D1191351

NOV 8 1976

JANE'S
FIGHTING SHIPS
1931

JANE'S
FIGHTING SHIPS
1931

A Reprint of the 1931 Edition of Fighting Ships
Founded by

FRED T. JANE

Edited by Francis E. McMurtrie

ARCO PUBLISHING COMPANY, INC.
New York

KALAMAZOO PUBLIC LIBRARY

R
359
J33
1931
Reprint

First published by Sampson Low Marston in 1931
This edition published 1973 by ARCO PUBLISHING COMPANY, INC.
219 Park Avenue South, New York, N.Y. 10003

Library of Congress Catalog Number 69–14519
ARCO Book Number 0668–02899–8

Printed in Great Britain

William Doxford & Sons Ltd. Sunderland

Telephone Nos. 1800-1-2-3

Telegrams : "DOXFORD, SUNDERLAND."

SHIPBUILDERS & ENGINEERS

BUILDERS OF
STEAM & MOTOR VESSELS
OF ALL TYPES

HIGH SPEED
WAR VESSELS

OPPOSED PISTON
AIRLESS INJECTION
OIL ENGINES
OF
PROVED HIGH EFFICIENCY

M.V. "FRESNO CITY" REARDON SMITH LINER 9000 TONS. 3300 H.P.

27 T.B.D. BUILT FOR BRITISH ADMIRALTY

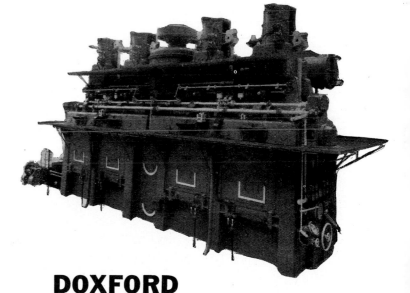

DOXFORD

BALANCED
Airless Injection
OIL ENGINES as fitted in
17 knot M.V. "BERMUDA"

MOTOR TANKER "PEGASUS" 14000 TONS. 12½ KNOTS

2 adv.

76-18665

ADVERTISERS IN 1931 EDITION.

ADVERTISEMENT RATES.

Two Pages	...	...	...	...	45 0 0	nett.
One Page	...	...	...	...	25 0 0	,,
Half ,,	...	...	...	...	15 0 0	,,
Quarter Page	...	...	...	...	8 0 0	,,

One Voucher Copy of the work is sent free to advertisers.

All communications in regard to Advertisements should be addressed to Advertisement Manager, Jane's "Fighting Ships,"
47, Gresham Street, LONDON, E.C.2.

VICKERS-ARMSTRONGS
LIMITED

SHIPBUILDERS AND ENGINEERS

BUILDERS OF EVERY CLASS OF VESSEL AND PROPELLING MACHINERY

"R" CLASS SUBMARINE.

SIAMESE GUNBOAT "SUKHODAYA."

H.M.S. "KEITH."

WARSHIPS AND ARMAMENTS OF ALL TYPES.
SHIP REPAIRS AND RECONDITIONING.
MARINE OIL ENGINES.
STEAM TURBINES.
STEAM RECIPROCATING ENGINES.

H.M.S. "NELSON."

MAIL AND PASSENGER STEAMERS.
CARGO VESSELS.
OIL TANKERS.
FLOATING DOCKS AND CRANES.
CROSS CHANNEL CRAFT.
ICE BREAKERS.

Head Office:
VICKERS HOUSE, BROADWAY, LONDON, S.W.1.

Shipyards:
BARROW-IN-FURNESS AND NEWCASTLE-ON-TYNE.

ADOPTED BY THE BRITISH & FOREIGN GOVERNMENTS for all classes of War Vessels including the largest and fastest vessels now in course of construction.

An interesting Album, profusely illustrated, and containing useful data, will be sent on request.

J. STONE & COMPANY LTD

COCKSPUR ST., LONDON, ENGLAND.
Works: DEPTFORD & CHARLTON, LONDON.

'Turbiston' *Bronze Propellers*

WACKRILL

CLASSIFIED LIST OF ADVERTISERS.

CLASSIFIED LIST OF ADVERTISERS—*continued*.

LOCOMOTIVES.

Cantieri Navali del Quarnaro-Fiume (**Italy**)	32	adv.
Partenopei, Officine E Cantieri (**Italy**)	30	,,

LOGS (for Ships, Motor Boats, and Yachts).

Heath & Co.,	32	,,
Walker, Thos. & Son, Ltd.	19	,,

LOUD SPEAKING TELEPHONES.

Graham, Alfred & Co., Ltd.	36	,,

MACHINE TOOLS.

Brown, John & Co., Ltd.	13	,,
Vickers-Armstrongs, Ltd.	4	,,

MARINE GLUE.

Jeffery, Alfred & Co.	29	,,

MATHEMATICAL INSTRUMENTS.

Ottway, W. & Co., Ltd.	33	,,

MEASURES (Inclination).

Barr & Stroud, Ltd.	30	,,

MECHANICAL SEARCHLIGHT CONTROL.

Chadburn's (Ship) Telegraph Co., Ltd.	34	,,

METALS (Copper, Brass, Alloys, Ingots, &c.).

Monel-Weir, Ltd.	35	,,
Stone, J. & Co., Ltd.	5	,,
Vickers-Armstrongs, Ltd.	4	,,
Yorkshire Copper Works, Ltd.	12	,,

METERS (Torsion).

Chadburn's (Ship) Telegraph Co., Ltd.	34	,,

MINE LAYERS.

Electric Boat Co. (**U.S.A.**)	24	adv.
Holland Torpedo Boat Co. (**U.S.A.**)	24	,,

MODEL MAKERS (Every Description).

Bassett-Lowke, Ltd.	29	,,

MONEL-METAL.

Monel-Weir, Ltd.	35	,,

MOTOR BOATS.

Bretagne, Ateliers et Chantiers de (**France**)	30	,,
Doxford, Wm. & Sons, Ltd.	2	,,
Lurssen, Fr. (**Germany**)	31	,,
Normand, Augustin (**France**)	25	,,
Thornycroft, John I. & Co., Ltd.	18	,,
White, J. Samuel & Co., Ltd.	15	,,
Yarrow & Co., Ltd.	34	,,

MOTOR CARS.

Thornycroft, John I. & Co., Ltd.	18	,,

MOTORS (ELECTRIC).

Vickers-Armstrongs, Ltd.	4	,,

NAILS (BOAT).

Stone, J. & Co., Ltd.	5	,,

NAVAL GUN SIGHTS.

Ottway, W. & Co., Ltd.	33	,,

OIL FUEL SPRAYERS.

Chadburn's (Ship) Telegraph Co., Ltd.	34	,,

OIL FUEL SYSTEMS AND BURNERS.

Thornycroft, John I. & Co., Ltd.	18	,,
Wallsend Slipway & Engineering Co., Ltd.	17	,,
White, J. Samuel & Co., Ltd.	15	,,

OIL PURIFIERS.

Chadburn's (Ship) Telegraph Co., Ltd.	34	adv.

OPTICAL INSTRUMENTS.

Ottway, W. & Co., Ltd.	33	,,

ORDNANCE.

Bofors, A. B. (**Sweden**)	23	,,
Vickers-Armstrongs, Ltd.	4	,,

OXYGEN APPARATUS FOR AIRMEN AND MEDICAL PURPOSES.

Siebe Gorman & Co., Ltd.	27	,,

PASSENGER AND CARGO BOATS.

Ansaldo, S. A. (**Italy**)	26	,,
Bethlehem Shipbuilding Corpn., Ltd. (**U.S.A.**)	22	,,
Bretagne, Ateliers et Chantiers de (**France**)	30	,,
Brown, John & Co., Ltd.	15	,,
Doxford, Wm. & Sons, Ltd.	2	,,
Hawthorn, R. & W. Leslie & Co., Ltd.	37	,,
Loire, Ateliers et Chantiers (**France**)	21	,,
Oderno-Terni-Orlando (**Italy**)	20	,,
Partenopei, Officine E Cantieri (**Italy**)	30	,,
St. Nazaire, Chantiers et Ateliers (Penhoët) (**France**)	25	,,
Thornycroft, John I. & Co., Ltd.	18	,,
Vickers-Armstrongs, Ltd.	4	,,
White, J. Samuel & Co., Ltd.	15	,,
Worms & Cie	32	,,
Yarrow & Co., Ltd.	34	,,

PERISCOPES (Submarine).

Barr & Stroud, Ltd.	30	,,

PRESSES (Power Plant).

Mactaggart, Scott & Co., Ltd.	31	,,

PROJECTILES.

Bofors, A. B. (**Sweden**)	23	,,
Brown, John & Co., Ltd.	13	,,

OIL PURIFIERS (continued)

Odero-Terni-Orlando (**Italy**)	20	,,
Vickers-Armstrongs, Ltd.	4	,,

PROPELLERS.

Bofors, A. B. (**Sweden**)	23	adv.
Darlington Forge, Ltd.	14	,,
Monel-Weir, Ltd.	35	,,
Stone, J. & Co., Ltd.	5	,,
Thornycroft John I. & Co., Ltd.	18	,,
Wallsend Slipway & Engineering Co., Ltd.	17	,,

PUBLISHERS.

Low, Sampson, Marston & Co. Ltd.	31, 38	,,

PUMPS.

Mactaggart, Scott & Co., Ltd.	31	,,
Partenopei, Officine E Cantieri (**Italy**)	30	,,
Stone, J. & Co., Ltd.	5	,,

PUMPS (Circulating).

Stone, J. & Co., Ltd.	5	,,

RAILWAY WHEELS, TYRES, SPRINGS, RAILS, AXLES, &c.

Brown, John & Co., Ltd.	13	,,
Vickers-Armstrongs, Ltd.	4	,,

RANGE FINDERS.

Barr & Stroud, Ltd.	30	,,

REDUCING GEARS.

Stone, J. & Co., Ltd.	5	,,

RESPIRATORS (Anti-Gas).

Siebe Gorman & Co., Ltd.	27	,,

RIVETS.

Stone, J. & Co., Ltd.	5	,,

SALVAGE BOATS.

White, J. Samuel & Co., Ltd.	17	,,

SCIENTIFIC INSTRUMENTS.

	PAGE
Ottway, W. & Co., Ltd.	33 adv.

SEARCHLIGHTS.

Sperry Gyroscope Co., Ltd. ..	11 ,,

SEARCHLIGHT CONTROL.

Chadburn's (Ship) Telegraph Co., Ltd.	34 ,,

SEXTANTS.

Heath & Co.	32 ,,

SHAFTING.

Bofors, A. B. (**Sweden**)	23 ,,
Brown, John & Co., Ltd.	13 ,,
Darlington Forge, Ltd.	14 ,,
Monel-Weir, Ltd.	35 ,,

SHIPBUILDERS.

(see also **Warship, Torpedo Craft Builders, Passenger and Cargo Boats, Tugs, Dredgers, Yachts, Launches, &c., Launches & Tenders, Motor Boats, Fire & Salvage Boats.**)

Ansaldo, S. A. (**Italy**)	26 ,.
Bethlehem Shipbuilding Corpn., Ltd. (**U.S.A.**)	22 ,,
Bretagne, Ateliers et Chantiers de (**France**)	30 ,,
Brown, John & Co., Ltd. ..	13 ,,
Cantieri Navali del Quarnaro-Fiume (**Italy**)	32 ,,
Doxford, Wm., & Sons, Ltd. ..	2 ,,
Hawthorn, R. & W., Leslie & Co., Ltd.	37 ,.
Loire, Ateliers et Chantiers (**France**)	21 ,,
Odero-Terni-Orlando (**Italy**) ..	20 ,,
Partenopei, Officine E Cantieri .. (**Italy**)	30 ,,
St. Nazaire, Chantiers et Ateliers (Penhoët) (**France**)	25 ,,
Thornycroft, John I. & Co., Ltd.	18 ,,
Vickers-Armstrongs, Ltd. ..	4 ,,
White, J. Samuel & Co., Ltd. ..	15 ,,
Worms & Cie	32 ,,
Yarrow & Co., Ltd.	34 ,,

SHIP LIGHTING PLANT & ACCESSORIES.

	PAGE
Thornycroft, John I. & Co., Ltd.	18 adv.

SHIP AND MACHINERY REPAIRS.

Ansaldo, S. A. (**Italy**)	26 ,,
Bethlehem Shipbuilding Corpn., Ltd. (**U.S.A.**)	22 ,,
Doxford, Wm. & Sons, Ltd. ..	2 ,,
Hawthorn, R. & W., Leslie & Co., Ltd.	37 ,,
Loire, Ateliers et Chantiers (**France**)	21 ,,
Partenopei, Officine E Cantieri (**Italy**)	30 ,,
Thornycroft, John I. & Co., Ltd.	18 ,,
Vickers-Armstrongs, Ltd. ..	4 ,,
Wallsend Slipway & Engineering Co., Ltd.	17 ,,
Worms & Cie	32 ,,

SHIPS' AUXILIARY MACHINERY.

Brown Bros. & Co., Ltd.	33 ,,
Mactaggart, Scott & Co., Ltd. ..	31 ,,
Metallic Valve Co., Ltd. ..	29 ,,

SHIPS' LOGS.

Walker, Thos. & Son, Ltd. ..	19 ,,

SHIP STABILIZERS.

Sperry Gyroscope Co., Ltd. ..	11 ,,

SHIPS' TELEPHONES.

Graham, Alfred & Co., Ltd. ..	36 ,,

SIGNALLING SYSTEMS AND APPARATUS.

Chadburn's (Ship) Telegraph Co., Ltd.	34 ,,
Evershed & Vignoles, Ltd. (**inside front cover**)	
Graham, Alfred & Co., Ltd. ..	36 ,,

SMOKE HELMETS.

Siebe Gorman & Co., Ltd. ..	27 ,,

SOUNDING MACHINES.

Heath & Co.	32 ,,

SPEED BOATS

Lurssen, Fr. (**Germany**)	31 ,,

SPRINGS.

	PAGE
Cockburns, Ltd.	32 adv.
Monel-Weir, Ltd.	35 ,,

SPRINGS (Steel).

Brown, John & Co., Ltd.	13 ,,
Cockburns, Ltd.	32 ,,

STEAM TRAPS.

Cockburns, Ltd.	32 ,,

STEAM TRAPS AND SEPARATORS.

Aiton & Co., Ltd.	27 ,,

STEEL CASTINGS.

Vickers-Armstrongs, Ltd. ..	4 ,,

STEEL FLANGES.

Aiton & Co., Ltd.	27 ,,

STEEL (High Speed).

Vickers-Armstrongs, Ltd. ..	4 ,,

STEEL FORGINGS.

Brown, John & Co., Ltd.	13 ,,
Darlington Forge, Ltd.	14 ,,
Hadfields, Ltd.	23 ,,

STEEL FOUNDERS.

Ansaldo, S. A. (**Italy**)	26 ,,
Bofors, A. B. (**Sweden**)	23 ,,
Brown, John & Co., Ltd.	13 ,,
Darlington Forge, Ltd.	14 ,,

STEEL (Tool and Mining).

Vickers-Armstrongs, Ltd. ..	4 ,,

STEEL TYRES, AXLES, SPRINGS, &c.

Vickers-Armstrongs, Ltd. ..	4 ,,

STEERING GEAR, &c.

Brown Bros. & Co., Ltd.	33 ,,
Mactaggart, Scott & Co., Ltd. ..	31 ,,
Sperry Gyroscope Co., Ltd. ..	11 ,,

STERN AND RUDDER FRAMES.

	PAGE
Bofors, A. B. (**Sweden**)	23 adv.
Stone, J. & Co., Ltd.	5 ,,

SUBMARINES.

Ansaldo, S. A. (**Italy**)	26 ,,
Bethlehem Shipbuilding Corpn., Ltd. (**U.S.A.**)	22 ,,
Cantieri Navali del Quarnaro-Fiume (**Italy**)	32 ,,
Electric Boat Co., (**U.S.A.**) ..	24 ,,
Hawthorn, R. & W., Leslie & Co., Ltd.	37 ,,
Holland Torpedo Boat Co. (**U.S.A.**)	24 ,,
Loire, Ateliers et Chantiers (**France**)	21 ,,
Normand, Augustin (**France**) ..	25 ,,
Odero-Terni-Orlando (**Italy**) ..	20 ,,
Vickers-Armstrongs, Ltd. ..	4 ,,
Worms & Cie	32 ,,

SUBMARINE PERISCOPES.

Barr & Stroud, Ltd.	30 ,,

SUPERHEATERS (Marine).

Yarrow & Co., Ltd.	34 ,,

SWITCHBOARDS.

Graham, Alfred & Co., Ltd. ..	36 ,,

SWITCHGEAR.

Graham, Alfred & Co., Ltd. ..	36 ,,

TELEGRAPHS (for Aeroplanes & Airships).

Chadburn's (Ship) Telegraph Co., Ltd.	34 ,,

TELEGRAPHS (Ship).

Chadburn's (Ship) Telegraph Co., Ltd.	34 ,,
Evershed & Vignoles, Ltd. (**inside front cover**)	
Heath & Co.	32 ,,
Stone, J. & Co., Ltd.	5 ,,

SPERRY

GYRO-COMPASSES
AND SEARCHLIGHTS

SPERRY 24″
high intensity
NAVAL SEARCHLIGHT

SPERRY MASTER GYRO
COMPASS, MARK VIII

THE SPERRY GYRO COMPASS is employed in nearly all the world's Navies. In numbers it is predominant, and in accuracy and reliability it is unequalled. It is the standard gyro compass of the British Navy.

The Sperry Compass is universal too, in the variety of shipping where it is employed, from battleships and liners to tankers and tramp steamers.

2,000 installed in warships

The Sperry is the only gyro compass which indicates true North at all speeds and in all latitudes. Other types have deviations necessitating reference to correction tables.

With the Gyro Pilot the steadiness of automatic steering, and the absence of yawing, are of great tactical advantage during gun and torpedo firing.

SPERRY SEARCHLIGHTS are robustly built of light weight castings, and have many patented special features which place them in the foremost class. Made in two types, high intensity and incandescent, and in a varied range of sizes and mountings, each searchlight stands pre-eminent for dependability and powerful illumination. Sperry Searchlights are absolutely automatic in action, true focus is always maintained, giving a steady brilliant beam without necessitating attention. When desired, the beam can be spread for floodlighting decks, etc.

We will gladly send descriptive literature to **anyone** *interested.*

THE SPERRY GYROSCOPE CO., LTD.

HEAD OFFICE AND WORKS
GREAT WEST ROAD, BRENTFORD, MIDDLESEX
(*near London*)

Phone: Ealing 6771

11 adv.

"*Yorcalbro*"

Protected under B.N.F. Patent 308647, 1929.

THE MOST ECONOMICAL CONDENSER TUBE IN THE WORLD

TUBES IN COPPER, BRASS, ALUMINIUM, ALUMINIUM BRASS, CUPRO NICKEL AND ALL NON-FERROUS ALLOYS

Contractors to British and Foreign Admiralties and all Government Departments

THE YORKSHIRE COPPER WORKS Ltd., LEEDS, ENGLAND

Telephone 20031 (6 lines)   London Office : 53 NEW BROAD STREET, E.C.2   Telegrams 'TUBES,' LEEDS

12 adv.

JOHN · BROWN
& · COMPANY · LIMITED.

Shipbuilders and Marine Engineers

WARSHIPS OF ALL
CLASSES

PASSENGER AND
CARGO VESSELS

up to the largest size
and power.

H.M.S. "HOOD."

Shipyard and Engine Works:
CLYDEBANK, NR. GLASGOW

Registered Office:
ATLAS WORKS, SHEFFIELD

London Office:
8 THE SANCTUARY, WESTMINSTER,
LONDON, S.W.1.

ATLAS WORKS,
SHEFFIELD,

& CLYDEBANK,
NR. GLASGOW.

13 adv.

Telegraphic Address: "FORGE, DARLINGTON."

Nat. Telephone No.: 2610, DARLINGTON.

STEEL AND IRON
FORGINGS

THE
DARLINGTON
FORGE LTD.
DARLINGTON

STEEL & BRONZE
CASTINGS

HYDRAULIC PRESSED STEEL FORGING FOR TURBINE DRUM
7'—1" diameter.   11'—11¼" long.
Forging Weight 52 Tons

"DARLINGTON FORGE" BRONZE PROPELLERS
up to 24 feet diameter:
Finished Complete

FORGED STEEL THREE-THROW SOLID TYPE
Hollow Bored Crankshaft.   18" diameter.   21'—6" long.
Weight 22 Tons

FORGED STEEL BUILT RUDDER FOR CUNARD TURBINE
MAIL BOAT "AQUITANIA"
Weight 54 Tons

14 adv.

Shipbuilders *and* Engineers

BUILDERS OF: Torpedo Boat Destroyers, High Speed Steam and Motor-driven Passenger and Cargo Vessels, Special Service, Shallow Draught Vessels, Steam and Motor Launches of every class.

J. SAMUEL WHITE & CO. LTD.

◆ EAST COWES ◆ ISLE OF WIGHT ◆

Telephone: Cowes 103 (3 lines).   *Telegrams: "White," East Cowes.*

MANUFACTURERS OF: Marine Steam Turbines, Reciprocating Engines, "White-Forster" Water Tube Boilers, Marine Return Tube Boilers, The "J. Samuel White" Oil Fuel Burning Installations (Low Pressure System) for Marine and Land purposes.

LONDON OFFICE:
28, VICTORIA STREET, WESTMINSTER, S.W.1

REPAIR DEPARTMENT:
PRINCE OF WALES DRY DOCK, SOUTHAMPTON.
Telephone: SOUTHAMPTON 4151.   Telegrams: "OVERHAUL, SOUTHAMPTON."

LIVERPOOL OFFICE:
707/711, ROYAL LIVER BUILDINGS.

Fifty Years of Electric Cable Making

Since 1882 Callenders have specialised in the manufacture of Electric Cables and for many years these have been installed in Fighting Ships both for the H.M. Admiralty and for Foreign Powers. Callender's engineers have made a special study of the arduous usage to which Electric Cables are subjected on all classes of sea-going vessels, and have introduced various types of cables to meet such conditions.

Callender's Marine Department and its experts are always at the service of Naval Architects and Shipbuilders to give quotations, and assist enquirers in every way possible.

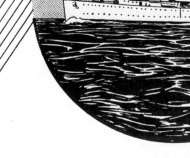

Contractors to   *H.M. Admiralty*

ALL OVER THE WORLD
CALLENDER CABLE

CALLENDER'S CABLE & CONSTRUCTION CO., LTD.
Hamilton House, Victoria Embankment,
LONDON E.C.4
Telephone. Central 5241 Telegrams. Callender. Fleet London

THE WALLSEND SLIPWAY & ENGINEERING CO. LTD.

Builders of Marine Steam Reciprocating Turbine and Wallsend-Sulzer Internal Combustion Engines for all types of War & Merchant ships

**Constructors
of
Cylindrical
and
Watertube
Boilers
of the
Yarrow
and
Johnson types**

Ship repairers
Graving Dock
540 feet long

Aerial View of the Works

**Licensees
and
Manufacturers
of
Installations
for
Burning Oil Fuel**

The aggregate power of boilers for which the Company has supplied Liquid Fuel Burning arrangements exceeds
**11,000,000
horse power**

London Office:
34 Great St. Helen's, E.C.3.

Head Office & Works: WALLSEND-ON-TYNE

Liverpool Office:
Cunard Building

17 adv.

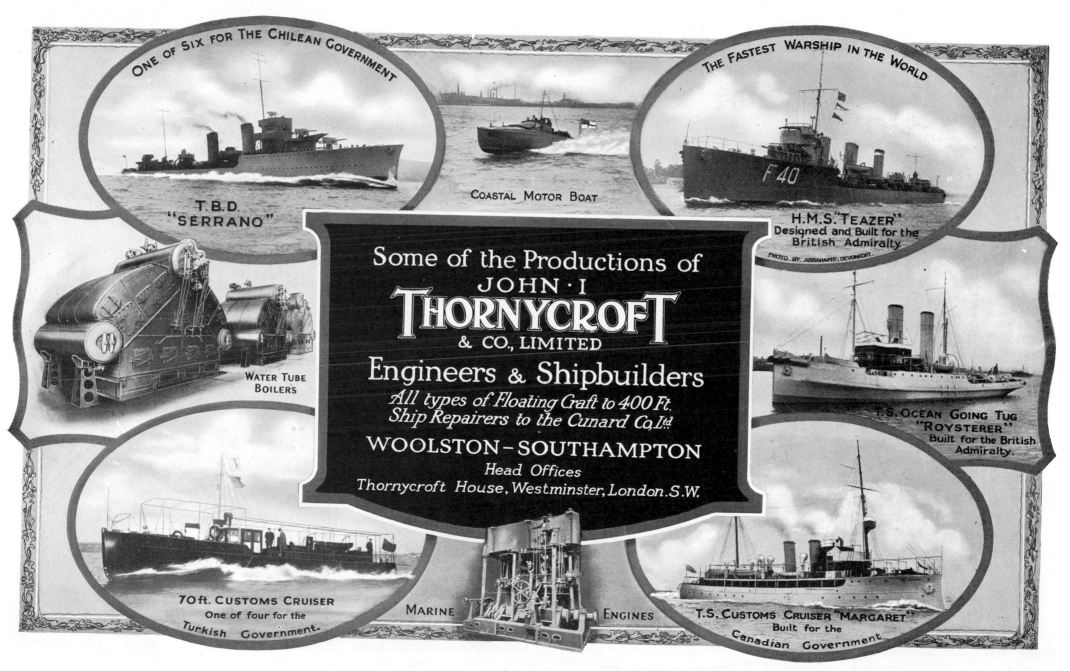

ONE OF SIX FOR THE CHILEAN GOVERNMENT

T.B.D. "SERRANO"

COASTAL MOTOR BOAT

THE FASTEST WARSHIP IN THE WORLD

H.M.S. "TEAZER"
Designed and Built for the British Admiralty
PHOTO BY ABRAHAMS, DEVONPORT

WATER TUBE BOILERS

Some of the Productions of
JOHN · I
THORNYCROFT
& CO., LIMITED
Engineers & Shipbuilders
All types of Floating Craft to 400 Ft.
Ship Repairers to the Cunard Co. Ltd.
WOOLSTON — SOUTHAMPTON
Head Offices
Thornycroft House, Westminster, London. S.W.

T.S. OCEAN GOING TUG "ROYSTERER"
Built for the British Admiralty.

70 ft. CUSTOMS CRUISER
One of four for the Turkish Government.

MARINE ENGINES

T.S. CUSTOMS CRUISER "MARGARET"
Built for the Canadian Government

18 adv.

Walker's "Trident" Electric Log

Watertight Taffrail Register Naval Pattern fitted with Resistance for 10/25 Volts

gives an accurate reading of " distance run," because it is streamed well clear of the ship and is therefore unaffected by hull disturbance. Recent trials on the measured mile at speeds varying between 10 and 25 knots gave Walker's towing log an error of + **0·7** % on the mean of means. Fitted above the water, it is readily maintained, and the log line and the rotator, if lost, are easily replaced at sea.

Write for illustrated booklet - price of Naval Pattern Log 10/25 volts complete ex works **£30 12 0**

AS SUPPLIED TO THE BRITISH NAVY

Thos. Walker & Son, Ltd.,
58, Oxford Street, Birmingham, Eng.
T.W

Watertight Chart House Receiver, Naval Pattern

ODERO TERNI ORLANDO

HEAD OFFICE : GENOA (ITALY) VIA B. BOSCO 37
TELEGRAMS : MOTONAVI - GENOVA

ITALIAN FLOTILLA LEADER
"USODIMARE" CLASS
2000 TONS   40 KNOTS

ITALIAN SUBMARINE
"BALILLA" CLASS
1450 TONS

	BUILT AND BUILDING		
WARSHIPS		295.000	TONS DISP.
SUBMARINES	" " "	34.000	" "
MERCHANT SHIPS	" " "	627.000	REG. TONS.
MARINE ENGINES	" " "	2.800.000	HP
ARTILLERY	" " "	OVER 6.000	GUNS

SHIPYARDS &
ENGINE WORKS:

GENOA (EX ODERO)

SPEZIA (EX FIAT)

LEGHORN (EX ORLANDO)

GUNS FACTORY:

SPEZIA (EX VICKERS-TERNI)

HARBOUR WORKS &
DRY DOCK:

GENOA

SPEZIA

LEGHORN

WARSHIPS OF ALL TYPE
MERCHANT SHIPS OF ALL SIZES
GUNS OF ALL CALIBRES
AMMUNITIONS
MARINE ENGINES
PARSONS
TURBINES
BOILERS

ARGENTINE "LIGHT CRUISER
"25 DE MAYO" CLASS
8500 TONS   34 KNOTS

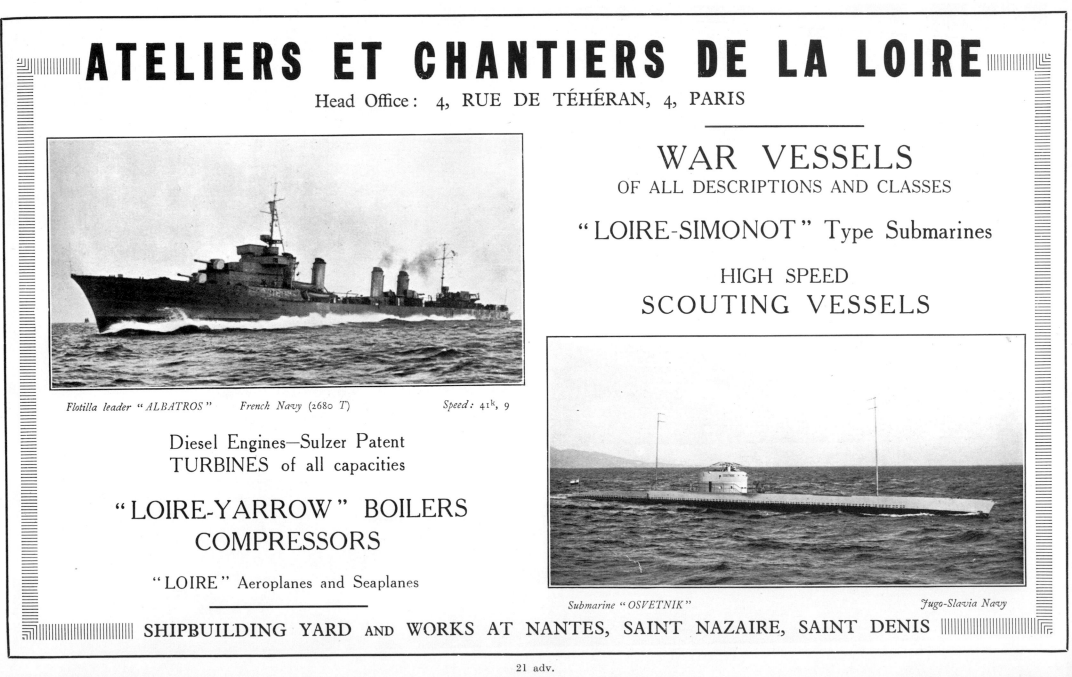

ATELIERS ET CHANTIERS DE LA LOIRE

Head Office : 4, RUE DE TÉHÉRAN, 4, PARIS

Flotilla leader "ALBATROS"   *French Navy (2680 T)*   *Speed: 41ᵏ, 9*

WAR VESSELS
OF ALL DESCRIPTIONS AND CLASSES

"LOIRE-SIMONOT" Type Submarines

HIGH SPEED
SCOUTING VESSELS

Diesel Engines—Sulzer Patent
TURBINES of all capacities

"LOIRE-YARROW" BOILERS
COMPRESSORS

"LOIRE" Aeroplanes and Seaplanes

Submarine "OSVETNIK"   *Jugo-Slavia Navy*

SHIPBUILDING YARD AND WORKS AT NANTES, SAINT NAZAIRE, SAINT DENIS

BETHLEHEM SHIPBUILDING CORPORATION, LTD.

Shipbuilders and Marine Engineers.

Subsidiary of Bethlehem *Steel Corporation*

DESIGNERS
AND
CONSTRUCTORS
OF

Naval and Government Ships—
Battleships, Cruisers, Airplane Carriers, Destroyers, Submarines, Cutters, Tenders, Tugs, Mine Sweepers, Light Ships, Colliers, etc.

Merchant Ships—
Passenger, General and Special Cargo Vessels, Oil Tankers, Car Floats, Tug Boats, Barges, Lighters, Ferry Boats, Yachts, etc.

PLANTS
FORE RIVER PLANT:
Quincy, Mass.

BOSTON PLANT:
Atlantic Works, Boston, Mass.
Simpson Works, Boston, Mass.

BALTIMORE PLANT:
Baltimore Dry Dock Works, Baltimore, Md.
Sparrows Point Works, Sparrows Point, Md.

UNION PLANT:
Hunters Point Works, San Francisco, Cal.
Potrero Works, San Francisco, Cal.
Almeda Works, Almeda, Cal.
San Pedro Works, East San Pedro, Cal.
(Los Angeles Harbor).

U.S.S. Northampton, 10,000-ton light cruiser built at Bethlehem's Fore River Plant, Quincy, Mass.

The extensive facilities of nine well-equipped ship yards located along the Atlantic and Pacific Coasts and convenient to main ocean routes, enable Bethlehem to offer efficient service to ship owners and operators.

BETHLEHEM

General Offices: **BETHLEHEM, PA., U.S.A.**
General State Offices:
25, Broadway, New York City.
Cable Address: "Bethship," New York City.

22 adv.

BOFORS ORDNANCE WORKS

A:B. BOFORS
BOFORS ✦ SWEDEN
GUN & ORDNANCE FACTORY

10.2 cm. Anti-Aircraft Naval Gun L/35.

MAKERS OF

Marine Guns. Coast Defence Guns.
Field Guns. Mountain Guns.
Anti-Aircraft Guns. Armour Shields.
Armour Gun Turrets.
Torpedo Air Vessels. Projectiles.
Forgings. Castings. Steel Propellers.
etc.

A:B. BOFORS' NOBELKRUT
BOFORS ✦ SWEDEN
POWDER FACTORY

7.5 cm. Anti-Aircraft Gun L/45.

MAKERS OF

Gunpowder. Flashless Powder.
Rifle Powder. Pistol Powder.
Explosives of all Kinds.
Dynamites. Gelignites. T.N.T.
Tetryl. Hexyl. Explosive Charges.

12 cm. Naval Guns L/45.

7.5 cm. Anti-Aircraft Naval Gun L/60

25 cm. Naval Guns L/46.

ELECTRIC BOAT CO.

(HOLLAND TORPEDO BOAT CO.)

SUBMARINES

DESIGNERS AND BUILDERS OF SUBMARINES OF ALL TYPES

DOUBLE HULL — SADDLE TANK AND SINGLE HULL — COAST DEFENCE — FLEET AND MINELAYERS

394 SUBMARINES BUILT AND BUILDING TO ELECTRIC BOAT CO. DESIGNS

BRANCHES AND SUBSIDIARY COMPANIES

NEW LONDON SHIP AND ENGINE WORKS   GROTON, CONN.

SUBMARINES   STEEL YACHTS   COMMERCIAL VESSELS   DIESEL ENGINES AND SHIP'S AUXILIARIES

ELECTRO DYNAMIC CO. BAYONNE, N.J.

ALTERNATING AND DIRECT CURRENT MOTORS AND GENERATORS

ELCO WORKS—BAYONNE, N.J.

WOODEN YACHTS, MOTOR BOATS AND SUBMARINE CHASERS

SUBMARINES BUILT FOR

UNITED STATES

GREAT BRITAIN	AUSTRIA-HUNGARY
JAPAN	DENMARK
ITALY	NORWAY
HOLLAND	PERU
RUSSIA	CHILE
SPAIN	CANADA

HEAD OFFICE: 40 WALL STREET   NEW YORK U.S.A.   TECHNICAL OFFICE: GROTON, CONN.

CHANTIER ET ATELIERS DE ST. NAZAIRE
PENHOET

HEAD OFFICE—7 rue AUBER, PARIS

SHIPYARDS & WORKS at PENHOET (St. Nazaire) and GRAND-QUEVILLY (near Rouen)

The new cruiser "JEANNE D'ARC" (6,600 tons, Washington Displacement)

entirely built and engined by the Société des Chantier et Ateliers de St. Nazaire Penhoët for the French Navy, especially designed for the training of Junior Officers.—Speed attained: 27·844 knots (contract speed: 26·5 knots).

WARSHIPS OF ALL CLASSES

Cruisers, Flotilla Leaders, Torpedo-Boats, Submarines, etc.

PARSONS TURBINES

DIESEL ENGINES (M.A.N. and B. & W. Licences)

CHANTIERS ET ATELIERS
AUGUSTIN NORMAND
LE HAVRE, FRANCE.

POLISH SUBMARINE "WILK."

DESTROYERS.   TORPEDO BOATS.
SUBMARINE and SUBMERSIBLE BOATS.
YACHTS and FAST BOATS.
MERCHANT and FISHING VESSELS.

LINER "AUSONIA..

LINER "DUILIO..

LINER "ROMA..

MOTORSHIP "AUGUSTUS..

FLOTILLA LEADER "PANTERA..

SUBMARINE MINELAYER "X. 3..

"ANSALDO" S.A.
GENOA, ITALY.

Naval Shipyard for Warships and Merchant Vessels of
every size and type.
Machinery Works for Steam Marine Engines of every type
(turbine and reciprocating) up to the highest powers.
Marine and Stationary Oil Motor Works.
Guns, Gun-mountings and Shell Factory.
Armour Plates and Steelmakers.
Steel, Cast-iron and Brass Foundry.
Land and Marine Electric Installations.
Ship Repairs and Refittings.
Steam and Electric Locomotive and Car Builders.

Head Office: GENOVA-CORNIGLIANO.

FLOTILLA LEADER "LUCA TARIGO,,

SUBMARINE "N. 1..

DESTROYER "BOREA..

CRUISER "LIBIA..

LIGHT CRUISER A. DA GIUSSANO

BATTLESHIP "G. CESARE..

SIEBE GORMAN & CO. LTD.

DIVING APPARATUS

OF EVERY — **DESCRIPTION**

DAVIS'S NEW PATENT

DEEP DIVING SYSTEM

DAVIS'S Patent Apparatus FOR ESCAPE FROM DISABLED SUBMARINES

AND ALL OTHER SUBMARINE APPLIANCES.

Contractors to British Admiralty and most Foreign Navies

GAS MASKS | **SMOKE HELMETS**

for NAVAL, MILITARY, and INDUSTRIAL PURPOSES. | for STEAMSHIPS, OIL TANKERS, OIL DEPOTS, DOCKS, etc. etc.

OXYGEN BREATHING APPARATUS for Airmen Flying at Great Altitudes.

OXYGEN RESUSCITATING APPARATUS for the apparently drowned or asphyxiated ; Oxygen and Oxygen + CO_2 systems.

SAFETY LAMPS   FIRE EXTINGUISHERS, Etc.   FIRST AID OUTFITS

And all other SAFETY and PROTECTIVE DEVICES

ILLUSTRATED CATALOGUES on application

187, WESTMINSTER BRIDGE ROAD, LONDON, S.E.1.

Telegrams: " SIEBE, LAMB, LONDON."
Cables: " SIEBE, LONDON."

Telephone No.: Hop 3401
(2 Lines.)

Codes used:
A.B.C. (5th and 6th Eds.), WESTERN UNION (Universal and 5 Letter Eds.),
LIEBER, MARCONI, ENGINEERING AND PRIVATE.

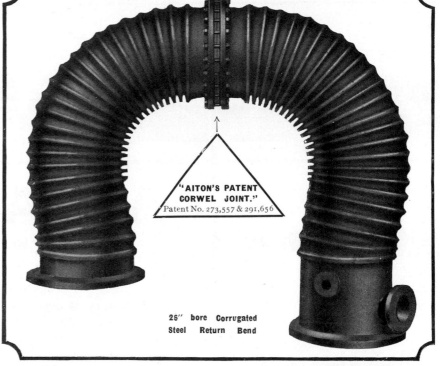

"AITON'S PATENT CORWEL JOINT."
Patent No. 273,557 & 291,656

26″ bore Corrugated Steel Return Bend

Aiton's corrugated pipes

Aiton's are specialists in pipework construction—they are intimately acquainted with the conditions of working and the difficulties to be met—for many years their pipes have maintained a reputation for long and reliable service.

Of particular interest are Aiton's Corrugated Bends ; the corrugations on these Pipes are so raised that the material is not stressed, and after corrugating the Pipe is bent without in any way thinning the wall. Aiton's Corrugated Bends have proved an outsanding success on board ship, where both the stress and the total weight of the installation have been reduced.

The illustration shows a 26-in. bore Corrugated Return Bend, fitted with Aiton Patent " Corwel " Joint, which is acknowledged to have no rival for the highest steam pressures and temperatures.

AITON & CO LTD
DERBY
PIPES

SILURIFICIO WHITEHEAD DI FIUME S.A. ITALY

ESTABLISHED 1872

TORPEDO RUNNING STATION

ELECTRICALLY DRIVEN COMPRESSOR FOR SUBMERSIBLES

STEAM DRIVEN COMPR. FOR SURFACE VESSELS

TRIPLE LAUNCHING TUBES ON RAILS

LAUNCHING TUBES FOR SUBMERSIBLES

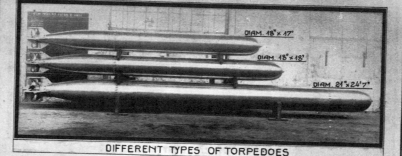

DIAM. 18" x 17"

DIAM. 18" x 18"

DIAM. 21" x 24'7"

DIFFERENT TYPES OF TORPEDOES

CONSTRUCTORS OF:
TORPEDOES OF 18" AND 21"
ELECTRICALLY DRIVEN COMPRESSORS
FOR SUBMERSIBLES
STEAM DRIVEN COMPRESSORS FOR
SURFACE VESSELS
COMPRESSORS FOR OXYGEN AND
OTHER GASES
TORPEDO LAUNCHING TUBES FOR SUR-
FACE VESSELS AND SUBMERSIBLES

FURNISHERS TO THE FOLLOWING GOVERNMENTS

ARGENTINA	FINLAND	MEXICO	
AUSTRIA-HUNGARY	FRANCE	NETHERLANDS	SOUTH AUSTRALIA
BELGIUM	GERMANY	NORWAY	SPAIN
BRAZIL	GREAT BRITAIN	PERU	SWEDEN
BULGARIA	GREECE	PORTUGAL	TASMANIA
CHILE	ITALY	ROUMANIA	TURKEY
CHINA	JAPAN	RUSSIA	UNITED STATES AMERICA
DENMARK	JUGOSLAVIA	SIAM	URUGUAY
			VICTORIA

JEFFERY'S PATENT MARINE GLUE.

ANTWERP. 1294.

JEFFERY'S MARINE GLUE

JEFFERY'S MARINE GLUE PITCH

PRIZE MEDAL LONDON 62

LONDON. 1884.

Original Patentees and only Manufacturers Patent Marine Glue.

Adopted by H.M. Navy and many Steamship Companies.

TRADE MARK.

Established Over 80 Years.

For DECK SEAMS OF SHIPS AND YACHTS

Also LIGHT-COLOURED MARINE GLUES.

Works: MARSH GATE LANE, STRATFORD, LONDON, E.15.

Telegrams: "MARINE GLUE, BOCHURCH, LONDON."   Tel.: MARYLAND 2457.

Æ CONDENSER TUBES Æ

Are used by the British Navy and all important foreign navies.
Are in service in many hundreds of ships, including the Atlantic Record Breakers.
Are fitted in all steamships of 30,000 tons and upwards.

Æ SUPER-NICKEL TUBES
ARE THE BEST FOR THE WORST CONDITIONS

Æ ALUMBRO TUBES
ARE RECOMMENDED FOR LESS SEVERE CONDITIONS

I.C.I. METALS LTD. (TUBE SECTION)

A subsidiary company of Imperial Chemical Industries, Ltd.

KINGSTON METAL WORKS, SMETHWICK, BIRMINGHAM

SCALE MODEL SHIPS

You cannot put a Liner in a shop window, nor a Harbour in Cockspur Street, but you can exhibit a realistic model and enable the world to appreciate your facilities for transport, and the comforts you offer to travellers. A good scale model tells this story efficiently; it will never lie nor offend, and works without a weekly paysheet. We specialise in models of Ships, Harbours or Docks, built with absolute fidelity and realism. Photographs and pictures are better, but they still fall far behind the combined realism and romance of the famous Bassett-Lowke Models. We have made these models for most of the greatest shipping companies in the world, and also, which is perhaps even more important, for the British Admiralty. Let a qualified representative call upon you and discuss the possibilities of publicity by means of scale models. Our Ships catalogue, section S/29, will be sent, post free, to all those interested in marine modelling.

London Branch: 112 HIGH HOLBORN, W.C.1   **BASSETT-LOWKE, Ltd.**   *Manchester Branch:* 28 CORPORATION STREET

Head Office and Works: NORTHAMPTON.

KINGHORN'S PATENT METALLIC VALVES FOR PUMPS OF EVERY DESCRIPTION

ROGLER-HOERBIGER PATENT RING PLATE VALVES FOR AIR AND GAS COMPRESSORS, SCAVENGE PUMPS, Etc.

THE

METALLIC VALVE CO. LTD.,

661, ROYAL LIVER BUILDING

LIVERPOOL

FIREBRICKS
with a CENTURY *of* EXPERIENCE *behind them*

Year after Year for almost a century the demand for Glenboig Firebricks has increased, until to-day they are known and used practically all over the world. The reason is their quality—quality which means economy and efficiency to the user. (Hundreds of unsought testimonials received). 60 Prize Medals awarded.

"Contractors to the Principal National Arsenals of Europe," and also "On the Admiralty List."

GLENBOIG BRICKS

Sole Proprietors & Manufacturers:
THE GLENBOIG UNION FIRECLAY CO. LTD.
48 West Regent Street, Glasgow, C.2

BARR & STROUD Ltd.
Engineers and Instrument Makers
OPTICAL—MECHANICAL—ELECTRICAL

RANGEFINDERS, HEIGHTFINDERS, INCLINOMETERS, GUNNERY CONTROL GEAR, TORPEDO CONTROL GEAR, SUBMARINE PERISCOPES, DEPTH & ROLL RECORDERS, TOPOGRAPHICAL STEREOSCOPES, BINOCULARS, OPTICAL GLASS,

ANNIESLAND, GLASGOW
AND
15, VICTORIA STREET, LONDON, S.W.1.

Telegrams:
"Telemeter, Glasgow.
Retemelet, Sowest, London."

TRADE MARK

Telephones:
GLASGOW—Scotstoun 1831.
LONDON — Victoria 6668.

ATELIERS ET CHANTIERS
DE BRETAGNE
PRAIRIE AU DUC - NANTES - FRANCE

DESTROYER "GERFAUT" Speed 43·32 knots (WORLD RECORD)

"Considering that the trials of French Warships are carried out under especially severe conditions, it is evident that the French shipbuilding industry has gained a great victory on this occasion by breaking the record of 42·3 knots hitherto held by Italy." (*Extract from "Journal of Commerce" of May 21st, 1931.*)

OFFICINE E CANTIERI PARTENOPEI
Telegraphic Address:
"MECCANICHE, NAPLES.
21, VIA BENEDETTO BRIN,
NAPLES.

SHIPYARDS, GRAVING DOCKS, ENGINE WORKS.

WORKS
- OFFICINE MECCANICHE E NAVALI DI NAPOLI
- OFFICINE E CANTIERI NAPOLETANI
- C. & T. T. PATTISON
- BACINI E SCALI NAPOLETANI

MARINE STEAM TURBINES "BELLUZZO" TYPE
MARINE RECIPROCATING AND TURBINE MACHINERIES
DIESEL O. M. KRUPP MARINE MOTORS
STEAM AND ELECTRIC LOCOMOTIVES
FITTINGS AND REPAIRS OF ALL TYPES OF SHIPS AND MARINE ENGINES

FORBES' PATENT
EXTENDING STRUCTURE TYPE CATAPULT

SUITABLE FOR LAUNCHING AIRCRAFT OF ALL TYPES & SIZES.

FEATURES

Long Launching Travel with Short Stowage Space.

Smooth Acceleration and Retardation.

Compressed Air or Cordite Operation.

Fixed or Rotative Type as Required.

Designs and Prices on Application.

Illustration shows Catapult in Extended Position

Sole Licencees and Manufacturers :-

MACTAGGART, SCOTT & Co. Ltd.

STATION IRONWORKS,   **LOANHEAD,**   **Nr. EDINBURGH**

Telegrams :- "VALVE" LOANHEAD.   'Phone 12 LOANHEAD

FOUNDED IN 1875

SPECIALISTS IN FAST BOATS

DISPLACEMENT SPEED BOAT

Length 90'   Speed 35 knots.

FR. LURSSEN - BREMEN / VEGESACK - GERMANY

Naval architects — Yacht and Boat Yard — Suppliers to the German navy.

LEAVES FROM AN UNWRITTEN LOG-BOOK
CAPTAIN WALTER H. PARKER, C.B.E., R.D., R.N.R., (Retd.)
(Lately Commanding R.M.S. " Olympic ")

Illustrated   12s. 6d. net

" *An interesting contribution to sea literature. Well worth reading.*"
" *DAILY TELEGRAPH* "

" *Rich in adventure of the sea.*"—" *EVENING STANDARD* "

A CENTURY OF ATLANTIC TRAVEL
FRANK C. BOWEN
Author of " The Golden Age of Sail," Etc. Etc.

Fully Illustrated   12s. 6d. net

Devoting a chapter to each decade of the last 100 years Mr. Bowen has written a fascinating history in which he discourses on all phases of Atlantic Travel development.

FULL BORE SAFETY VALVE

(Cockburn-MacNicoll Patent)

AS FITTED TO ALL THE MODERN BRITISH & FOREIGN BATTLESHIPS

Maximum Evaporation dealt with on Minimum Weight and Space

SOLE MAKERS

COCKBURNS
LIMITED
CARDONALD
GLASGOW

The World Renowned Steam Valve Specialists

Telephone:
361 GOVAN (2 lines)

Telegrams:
"COCKBURN, GLASGOW."

NAVIGATION INSTRUMENTS

MAKERS TO
BRITISH AND FOREIGN GOVERNMENTS

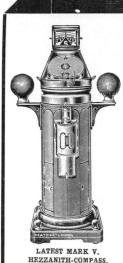

ACCURACY

TRADE **HEZZANITH** MARK

RELIABILITY

SEXTANTS
SOUNDERS
TELESCOPES
THERMOMETERS

CLOCKS
BAROMETERS
HYDROMETERS
RULES, ETC.

SEND FOR

LIST. N. I.

ALL OPTICAL AND SCIENTIFIC INSTRUMENTS

"DAY & NIGHT" SEXTANT

COMPLETE NAVIGATION OUTFITS

LATEST MARK V.
HEZZANITH-COMPASS.
WITH
PATENT VERTICAL
CARD MAGNIFIER

HEATH & Co
NEW ELTHAM, LONDON, S.E.9.

CABLES: "Polaris," London.   PHONES: Eltham 1301 (3 lines)

MARK II.
HEZZANITH
NAVY
TAXIMETER

CANTIERI NAVALI DEL QUARNARO-FIUME (ITALY)

CONSTRUCTION OF WAR, PASSENGER AND CARGO VESSELS OF ALL TYPES AND DISPLACEMENT. BOILERS OF ALL KINDS AND DESCRIPTION.

2000 TONS ESPLORATORI "DA MOSTO" of the series "ZENO," "DA VERAGGAN," "DA MOSTI," and "PIGAFETTA." Maximum speed over 44 knots.

SHIPS REPAIRS OF ALL DESCRIPTION, BOTH HULL AND MACHINERY COMBINED WITH THE BEST OF DOCKING FACILITIES.

SUBMARINE BOAT "DELFINUL" for the Rumanian Navy.

ATELIERS ET CHANTIERS
DE LA
SEINE MARITIME

WORMS & CIE

LE TRAIT (Seine Inférieure).

EIGHT BUILDING BERTHS

DESIGNERS & CONSTRUCTORS OF ALL CLASSES OF WARSHIPS

DESTROYERS, TORPEDO BOATS, SUBMARINES AND CARGO VESSELS, TANKERS, TRAWLERS

MARINE ENGINES AND BOILERS

HEAD OFFICE:—45 Boulevard Haussman, PARIS
Telegrams: LOCATOR, PARIS — WORMS, LE TRAIT

BROWN'S STEERING GEARS
STEAM, HYDRAULIC & ELECTRO-HYDRAULIC

STEERING TELEMOTORS

DIRECT-ACTING REVERSING ENGINES
FOR CONTROLLING
STEAM ENGINES, TURBINES & DIESEL ENGINES

HIGH SPEED HYDRAULIC CRANES & HOISTS
SPECIALLY SUITABLE FOR DIESEL ENGINED SHIPS

CAPSTANS, WINDLASSES, WINCHES BOAT-HOISTS, Etc.
COMPLETE INSTALLATIONS, INCLUDING STEAM OR ELECTRICALLY
DRIVEN PUMPING PLANT

Electro-Hydraulic Steering Gear
FOR
Q.S.T.S. "Empress of Britain"
ON TEST BED AT OUR WORKS.

Latest design 4-ram Type, Telemotor Controlled with Reserve Pumping Unit which
can be instantaneously brought into action.
As Fitted on Latest Warships of
H.M. NAVY, ITALIAN, FRENCH, NETHERLANDS, JAPANESE, ARGENTINE
AND CHILEAN NAVIES
and on
STEAMSHIPS AND MOTORSHIPS OF THE LEADING MERCHANT AND PASSENGER LINES

BROWN BROS. & CO. LTD.

Telegraphic Address	**ROSEBANK**	*Telephone No.*
"Hydraulic, Edinburgh"	**IRONWORKS**	Edinburgh 26231 & 26232
LIVERPOOL	**EDINBURGH**	**NEWCASTLE**
L. S. Taylor & Co.		H. K. Denton & Co.
610 Royal Liver Buildings		Prudential Buildings

W. OTTWAY & CO. Ltd.

ORION WORKS
EALING, LONDON, W.5.

ESTABLISHED 1640

Manufacturers of

W. OTTWAY & CO.'S PATENT VARIABLE POWER
GUN-SIGHTING TELESCOPES

AERO GUN SIGHT
(PATENT)

Manufacturers of

Naval and Military Telescopic Gun Sights, Theodolites, Tacheometers, Levels, Miners' Dials, Prismatic Compasses, Heliographs, Equatorials, Driving Clocks, Micrometers, Ceolostats, Transits, Mirrors, Flatts, Naval, Military and Astronomical Telescopes, Prismatic Binoculars, Sextants, Telescopic Lenses, Object Glasses, Prisms, etc. etc.

Contractors to ADMIRALTY, WAR OFFICE, INDIA OFFICE, Etc.

ESTABLISHED 1640

CHADBURN'S

(SHIP) TELEGRAPH CO. LTD.

NAVAL PATTERN TELEGRAPHS

ENGINE, STOKEHOLD REVOLUTION
SPEED INDICATORS AND COUNTERS

MECHANICAL SEARCHLIGHT CONTROL

FITTED DURING THE WAR THROUGHOUT THE WHOLE OF
THE VESSELS OF H.M. GRAND FLEET

MECHANICAL TORPEDO CONTROL

AS FITTED THROUGHOUT ALL DESTROYERS BUILT SINCE 1916
AND A LARGE NUMBER OF H.M. SHIPS OF THE GRAND FLEET

DE LAVAL OIL PURIFIER

FOR GEARED TURBINES, DIESEL ENGINES AND FUEL OIL

CYPRUS ROAD, BOOTLE, LANCS.

Also at LONDON, GLASGOW, NEWCASTLE
BELFAST, SOUTHAMPTON and HULL

One of the eight latest destroyers all designed by YARROW & CO., LTD., for the Royal Netherlands Navy

Four of these vessels are equipped with special high-pressure, high
temperature steam machinery

The YARROW design destroyer combines heavy armament
with high-speed large radius of action and exceptionally
good sea-going qualities

YARROW & Co. LIMITED, GLASGOW

also CONSTRUCTORS of

GUNBOATS, YACHTS, TUGS, LAUNCHES
PASSENGER AND CARGO STEAMERS
SHALLOW-DRAUGHT VESSELS

YARROW PATENT HIGH PRESSURE WATER TUBE BOILERS
YARROW SUPERHEATERS, YARROW AIR HEATERS, ETC.

**Outboard Set of
H.P. & I.P. Turbines
for T.S.S. "Empress of Britain"**

2¾ *tons*
of
MONEL METAL
TURBINE BLADING
in one installation alone!

Power Units in the modern battleship or liner must be capable of a performance hitherto unknown.

The enormous power to be developed in small space involves the utmost practicable pressures, temperatures and speeds, but the equally enormous responsibilities demand unquestionable reliability.

Monel Metal Blading to the amount of 2¾ tons was chosen for the "Empress of Britain" because

Monel Metal remains strong and tough at high steam pressures.

It is not cut by superheated steam.

It is not corroded.

It is immediately available in accurately-drawn sections of correct strength, hardness and toughness.

It is readily machined and easily brazed.

Monel Metal Blading is extensively, and in more recent cases exclusively, fitted in British and Foreign Warships and in the fastest liners, *e.g.* "Empress of Japan," C.P.S. Duchess and Beaver Class, "Statendam," "Bremen," "Europa," "Conte Rosso," "El Duce," "Rex," etc. etc.

MONEL-WEIR, LIMITED.
CATHCART - - - GLASGOW

GRAHAM MARINE EQUIPMENT

(15 Line)

A Graham Exchange Switchboard complete with operator's handsets

Dimensions:— Height—5 ft.
Width—19 inches.

GRAHAM DIN-PROOF PHONE

Approx. height overall—11½ inches. Approx. width overall—7½ inches.

This instrument provides for the exclusion of extraneous sounds while permitting clear and distinct transmission of messages at ample volume through the medium of an "OPEN MOUTHPIECE." The instrument is entirely weatherproof.

THE GRAHAM NAVAL MULTIPHONE

This instrument is intended for use where it is desired to transmit orders through a loud speaking receiver or receivers (right of illustration) from a central station to one or more distant stations. Owing to the circuit employed, receivers up to five in number may be used without serious diminution in volume.

Dimensions:— Transmitter Box { Approx. width overall—5½ inches
,, height ,, —10¾ ,,
Receiver . . . { ,, width ,, 9 inches
,, height ,, 14¼ ,,

ALFRED GRAHAM & CO. LTD.
St. Andrews Works
SLOUGH, BUCKS.

Suppliers to the British Navy ; also to the Japanese Navy as well as to the Navies of many other foreign Powers.

R. & W. HAWTHORN LESLIE & Co. Ltd.

ESTABLISHED 1817

ENGINES

TURBINE
RECIPROCATING
DIESEL (4-CYCLE
& 2-CYCLE)
WATERTUBE &
CYLINDRICAL
BOILERS
LOCOMOTIVES

TORPEDO BOAT DESTROYER FOR BRITISH ADMIRALTY

SHIPS

CRUISERS
DESTROYERS
MINESWEEPERS
SLOOPS
PASSENGER &
CARGO VESSELS
OIL TANKERS
TUGS

NEWCASTLE-ON-TYNE

FRENCH SUBMARINE CRUISER "SURCOUF"

1931 *Photo, Official*

JANE'S FIGHTING SHIPS
1931

FOUNDED IN **1897** BY FRED T. JANE

THIRTY-FIFTH YEAR OF ISSUE

EDITOR:
OSCAR PARKES, O.B.E., M.B., Ch.B.

SAMPSON LOW, MARSTON
& CO., LTD: LONDON
MCMXXXI

CONTENTS.

FOREWORD

DESPITE the effects of Treaties and Conferences in limiting naval construction, sufficient fresh material has been collected to justify the hope that this edition of "FIGHTING SHIPS" will be found well up to the usual standard. Interest in a new design does not depend upon the number of ships to be built to it, and limitation of construction does not lessen the necessity for keeping abreast of development. Far-reaching changes are maturing in warship design the world over, and the present lull in construction in this country is mainly due to a policy of marking time pending the completion of certain experiments, both in methods of construction and propulsion. However, next year there is to be held a Disarmament Conference, and maybe once again Yard-stick will be calling to Yard-stick across the Vasty Deep—which, judging by past experience, will result in a filip to construction along new lines.

In the British section, the most interesting addition is the picture of *Leander* as she will appear when completed. The original lay-out of the upper works has undergone modification to allow for a hangar to be worked in forward of the main mast, the rig has been lightened, and a really noble funnel installed. With vertical side armour of about 4 inches, very adequate deck and internal protection she bids fair to prove a really satisfactory cruiser. Details of the new 5,000 tonner are confidential, and it is to be hoped that the novel features rumour ascribes to her will materialise. Some very fine photos of *Hood* after her refit, *Exeter*, *York*, *Eagle* and *Furious*, the new destroyers, submarines and small craft will

be found, but the removal of the four *Iron Dukes*, the splendid *Tiger*, the "C" cruisers, "S" destroyers, sloops and "L" submarines has made the preparation of the British section a melancholy business.

It will be seen that the "B," "C," and "D" classes of destroyers have been grouped together as their differences are only in minor detail, and the so-called "leaders" of the same programmes are not really worthy of separate classification for the same reason. A plan of the *Swordfish* class of submarines is given in the addenda, together with a photo of *Falcon*—a modified *Tern* with two deck accommodation.

This year the French section must be awarded the palm for interest, as plans and photos of all the new ships have been secured. *Algerie* strikes a fresh note with her tower bridge-mast *à la Nelson*—a striking contrast to the much reduced bridgework and rig in our *Exeter*—and a return to side armour; *Foch* appears with an equally striking foremast which apparently has yet to justify its existence as *Dupleix* has reverted to the *Colbert* rig. In being, *Commandant Teste* is even more bizarre than her plans suggested, and a special set of photos show her at all angles. *Jeanne D'Arc* and *Pluton* are illustrated by large blocks which show them to their best advantage. The plan of *Emile Bertin* reveals her as a cruiser fitted for mine-laying, and she is to serve as a model for the later 7,600 ton *La Galisonnière* class. She marks the introduction of the triple mounting in the French service, a grouping to which we have not yet become reconciled. Among the new leaders, *Milan* and *Epervier* have

been built as trial ships for the later *Malin* class, of which the plan shows the new arrangement of torpedo tubes. In the experimental leader and destroyer of the 1931–32 programme the guns are to be paired on the Italian pattern, and the torpedo armament increased.

This year the French Ministry of Marine has been especially generous in the matter of photographs, and especial thanks are due for the splendid view of *Surcouf* which forms the frontispiece. The appearance of this, the biggest submarine afloat, has been kept strictly confidential and "FIGHTING SHIPS" is very conscious of the privilege of being allowed to make public the secret of her grim profile. Reference to the addenda will show the modifications in her armament, and during the next twelve months the results of her trials will be awaited with the keenest interest.

At the moment of writing no decision has been come to as regards the 25,000 ton armoured ships, nor have the credits been voted. The preliminary design, it is understood, included three quadruple turrets, which was followed by one in which eight guns were disposed in four turrets, of which A mounted two, B three, X two and Y one only, giving a broadside of eight, ahead of five and astern fire of three guns. Latest information indicates that the customary arrangement of four twin 13.4″ turrets in pairs fore and aft will be adopted after all.

The provision of two "sailing gunboats" and a sailing training ship, *Belle Poule*, will be welcomed by those who maintain that training in sail is still the best school for developing essential nautical qualities in both officers and men whatever subsequent scientific and mechanical skill is required. Sail has been adopted for training purposes in most navies, and now that France has joined the majority only Japan (who possesses auxiliary sailing ships for training her mercantile marine), the U.S.A. and the British Navy stand alone in favour of utilitarian training.

In the Italian section will be found *Zara* as finally completed, minus the tiers of bridges around the quadrupled foremast; and the *Condottieri* class of 40 knot cruisers as modified by removal of a certain amount of upperworks and the after tripod mast. These wonderful ships continue to improve upon their speed figures, and the *A. di Barbiano* now holds the record with 42 knots. Additional space has been allotted to the big destroyer-scouts which form such an important part of the fleet. During the past year the destroyer record has been raised to 44 knots by the *A. Cadamosto*, completely equipped and with fuel and water at the beginning of the trials approximately equal to the normal load. The curious alteration to the bridgework of this class should be noted. The photo of the big submarine *E. Fieramosca*, shows up well her unusually large conning tower; while that of the *A. Vespucci*, second of the Diesel-sail training ships, is a striking contrast to the ever-growing submarine fleets in the Mediterranean.

During the past year Japan has pressed forward with the construction of the last ships of the *Nachi* class, of which new photos are included, and from the new programme, 1931–36, it will be seen that she is embarking upon large 6″ gunned cruisers and a variety of new types of smaller craft. Further details of the carrier *Ryugo* are given, but unfortunately little can be learned as to her appearance when completed from the launch photo. It will be interesting to see how the funnel problem is tackled and whether the reported *Hosho* arrangement is still in favour. A study of the *Shinonome* on page 335 will show the shields to the torpedo tubes—an innovation which will doubtless be extensively copied. Japan has led the way in protecting the crews of her destroyers from machine gun attack, and these last boats of the *Fubuki* class are probably the most efficient destroyers afloat in general all round qualities.

American new construction is confined to the 8″ gun cruisers and destroyers—of which details are still confidential—the flight-deck cruisers being projected only, as is the 6″ cruiser programme. Reconstruction of the *Idaho* class is proceeding, and they will be altered similarly to the *Arizona*.

Alterations to the Spanish 10,000 ton *Canarias* class are shown in plan and picture, and it is still uncertain which of the alternative designs will be chosen. The change over to the single funnel makes them vastly more imposing looking, and the distribution of the A.A. guns differentiating the designs is a minor feature.

A number of changes and additions will be found in the Russian pages, but mainly in the smaller craft. The re-appearance of the *Novik* as altered for cruiser duties confirms reports that a number of the destroyers thought to be scrapped have been renovated and put into commission again, while the long delayed completion of the remaining ships of the *Profintern* type has at last been achieved. The re-arming of the old gunboats has been done on the generous plan of "space without a gun is wasted" and it is refreshing to find ships forty years old still employed at sea.

Interest in the German Navy is still centred around the *Deutschland*, now completing for sea, about which very little new information has been forthcoming. Two photos were obtained of *Leipzig* when she went out on trials, and the picture of *Bremse* is based on reliable data—although two funnels seems rather superfluous. A number of the older ships have been scrapped and the small craft have been brought up-to-date.

Considerable interest is attached to the Finnish coast defence ships, which bear a close resemblance to the *Gorgon* class we took over from Norway during the War. In them the armour is less than was expected, but owing to their Diesels the sub-division has been carried out in such a way as to render them relatively as safe as would the amount of medium-armour which might have been worked into the design. The Yugo-Slav section has been re-cast, and illustrated by fresh photos, while the Greek Navy is almost entirely illustrated afresh.

The new destroyers for the Greek and Turkish fleets are of interest, the *Hydra* being a *Dardo* with the British arrangement of guns. It may be of interest to note that the one funnel idea was incorporated in an alternative plan submitted by Messrs. Thornycroft for the Chilean destroyers of the *Rioja* class, and is likely to appear in several forthcoming designs.

FOREWORD—*continued*.

The new ships now under construction for the Portuguese Navy show a certain similarity in design which somewhat detracts from their general interest, and the carrier pays tribute to the R.A.N. *Albatross* of which she appears almost a replica.

We welcome the new Czecho-Slovac section and the photo of the *P. Massaryk* will interest those correspondents who have reported the appearance of this little monitor.

Most of the old black silhouettes have disappeared, and the Chinese, Esthonian, Finnish, Greek, Norwegian, Polish, Portuguese, Roumanian, Russian, Siamese, Swedish, Turkish and Yugo-Slav navies have been entirely re-drawn, and a large number of new or replace silhouettes have been added to the other navies.

Drawings of new ships include the *Leander*, *Algerie*, *Canarias*, *Bremse*, *Vainomoinen*, *Hydra*, *Folgore*, *Novik* and three other Russian ships, of which the photos were unsuitable for reproduction. These are referred to as "1931 Illustrations." The only omissions from the new construction pages (of which plans or illustrations could not be given) are those which are still confidential, like the U.S.S. *Ranger* and new cruisers, our own 5,000 tonner, and those ships of which the plans are not yet settled, like the Netherlands cruiser and leader.

A more personal note may be forgiven in the acknowledgment of assistance received during the past year. In these lean years

"FIGHTING SHIPS" has to count on being able to obtain every available scrap of information, and the postponement of construction until late in the year together with the chopping and changing of design has made the compilation this year rather more difficult than formerly. For this reason we are doubly grateful to the various Naval Attaché's for the trouble they have taken in dealing with repeated questionnaires and obtaining photographs. The number of official photographs in the Chinese, French, Italian, Greek, Yugo-Slav and U.S. sections, for instance, are eloquent of more than generous help and we are sorry that it was not possible to make use of the replace photos in many instances. In other sections the additions and alterations to the text, flags and uniforms is of equal importance, and for the painstaking assistance of the "Home Authorities" one and all, we proffer most sincere thanks.

To the "Special Correspondents" abroad this annual tribute for their brotherly co-operation is as deep as words can convey, and as they wish to remain anonymous, will they accept this assurance that their association with "FIGHTING SHIPS" makes the editorship a much lighter and more pleasureable task. Those readers who have sent in photos and information from all over the World will have received acknowledgments, and we can only say how much their contributions are appreciated, and beg their continuance.

For his invaluable assistance in preparing the plans and providing so many excellent photos we are, as before, vastly indebted to Mr. R. Perkins, and Captain Frank Bowen will see evidence of his notes in every section of the book. Commdt. P. Vincent-Brechignac (Editor of the *Flottes de Combat*) and Mons. H. le Masson have again proved real friends, and as always, we are deeply grateful for their help. Lt.-Commdr. R. Steen Steensen, R.D.N., and Herr Ossi Janson will again see their names under many photos, and Herr Torsten Hallonblad's last minute contributions were indeed welcome. Capitan Mateo Mille, Dr. Ing. V. Mendl, and Commdr. A Raninen, three of "FIGHTING SHIPS'" earliest contributors have again rendered most valuable and welcome help.

For photos and information we are indebted to Messrs. Thornycroft, Messrs. Yarrow, Messrs. Vickers-Armstrong, Messrs. Ansaldo, the Cant. Nav. Riunitis of Ancona and Palermo, Messrs. Normand and Messrs. The Bethlehem S.B. Co., whom we cordially thank.

Finally, may we acknowledge the valuable assistance given by those departments at the Admiralty to whom we turned for information, and say how grateful we are for the material furnished.

THE PUBLISHERS.

GENERAL INDEX (Named Ships only.)

ABBREVIATIONS: (A) signifies Argentina, (Br) Brazilian, (Chil) Chilian, (C) Chinese, (Cu) Cuban, (Da) Danish, (F) French, (G) German, (Gr) Grecian, (I) Italian, (J) Japanese, (N) Netherlands (Nor) Norwegian, (P) Peruvian, (Po) Polish, (Port) Portuguese, (Ro) Roumanian, (Rus) Russian, (Sp) Spanish, (Sw) Swedish, (T) Turkish, (U.S.) United States. No descriptive term implies British Empire.

NOTE :—The following pages, descriptive of H. M. Navy, have been inspected and approved for publication by the Admiralty. The Admiralty accepts no responsibility whatever for the accuracy of any of the statements made in " Fighting Ships " as regards H. M. Navy.

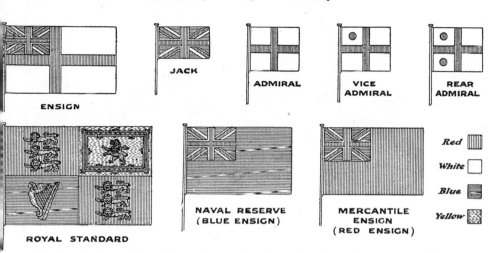

ENSIGN

JACK

ADMIRAL

VICE ADMIRAL

REAR ADMIRAL

ROYAL STANDARD

NAVAL RESERVE (BLUE ENSIGN)

MERCANTILE ENSIGN (RED ENSIGN)

Red

White

Blue

Yellow

Note.—M (International Code) at masthead indicates that Submarines are in company and/or exercising. When accompanied by group from Numerical Table (Int. Code), number of Submarines are indicated by group hoist. R.F.A. fly Blue Ensign with Admiralty Badge (Foul Anchor). Mercantile F.A. fly Red Ensign.

Colour of Ships.

Warships in Home Waters, dark grey ; in Mediterranean, light grey. Cruisers and Sloops on China Station, white hulls, grey upperworks. Sloops in East Indies and Red Sea, and Cruisers in East Indies, North America and West Indies, white with primrose-yellow masts, funnels and yards. Sloops for North America and West Indies, New Zealand and Africa Stations, grey all over. Fishery Protection Vessels, Depot Ships and many auxiliaries in Home Waters, black hulls and light grey upperworks ; funnels may be varied between black, white and grey, and may have rings for identification purposes. Surveying Ships have white hulls with yellow funnels. All Destroyers have their Pendant Numbers on bows and across sterns. Submarines have their Class Letter and Numbers painted on sides of Conning Tower.

Future Construction.

1929 Programme. 1 Cruiser (Leander), 1 Leader, 4 Destroyers, 4 Sloops, 3 Submarines.

1930 Programme. 3 Cruisers, 1 Leader, 8 Destroyers, 3 Submarines, 4 Sloops, 1 Net Layer.

1931 Programme. 3 Cruisers, 9 Destroyers, 4 Sloops, 3 Submarines, 1 China G.B., 1 Mining Tender, 1 Gate Vessel.

Uniforms.

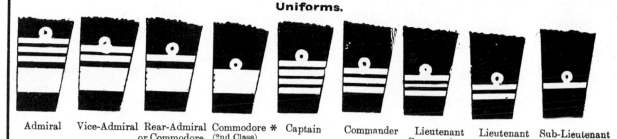

Admiral	Vice-Admiral	Rear-Admiral or Commodore (1st Class)	Commodore ✱ (2nd Class)	Captain	Commander	Lieutenant Commander	Lieutenant	Sub-Lieutenant

Admiral of the Fleet has one stripe more than Admiral, i.e., four in all.

Relative Ranks. Non-Executive Branches (as modified, 1926). Engineer Officers have same as above, with purple between stripes.

Medical	"	"	"	" scarlet " "
Dental	"	"	"	" orange " "
Accountant	"	"	"	" white " "
Instructor	"	"	"	" light blue " "
Shipwright	"	"	"	" silver grey " "
Wardmaster	"	"	"	" maroon " "
Electrical	"	"	"	" dark green " "
Ordnance	"	"	"	" dark blue " "

✱ Ring separated from top stripe.

Navy Estimates and Personnel.

(1931) £54,679,560 net.

Personnel : 95,000.

Board of Admiralty.

First Lord : The Rt. Hon. Sir Bolton Eyres-Monsell, G.B.E.
First Sea Lord and Chief of Naval Staff : Admiral Sir F. L. Field, K.C.B., K.C.M.G.
Second Sea Lord : Admiral Sir T. M. Fuller, K.C.B., C.M.G., D.S.O.
Deputy Chief of the Naval Staff : Vice-Admiral F. C. Dreyer, C.B., C.B.E.
Third Sea Lord and Controller : Vice-Admiral Roger Roland C. Blackhouse, C.B., C.M.G.
Fourth Sea Lord : Vice-Admiral L. G. Preston, C.B.
Civil Lord : Capt. D. Euam Wallace, M.C.
Parliamentary and Financial Secretary : Lord Stanley.
Permanent Secretary : Sir Oswyn A. R. Murray, K.C.B.

Committee of Imperial Defence.

President : The Lord President of the Council.
Members : H. M. Secretaries of State for War, Air, Colonies, India ; The First Lord of Admiralty ; The First Sea Lord and Chief of Naval Staff ; Chief of the Imperial General Staff ; Chief of the Air Staff.
Also representatives of H.M. Treasury and other Government Departments are called in, as requisite.

Director of Naval Construction.

A. W. Johns, Esq., C.B., C.B.E.

Mercantile Marine.

(From "Lloyd's Register," 1931).
Total for whole of British Empire, 23,379,999 tons *gross*, including 328 vessels of 16 knots and over.

BRITISH NAVAL ORDNANCE.

NOTE.—All details unofficial, but believed to be approximately correct. (Particulars formerly given of some older marks of guns, no longer mounted in H.M. Ships, have been deleted).

Calibre. ins.	Mark.	Length of Bore in Calibres.	Weight of piece without B.M.	Weight of Projectile.	M.V.	M.E.	Weight of Full Charge.	REMARKS.
			tons cwts. qrs.	lbs.	f. s.	f. t.	lbs.	
				HEAVY B.L.				
16	I	45	103 10 0	2461	2953	..	640	" Nelson " and " Rodney."
15	I	42	97 3 0	1920	2450	84,070	428	Mounted in " Royal Sovereign," " Queen Elizabeth," " Hood," " Repulse," and " Erebus " classes.
13.5	VI	45	75 8 0	{ 1250 L. } { 1400 H. }	2700	63,190	{ 293 L. } { 297 H. }	Mounted in " Tiger."
	V	45	74 18 1	..	2500	63,190	..	" Iron Duke " class.
				MEDIUM B.L.				
8	I	55	16 10 0	256	3150	17,615	..	" Kent," " London," " Dorsetshire " and " York " classes.
7.5	VI	45	13 11 0	200	2800	12,500	61	" Frobisher " and " Effingham."
	V	50	15 16 2	200	2800	12,500	61	" Hawkins " and " Vindictive."
6	XVIII	50	8 9 2	100	2800	..	$28\frac{5}{8}$	Cruisers and Secondary Armament Battleships and Battle Cruisers.
	XVI	50	7 19 1	100	3100	6665	33	
	XII	45	6 14 2	100	2750	..	$27\frac{1}{4}$	
	XI*	50	8 8 2	100	2937	5990	$32\frac{1}{12}$	
	XI	50	8 8 2	100	2937	5990	$32\frac{1}{12}$	Secondary Armament " Iron Duke " class and " Tiger."
	VII	44.9	7 7 2	100	2493	5250	$28\frac{5}{8}$	
5.5	I	50	6 1 0	82	2725	4222	$22\frac{1}{4}$	Breech mechanism of the Holmstrom type. Aircraft Carriers and Secondary Armament " Hood."
4.7	II	40	3 1 0	48.5	2560	2205	..	AA. mounted in " Nelson " and " Rodney."
	I	45	3 1 0	50	3000	2800	$11\frac{3}{8}$	Mounted in later Flotilla Leaders and Destroyers.
				LIGHT B.L.				
4	XI	40	1 4 3	31	2100	..	..	Secondary armament, Battle Cruisers and Monitors.
	IX*	44.35	2 1 1	31	2625	1934	$7\frac{11}{16}$	
	IX	44.35	2 1 1	31	2625	1934	$7\frac{11}{16}$	
	VIII	39.8	1 4 2	31	2287	..	$5\frac{3}{8}$	Earlier Destroyers.
				MEDIUM Q.F.				
6	III	40	7 0 0	100	2025	..	$13\frac{1}{4}$	In reserve for D.A.M.S.
4.7	VII	50	3 5 0	45	..	..	$8\frac{11}{16}$	In reserve for D.A.M.S.
	V*	43.9	2 10 0	45	..	..	$8\frac{11}{16}$	
	V	43.9	2 10 0	45	..	..	$8\frac{11}{16}$	

BRITISH NAVAL ORDNANCE.

LIGHT GUNS.—(See Note on previous page).

Calibre. ins.	Mark.	Length of Bore in Calibres.	Weight of piece without B.M.	Weight of Projectile.	M.V.	M.E.	Weight of Full Charge.	REMARKS.
			tons cwts. qrs.	lbs.	f. s.	f. t	lbs.	
LIGHT Q.F.								
4	XII	40	1 6 0	31	2100	..	$5\frac{1}{6}$	Semi-automatic. Fixed Ammunition. A.A. mounting. Battleships, Battle Cruisers, Cruisers and Aircraft Carriers.
	VII	40.5	1 4 4	31	2750	1970	$5\frac{7}{16}$	Do. do. do. do.
	V*	45	2 1 2	31	2625	1934	$5\frac{7}{8}$	Do. do. do. do.
	V	45	2 1 2	31	2625	1934	$7\frac{11}{16}$	Semi-automatic. } Earlier Destroyers and Submarines.
	IV	40	1 3 3	31	2225	1137	$5\frac{1}{6}$	Do. } Earlier Destroyers and Submarines.
	III	40	1 3 0	25	2456	1200	$3\frac{9}{16}$	D.A.M.S.
3	I	45	1 0 0	{ 16 $12\frac{1}{2}$ }	2500	..	{ $2\frac{1}{6}$ $2\frac{1}{2}$ }	Semi-Automatic. Fixed ammunition. AA. mounting. Earlier Cruisers, Flotilla Leaders and Destroyers.
3	I	23	5 3	$12\frac{1}{2}$	1700	..	$1\frac{5}{16}$	Fixed ammunition. In reserve for D.A.M.S.
3	I	40	11 2	$12\frac{1}{2}$	2197	..	2	Minesweepers, Sloops and Gunboats.
2.24	II	40	7 0	6	1735	..	ozs. $8\frac{3}{4}$	Fixed ammunition. Auxiliary patrol.
1.85	II	40	5 0	$3\frac{5}{16}$	1873	..	$7\frac{1}{4}$	Fixed ammunition. Hotchkiss. Saluting guns in all classes.
	I	50	6 0	$3\frac{5}{16}$	2575	152	$13\frac{1}{8}$	Fixed ammunition. Vickers. Auxiliary Patrol. Aircraft Carriers.
	II	39.37	1 3	2	2000	55.5	3	} Automatic. AA. mounting. Cruisers, Flotilla Leaders and Destroyers.
	I	39.37	1 3	2	2000	55.5	3	} Automatic. AA. mounting. Cruisers, Flotilla Leaders and Destroyers.
ANTI-SUBMARINE HOWITZERS, B.L.								
							lbs.	
11	I	8.5	1 14 2	200	..	..	..	} In reserve for D.A.M.S. and Auxiliary Patrol.
7.5	I	8.5	6 0	100	390	105.5	$1\frac{1}{4}$	} In reserve for D.A.M.S. and Auxiliary Patrol.

STICK BOMBS.

Gun.	Weight of Bomb.	Charge.		
4.7 in. Q.F.	{ 600 500 250 200 }	3 lbs. 14 ozs.		
4 in. B.L. or Q.F.	{ 350 200 }	2 lbs. 2 ozs. 3 lbs. 4 ozs.	Mark IV. & VIII. Mark V & IX.	
12 pdr. 12 cwt. Q.F.	200	1 lb.		

Torpedoes.

No official details obtainable. Standard torpedo used is the 21 inch Mk 5 heater type, 18 inch tubes being obsolete and only fitted for instructional purposes in certain destroyers and submarines. Specially strengthened 14 inch torpedoes are used for dropping from seaplanes. In all new cruisers tubes are of the above-water pattern; the great height of these above the waterline has necessitated modifications of construction and depth-keeping mechanism to avoid breaking up the torpedo, and deep diving when fired. Torpedoes are fired by air or a cordite charge, and are of the improved heater type fitted with high and low speed settings with a corresponding short or long range, and are directed by an angled gyro to give increased firing arc.

Searchlights.

These are of 36 inch and 24 inch diameters. The number of 36 inch pattern has been reduced to six in capital ships with 2—24 inch for signalling. Cruisers carry 4—36 inch lights, while 1—24 inch is mounted in destroyers. The searchlights are elevated and trained from remote positions, and are controlled by an electrical 'follow-the-pointer' device. In the Mk 5—36 inch arc lamp the carbons revolve and the size of the arc is regulated by an electro-magnetic arc beater, which gives a nearly parallel beam reflected from the mirror. As the carbons no longer burn in a spirit flame the beams have lost their characteristic blueish tint. Carbons are fed automatically with alternative hand operation, while an improved pattern of arc striker minimizes the risk of ' broken carbon.'

Mining.

Mk H2 mine, extensively used in the War, is still the standard type used from surface minelayers, with a modification for use by submarines. Weight 650 lbs., diameter 38 inches, buoyancy 400 lbs., fitted with 6 " horns " for exploding charge. Several marks of sinker are used in conjunction with this mine according to the depth, tides, etc. No details are obtainable of further types of mine, e.g., observation.

Protective paravanes are carried by all deep draught ships, of a similar design to that used during the War.

BRITISH WARSHIP BUILDERS.

Note.—The headings give the abbreviated titles by which builders are mentioned on later Ship Pages. With a few exceptions, all details given below were kindly approved or furnished by the firms mentioned.

Vickers—Armstrongs. (A)
(See also Vickers—Armstrongs. (B) on following page).

SIR W. G. ARMSTRONG, WHITWORTH & CO., LTD. (NEWCASTLE-ON-TYNE). *Armstrong Yard*, opened 1913, and now engaged on the construction of both warships and mercantile vessels. Area 81 acres. Frontage about a mile. Ten slips, 1000 to 500 ft. long. *Walker Shipyard*. Area 30 acres. Frontage 317 yards. Six slips from 650 to 450 ft. long. (The former Elswick yard ceased to function as such in 1918, the land and shops being absorbed by the Ordnance and Steel Departments of the firm.) The Dobson and Tyne Iron Shipbuilding Yards are now included in the organisation.

Cammell Laird.

CAMMELL LAIRD & CO., LTD. (BIRKENHEAD AND TRANMERE). Area of yard, 108 acres. Six slips (longest 1000 ft.), six small slips. Seven graving docks, five small and No. 6, 708 × 80 ft.; No. 7, 861 × 90 ft. Outer basin, 14½ acres ; inner basin, 2¾ acres. Annual capacity, 100,000 tons *gross* and 400,000 H.P. output. Establishment consists of North Yard, where vessels up to 500 feet in length can be constructed, and the South Yard, in which are slips suitable for vessels between 600 and 900 feet in length. Builders of heavy armoured ships, cruisers, flotilla leaders, destroyers, submarines, &c., as well as of merchant vessels of all classes. Equipment of yard thoroughly up-to-date.

Clydebank.

JOHN BROWN & CO., LTD. (SHIPBUILDING & ENGINEERING WORKS, CLYDEBANK, GLASGOW). Area, 80 acres. River frontage, 1050 yards. Building berths : Five of 950 to 600 ft. in length, and three 600 to 450 ft. in length. Building berths are commanded by derricks, tower and gantry cranes ; two of berths are covered. Tidal basin : 5¼ acres in area, 30 ft. depth, L.W.O.S.T. with two entrances of 130 and 180 ft. width respectively. Basin commanded by two 150-ton cranes ; also four wharf cranes of 5 to 30 tons capacity. Builders of war and mercantile vessels of all types and the largest dimensions, inclusive of machinery and equipment. Steam engines of reciprocating type, Parsons and Brown-Curtis turbine types ; and Diesel oil engines.

Denny.

WM. DENNY & BROS., LTD. (LEVEN SHIPYARD, DUMBARTON.). Area : 60 acres. Building berths up to 550 ft. in length. Two wet basins, one 475 ft., one 910 ft. Numerous cranes with lifts up to 110 tons. Destroyers, torpedo boats, submarines and mercantile vessels built, with necessary machinery, &c.

Doxford.

WM. DOXFORD & SONS, LTD. (PALLION YARD, SUNDERLAND). Builders of vessels up to 20,000 tons dead-weight. Output over 100,000 tons *gross* per annum. Build Diesel marine engines of opposed piston, airless injection type, up to any size.

Fairfield.

THE FAIRFIELD SHIPBUILDING & ENGINEERING CO., LTD. (GOVAN, GLASGOW). Area: 70 acres. Water front: 2600 ft. 11 slips to build ships up to 900 ft. in length. Dock: 6 acres with 270 ft. entrance. 250-ton crane. Wet basin: 900 ft. long and ten docks up to 900 ft. Naval and mercantile ships, engines, boilers, &c., of all types. Associated with Northumberland S.B. Co. and Workman, Clark & Co.

Harland & Wolff.

HARLAND & WOLFF, LTD. (BELFAST). Eight large slips in main yard (two 860 × 99 ft.). Six large slips in East Yard. Two large docks and three smaller in the vicinity of the works. Also at Govan, Glasgow, 7 large slips; Greenock, 6 large slips. Engineering establishments: Diesel Engine Works, Finnieston and Scotstoun, Glasgow; Clyde Foundry, Govan, Glasgow. Exceptional facilities at London, Liverpool, and Southampton, for the repair of ships and machinery.

Hawthorn Leslie.

R. & W. HAWTHORN, LESLIE & CO., LTD. (HEBBURN YARD, HEBBURN-ON-TYNE). Twelve slips up to 700 ft. long. One dock: 460 × 68 × 21 ft. on blocks; 26 ft. draught at quay at low water. Engine department of 150,000 I.H.P. per annum. Designers and builders of cruisers, destroyers and other warship types. Engine every type of war vessel. Builders of locomotives for main line service and works.

Palmers.

PALMERS SHIPBUILDING & IRON CO., LTD. (JARROW AND HEBBURN-ON-TYNE). All classes of war and mercantile vessels. Build internal combustion, steam turbine and reciprocating engines, water-tube and Scotch boilers. Fully equipped for all classes of repairs to hulls and machinery. Twelve slips. Employees: 9000. Has two docks: Hebburn, 700 × 90 × 29 ft.; Jarrow, 440 × 70 × 18 ft.; also patent slipway (Jarrow), and dry dock at Swansea, 560 × 75 × 26 feet—all suitable for warships and mercantile vessels.

Scotts'.

SCOTTS' SHIPBUILDING & ENGINEERING CO., LTD. (GREENOCK). Slips for eight large vessels; fitting-out basin; graving dock. Makers of heavy oil engines and licensees for Laurenti type of submarines.

Stephen.

ALEX. STEPHEN & SONS, LTD. (LINTHOUSE, GOVAN, GLASGOW). Build destroyers and torpedo craft; also mail, passenger and cargo steamers. Machinery: all types, 40,000 H.P. output per annum. Boilers: Scotch, cylindrical and all water-tube types. Seven building berths for building ships up to 700 ft. long. Water front: 1500 ft. Area of yard: 52 acres. Repairs of all classes to hulls and machinery at firm's Govan graving dock. Works adjacent to Glasgow Docks.

Swan Hunter.

SWAN, HUNTER & WIGHAM RICHARDSON, LTD. (WALLSEND-ON-TYNE). Nineteen building berths, served by overhead electric cranes. Four of the largest berths covered in. Annual *gross* shipbuilding capacity, 150,000 tons. Engine works: 60,000 H.P. output per year.

The dry dock dept. includes a large repairing yard with two graving docks and a floating dock. Engine works build marine oil engines of the Neptune type, also Metropolitan-Vickers Rateau marine steam turbines, and reciprocating steam engines. Total area of works: 78 acres. Water frontage: 4000 ft. Shipyard also at Southwick-on-Wear, with four building berths. Allied firms are the Wallsend Slipway & Engineering Co., Ltd., Wallsend; Barclay Curle & Co., Ltd., of Whiteinch, Govan, Elderslie and Glasgow; North of Ireland Shipbuilding Co., Ltd., Londonderry; Philip & Son, Ltd., Dartmouth; Harris Bros., Ltd., Cambrian Dry Docks, Swansea; Lindsay, Swan, Hunter, Ltd., salvage contractors, Sunderland.

Thornycroft.

JOHN I. THORNYCROFT & CO., LTD. (WOOLSTON, SOUTHAMPTON). Builders of torpedo boats, destroyers, light cruisers, merchant vessels up to 400 ft. Thirteen building berths, including three covered in. One hauling-up slip for ships up to 170 ft. long. Water frontage: 2000 ft. Opposite Southampton Docks. Specialities: Turbines, water-tube boilers, oil fuel gear. Workshops in Southampton Docks, adjacent to fitting-out dock for hull and machinery repairs. Total floor area: 25,000 sq. ft.

Vickers—Armstrongs. (B)

(See also Vickers—Armstrongs (A) details on preceding page).

VICKERS, LTD. (BARROW-IN-FURNESS). Area of works: 105 acres. Thirteen building berths, of length respectively 800 ft.; 750 ft.; 700 ft.; 630 ft.; two of 600 ft.; three of 550 ft.; 450 ft.; 400 ft.; and 350 ft.—the two latter being entirely under cover; all berths efficiently served by modern cranes, lattice work derricks and electric winches. Fitting-out basin equipped with two 150-ton Giant Hammer-head cranes, 30-ton electric jib crane, two 10-ton steam derrick cranes, one 18-ton steam travelling crane, and numerous others, with a full complement of winches and capstans. Floating dock, 420 × 59½ ft., to lift 5200 tons. Graving dock, 500 × 60 × 22 ft. Extensive shops fully equipped with the most modern machinery for the construction of steam and internal combustion engines, boilers, electric equipment, gun mountings, and every kind of naval and mercantile engineering work. (Overseas Branch: Canadian Vickers Co., Montreal.) Agencies all over the world.

White.

J. SAMUEL WHITE & CO., LTD. (COWES). The oldest shipyard on the Admiralty List. Light cruisers, gunboats, flotilla leaders, destroyers, submarines, minelayers, patrol boats, turbine pinnaces, and small naval craft of every kind. Seven building berths. Engine works for reciprocating and turbine engines of highest powers, "White-Forster" water-tube boilers, "White" Diesel engines, and "White" patent oil fuel installations. Hammer-head 80-ton crane.

Yarrow.

YARROW & CO., LTD. (SCOTSTOUN, GLASGOW). Area of yard: 16 acres. Water frontage: 750 ft. Six building berths, for ships up to 400 ft. long. Wet basin for fitting-out, 350 × 85 ft., served by 50-ton crane. Specialities are destroyers, fast yachts, vessels for shallow river navigation, both of stern-wheel type and of type propelled by screws working in tunnels. Yarrow water-tube boilers and Yarrow superheater, both for land and marine use. Also vessels propelled by internal-combustion motors. (Overseas Branch: Yarrows, Ltd., Victoria, B.C.)

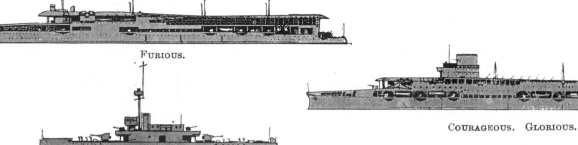

FURIOUS.

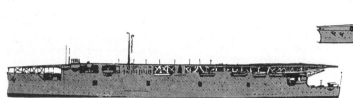

ARGUS.

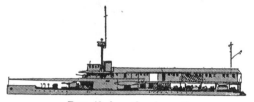

SCARAB class (2 funnels abreast).

COURAGEOUS. GLORIOUS.

SPEY.

BEE (2 funnels abreast).

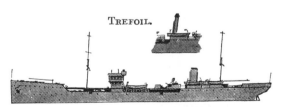

DART and PC 74.

P40, P59.

TREFOIL.

PETROBUS class (3).

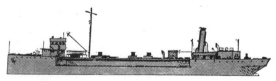

BIRCHOL (8), DISTOL (4), ATTENDANT (2).

TURMOIL.

DREDGOL.

SCOTOL.

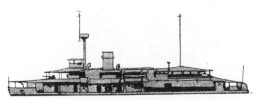

WAR KRISHNA type.

MIXOL.
THERMOL. }

BRITISH BEACON class (4).

BURMA.

SEAMEW, TERN.
GANNET, PETREL.

FRANCOL (3).

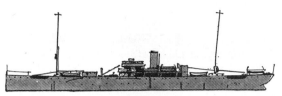

PERTHSHIRE.

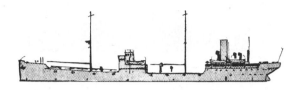

OLEANDER OLNA.

WAR AFRIDI *type*.

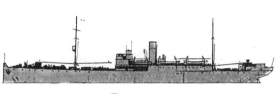

BACCHUS.

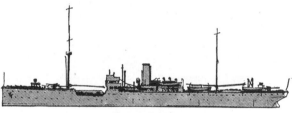

GREENWICH.

PLUMLEAF *type*.

NUCULA. (N.Z.)

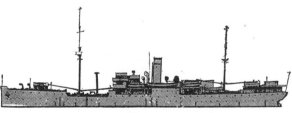

LUCIA.

BELGOL (6).

PETROLEUM.

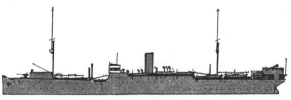

CYCLOPS.

HINDUSTAN (R.I.M.)

BRIDGEWATER *Class*

CHRYSANTHEMUM.

SANDHURST

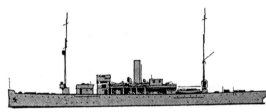

BRYONY.

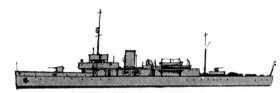

Twin Screw Minesweepers.

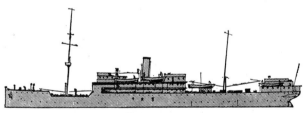

TITANIA.

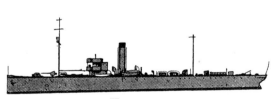

HEATHER.

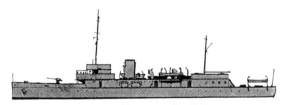

Twin Screw Minesweepers as Tenders.

HERALD (3), MORESBY. (R.A.N.)

HAREBELL.

FLINDERS (4).

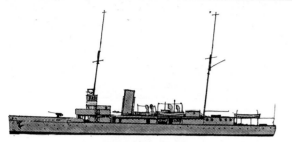

PETERSFIELD.

ALECTO, ADAMANT.

HERMES.

CACHALOT.

ENDEAVOUR.

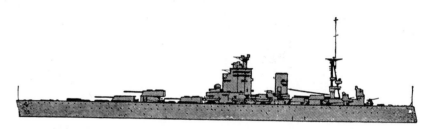

NELSON & RODNEY.

RESOLUTION.

DEE Type Trawlers.

EREBUS.

ROYAL SOVEREIGN *Class.*

MERSEY Type Trawlers.

TERROR.

Q. ELIZABETH *Class.*

TRIAD.

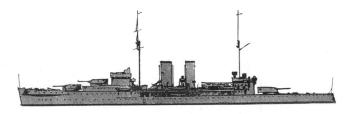

EXETER.

RENOWN, REPULSE.

CYCLAMEN (4), GODETIA.

YORK.
(Catapult now fitted abaft funnels).

HOOD.

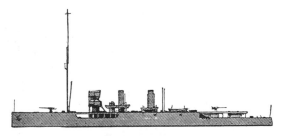

CORNFLOWER.

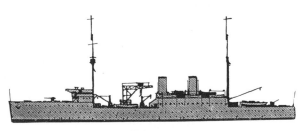

RESOURCE.

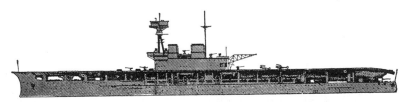

EAGLE.

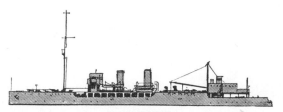

SNAPDRAGON.

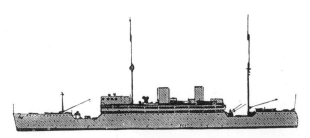

MEDWAY.

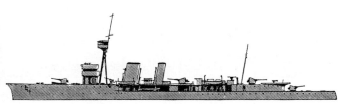

CAMBRIAN, CANTERBURY, CASTOR, CONSTANCE.

CONCORD.
(CENTAUR similar with deckhouse in place of gun abaft foremast).

Diomede (note turret.)

DELHI, DURBAN, DESPATCH, DIOMEDE (N.Z.), DUNEDIN (N.Z).
(Trawler bow.)

CHAMPION. (S.L. Control Tower amidships.)

CERES, CARDIFF, COVENTRY, CURAÇOA, CURLEW.
(Note No. 2 gun on shelter deck forward.)

CALYPSO.

CARADOC, CALYPSO.

CAPETOWN, CAIRO, CALCUTTA, CARLISLE, COLOMBO.
(Trawler bow.)

HAWKINS, EFFINGHAM, FROBISHER.

CALEDON.
(Note flight platform.)

DANAE, DAUNTLESS, DRAGON.
(No. 3 gun abaft foremast.)

VINDICTIVE.

13

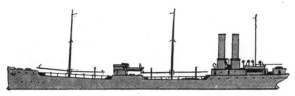

DELPHINULA.

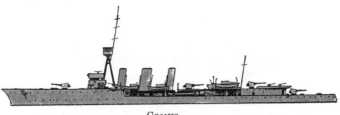

COMUS.

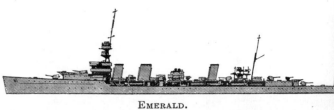

EMERALD.

IRON DUKE.

ENTERPRISE (Note forward turret).

ADVENTURE.

BERWICK, CORNWALL, CUMBERLAND, KENT, SUFFOLK.

DORSETSHIRE, NORFOLK, SUSSEX, DEVONSHIRE, LONDON, SHROPSHIRE.
(Note position of main mast).

TYRANT.

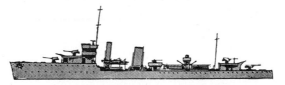

VICEROY, VISCOUNT, WOLSEY, WOOLSTON.

"A" class.

"S" class.

"V" and "W" classes (50).

"B" class.

CODRINGTON (Leader).

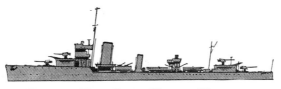

VETERAN, WILD SWAN, WIVERN, WHITSHED,
WITHERINGTON, WOLVERINE, WORCESTER.

Admiralty "R" class (9).

BRUCE, CAMPBELL, MALCOLM, DOUGLAS, MACKAY,
STUART. (Leaders.)

WISHART, WITCH.

GRENVILLE. (Leader.)

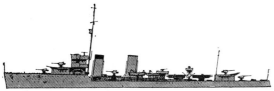

BROKE, KEPPEL, SHAKESPEARE, SPENSER, WALLACE.
(Leaders.)

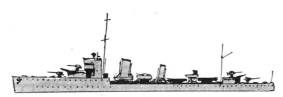

AMAZON, AMBUSCADE.

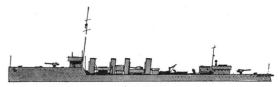

ABDIEL.

SUBMARINES.

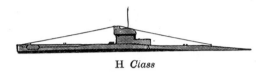

H *Class*

L 18—33.

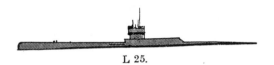

L 25.

L 52—71.

X 1.

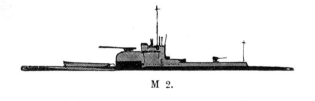

M 2.

OBERON.

M 3.

"P" and "R" *Class.*
(Note bow).

ODIN *Class* (6).
(Note bow).

NELSON.   (NELSON CLASS.)   *1927 Photo, Cribb.*

NELSON (September 3rd, 1925), RODNEY (December 17th, 1925).

Standard displacement, 33,500 tons (*Nelson*), 33,900 tons (*Rodney*), (*full load*, about 40,000 tons).
Length, (*p.p.*) 660 feet, (*w.l.*) 702 feet, (*o.a.*) 710 feet. Beam, 106 feet. *Mean* draught, 30 feet.
Complement, as flagship, 1361; as private ship, 1314.

Guns:
- 9—16 inch.
- 12—6 inch.
- 6—4·7 inch AA.
- 4—3 pdr.
- 2—Multiple AA.
- 8—2 pdr. pom-pom AA.
- 1—12 pdr. landing.
- 5—M.G.
- 10—Lewis.

Torpedo tubes (*submerged*)
- 2—24 inch.

Armour:
Is largely concentrated over guns and magazines in fore part of ship. Internal bulge protection.
- 14″ Belt ......
- 16″—9″ Turrets
- 6¼″ Deck ....

NELSON.   *1927 Photo, Frank & Son.*

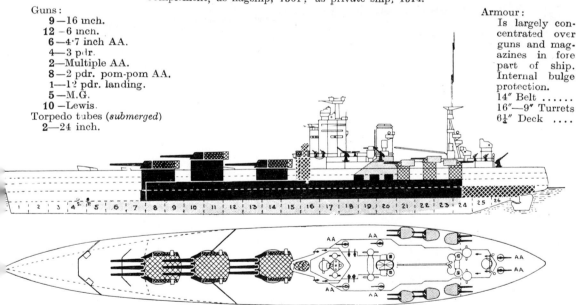

Machinery: Geared turbines. Boilers: 8 Yarrow. Designed H.P. 45,000 = 23 kts. Oil fuel: 4000 tons. Consumption: full speed, 16 tons per hour; cruising speed, 2·7 tons per hour.

General Notes.—Both laid down under 1922-23 Estimates, being the last battleships designed by Sir E. Tennyson D'Eyncourt while D.N.C. They are reduced editions of the 48,000 ton battle-cruisers ordered in 1921 and cancelled under the Washington Treaty, in which 16″ gunned triple turrets were to have been mounted. Designed to Treaty limits which could not be exceeded, and yet must be approached as closely as possible, weight estimation and economy was a far more important factor than in previous designs. The grouping of the main armament forward allows for a minimum length of armoured citadel with maximum protection to hull and magazines, and is considered to more than compensate for the loss of fire astern. The design is therefore peculiar, in that it is governed more by constructional than tactical principles. By placing the boiler room abaft the engine rooms smoke interference with the control positions is obviated. The bridge structure carries the directors for the 16″ 6″ and AA. guns, admirals bridge, torpedo controls, signalling and navigating bridges, sea cabins and offices. Special measures have been taken to protect personnel and instruments from the blast of the after guns when fired abaft the beam at full elevation.

Cost.—Nelson £7,405,269; *Rodney* £7,488,274. Annual upkeep with indirect personnel charges £432,960. Cost of guns and turret armour approx. £3,000,000; engines: £490,000. Steering gear is of novel design and rudder can be swung over in 30 secs. at full speed. Accommodation is on specially generous lines and all living spaces have natural lighting and ventilation.

Gunnery Notes.—The 16″ gun is a new calibre in the Service. Elevation is 40° and range 35,000 yards. Cost of firing a triple salvo is £700. The 6″ guns have 60° elevation and can be used as AA. They are the first power worked 6″ guns in the Service. Multiple AA. guns are now mounted in these ships.

Armour Notes.—Citadel belt extends from foremost 16″ to aftermost 6″ turret, with thick armour deck over same area with specially designed hatches. Underwater protection is most efficient and the usual external bulges have been replaced by an alternative system of hull construction developed from a long series of experiments.

Name	Builder	Machinery	Laid down	Completed	Trials	Boilers
Nelson	Armstrong	Wallsend Co.	Dec. 28, 1922	June, 1927	46,000 = 23·5 = 23·8	Yarrow
Rodney	Cammell Laird	Cammell Laird		Aug., 1927		

NELSON.

1927 *Photo, Frank & Son.*

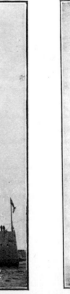

Bow view.   1929 *Photo, R. Perkins, Esq.*   RODNEY.   1928 *Photo, C. Cozens, Portsmouth.*   Stern view.   1927 *Photo, Frank & Son.*

RESOLUTION (taken before extensive refit, 1930).

1930 *Photo, Abrahams, Devonport.*

Note.—All the ships of this class now carry flying topmast on main.

ROYAL OAK (showing bulge protection).   1924 *Photo, Cribb.*

ROYAL OAK (bow).   1923 *Photo, Abrahams, Devonport.*

REVENGE (note sternwalk). 1924 *Photo, W. A. Fuller. Esq.*

(ROYAL SOVEREIGN CLASS.)—All fitted as Flagships.

ROYAL SOVEREIGN (29th April, 1915), **ROYAL OAK** (17th Nov., 1914), **RESOLUTION** (14th Jan., 1916), **RAMILLIES** (12th Sept., 1916), **REVENGE** (29th May, 1915).

Standard displacement, 29,150 tons (about 33,500 tons *full load*). Complement, 1009-1146.
Length (*p.p.*) 580 feet, (*w.l.*) 614½ feet, (*o.a.*) 620½ feet.†   Beam, about 102½ feet.*   *Mean* draught, 28½ feet.
*With bulge protection.   †*Revenge* 624½ feet (*o.a.*)

Guns :
  8—15 inch, 42 cal. } **Dir. Con.**
  12—6 inch, 50 cal. }
  4—4 inch (anti-aircraft)
  4—3 pdr.
  1—12 pdr. Field
  5 M.G.
  10 Lewis
Torpedo tubes (21 inch) :
  4 *submerged.*
  (2 only in *Revenge* and
  Resolution.)
Armour (H.T.) :
  1″ Fo'xle over Battery
  1¼″—1½″ Upper ......
  2″, 1½″, 1″ Main ......
  2½″, 1″ (forw'd) } Lower
  4″, 3″, 2½″ (aft) }
  Special Protection :
  1½″—1″ Torp. Prot. b.h.
    between end barbettes.
  (Also bulges, of varying types.)

Armour (K.C.) :
  13″ Belt ....
  6″—4″ Belt (ends) ....
  1″ Belt (bow) ....
  6″, 4″ Bulkheads (f. & a.)
  6″ Battery....
  10″—7″ Barbettes .....
  13″—5″ Gunhouses.....
  1½″ Funnel uptake ....
  6″—3″ C.T. Base .....
  11″ C.T. (6″—3″ hood) .
  6″ Fore com. tube ....
  6″ Torp. con. tower ...
  4″ Tube (T.C. tower) ..

ROYAL SOVEREIGN.

1928 *Photo, Stephen Cribb, Southsea.*

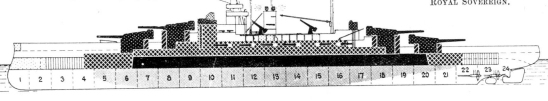

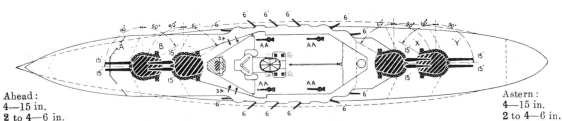

Ahead :
4—15 in.
2 to 4—6 in.

Astern :
4—15 in.
2 to 4—6 in.

Broadside : 8—15 in., 7—6 in., 2—21 in. tubes.

Machinery : Turbine, Parsons. Boilers : (see *Notes*). 4 screws. Designed H.P. 40,000 = 23 kts. *without* bulges, about 22 *with* bulges. Fuel : Oil only, *normal*, 900 tons ; *maximum*, 3,230 tons. Coal : 140 tons (for culinary purposes and boats).

Gunnery Notes.—Much as *Queen Elizabeth* class. Battery differently disposed in these ships. 6 inch batteries are wet in head seas, but dwarf walls in battery retain water and it is rapidly drained away. 4 inch AA, mounted in place of former 3 inch AA, in most of class, 1924-25. Two superstructure 6 inch removed in 1927-28.

Armour Notes.—Thicknesses much as *Queen Elizabeth* class, but armour differently distributed. Barbettes 6″—4″ as they descend behind belt. Gunhouses, 13″ face, 11″ sides and rear ; crowns 5″. In these ships 2″ protective deck has a high 2″ slope behind belt, so that flat part of protection can be put on main deck and at top of belt, instead of a deck lower. Internal protection is very good, and with protective bulges, defence against underwater attack is very strong. *Royal Oak* refitted, 1922-23, bulges now extending almost up to battery deck.

Engineering Notes.—Designed to burn coal, but while building "all oil fuel" was adopted, so that 23 kts. would be secured with the resulting increase of H.P. Addition of bulges has brought speed down again to about 22 kts.

General Notes.—Begun under 1913-14 Estimates. *Revenge* first named *Renown*. *Ramillies* injured herself at launch and was delayed in completion. They are fine ships, but suffer rather from reduced freeboard. Searchlights or main mast removed 1922. Refits : R. Sovereign, 1927-28 ; Royal Oak, 1922-24 ; Ramillies and Resolution, 1926-27 ; Revenge, 1928. Resolution 1930. All to have catapult fitted on quarter deck.

REVENGE.

1929 *Photo, Abrahams & Son, Devonport.*

Name	Builder	Machinery	Laid down	Completed	Trials :—	Boilers
Royal Sovereign	Portsmouth Y.	Parsons	Jan.'14	May, '16	41,115 = 21·6	18 Babcock
Royal Oak	Devonport Y.	Hawthorn	Jan.'14	May, '16	40,360 =	18 Yarrow
Resolution	Palmer	Palmer	Nov.'13	Dec.,'16	41,406 =	18 Yarrow
Ramillies	Beardmore*	Beardmore	Nov.'13	Sept. '17	42,356 = 21·5	18 Babcock
Revenge	Vickers	Vickers	Dec.'13	Mar.,'16	42,962 = 21·9	18 Babcock

*Towed to Liverpool and completed by Cammel Laird & Co.

20

Guns :
　8—15 inch, 42 cal. ⎫ **Dir. Con.**
　12—6 inch, 50 cal. ⎭
　4—4 inch AA.
　4—3 pdr.
　1—12 pdr. Field.
　5 M.G.
　10 Lewis.
Torpedo tubes (21 inch) :
　2 *submerged* (broadside).

Armour (H.T.) :
　1″ Fo'xle (over battery).
　2″—1¼″ Upper ....
　1¼″ Main fwd. & aft...
　1″ Middle ....
　3″ (ends) ⎫
　1″ (amidships) ⎭ Lower.
Special Protec. :
　2″—1″ Torp. pro. b'lkh'ds.
　　between end barbettes.

Vertical.

Armour (K.C.) :
　13″ on waterline ..⎫
　6″—4″ over w.l. ..⎬ Side
　6″—4″ (ends) ....⎭
　6″, 4″ Bulkheads (f. & a.)
　6″ Battery ....
　0″—7″ Barbettes .....
　11″ Gunhouses ....
　11½″ Funnel uptakes ...
　6″—3″ C.T. base .....
　14″ C.T. (6″—2″ Hood)..
　4″ Fore com. tube ....
　6″ Torpedo C.T. ......

Deck.

(QUEEN ELIZABETH CLASS.)
QUEEN ELIZABETH (16th Oct., 1913), **WARSPITE** (26th Nov., 1913), **VALIANT** (4th Nov., 1914),
BARHAM (31st Dec., 1914), **MALAYA** (18th Mar., 1915).
Standard displacement, 31,100 tons (about 33,000 *full load*). Complement, 1124-1184. All fitted as flagships.
Length (*p.p.*), 600 feet. Beam, 90½ feet {*Mean* draught, 30⅔ feet. } Length (*o.a.*) {B., W. 643¾ ft. } (*w.l.*) 634½ feet.
(without bulges.) {*Max.* ,, 33½ ,, } Q.E., M., V. 639¾ ft. }

VALIANT.　　　　　　　　　　　　　　　　1930 *Photo, R. Perkins, Esq.*

Note.—6″ battery armour should be shown
ending at second (B) turret.

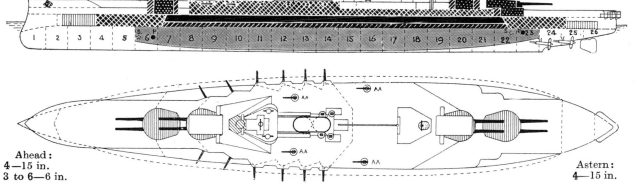

Ahead :
4—15 in.
3 to 6—6 in.

Astern :
4—15 in.

1924 *Photo, W. A. Fuller, Esq.*

1930 *Photo, R. Perkins, Esq.*

Broadside : 8—15 in., 6—6 in., 2—21 in. tubes.
　Machinery : Parsons turbine, but *Valiant* and *Barham* have Brown-Curtis. Geared cruising
turbines in all ships. Boilers : 24 large tube (see *Notes*). Designed H.P. 75,000 = 25 kts. Fuel :
Only oil, 650 tons *normal*, 3400 tons *max.* Coal : 100 tons, for culinary purposes and boats.
Radius of action : *about* 4400 miles.

General Notes.—First four begun under 1912 Estimates. *Malaya*, extra ship, gift of Federated Malay States.
　Estimated cost (average), exceeds £3,000,000 per ship. (Q. E. cost £3,014,103.) Annual upkeep = £170,416 per ship.
　Q.E., *Barham* and *Warspite* have stern walks. Re-construction includes the remodelling of control top and
　bridgework, addition of bulges of a modified pattern, the trunking of the forefunnel into the second, and the
　doubling of the anti-aircraft armament. Two Torpedo tubes removed during last refit.
Gunnery Notes.—15 inch guns and mountings designed for 20° elevation. 6 inch controlled in two groups from director
　towers on middle bridges. Anti-aircraft armament is being doubled as ships are refitted.
Armour Notes.—Belt is 13″ at w.l. only, 6″ on upper edge, 8″ on lower, and applied in vertical strakes. Barbettes,
　6″ and 4″ within belt. 1½″ traverses to battery, but no rear screens—only dwarf walls to retain and drain away
　water admitted to battery. Rear bulkhead to battery is 6″ diagonal and 4″ where it crosses centre line. Internal
　protection of these ships is very good. All this class are fitted with bulges.
Engineering Notes.—"All oil" installation very successful. These ships steam splendidly, and can maintain a high
　average speed for long periods. H.P. turbines on wing shafts, with cruising turbines geared at forward end ; L.P.
　turbines on inner shafts.

Name.	Builder.	Machinery.	Laid down.	Com- pleted.	Trials.	Boilers.
Queen Elizabeth	Portsmouth	Wallsend	Oct. '12	Jan., '15	57,130 =	24 Babcock
Warspite	Devonport	Hawthorn	Oct. '12	Mar., '15	77,510 =	24 Yarrow
Valiant	Fairfield	Fairfield	Jan. '13	Feb., '16	71.112 =	24 Babcock
Barham	Clydebank	Clydebank	Feb. '13	Oct., '15	76.575 =	24 Yarrow
Malaya	Elswick	Wallsend	Oct. '13	Feb., '16	76.074 =	24 Babcock

WARSPITE.   1926 *Photo, Cribb.*

Q. ELIZABETH.   1930 *Photo, R. Perkins, Esq.*

WARSPITE. Details of control top, bridgework and funnel.   1926 *Photo, Cribb.*

QUEEN ELIZABETH.   1928 *Photo, Cribb.*

Guns :
  8—15 inch, 42 cal. } **Dir. Con.**
  12—5·5 inch, 50 cal. }
  2—4·7 inch AA.
  4—4 inch (anti-aircraft.)
  4—3 pdr.
  1—12 pdr. Field.
  5 M.G. and Multiple AA.
  10 Lewis.
Torpedo tubes (21 inch)
  2 submerged (P. & S.)
  4 above water in pairs.
Aircraft :
  1—Fairey III F.

HOOD*.(J. Brown & Co., Clydebank. Begun 1st Sept., 1916, Launched 22nd August, 1918, completed 5th March, 1920.)

Standard displacement, 42,100 tons (46,200 tons *full load*). Complement, 1341.

Length { p.p. 810 ft. / o.a. 860 ft. 7 in. } Beam { w.l. / outside bulges 105 ft. 2½ in. } Draught { mean 28½ ft. / max. 31½ ft. }

*Fitted as Flagship.

Notes to Plan.—Combined thicknesses of side armour and conning tower shown by dark patch in section 11. Now carries flagstaffs on both masts, with gaff on main.

Armour (K.C.) :
  3″ Side (submerged) ..
  12″, 7″, 5″ Side (amidships) ....
  6″—5″ Side (forward)..
  6″ Side (aft) ....
  5″ 4″ Bulkh'ds (f. & a.)
  12″— ″ Barbettes ....
  15″ Face } Turrets
  12″—11″ Sides }
  12″ & 9″ C.T. ....
  6″ C.T. Base ....
  6″ Director tower ....
  4″—3″ Torp. control tower ....
  —″ P. & S. R.F. towers (5.5″) ....
  —″ Funnel uptakes ...
  1″ (H.T.) Shields to 5.5″ guns ....

Vertical. *Decks.* *Crowns.*

Armour (H.T.) :
  2″ Forecastle ....
  1″ U.D. amidships ....
  1½″—3″ Main deck ...
  3″ M.D. over magazines
  1½″—1″ L.D. forward
  3″—1″ L.D. aft ......
  3″ Director tower ...
  5″ C.T. ....
  3″ Torpedo control T.
  5″ Turrets ....

Special protection (H.T.) :
  1½″ and ¾″ Torp. pro. b'lk'd over magazines, boiler and engine rooms, bulges and buoyancy spaces.

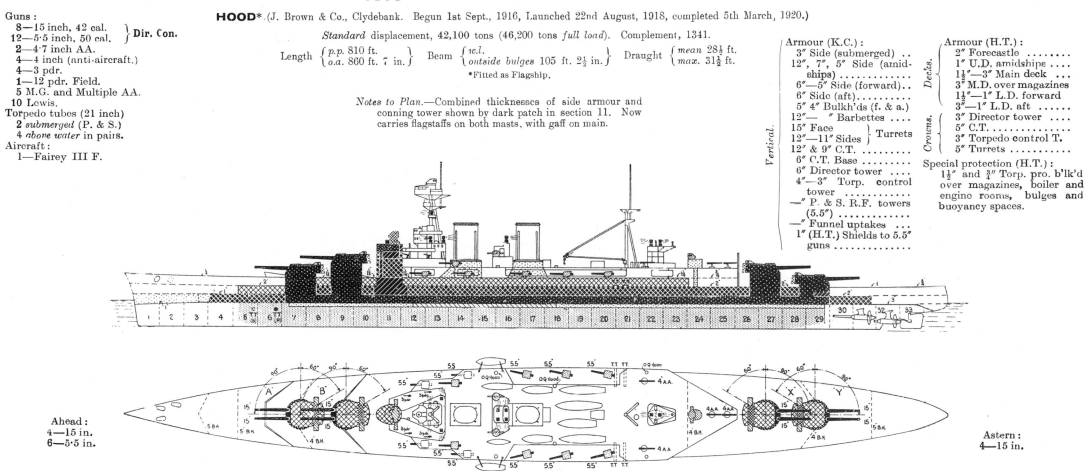

Ahead :
  4—15 in.
  6—5·5 in.

Astern :
  4—15 in.

Broadside : 8—15 in., 6—5·5 in., 3—21 in. tubes.

Machinery (by Builders) : Brown-Curtis (geared) turbines. 4 screws. Boilers : 24 Yarrow (small tube). Designed S.H.P. 144,000 = 31 kts. Fuel : Oil only. 1200 tons *normal*, 4,000 tons *maximum*.

Gunnery Notes.—Barbette heights over l.w.l.: A, 32 ft. ; B, 43 ft. ; X, 31¾ ft. ; Y, 21¾ ft. All turrets bear 150° on each beam. Designed to mount 16—5.5 inch, but the four after guns were removed before completion. Elevation of 15 inch guns, 30°. 8—36 inch controlled, and 4—24 inch signalling S.L. Stem attachment for PVs. of new design.

Armour Notes.—Vertical side armour is backed by strong 2″—1″ H.T. plating, not included in thicknesses given. Area of 12″ armour at w.l., 562 ft. long by 9½ ft. deep. Gun houses, new type with flat crowns, small square sighting ports cut low in face for laying over open sights. On roofs, armoured cases slightly wider than R.F. to allow R.F. to be traversed for fine adjustments. Barbettes, 6″—5″ as they descend through decks. C.T. is an enormous, elaborate, most expensive and ponderous structure : in upper stages, it consists of two shells, 12″ outer, 9″ inner, with narrow passage between. The slope inboard of hull side detracts from effects of plunging fire by virtual increase of armour thickness. A perpendicular, dropped from top sides, just meets outer edges of bulges, which are of the improved " D'Eyncourt-Hopkinson " type. Total weight of armour and protection, 13,800 tons.

Engineering Notes.—During world cruise, economical speed worked out at 288 miles in 24 hours on 180 tons of oil. *Trials* (unofficial figures).—At 42,200 tons, 151,000 S.H.P. = 32.07 kts. (run in bad weather, wind force 6 Beaufort scale) on Arran mile. At 44,600 tons, 31.89 kts. *mean* attained. On ⅔ power, 25 kts. easily secured. Total weight of machinery (with water in boilers to working level) = 5,350 tons.

Notes on Original Design.—The original 1915 Design embodied same length and beam, but draughts were 25½ feet *normal* = 36,300 tons, and 29 feet deep. Speed : 32 kts. Belt 8″, barbettes 9″, much thinner deck armour, and only 2—21 inch *submerged* T. T. Four ships ordered to this design April, 1916. In the design produced after Jutland (not approved till 1917), 5,000 tons extra protection was worked in. By use of small-tube boilers, 24,000 S.H.P. gained on *same* machinery weights as for *Renown* class.

General Notes.—Begun under Emergency War Programme. Originally, there were four ships in this class, *Anson, Hood, Howe, Rodney*. They were begun in the autumn of 1916, to meet the German Battle Cruisers, *Graf Spee, Mackensen, Ersatz Freya* and *Ersatz "A,"* which were laid down in 1916. Contractors were : *Anson* (Armstrong), *Howe* (Cammell Laird), *Rodney* (Fairfield), *Hood* (Brown). The enemy having ceased work on all his large ships, in 1917, *Anson, Howe* and *Rodney* were stopped in March, 1917, and dismantled to clear slips after the Armistice, but not before £860,000 had been expended on them. These ships were redesigned to meet the lessons of Jutland. In *Hood*, the outstanding feature is the huge areas covered by heavy armour, strong framing, &c.—in fact, the general scheme of protection is most comprehensive. Cost. *about* £6,025,000 = £145 per ton. Annual upkeep, £427,270. Due for replacement, 1941. General refit, 1929–30.

HOOD.

1931 *Photo, Wright & Logan.*

HOOD.

1931 *Photo, Kestin.*

(RENOWN CLASS.)

REPULSE (8th January, 1916), **RENOWN** (4th March, 1916).

Standard displacement, 32,000 tons (36,800—37,400 *full load*).   Complement, 1181/1205.

Length $\begin{cases} (p.p.) \text{ 750 feet.} \\ (w.l.) \text{ 787}\frac{3}{4} \text{ feet.} \end{cases}$ $\begin{cases} o.a. \text{ 794 feet 2}\frac{1}{2} \text{ in. } Repulse \\ o.a. \text{ 794 feet 1}\frac{1}{2} \text{in. } Renown \end{cases}$ Beam 102$\frac{2}{3}$ feet†   Draught $\begin{cases} Repulse \text{ — feet (mean), 31}\frac{3}{4} \text{ feet (max.)} \\ Renown \text{ 26}\frac{2}{3} \text{ feet (mean), 30}\frac{1}{4} \text{ feet (max.)} \end{cases}$

Both fitted as flagships.   †Outside bulges.

(See Armour Notes.)

Guns :
6—15 inch, 42 cal. } Dir.
15—\ inch, 40 cal. } Con.
4—4 inch AA.
4—3 pdr.
1—12 pdr. Field
5 M.G.
10 Lewis
Torpedo tubes (21 inch) :*
2 *submerged* (both ships)
8 *above water* in pairs (*Repulse*)

*See Torpedo Notes.

For illustrations, vide following page.

Notes to plan :

Now have range-finders mounted on turrets and additional control top at foremast head.

Renown is without main deck 6″ side armour.

Armour (K.C.) :
9″— 6″ Side (amidships) }
6″—4″ Side (within bow) } Lower belt
3″ (stern) }
4″ Fore b'lkhead
3″ After b'lkh'd
1½″ Upper belt ....
7″—4″ Barbettes .....
11″—7″ Gunhouses.....
1½″ Funnel uptakes ..
2″ C.T. base (3″ tube within)............
10″ C.T. ....
6″ Sighting hood over C.T.
3″ Torpedo C.T. ......

Vertical.

Armour (H.T.) :
1½″—½″ Fo'xle..........
$\frac{7}{16}$″—1½″ Upper ....
3″—¾″ Main (2″ slopes
2½″ Bow
3½″—3″ Stern } Lower
—″ Barbettes ....
3″ C.T. and hood ..
1½″ Torpedo C.T. .....
Special protection :
Modified bulges.......

Crowns Decks

Ahead :
4—15 in.
8—4 in.

Astern :
2—15 in.
12—4 in.

Broadside : 6—15 in., 13—4 in., 4—21 in. tubes.

Machinery : Brown-Curtis (direct drive) turbines. 4 screws. Boilers : 42 Babcock & Wilcox. Designed H.P. not exactly specified, but expected to be 110,000 to 120,000 S.H.P. for 30 kts. In service, S.H.P. 112,000 = about 31.5 kts. Fuel (oil only) : 1000 tons *normal* ; *Repulse* 4243 tons *maximum* ; *Renown* 4289 tons *maximum*. Radius of action, *about* 3650 miles. Tactical diameter : 4$\frac{1}{3}$ times length.

Gunnery Notes.—15-inch have range only limited by maximum visibility and Director tower is under control tower on foremast. 4 inch triples have 2 director towers, and all guns can be worked from either tower or half the 4-inch from one tower. If towers are destroyed, 4-inch can work independently. 4-inch triples are clumsy and not liked. They are not mounted in one sleeve ; have separate breech mechanism ; gun crew of 23 to each triple. It is said that first salvo fired by forward 15-inch of *Renown* did considerable damage forward, and she had to be docked for repairs.

Torpedo Notes.—*Repulse*, on 1919 re-fit, had 8 *above water* tubes in 4 twin mountings fitted on main deck above sections 19 and 23.

Armour Notes.—Armouring adapted from *Invincible* and *Indefatigable* classes. On re-fit 1919-20, *Repulse* re-armoured on w.l. with 9″ K.C. and 6″ K.C. between main and upper decks, extending over sections 8-27 on plans. Belt, *about* 9 ft. deep.

Engineering Notes.—Turbines similar to *Tiger*. For full description, v. "Engineering," April 11th, 1919. Boilers : 250 lbs. per sq. in. Heating surface : 157,206 sq. ft. Consumption at full speed : *about* 1400 tons oil fuel per day ; at economical speed, *about* 180 tons per day.

Name	Builder	Machinery	Begun*	Completed	Trials : H.P. kts.
Repulse	Clydebank Fairfield	Clydebank Fairfield	Jan.25,'15	Aug.,1916	119,025=31.7*
Renown			Jan.25,'15	Sept.,1916	126,300=32.68

*To Battle Cruiser design.   *30 kts. on Arran mile after being re-armoured.

General Notes.—Provided for by 1914-15 Navy Estimates ; first designed as slightly modified *Royal Sovereigns*, contracted for on that basis, and begun 1914, but building was not pushed on actively after the outbreak of War. After the Falklands Battle it was decided that these two ships should be re-designed as Battle Cruisers. Outline design was prepared in ten days, and builders received sufficient details by January 21st, 1915, to begin building, but full designs were not finished and approved till April, 1915. Intended that they should be completely built in fifteen months, but this time was somewhat exceeded. Both ships have turned out remarkably well and reflect great credit on their designers and builders. Internally, they are most spacious, but it has been stated that their guns " shake them up " considerably. Costs : *Repulse*, £2,627,401 ; *Renown*, £3,111,266 ; but former total is not inclusive of all charges, and is liable to revision. Refits : *Renown* (1919-20), £100,738, (1921-22) £175,518. *Repulse* (1918-22), £860,684 ; which is equivalent to the cost of a new *Carlisle* type Light Cruiser. *Renown* re-constructed, 1923-26, with addition of conspicuous bulge ; bridge built up abaft fore tripod, as in *Revenge* ; heavy upper control top on foremast and short topmast removed ; gaff on main at heel of topmast.

(*All Photos on this page, by Stephen Cribb, Southsea.*)

RENOWN.   1926 *Photo.*   RENOWN (bow view.)   1927 *Photo.*

RENOWN.   1927 *Photo.*   RENOWN.   1926 *Photo.*

1915 BRITISH BATTLE CRUISER (Illustrations.)
(Described on an earlier page.)

Battle Cruiser—**BRITISH**

REPULSE.

1925 *Photo, Abrahams, Weymouth.*

REPULSE.

1922 *Photo, Gieves, Ltd.*

ARGUS (2nd Dec., 1917). Late Liner.

Normal displacement, 14,450 tons. Complement, 373.

Length, (*p.p.*) 535 feet (*w.l.*) 560 feet (*o.a.*) 565 feet.

Beam, 68 feet (excluding bulges).

Draught, 21 feet, *mean.*

Guns :
6—4 inch AA.
4—3 pdr.
4 M.G.
10 Lewis.
Flights carried :
1 Fighter (Flycatcher).
2 Spotter Reconnaissance
(1 flight Fairey III F,
1 flight Blackburn).

Armour :
Nil.
(Bulges—see *General Notes.*)

ARGUS. 1929 *Photo, R. Perkins, Esq.*

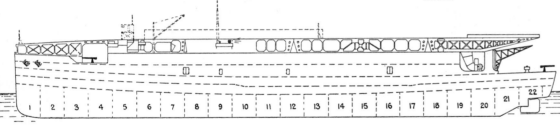

ARGUS. 1927 *Photo, Cribb, Southsea.*

Machinery (by builders) : Parsons turbines. 4 screws. Designed S.H.P. 20,000=20·2 kts. Can make 20·75 kts. for short periods, but 20 kts. is usually best speed under ordinary conditions. Boilers : 12 cylindrical (6 D.E. and 6 S.E.), with Howdens forced draught. Fuel : 2000 tons oil.

Capacity, &c.—Hangar is 350 ft. long by 68 ft. wide (*over all*) and 48 ft. clear width, 20 ft. clear height. It is divided into four sections by fire-proof screens, and can accommodate 20 aeroplanes of sea and land types.

Stores, &c.—Torpedoes are carried for torpedo-dropping aeroplanes ; aero-bombs, spare parts, wings, propellers, &c. Full equipment is carried for maintenance and repair of aircraft. There are large carpenters' and engineers' workshops, for executing rapid repairs.

Handling Gear.—Two electrically controlled lifts for raising aircraft from hangar to flight deck. Forward lift, 30 ft. × 36 ft. After lift, 60 ft. × 18 ft. When forward lift is at flight deck level, two roller platforms slide to the sides and uncover well opening. When lift descends, the platforms are closed together and give a 20-ft. platform for flying off. When a deck load of aeroplanes is carried, wind-breaking palisades can be raised simultaneously to 14 ft. above flying deck. Two derricks with electric winches amidships on flight deck and two electric cranes at stern on hangar deck level ; all to pick up aeroplanes from the water.

Engineering Notes.—At the time designs were got out, a ½-inch scale model was prepared for testing in the air tunnel at the National Physical Laboratory, Teddington, to solve various structural problems and to test eddy-making effects of hull. It was found that the emission of hot furnace gases from the usual type of funnels created such serious air disturbances, safe landings would be very difficult. Accordingly, horizontal smoke-ducts with big expelling fans were fitted, to deliver all furnace gases and smoke out abaft hangar, or alternatively through flight deck. Designed for 18 kts., but modifications during conversion raised speed by 2 kts. Mean H.P. on trial, 21,376 = 20·5 knots.

General Notes.—Begun 1914, by Beardmore, for Italian Lloyd Sabaudo Line, as S.S. *Conte Rosso.* All work on her ceased in 1914. She was purchased in 1916 and converted to Aircraft Carrier. Completed September, 1918. Refitted 1925-26, and Bulges fitted, extending from Section 4 to Section 19.

HERMES (11th September, 1919).

Displacement, 10,950 tons *normal.*   Complement, 664.

gth $\begin{cases} p.p. & 548 \text{ feet} \\ o.a. & 598 \quad ,, \end{cases}$ Beam $\begin{cases} w.l. \\ \text{outside bulges, 70 feet} \\ \text{over flight deck, 90 feet} \end{cases}$ Draught $\begin{cases} mean \ 18\frac{3}{4} \text{ feet.} \\ max. \ — \quad ,, \end{cases}$

uns :
6—5·5 inch, 50 cal. (**Dir. Con.**)
3—4 inch AA.
26 Smaller.

lights carried :
1 Fighter (9 Flycatchers in all).
1 Spotter Reconnaissance.
6 Fairey III F.

Armour :
 Not known—probably
 of Light Cruiser
 type.

Anti-Torp. Pro.
 Bulges.

HERMES.

1924 *Photo, Abrahams, Devonport.*

SECTIONS

MAST
FROM FORD

Note to plan :
 There is another S.L. on superstructure
 abaft funnel.

SECTIONS

HALF-PLAN AT FLIGHT D^K

4"AA. 4"AA.   4"AA

HALF-PLAN AT UPPER D^K

Machinery : Parsons (all geared) turbines.   Designed S.H.P. 40,000=25 kts.   2 screws.
Boilers : Yarrow or Babcock.   Fuel (oil only) : 1000 tons *normal.*   2000 tons *max.*

Name	Builder	Machinery	Ordered	Begun	Completed	Trials
Hermes	Armstrong Whitworth Devonport D.Y.*	Parsons	July, '17	15 Jan., '18	1923	

* Towed here for completion, January, 1920.

General Notes.—Begun under Emergency War Programme. First vessel specially designed by Admiralty as an Aircraft Carrier. Is a splendid sea boat, very steady, with remarkably little rolling propensity.

To carry 20 sea or aeroplanes. Special ventilation system to lessen danger of fire from petrol fumes, and new types of gear for handling, landing and flying-off aircraft. Hangar aft, with electric lift from quarterdeck to flight deck, 'planes being wheeled out from hangar on to lift through an opening normally closed by shutters. Transporter cranes fitted forward and aft.

HERMES (bow view).   1923 *Photo, Abrahams,
Devonport.*

BRITISH NAVY—AIRCRAFT CARRIER.

HERMES (port quarter).

HERMES (amidships, starboard side).

HERMES.

All Photos, Abrahams, Devonport (1923).

EAGLE (8th June, 1918), late Battleship.

Normal displacement, 22,600 (*deep load*, 26,200) tons. Complement, 748.

Length $\left\{ \begin{array}{l} (p.p.)\ 625\ \text{feet} \\ (o.a.)\ 667\ ,, \end{array} \right\}$ Beam $\left\{ \begin{array}{l} 92\frac{3}{4} \\ 105\frac{1}{6}\ (max.) \end{array} \right\}$ feet.* Draught $\left\{ \begin{array}{l} 24\ \text{feet } mean. \\ 27\ \text{feet } max. \end{array} \right\}$

* 100 feet, flight deck.

Guns :
  9—6 inch, 50 cal. (**Dir. Con.**)
  5—4 inch A A.
  36 Smaller.

Flights carried :
  1 Spotter Reconnaissance
    (Fairey III F).
  1 Fighter (Flycatcher).
  1 Torpedo (Dart).

Armour :
  ...″ Side (amidships)......
  ...″ Deck ....
Special protection :
  Bulges over about four-
  fifths of length, project-
  ing about 6 feet from
  side.

Bow view. *1924 Photo, Abrahams, Devonport.*

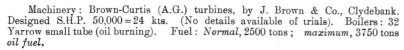

Machinery : Brown-Curtis (A.G.) turbines, by J. Brown & Co., Clydebank. Designed S.H.P. 50,000 = 24 kts. (No details available of trials). Boilers: 32 Yarrow small tube (oil burning). Fuel : *Normal,* 2500 tons ; *maximum,* 3750 tons *oil fuel.*

General Notes—Designed and begun by Armstrong Whitworth, February, 1913, for Chile, as *Almirante Cochrane,* a Dreadnought Battleship and sister to Chilean *Almirante Latòrre.* All work on this ship ceased in August, 1914, and she lay on her slip until 1917, when her purchase was negotiated with the Chilean Government. Her design was modified to an Aircraft Carrier by Sir E. H. Tennyson d'Eyncourt. Commissioned for ship and flying trials with one funnel and no masts, 13th April, 1920. As a result of trials made off Scilly Islands, put in hand at H.M. Dockyard, Portsmouth, for modifications, November, 1920. Finally completed in 1923. Bought from Chile for £1,334,358, sums subsequently expended have raised total cost to £4,617,636 (Statement by First Lord, April 1927).

EAGLE.

1927 Photo, Cassar.

EAGLE

1931 Photo, R. Perkins, Esq.

EAGLE

1924 Photo, Abrahams, Devonport.

FURIOUS.

1925 *Photo, Abrahams, Devonport.*

1926 *Photo, Cribb, Southsea.*

FURIOUS (15 August, 1916). Late Cruiser.

Normal Displacement, *about* 19,100 tons, (about 22,450 tons *full load*). Complement, 748. †

Length, (*p.p.*) 735 feet, (*o.a.*) 786¼ feet. *Beam, 89¾ feet. Draught, $\begin{cases} mean & 21\frac{2}{3} \text{ feet.} \\ max. & 25 \text{ feet.} \end{cases}$

*Outside bulges.

Guns (**Dir. Con.**):
10—5·5 inch, 50 cal.
6—4 inch AA.
54 Smaller.
Flights carried:
1 Fighter (Flycatcher).
3 Spotter Reconnaissance.
(2 flights Fairey III F,
1 flight Blackburn).
2 Torpedo (1 Dart, 1 Ripon II).

NOTE TO PLAN.

Quarter deck to be raised one deck
during present refit, 1931.

Armour:
3″ Belt (amidships)................
2″ Belt (bow). ....
3″—2″ Bulkheads F. & A.........
1″ Decks (H.T at stern)..........
3″—1½″ Decks (H.T. at stern)...
Anti-Torp. Pro.
Shallow bulges ....
1″ H.T. vertical. ....
†With flying personnel added,
complement is about 1100.

1926 *Photo, Cribb, Southsea.*

1926 *Photo, Cribb, Southsea.*

Machinery (by Wallsend Co.): Brown-Curtis (all geared) Turbines. 4 screws. Boilers: 18 Yarrow.
Designed S.H.P. 90,000 = 31 kts. *Trials*: 90,820 = kts. Fuel (oil only): 4010 tons.

Armour Notes.—3″ Belt consists of 2″ plating over 1″ shell plating, as in Light Cruisers.

General Notes.—Built under Emergency War Programme, by Armstrong Whitworth. Begun June, 1915 ; completed July, 1917 : re-built November, 1917, March, 1918. Designed as a modified *Courageous* but altered to Aircraft Carrier. Since conversion, she is said to be rather light, and is good now for 32-33 kts. Including cost of alterations, this ship is said to have absorbed over six million pounds. Underwent re-fit and alteration at H.M. Dockyards, Rosyth and Devonport, 1921-25, after which her appearance was completely altered, the funnel and mast being removed and a new hangar built forward. Smoke is discharged from vents at after end of hangar, or alternatively through flight deck, which measures 700 × 80 feet. Height of flight deck from water line is 75 feet. There are 2 hydraulic lifts from hangars to flight deck.

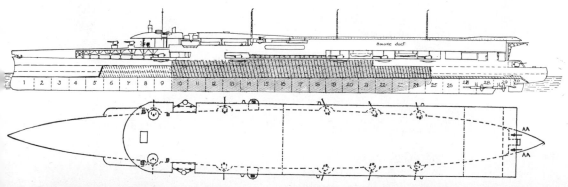

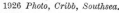

Smoke duct

FURIOUS (during present refit (1931) quarter deck is being raised a deck).

1931 *Photo, R. Perkins, Esq.*

FURIOUS.

1931 *Photo, R. Perkins, Esq.*

1931 *Photo.*

(COURAGEOUS CLASS—2 Ships).

COURAGEOUS (5th February, 1916), **GLORIOUS** (20th April, 1916). (Late Cruisers.)

Normal displacement, *about* 18,600 tons (*about* 22,700 tons *full load*). Complement, 748 (with flying personnel included, *about* 1100).

Length $\begin{cases} p.p. \text{ 735 ft.} \\ o.a. \text{ 786}\frac{1}{4}\text{ ft.} \end{cases}$ Beam (outside bulges), 81 ft. Draughts $\begin{cases} mean \text{ 22}\frac{1}{8}\text{ ft.} \\ max. \text{ 26 ft.} \end{cases}$

Guns :
16—4·7 inch HA. and LA.
4—3 pdr.
50 Smaller.
Flights carried :
2 Fighter (Flycatcher)
2 Spotter Reconnaissance
(Fairey III F)
2 Torpedo (Dart)

Armour :
3″ Belt (amidships) ...
2″ Belt (forward) ....
2″ (H.T.) Fore bulkhead
3″—1″ (H.T.) After
Bulkhead ....
1½″ Side over belt ....
1″ Upper deck ......
1½″ Lower (stern, flat)
3″ Lower (stern, over
rudder) ....
2″ Lower (on slopes) ..
Torpedo protection (H.T.) :
Modified bulges 25 ft.
deep ....
¾″ Inner screen to boiler
and engine room vents.

COURAGEOUS.

1928 *Photo, Abrahams & Sons.*

Machinery : Parsons (all-geared) turbines. 4 screws. Boilers : 18 Yarrow (small tube). Designed H.P. 90,000 = about 31 kts. Fuel (oil only) : *normal,* 750 tons ; *maximum,* 3250 tons.

Armour Notes.—General scheme of armouring on Cruiser lines, the 3″ belt being built up of 2″ plating on 1″ shell plating. Decks round magazines thickened during completion.

Engineering Notes.—General arrangement of machinery as in Cruiser *Champion.* 4-shaft geared turbines and double helical gearing. Have done 32 kts. in service.

General Notes.—Emergency War Programme ships. Original cruiser design formulated by Lord Fisher in 1915, with a view to Baltic operations—hence the shallow draught. The lines are remarkably fine. On *trials, Courageous* met heavy weather and was driven into a head sea. straining her hull forward. Doubling plates were added here, and subsequent trials showed the defect had been overcome. *Glorious* strengthened in the same way a year later as a precautionary measure. No figures are available as to cost, but they are said to have run to three millions apiece. *Furious,* of slightly modified design, was converted while building into an Aircraft Carrier. *Courageous* and *Glorious* taken in hand for similar conversion at Devonport (June, 1924 and Feb., 1924 respectively). Work on *Glorious* was started at Rosyth, but on that yard being closed she was towed to Devonport for completion. *Courageous* completed March, 1928, her conversion having cost £2,025,800. *Glorious* completed January 1930.

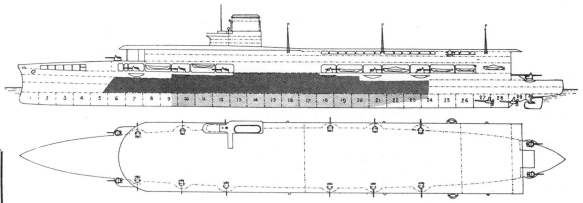

Name	Builder	Machinery	Begun	Completed	Trials
Courageous	Armstrong	Parsons	May, 1915	Jan., 1917	93,780 = 31·58
Glorious	Harland & Wolff, Belfast	Harland & Wolff	Mar., 1915	Jan., 1917	91,165 = 31·6

COURAGEOUS.

1928 *Photo, Cribb.*

COURAGEOUS.

1928 *Photo, R. Perkins, Esq.*

COURAGEOUS.

1928 *Photo, Cribb.*

Shewing extension of flight deck aft.

1929 *Photo, N. J. Tangye, Esq.*

GLORIOUS.   1930 *Photo, Abrahams, Devonport.*

1930 *Photo, R. Perkins Esq.*

EXETER (July 18th, 1929).

"Standard" displacement, 8400 tons.

Length, 540 (*p.p.*), 575 (*o.a.*) feet.   Beam, 58 feet.   Draught, 17 feet.

Guns :
  6—8″ 50 cal.
  4—4″ A.A.
  4—3 pdr.
  8—2 pdr. pom-pom.
Torpedo Tubes :
  6—21″ (tripled)
Aircraft :
  1—Fairey III F.

Armour :
  2″ Deck
  3″ C.T.

Exeter.

1931 *Photo, R. Perkins, Esq.*

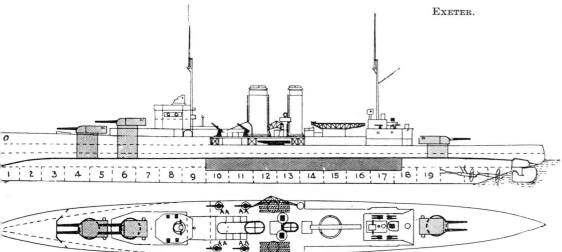

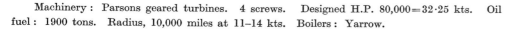

Machinery : Parsons geared turbines.   4 screws.   Designed H.P. 80,000=32·25 kts.   Oil fuel : 1900 tons.   Radius, 10,000 miles at 11–14 kts.   Boilers : Yarrow.

General Notes.—Designed by Sir William Berry and laid down at Devonport in August, 1928.   Completed at the end of 1930.   Design is similar to *York*, with an increase in beam of 1 foot.   Originally she had three raking funnels and catapult on raised turret, with masts spaced as in *York*, but the foremost funnel was trunked into the second in order to improve the habitability of the bridge and save space and weight.   The catapult on the second turret having been dispensed with, the bridge has been lowered so that the director is only 60 feet above water. Note the absence of wings to the bridge and the searchlight arrangement similar to that in the *Nelson* class.   The absence of rake to the masts and funnels, which brings the main mast up through the superstructure, is a break-away from traditional cruiser practice and (like the thickening of the second funnel by 4 feet) has been effected in order to improve her appearance.

1931 *Photo, R. Perkins, Esq.*

1931 *Photo, R. Perkins, Esq.*

1931 *Photo, Cribb.*

1931 *Photo, R. Perkins, Esq.*

YORK (July 17th, 1928).

"Standard" displacement, 8400 tons.

Length, 540 (*p.p.*), 575 (*o.a.*) feet. Beam, 57 feet.

Draught, 17 feet.

Guns :
  6—8 inch, 50 cal.
  4—4 inch AA.
  4—3 pdr.
  2—2 pdr. pom-pom
Torpedo Tubes :
  6—21 inch (tripled).
Aircraft :
  1—Fairey III F.

Armour :
  2″ Deck
  3″ C.T.

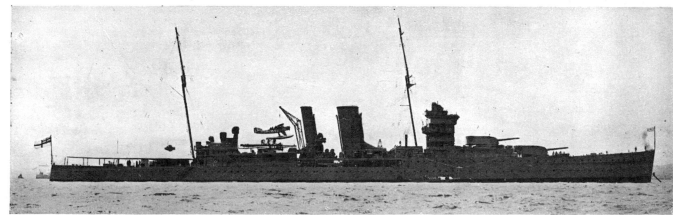

YORK.

1931 *Photo, R. Perkins, Esq.*

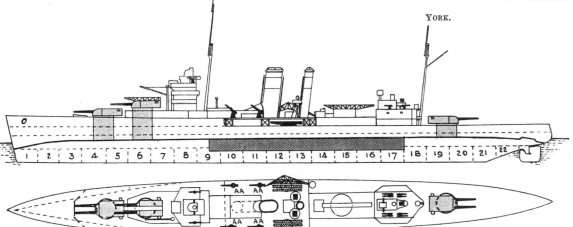

YORK.

Ahead :
4—8 in.

Broadside 6—8 in.

Astern :
2—8 in.

Machinery : Parsons geared turbines. 4 screws. Designed H.P. 80,000 = 32·25 kts. Oil fuel : 1900 tons. Radius, 10,000 miles at 11—14 kts. Boilers : Yarrow.

General Notes.—Designed by Sir William Berry and marks the first attempt on the part of one of the Treaty Powers to break away from the 10,000 ton type of cruiser. For a saving of 1600 tons, two 8″ guns are sacrificed, speed and protection being the same as in the *Kent* class, the resulting ship being little inferior to the 10,000 tonners, all things being considered. *York* was laid down at Messrs. Palmer's yard at Jarrow in May, 1927, and completed in June, 1930. The original design allowed for three funnels, but during 1928 the plans were modified and the foremost funnel was trunked into the second. In order to clear the catapult shown in the plan on the second turret, the bridge was raised, and consequently the funnels. It has been found, however, that the turrets are too light for the catapult to be carried, and it and the derrick have been dispensed with. The reversion to the triple torpedo tubes is due to limitation of training space only.

YORK.

1931 *Photo R. Perkins, Esq.*

1930 *Photo, Cribb.*

YORK.   1930 *Photo, Cribb.*

NORFOLK.

1930 *Photo, Cribb.*

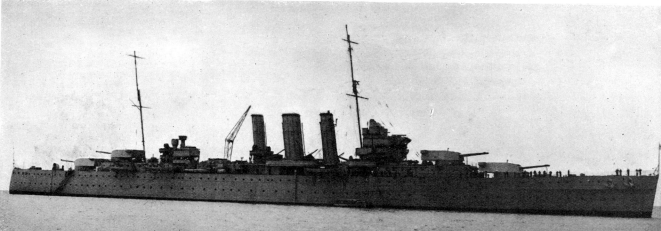

NORFOLK.

1930 *Photo, Cribb.*

DORSETSHIRE CLASS.

DORSETSHIRE (January 29th, 1929). Portsmouth Dockyard.
NORFOLK (December 12th, 1928). Fairfield.

" Standard " displacement, 10,000 tons.

Length, 590 (*p.p.*), 630 (*o.a.*) feet. Beam, 66 feet. Draught, 17 feet.

Guns :
  8—8", 50 cal.
  4—4" AA.
  4—3 pdr.
  4—2 pdr. pom-pom
Torpedo Tubes :
  8—21" (quadruple)
Aircraft :
  1—Fairey III F.

Armour :
  Similar to
  Devonshire
  class

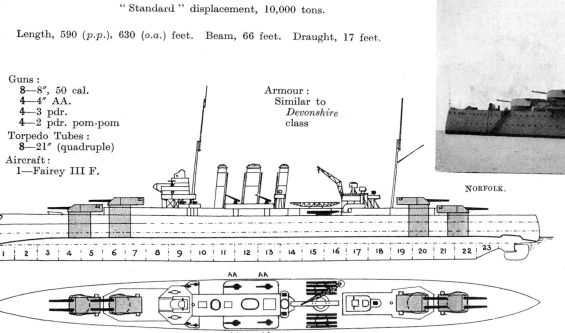

NORFOLK.

1930 *Photo, Cribb.*

Machinery : Geared turbines. 4 screws. Designed S.H.P. 80,000=32·25 kts. Oil fuel : 3200 tons. Boilers : Yarrow. Machinery of *Dorsetshire* by Cammell Laird, *Norfolk* by Fairfield.

General Notes.—Designed by Sir William Berry and built under the 1926-27 Estimates. *Dorsetshire* begun September, 1927, and completed July, 1930 ; *Norfolk* in July, 1927, and completed in June, 1930. Differ from the *London* class in position of A.A. guns, height of bridge (the topmost deck has been removed) and dimensions. Catapult will be fitted when design is approved : crane mounted on starboard side and can be stowed below searchlights on third funnel.

Ahead: **4—8"**   Broadside: **8—8"**   Astern: **4—8"**   41

SUSSEX.

1929 *Photo, Cribb, Southsea.*

LONDON.

1929 *Photo, Cribb, Southsea*

(LONDON CLASS—4 SHIPS.)
DEVONSHIRE (Oct. 22nd, 1927).
LONDON (Sept. 14th, 1927).
SHROPSHIRE (July 5th, 1928).
SUSSEX (Feb. 22nd, 1928).

"Standard" displacement, 10,000 tons (*about* 14,000 tons *full load*).
Length $\begin{cases} p.p.\ 595\ \text{feet} \\ o.a.\ 633\ \text{feet} \end{cases}$ Beam, 66 feet. Draught, 17 feet.

DEVONSHIRE.

1929 *Photo, Abrahams, Devonport.*

Guns :
  8—8 inch, 50 cal.
  4—4 inch AA.
  4—3 pdr.
  4—2 pdr. pom-pom.
Torpedo tubes :
  8—21 inch (quadrupled).

Armour :
  Similar to *Kent* class, without
    external bulges.

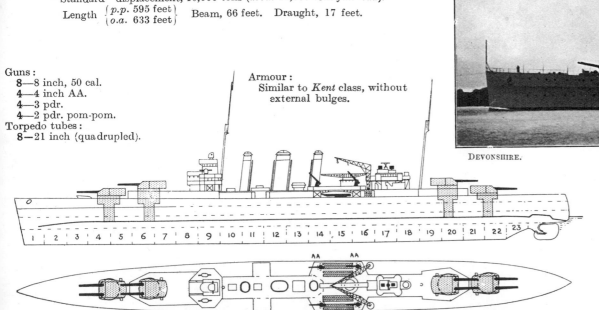

Machinery : Geared turbines. 4 screws. Designed S.H.P. 80.000 = 32·25 kts. Oil fuel : 3200 ton

Name	Builder	Machinery	Ordered	Begun	Completed	Trials	Boilers
Devonshire	Devonport Y.	Vickers		16/3/26	3/29		Yarro
London	Portsmouth Y.	Fairfield	1925	23/2/26	1/29		in
Shropshire	Beardmore	Beardmore	-26	2/26	9/29		all
Sussex	Hawthorn, Les.	Hawthorn		1926	3/29		

General Notes.—All designed by Sir William J. Berry. *London* class authorised by 1925-26 Estimates. Aeropl
derrick on Starboard side only. Catapult to be fitted when design is approved

KENT.

1928 *Photo, Stephen Cribb, Southsea.*

1928 *Photo, Cribb.*

CORNWALL.

1928 *Photo, Cribb.*

(KENT CLASS—5 SHIPS.)

BERWICK (March 30th, 1926), **CORNWALL** (March 11th, 1926), **CUMBERLAND** (March 16th, 1926), **KENT** (March 16th, 1926), **SUFFOLK** (Feb. 16th, 1926).

"Standard" displacement, 10,000 tons (13,630 *deep load*).

Complement, 679 (710 as flagship).

Length (*p.p.*) 590 feet, (*o.a.*) 630 feet. Beam, 68¼ feet. Draught, 16¼ feet (*mean*).

Guns :
8—8 inch, 50 cal.
4—4 inch AA.
4—3 pdr.
4—2 pdr. pom-pom.
4 Machine, 8 Lewis.
Torpedo tubes :
8—21 inch in two sets
  of 4.

Armour :
3—1½″ Deck over vitals
3″ C.T. ....
Bulges ....

Machinery : Geared turbines. 4 screws. Designed S.H.P. 80,000 = 31·5 kts. Boilers : 8 Yarrow in all. Oil fuel : 3400 tons. Radius at full speed, 2300 miles ; at economical speed (11—14 kts.), 10,400 miles.

General Notes.—Built under 1924-25 Estimates ; designed by Sir Eustace Tennyson d'Eyncourt. Although on paper these ships appear to be inferior to foreign Treaty cruisers, they are in practice, superior in sea-going qualities and have accommodation and habitability which is not equalled by any other cruisers. In addition, a considerable amount of weight has been expended in structural strength and internal protection. No attempt has been made to attain the high speeds which have been recorded by the *Tourville* and *Trento* types, the ideal aimed at being the ability to sustain the designed speed indefinitely and in all weathers, without exceeding the normal S.H.P. and over 34 knots has been maintained in service without in any way pressing the boilers. A catapult is to be fitted amidships when the design is approved. Two ships of the class *Australia* and *Canberra* have been built for the Australian Navy. Average cost is £1,970,000 and annual upkeep £238,850 per ship.

Gunnery Notes.—Exceptional elevation has been given to the 8″ guns, more than 65° having been observed. By means of an improved ammunition supply a rate of fire of four rounds per gun per minute can be maintained under D.C. Weight of 8″ broadside 2,048 lbs. Total cost of armament £700,000 ; of firing a single broadside £408.

Armour Notes.—No side armour is included in the design, protection being afforded by a 3″—1½″ deck. External bulges are fitted and the internal subdivision is particularly well planned.

Torpedo Notes.—These ships carry the first quadruple tubes to be fitted in any navy, and despite their height above water are satisfactory in every way.

Engineering Notes.—Boiler pressure is 250 lbs.

1928 *Photo, Cribb.*   1928 *Photo,*

Name	Builder	Machinery	Ordered	Begun	Completed	Trials	Turbines
Berwick	Fairfield	Fairfield		11/24	9/27	= 32·5	Brown-Curtis
Cornwall	Devonport Y.	Beardmore		9/10/24	11/27		Parsons
Cumberland	Vickers	Vickers	1924	10/24	10/27		Parsons
Kent	Chatham Y.	Hawthorn		15/11/24	2/28		Parsons
Suffolk	Portsmouth Y.	Parsons		30/9/24	1/28		Parsons

New Construction.

1 Cruiser about 5000 Tons.

(LEANDER CLASS—6 Ships.)

LEANDER (Devonport. September 24, 1931).

NEPTUNE (Portsmouth.).

ORION (Devonport.).

ACHILLES (Cammell Laird.).

" E."

" F."

" Standard " displacement, 7,000 tons.

Length (*o.a.*) 554½ feet. Beam, 55' 2". Draught, (*mean*) 16 feet.

Guns :
8—6"
4—4" A.A.
4—3 pdr.
2—2 Multiple AA.
Torpedo Tubes :
6—21" in Triple mounts.

Armour :
—Deck
—Side amidships.

LEANDER.

1931 *Illustration.*

Machinery : Parsons Geared Turbines. 4 screws. Designed S.H.P. 72,000 = 32 kts. Oil fuel : tons. Radius, miles at kts. Boilers :

General Notes.—This class represents a return to sanity in cruiser design compared with the overgrown and overgunned 10,000 ton Treaty type. The eight guns in four turrets is a disposition of armament which is regarded by the gunnery branch as the best number and arrangement for satisfactory control, and superior in practice to nine guns in triple mountings as in the German *Köln* class. The 6 inch guns are of an entirely new model produced by the " auto-frettage " system instead of being wire wound. The original design has been modified to accommodate a hanger in the after superstructure, the illustration showing her appearance according to provisional drafts. Although listed as being of the same class, it is probable that the later ships will differ in detail. *Leander* was laid down under 1929 Estimates ; remainder under 1930 and 1931 Estimates.

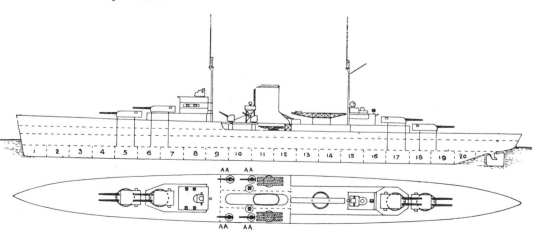

Name	Builder	Machinery	Begun	Completed
Leander	Devonport	V.-Armstrong	8/9/30	......
Neptune	Portsmouth		/9/31	
Orion	Devonport		26/9/31	
Achilles	Cammell Laird		/9/31	

("E" CLASS—FIRST SHIP.)

ENTERPRISE (23rd December, 1919).

"Standard" displacement, 7100 tons; *normal* displacement, 7580 tons.
Complement, 572/577.

Length $\begin{cases} p.p. \text{ 535 feet} \\ o.a. \text{ 570 feet} \end{cases}$ Beam 54½ feet. Draught $\begin{cases} mean \text{ 16½ feet.} \\ max. \text{ feet.} \end{cases}$

Guns :
7—6 inch, 50 cal. (**Dir. Con.**)
3—4 inch AA.
4—3 pdr.
2—2 pdr. pom-pom.
2 M.G.
8 Lewis.
Torpedo tubes (21 inch) :
16, in four quadruple mountings, *above water.*

Armour (H.T.) :
3″ Side (amidships) ....
2½″—1½″ Side (bow) ....
2″ Side (stern) ....
1″ Upper deck (amidships) ..
1″ Deck (over rudder) ......
″ Turret ....

Machinery : Turbines, 4 sets Brown-Curtis (geared). **4** screws. Designed
S.H.P. 80,000 = 33 kts. (light), 32 kts. (*full load*). Boilers : 8 Yarrow small
tube. Fuel (oil only) : *normal,* 650 tons ; *maximum,* 1600 tons.

ENTERPRISE.

1926 *Photo, Abrahams & Sons, Devonport.*

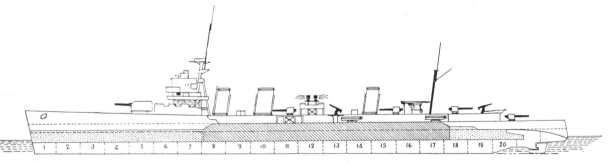

Note to plan : Torpedo Tubes now quadrupled.

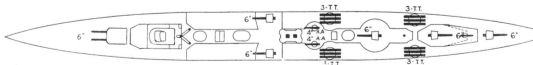

Ahead :
3 to 4—6 inch).

Broadside : 6—6 inch, 8—21 inch T.T.

Astern :
3 to 4—6 inch.

ENTERPRISE.

1926 *Photo, Abrahams & Sons, Devonport.*

General Notes.—It will be observed that the bridge is of a novel type, which has attained fuller development in the
Kent class. This and the twin turret forward render it easy to distinguish this ship from *Emerald*.

Gunnery Notes.—Pairing of forward 6 inch guns adopted as an experiment in this ship, has been followed closely
the *Nelson* and *Rodney.* (Additional notes will be found on a later page, under sister ship *Emerald*.)

EMERALD.

1929 *Photo, Abrahams, Devonport.*

ADDITIONAL VIEWS OF "E" CLASS

ENTERPRISE.   1926 *Photo, Abrahams & Sons, Devonport.*

EMERALD.

1929 *Photo, Abrahams, Devonport.*

Details of bridgework, ENTERPRISE.   1926 *Photo, Abrahams & Sons, Devonport.*

BRITISH—Cruisers

("E" Class—Second Ship).

EMERALD (19th May, 1920).

"Standard" displacement, 7100 tons; *normal* displacement, 7550 tons.
Complement, 572/577.

Length $\begin{cases} p.p. \ 535 \text{ feet} \\ o.a. \ 570 \text{ feet} \end{cases}$ Beam 54½ feet.   Draught $\begin{cases} mean \ 16½ \text{ feet} \\ max. \ \ \ \text{feet.} \end{cases}$

Guns :
7—6 inch, 50 cal. (**Dir. Con.**)
3—4 inch AA.
4—3 pdr.
2—2 pdr. pom-pom
2 M.G.
8 Lewis
Torpedo tubes (21 inch) :
16, in four quadruple mountings, *above water.*

Armour (H.T.) :
3" Side (amidships)
2½"—1½" Side (bow)
2" Side (stern)
1" Upper deck (amidships)
1" Deck (over rudder)

Machinery : Turbines, 4 sets Brown-Curtis (geared). 4 screws.
Designed S.H.P. 80,000=33 kts. (light), 32 kts. (*full load*). Boilers : 8
Yarrow small tube. Fuel (oil only) : *normal,* 650 tons ; *maximum,*
1746 tons.

EMERALD.

1926 *Photo, Grand Studio, Malta.*

Notes to Plan.—Now has aeroplane
platform. AA. gun mounted
on after blast screen as in
Enterprise
Torpedo tubes quadrupled.

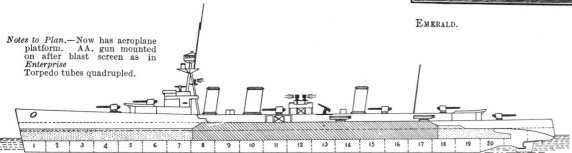

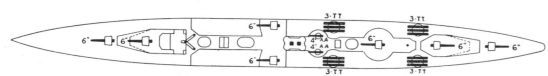

Ahead :
3 to 4—6 inch.

Broadside : 6—6 inch, 8—21 inch T.T.

Astern :
3 to 4—6 inch.

Notes for both Ships, "E" Class.

Gunnery Notes.— Elevation of 6-inch, up to 40°. Heavy Director on foremast. R.F. on forward bridge.

Engineering Notes.—Geared turbines, 4 shafts. For wing shafts, engine-rooms are forward ; for inner shafts, engine-rooms
are aft. H.P. and L.P. turbines in same casing ; astern turbine in exhaust casing of L.P. turbines. 8 boilers in
4 w.t. compartments, part forward of amidships magazines and part abaft forward engine-room. This arrangement
of boiler rooms is responsible for the somewhat unusual spacing of the funnels.

General Notes.—Begun under Emergency War Programme. A third ship, *Euphrates,* ordered from Fairfield Co.,
cancelled. They were designed early in 1918, to have a speed equal to that of any of the German Light Cruisers
then existing or likely to be built. The distribution of guns was recommended by Gunnery Officers on the basis
of war experience and is generally the same as that for *Hawkins, Raleigh,* &c., described hereafter. Owing to their high
speed and fine entry, the "C" and "D" classes of Light Cruisers without trawler bows, proved very wet forward.
To remedy this defect, these "E" class Cruisers have been given a very high freeboard for the whole length of
forecastle. Cost of these ships was £1,617,062 for *Emerald* and £1,751,854 for *Enterprise.* Full load displacement said to exceed 9000 tons. Refit 1931.

Name	Builder	Machinery	Ordered	Begun	Completed	Trials: H.P. kts.	Turbines
Emerald *Enterprise*	*Armstrong †Clydebank	Wallsend Clydebank	7/3/18 7/3/18	Sept.23/18 June 28/18	Jan. 14/'26 Jan., '26	80450=32.9 (*Enterprise* not tried).	Brown-Curtis Brown-Curtis

* Towed to Chatham D.Y., †Devonport D.Y. for completion.

(IMPROVED BIRMINGHAM CLASS—FIRST 3 SHIPS.)

EFFINGHAM (8th June, 1921), **FROBISHER** (20th March, 1920), **HAWKINS** (1st Oct., 1917).

Normal displacement, *Effingham* 9770 tons, *Frobisher* 9860 tons, *Hawkins* 9750 tons (as completed, all displace over 10,000). Complement, 712/749.

Length $\begin{Bmatrix} p.p. & 565 \text{ feet} \\ o.a. & 605 \text{ ,,} \end{Bmatrix}$ Beam $\begin{Bmatrix} w.l. & 58^* \text{ feet.} \\ \text{outside bulges } 65 \text{ ,,} \end{Bmatrix}$ Draught $\begin{Bmatrix} \text{mean } 17\frac{1}{4} \text{ feet.} \\ \text{max. } 20\frac{1}{2} \text{ ,,} \end{Bmatrix}$
*Approximate.

FROBISHER.

1924 *Photo Abrahams, Devonport.*

Guns :
7—7·5 inch, 45 cal., Mk. VI **(Dir.)**
3 or 4—4 inch ΛΛ.   **Con.)**
4—3 pdr.
2—2 pdr. pom-pom.
2 M.G.
8 Lewis
Torpedo tubes (21 inch) :
4 *above water*
2 *submerged* (*Effingham* 1.)

All fitted as Flagships.
Hawkins has 7·5 in. 50 cal., Mk. V and a fourth 4 inch.

Armour (H.T. or Nickel) :
3″—2″ Side (amidships)
2½″—1½″ Side (bow) ..
2½″—2¼″ Side (stern)
1″ Upper deck (amids.)
1½″—1″ Deck over rudder (Hadfield) ..
3″ C.T. ....
Anti-Torpedo Protection :
Bulges, 5 ft. deep ...
Unpierced Bulkheads, below lower deck ...

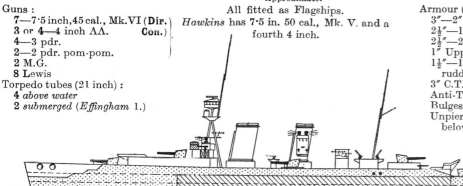

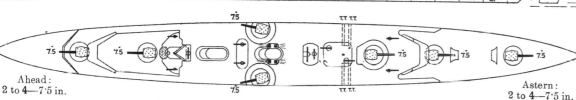

Ahead :
2 to 4—7·5 in.

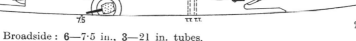

Astern :
2 to 4—7·5 in.

Broadside : 6—7·5 in., 3—21 in. tubes.

General Notes.—Begun under Emergency War Programme. One unit of this class was accelerated in building, and completed as the Aircraft Carrier *Vindictive*, but was re-converted into a Cruiser, 1923 (see later page for particulars). Another, *Raleigh*, was wrecked in August, 1922. *Hawkins* cost £1,636,745 ; *Effingham*, £2,175,000 ; *Frobisher*, £2,035 915. Refits *Frobisher*, 1928 ; *Hawkins*, 1929. All vessels of this class are excellent seaboats.

Machinery : Turbines, Brown-Curtis or Parsons (geared cruising). Designed S.H.P. in *Hawkins*, 60,000 = 30 kts. *Effingham* and *Frobisher*, 65,000 = 30·5 kts. 4 screws. Boilers : 12 Yarrow (small tube). Fuel : as completed, 1000 tons oil *normal*, 2150 *maximum*. *Hawkins*, as reconstructed, 2600 tons *maximum*.

Gunnery Notes.—7.5's are a Vickers type B.L. on centre-pivot mountings and with H.A. elevation. Very handy guns, but at H.A. (30°) elevation breeches close to deck. Hoists very noisy and interfere with telephonic communication with control stations. Unofficially stated that muzzle velocity is high, so that guns have practically a range only limited by *maximum* visibility. Armaments originally projected for this class were (*a*) mixed battery of 9.2 inch and 6 inch, (*b*) 14—6 inch. Heavy type director on foremast. Third AA. gun in *Effingham* and *Frobisher* is on Q.D. between 7.5 inch guns.

Torpedo Notes.—*Above water* tubes are single, mounted athwartships on upper deck below mainmast. *Submerged* tubes abeam of C.T.

FROBISHER with catapult.

1928 *Photo, Abrahams & Sons, Devonport.*

Name	Builder	Machinery	Begun	Completed	Trials : H.P. kts.	Turbines
Effingham *Frobisher* *Hawkins*	Portsmouth D.Y. Devonport D.Y. Chatham D.Y.	H. & Wolff Wallsend Parsons	2 Ap', '17 2 Aug., '16 June, '16	July, '25 20 Sept. '24 July 25, '19	60980 = 28·7	Brown-Curtis Brown-Curtis Parsons

EFFINGHAM.

1925 *Photo, Abrahams, Devonport.*

EFFINGHAM.

1925 *Photo, Abrahams, Devonport.*

(IMPROVED BIRMINGHAM CLASS— 4TH SHIP.)

VINDICTIVE (ex *Cavendish*) (17th January, 1918.)

Normal displacement, 9750 tons (as completed, over 10,000).

Complement, 717.

Length $\begin{cases} \text{p.p., } 565 \text{ feet} \\ \text{o.a., } 605 \text{ feet} \end{cases}$ Beam $\begin{cases} \textit{waterline,} & 58 \text{ feet} \\ \textit{outside bulges,} & 65 \text{ feet} \end{cases}$

Draught $\begin{cases} \textit{mean,} & 17\frac{1}{4} \text{ feet} \\ \textit{max.,} & 20\frac{1}{2} \text{ feet} \end{cases}$

uns :
6—7.5 inch, 50 cal. Mark V. (**Dir. Con.**)
3—4 inch AA.
4—3 pdr.
2—2 pdr. pom-pom.
8 Lewis.
rpedo tubes (21 inch) :
4 *above water*.
2 *submerged*.
ights carried :
1 Spotter Reconnaissance.
3 Fairey IIID seaplanes.

Armour (H.T. or Nickel) :
3″—2″ Side (amidships) ...
2½″—1½″ Side (forward and
    aft) ....
1″ Upper deck (amidships).
1½″ Deck over rudder (Had-
    field) ....
3″ C.T. ....
Anti-Torpedo Protection :
Bulges, 5 feet deep.
Unpierced bulkheads below
    lower deck.

VINDICTIVE (showing hangar and hydraulic crane).

1925 *Photo, Abrahams, Weymouth.*

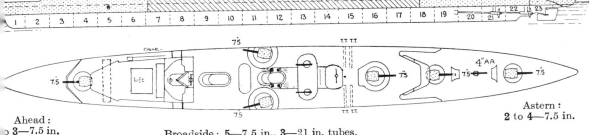

Ahead :
3—7.5 in.

Broadside : **5—7.5 in., 3—21 in. tubes.**

Astern :
2 to **4**—7.5 in.

Machinery : Parsons (geared) turbines. 4 screws. Boilers : Yarrow. Designed S.H.P.
60,000 = 30 kts. (trials, 63,600 = 29.12 kts.). Fuel : 800 tons coal and oil *normal* ; 800 tons
coal + 1420 tons oil *maximum*.

Gunnery and Torpedo Notes.—As *Hawkins, Effingham* and *Frobisher* on previous page.

General Notes.—Built under Emergency War Programme by Harland & Wolff, Ltd. Commenced 29th June, 1916, under
name of *Cavendish* as a unit of "Improved Birmingham" class. but renamed *Vindictive* and completed as an Aircraft
Carrier, October, 1918. Re-converted into a cruiser 1923-25, but still retains aeroplane hangar and catapult forward,
(on starboard side of superstructure). Refitted 1928.

VINDICTIVE.

1925 *Photo, Cribb, Southsea.*

("D Class.")

DESPATCH (24th Sept., 1919),

DELHI (23rd Aug., 1918),

DURBAN (29th May, 1919), **DANAE** (26th Jan., 1918),

DAUNTLESS (10th April, 1918), **DRAGON** (29th Dec., 1917).

Length $\begin{cases} p.p.\ 445\ \text{feet} \\ w.l.\ 465\frac{1}{2}\ ,, \\ o.a.\ 472\frac{1}{2}\ ,, \end{cases}$ Beam, $46\frac{1}{2}$ ft. Draught $\begin{cases} mean\ 14\frac{1}{4}\ \text{ft.} \\ max.\ 16\frac{1}{4}\ \text{ft.} \end{cases}$ = $\begin{array}{l} 4765\ \text{tons (first 1).} \\ 4650\ \text{tons (other 5).} \end{array}$

Complements of all, 450/469. All except *Despatch* fitted as Flagships.

Guns :
6—6 inch, 50 cal. (**Dir. Con.**)
3—4 inch AA.
4—3 pdr.
2—2 pdr. pom-pom.
2 M.G.
8 Lewis.
Torpedo tubes (21 inch) :
12 in 4 triple deck mountings.

Armour (H.T.) :
  3″ Side (amidships) ...
  2″, 1¾″, 1½″ Side (bow and stern) ....
  1″ Upper deck (amids.)
  1″ Deck over rudder ..
  (Hull and armour, 2940 tons.)

DURBAN, DELHI, DESPATCH. *Photo added 1925.*
(Note revolving aeroplane platform and trawler bows.)

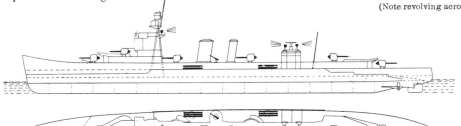

Ahead :
2—6 in.

Astern :
2 - 6 in.

Broadside : 6—6 in., 6—21 in. tubes.

Machinery : Turbines (all-geared), Brown-Curtis or Parsons types. Designed S.H.P. 40,000 = 29 kts. 2 screws. Boilers : 6 Yarrow (small tube). Oil fuel only : *normal*, 300 tons ; *maximum*, 1050 tons. Machinery and engineering stores = 945 tons.

Name	Builder	Machinery	Ordered	Begun	Completed	Trials: H.P. kts.	Turbines
Despatch	Fairfield*	Fairfield	Mar., 1918	July, 1918	2 June, 1922		Brown-Curtis
Delhi	Armstrong	Wallsend	Sept., 1917	29 Oct., '17	June, 1919	41,381 = 28·5†	Brown-Curtis
Durban	Scotts*	Scotts	Sept., 1917	Jan., 1918	1 Sept. 1921	41,026 =	Brown-Curtis
Danae	Armstrong	Wallsend	Sept., 1916	Dec., 1916	July, 1918	40,463 =	Brown-Curtis
Dauntless	Palmer		Sept., 1916	Jan., 1917	Dec., 1918	42,808 =	Parsons
Dragon	Scott	Scott	Sept., 1916	Jan., 1917	Aug., 1918	40,035 =	Brown-Curtis

*Towed to following Dockyards for completion : *Despatch* to Chatham, *Durban* to Devonport.
† With PVs. out, and on deep draught.

DAUNTLESS. 1928 *Photo. Cribb.*

General Notes.—Emergency War Programme ships. Note that first three were ordered *before Carlisle* class. Design generally as *Ceres* class, but lengthened *about* 20 feet, to add a sixth 6-inch between foremast and first funnel ; also triple tubes. Cost of *Delhi*, £840,182. Heavy director on foremast. *Dunedin* and *Diomede*, of this class, both transferred to New Zealand Navy, May, 1924 and October, 1925, respectively. *Dauntless* badly damaged by grounding off Halifax, Nova Scotia, July, 1928, and completely refitted 1929-30. *Danae, Delhi, Dragon*, all refitted 1929-30.

(CARLISLE CLASS—5 SHIPS.)
CAIRO* (19th Nov., 1918), **CALCUTTA*** (9th July, 1918), **CARLISLE*** (9th July, 1918), **CAPETOWN*** (28th June, 1919), **COLOMBO*** (18th Dec., 1918).

(CERES CLASS—5 SHIPS.)
CARDIFF* (ex *Caprice*, 12th April, 1917), **CERES** (24th March, 1917), **COVENTRY*** (ex *Corsair*, 6th July, 1917), **CURACOA*** (5th May, 1917), **CURLEW** (5th July, 1917).

Displacement, 4190 tons.   Complement, 400/437.

Length $\begin{cases} p.p. & 425 \text{ feet} \\ o.a. & 450 \text{ ,,} \end{cases}$ Beam, 43½ feet. Draught $\begin{cases} mean & 14 \text{ feet 1 inch.} \\ max. & 16\frac{1}{4} \text{ ,,} \end{cases}$

Guns :
5—6 inch, 50 cal. (**Dir. Con.**)
2—3 inch AA.
4—3 pdr. (Some mount 2 only).
2—2 pdr. pom-pom.
2 M.G.
8 Lewis.
Torpedo tubes (21 inch) :
8 *above water*, in 4 *double* mountings.

*Fitted as Flagships.

Armour (H.T.) :
3″ Side (amidships) ...
2¼″—1½″ Side (bow) ..
2″ Side (stern) ....
1″ Upper deck (amids.)
1″ Deck over rudder ..
(Harvey or Hadfield)
3″ C.T. ....
— Tube ....

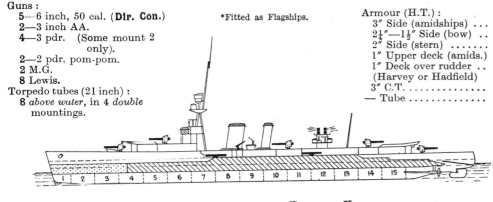

Ahead :
2—6 in.

Broadside : 5—6 in., 4—21 in. tubes.

Astern :
2—6 in.

Machinery : Turbines (all-geared), see Table. 2 screws in all. Designed S.H.P. 40,000 = 29 kts. Boilers : Yarrow. Fuel (oil only) : 300 tons, *normal* ; maximum, 950 tons.

General Notes.—*Cardiff* class Emergency War Programme ships, ordered April, 1916. Very wet forward, to remedy which defect the later *Carlisle* and *Dragon* classes were given " trawler " bows. Heavy type Director on foremast. *Cairo* class Emergency War Programme ships, ordered June-July, 1917, that is *after* the first three units of "D Class" (*Danae, Dragon, Dauntless*) were ordered. In these, ships "trawler" bows were added, to remedy defects shown by *Ceres* and *Calypso* classes. Conning tower also abolished. Heavy director on foremast. *Curacoa* was mined in 1919, and refitted 1919-20. Recent refits : *Carlisle, Coventry, Curacoa, Curlew*, 1928-29 ; *Cardiff, Ceres, Colombo*, 1929-30.

To distinguish : From *Dragon* and " D " Cruisers.—No 6 inch between foremast and first funnel. The same point separates this class from the *Caledon* class.

COLOMBO.   *1926 Photo, Grand Studio, Malta.*
Carlisle and *Capetown* originally had a hangar forward, but this has been removed and replaced by standard bridge work. *Curacoa* and several others now carry maintopmasts.

Name	Builder	Machinery	Begun	Completed	Trials H.P. kts.		Turbines
Cardiff	Fairfield	Fairfield	July, 1916	July, 1917	41,450 =	28·96	B.-Curtis A.G.
Ceres	Clydebank	Clydebank	Apl.26,'16	June, 1917	39,425 =	29·1	B.-Curtis A.G.
Coventry	Swan, Hunter	Wallsend	Aug., 1916	Feb., 1918	39,967 =		B.-Curtis A.G.
Curacoa	Pembroke D.Y.	Harland & Wolff	July, 1916	Feb., 1918	40,428 =		B.-Curtis A.G.
Curlew	Vickers	Vickers	Aug., 1916	Dec., 1917	40,240 =	28·07	Parsons A.G.
Cairo	Cammell Laird	Cammell Laird	28 Nov.,'17	24 Sep.'19			Parsons
Calcutta	Vickers	Vickers	Oct., 1917	21 Aug.,'19			Parsons
Carlisle	Fairfield	Fairfield	Oct., 1917	11 Nov.'18	40,930 =	28·45	B.-Curtis
Capetown	Cammell Laird*	Cammell Laird	23 Feb.,'18	Feb., '22			Parsons
Colombo	Fairfield	Fairfield	Dec., 1917	June, '19			B.-Curtis

*Towed to Pembroke D.Y. for completion.

   CURACOA (and others of *Ceres* class).   *1926 Photo, S. T. Abrahams, Weymouth.*

CALEDON. (Revolving aeroplane platform).   *1921 Photo, Abrahams, Devonport.*

(CALEDON CLASS—3 SHIPS.)

CALEDON* (25th Nov., 1916), **CALYPSO** (24th Jan., 1917), **CARADOC** (23rd Dec., 1916).

Displacement, 4120 tons. Complement, 400/437.

Length $\begin{Bmatrix} p.p. & 425 \text{ feet} \\ o.a. & 450 \text{ ,,} \end{Bmatrix}$ Beam, $42\frac{3}{4}$ feet.   Draught $\begin{Bmatrix} mean & 14 \text{ ft. 1 in.} \\ max. & 16\frac{1}{4} \text{ feet.} \end{Bmatrix}$

Guns :
5—6 inch, 50 cal. (**Dir. Con.**)
2—3 inch AA.
4—3 pdr.
2—2 pdr. pom-pom.
2 M.G.
8 Lewis.
Torpedo tube (21 inch) :
8 *above water*, in 4 double
mountings.

* Fitted as Flagship.

Armour (H.T.) :
3″ Side (amidships) ...
$2\frac{1}{4}″$—$1\frac{1}{4}″$ Side (bow) ..
$2\frac{1}{2}″$—2″ Side (stern) ..
1″ Upper deck (amids.)
1″ Deck over rudder ..
(Harvey or Hadfield)
6″ C.T. ....
4″ Tube..............

Ahead :
1—6 in.

Broadside : 5—6 in., 4—21 in. tubes.

Astern :
2—6 in.

Machinery : Turbines (all-geared), Parsons. 2 screws. Designed S.H.P. 40,000 = 29 kts.
Boilers : 8 Yarrow. Fuel (oil only) : *normal*, 300 tons ; *maximum*, 935 tons.

Gunnery Notes.--Mark of 6-inch gun introduced in this class and mounted in later Cruisers has about 40° elevation.
Heavy type Director.

Name	Builder	Machinery	Begun	Completed	Trials : H.P. kts.
Caledon	Cammell Laird	Cammell Laird	Mar.17,'16	Mar., '17	47,887 =
Calypso	Hawthorn Leslie	Hawthorn Leslie	Feb.7, '16	June 21,'17	43,312 =
Caradoc	Scott S.B. Co.	Scotts	Feb., '16	June, '17	41,196 =

General Notes.—Emergency War Programme. When new, they could make 29-30 kts. Are very wet forward, the fo'sle 6 inch being almost unfightable in a head sea. *Cassandra*, of this class, built by Messrs. Vickers Ltd , lost in Baltic by mine, soon after Armistice was signed. *Caledon* refitted 1926-1927, *Caradoc* 1927-28, *Calypso* 1929.

To distinguish

Caledon class   from   *Centaur* class

1. AA. guns abeam *between* funnels.
2. *Deck* tubes.
3. *Raking* stem.

Note.—Revolving aeroplane platform before SL. Tower added to *Caledon* 1919.

1. AA. guns on centre line *before and abaft* SL. tower.
2. Tubes *submerged*.
3. " *Yacht* " stems.

CALYPSO.   *1921 Photo, S. L. Cassar, Valetta, Malta.*

CONCORD.   (CENTAUR CLASS—2 SHIPS.)   1923 *Photo, Abrahams, Devonport.*

CENTAUR (6th Jan., 1916), **CONCORD** (1st April, 1916).

Displacement, 3750 tons. Complement, 370.

Length (*p.p.*) 420, (*o.a.*) 446 feet. Beam, 42 feet. Draught { mean 13½ feet. / max. 16⅓ „

Guns :

Both fitted as flagships.

Concord, **3**—6 inch, 50 cal., Mark XI. ⎫
Centaur, **4**—6 inch, 45 cal., Mark XII. ⎬ **(Dir. Con.).**
2—3 inch AA. (12½ pdr.)
4—3 pdr. (*Centaur* only 2).
2—2 pdr. pom-pom.
2 M.G.
8 Lewis.

Torpedo tubes (21 inch) :
2 *submerged.*

Plans :—Generally same as *Caledon* class.

Armour (H.T.) :
3″ Side (amidships) ...
2¼″—1¼″ Side (bow) ..
2½″—2″ Side (stern) ..
1″ Upper deck (amidships)
1″ Deck over rudder ..

Ahead :
1—6 in.   Broadside : **3 or 4**—6 in., **1**—21 in. tube.   Astern : **2**—6 in.

Machinery : Parsons I. R. turbines. 4 screws. Boilers : 8 Yarrow (*Centaur* 6). Designed S.H.P. 40,000 = 29 kts. Fuel (oil only) : *normal,* 300 tons ; *full load,* 824 tons.

Name	Builder	Machinery	Begun	Completed	Trials : H.P. kts.
Centaur	Armstrong	Vickers	Jan., 1915	Aug., 1916	31,679 = 26·8
Concord	Armstrong	Vickers	Feb., 1915	Dec., 1916	40,908 =

General Notes.—Emergency War Programme ships originally ordered for Turkish Navy. When new, could make 30-32 kts. Specially well sub-divided. Roll a lot and very wet forward. Heavy Director Control introduced in this type, these being the first small cruisers *designed* with guns on centre line. *Concord* refitted 1923-24. *Centaur* refitted 1923-25, and **1**—6 inch removed. *Concord* now employed as Signal School cruiser, and has had second and fourth 6 inch guns removed. *Centaur* to be scrapped, 1932.

CAMBRIAN.   1928 *Photo, Abrahams & Sons.*

(CAMBRIAN CLASS—LATER 4 SHIPS.)

CAMBRIAN (3rd March, 1916), **CANTERBURY** (21st Dec., 1915),
CASTOR (28th July, 1915), **CONSTANCE** (12th Sept., 1915).

Displacement, 3750 tons. Complement, 348/357.

Length (*p.p.*) 420, (*o.a.*) 446 feet. Beam, 41½ feet. Draught, 16¼ feet *max,* 13½ *mean.*

Guns :
4—6 inch, 50 cal. **(Dir. Con.)**
2—3 inch AA.
4—3 pdr.
2—2 pdr. pom-poms.
1 M G
8 Lewis

Torpedo tubes (21 inch).
2 *submerged.*

For Plans v. next page.

Armour (H.T. and Harvey) :
3″ side (amidships) ...
2¼″—1½″ Side (bow) ..
2½″—2″ Side (aft) ....
1″ Upper deck (amidships)
1″ Deck over rudder ..
6″ C.T. } Removed
4″ Tube } from some

Machinery : Turbines, as *Notes.* 4 screws. Boilers : 8 Yarrow in all. Designed S.H.P. 40,000 = 29 kts. Fuel (oil only) : *normal,* 420 tons ; *maximum,* 841 tons.

Name	Builder	Machinery	Begun	Completed	Trials : H.P. kts.	Turbines
Cambrian	Pembroke	Cammell Laird	Dec., 1914	May, 1916	40,100=	Parsons I.R.
Canterbury	Clydebank	Clydebank	Oct.14,'14	May, 1916		Brown-Curtis
Castor	Cammell Laird	Cammell Laird	Oct.28,'14	Nov., 1915	42,337=	Parsons I.R.
Constance	Cammell Laird	Cammell Laird	Jan.25,'15	Jan., 1916	41,892=	Parsons I.R.

General Notes.—Begun under 1914-15 Estimates. Design generally same as *Champion* and *Calliope*. Light director in foretop. *Cambrian* and *Canterbury* completed refits March and Jan., 1926, respectively. *Castor* refitted 1925-26, *Constance* 1926-27.

(CAROLINE CLASS)

CHAMPION (May 29th, 1915),   **COMUS** (16th Dec., 1914).

Displacement, 3750 tons (about 4780 tons *full load*).   Complement, 348.

Length (*p.p.*), 420 feet.   Beam, 41½ feet.   Draught, (*max.*) 16, (*mean*) 13½ feet.   Length (*over all*), 446 feet.

Guns :
  4—6 inch (**Dir. Con.**)
  2—3 inch AA.
  4—3 pdr.
  2—2 pdr. pom-poms.
  1 M.G.
  8 Lewis.
Tubes :
  4—21 inch *above water*
    in 2 pairs.
  Plus 2 submerged in
    Champion.

Armour (H.T.) :
  3″ Side (amidships), 2¼″—1½″
  forward, 2½″—2″ aft, 1″ Upper
  Deck (amidships), 1″ Deck over
  rudder head.   C.T. removed
  from all.

CHAMPION   *1921 Photo, Cribb, Southsea.*

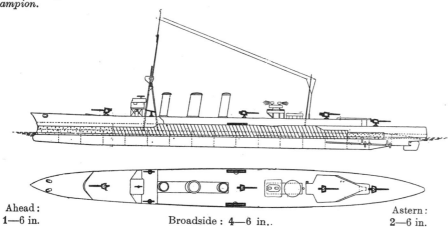

Ahead :
1—6 in.

Broadside : 4—6 in..

Astern :
2—6 in.

Machinery : Turbine : Parsons or Brown-Curtis.   (See notes tabulated below).
Boilers : 8 Yarrow.   Designed H.P. 40,000 = 29 kts.   Fuel (oil only) : *normal,* 482 tons ;
maximum, 917 tons.   (895 tons in *Champion*).

Name	Builder	Machinery	Laid down	Completed	Trials	Turbines	Boilers	Best recent speed
Champion *Comus*	Hawthorn Swan, Hunter	Hawthorn Wallsend	Mar.'14 Nov.'13	Dec. '15 May, '15	41,000 = 29 32,736 =	Parsons A.G. Parsons L.R.	Yarrow	

General Notes.—Belong to the 1913-14 Estimates. Originally had 2—6 inch and 8—4 inch ; in 1916-17, 3—6 inch and
6—4 inch and tripod mast added ; in 1918, 4—6 inch and no 4 inch. Much overloaded and roll badly, but very
strongly built. Light Director on foretop. *Conquest* placed on disposal list, 1927. *Caroline* now a harbour
drillship for R.N.V.R., at Belfast. *Calliope, Carysfort* and *Cleopatra* scrapped 1931.

COMUS.   *1927 Photo, R. Perkins, Esq.*

MARSHAL SOULT.   1023 *Photo, Abrahams, Devonport.*

EREBUS (19th June, 1916), TERROR (18th May, 1916).

Displacement, 8000 tons.   Complement, 300.

Length, (*p.p.*) 380, (*o.a.*) 405 feet.   Beam, 88 feet.   *Mean* Draught, 11 feet.

Guns :
2—15 inch, 42 cal. (**Dir. Con.**)*
5—4 inch in *Terror*, 2 in *Erebus*.
2—3 inch (anti-aircraft)
2—2 pdr. (anti-aircraft)
4 M.G. or Lewis

* and H.A. elevation.

Armour :
4″ Bulkheads, F. & A.
8″ Barbette ....
13″—4¼″ Gunhouse ....

4″ Box citadel (over magazines) ......
6″ C.T. ....
1″ Fo'xle & upper decks
4″ Main deck (slopes)
2″ Main deck ....
1½″—¾″ Lower deck ..
Anti-torpedo pro.
       bulges.

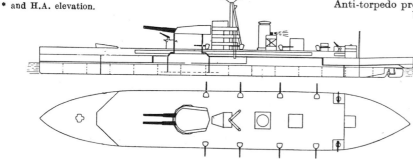

Machinery : Triple expansion.   2 screws.   Boilers : Babcock.   Designed H.P. 6000=12 kts.
Fuel : 650 tons *normal,* 750 tons, *maximum,* oil only.
Gunnery Notes.—15 inch are high angle and can range up to 40,000 yards. Smoke screen apparatus fitted. *Erebus* has 15 inch removed from *M. Ney.*
Special Protection.—Bulges about 15 feet deep, sub-divided into 50 w.t.c.

Name	Builder and Machinery	Begun	Completed	Trials
Erebus	Harland & Wolff (Govan)	Oct., 1915	Sept.,1916	7244 H.P. = 14·1 kts.
Terror	Harland & Wolff (Belfast)	Oct., 1915	Aug., 1916	6235 H.P. = 13·1 kts.

General Notes.—Both Emergency War Programme. *Erebus* fitted out as Cadets' T.S., with extra cabin accommodation on upper deck, and other alterations.

MARSHAL SOULT (17th June, 1915).

Displacement, 6670 tons.   Complement, 228.

Length, 340 (*p.p.*), 355⅔ (*o.a.*) feet.   Beam, 90¼ feet.   Draught, 10½ feet.

Guns : 2—15 inch (Dir. Con.), H. A. elevation, 8—4 inch, 2—3 inch AA., 2—2 pdr. AA., 4 Lewis (disposed similarly to *Erebus* and *Terror*). Armour : 8″ Barbette, 13″—4¼″ Gunhouse; 4″ Bulkheads fore and aft, 6″ C.T., 4″—1″ Box Citadel over Magazine, 1″ Fo'xle Deck, 2″—1½″ Upper Deck, Lower Deck 3″ at bow, 1½″ at stern, 1″ Navig. Position. Deep bulge Protection.
Machinery : 2 sets Diesel.   4 screws.   Designed H.P. 1500 = 6.7 kts.   Fuel : 235 tons, *maximum* oil only.

Name	Builder	Machinery	Begun	Completed	Trials
M. Soult	Palmer	Vickers	Jan., 1915	Nov., 1915	1898 H.P. = 6·6 kts.

General Notes.—Emergency War Programme. Serves as Gunnery Training Ship at the Nore. Sister Ship *M. Ney* now Hulk *Vivid,* at Devonport.

TERROR.   1919 *Photo.*

Pendant Numbers.

The following is a list of Flotilla Leader and Destroyer Pendant Numbers, as officially communicated to *Fighting Ships* by the Admiralty, Oct., 1931 :—

D Flag Superior.

Pendants.	Ship.	Pendants.	Ship.	Pendants.	Ship.	Pendants.	Ship.
D, 00	Stuart	D, 50	Shakespeare.	H, 05	Stormcloud.	H, 65	Boadicea.
D, 01	Montrose.	D, 51	Vectis.	H, 06	Shamrock.	H, 66	
D, 02	Senator.	D, 52	Vega.	H, 07	Defender.	H, 67	
D, 03	Sepoy.	D, 53	Vehetia.	H, 08		H, 68	
D, 04	Serapis.	D, 54	Vanquisher.	H, 09	Acasta.	H, 69	
D, 05		D, 55	Vesper.	H, 10	Umpire.	H, 70	
D, 06		D, 56	Wolfhound.	H, 11	Basilisk.	H, 71	Tempest.
D, 07	Somme.	D, 57	Violent.	H, 12	Achates.	H, 72	Thisbe.
D, 08		D, 58	Serapis.	H, 14	Active.	H, 73	Thruster.
D, 09		D, 59	Sirdar.	H, 15	Seymour.	H, 74	
D, 10	Tourmaline.	D, 60	Campbell.	H, 16	Daring.	H, 75	Decoy.
D, 11		D, 61	Valkyrie.	H, 17		H, 76	
D, 12	Sportive.	D, 62	Wild Swan.	H, 18	Sabre.	H, 77	Boreas.
D, 14	Swallow.	D, 63	Verity.	H, 19	Seafire.	H, 78	
D, 15		D, 64	Vansittart.	H, 20	Searcher.	H, 79	
D, 16	Tribune.	D, 65	Codrington.	H, 21	Scimitar.	H, 80	Brazen.
D, 17	Trinidad.	D, 66	Wivern.	H, 22	Diamond.	H, 81	Torrid.
D, 18		D, 67	Wishart.	H, 23		H, 82	Restless.
D, 19	Malcolm.	D, 68	Vampire.	H, 24	Champlain, H.M.C.S.	H, 83	Cygnet.
D, 20	Wallace.	D, 69	Vendetta.	H, 25	Serene.	H, 84	Brilliant.
D, 21	Wrynech.	D, 70	Mackay.	H, 26	Sardonyx.	H, 85	Rowena.
D, 22	Waterhen.	D, 71	Volunteer.	H, 27	Grenville.	H, 86	
D, 23	Vimiera.	D, 72	Veteran.	H, 28	Sturdy.	H, 87	
D, 24	Walrus.	D, 73	Vivien.	H, 29	Thanet.	H, 88	Wakeful.
D, 25	Warwick.	D, 74	Wanderer.	H, 30	Beagle.	H, 89	
D, 26	Watchman.	D, 75	Venomous.	H, 31	Sterling.	H, 90	
D, 27	Walker.	D, 76	Witherington.	H, 32	Abdiel.	H, 91	Bulldog.
D, 28	Vanity.	D, 77	Whitshed.	H, 33	Vanoc.	H, 92	
D, 29	Vanessa.	D, 78	Wolverine.	H, 34	Turbulent.	H, 93	
D, 30	Whirlwind.	D, 79		H, 35	Sesame.	H, 94	
D, 31	Voyager.	D, 80	Tuscan.	H, 36	Antelope.	H, 95	Winchester.
D, 32	Versatile.	D, 81	Bruce.	H, 37	Steadfast.	H, 96	
D, 33	Vimy.	D, 82	Valorous.	H, 38	Delight.	H, 97	
D, 34	Velox.	D, 83	Broke.	H, 39	Skate.	H, 98	
D, 35	Wrestler.	D, 84	Keppel.	H, 40	Anthony.	H, 99	
D, 36	Vivacious.	D, 85	Shikari.	H, 41	Ardent.		
D, 37	Vortigern.	D, 86	Thracian.	H, 42	Arrow.	H, 1 Ans.	
D, 38	Ambuscade.	D, 87	Venturous.	H, 43		H, 2 Ans.	
D, 39	Amazon.	D, 88	Wren.	H, 44	Trojan.	H, 3 Ans.	Anzac, R.A.N.
D, 40	Spencer.	D, 89	Witch.	H, 45	Acheron.	H, 4 Ans.	Stalwart, R.A.N.
D, 41	Walpole.	D, 90	Douglas.	H, 46	Tyrant.	H, 5 Ans.	Success, R.A.N.
D, 42	Windsor.	D, 91	Viceroy.	H, 47	Blanche.	H, 6 Ans.	Tattoo, R.A.N.
D, 43	Wessex.	D, 92	Viscount.	H, 48	Crescent.	H, 7 Ans.	Tasmania, R.A.N.
D, 44	Valhalla.	D, 93	Verdun.	H, 49	Diana.	H, 8 Ans.	Swordsman, R.A.N.
D, 45	Westminster.	D, 94	Whitehall.	H, 50	Stronghold.	H, 9 Ans.	
D, 46	Winchelsea.	D, 95	Woolston.	H, 51	Scout.	H Ans. 0	
D, 47	Westcott.	D, 96	Worcester.	H, 52	Scotsman.	H Ans. 1	
D, 48	Vidette.	D, 97	Whitley.	H, 53	Dainty.	H Ans. 2	
D, 49	Valentine.	D, 98	Wolsey.	H, 54	Saladin.	H Ans. 3	
		D, 99		H, 55	Vancouver, H.M.C.S.	H Ans. 4	
				H, 56	Trusty.	H Ans. 5	
				H, 57	Spindrift.	H Ans. 6	
		H Flag Superior—Destroyers		H, 58	Salmon.	H Ans. 7	
				H, 59	Tetrach.	H Ans. 8	
		H, 00	Comet.	H, 60	Crusader.	H Ans. 9	
		H, 01		H, 61			
		H, 02	Turquoise.	H, 62			
		H, 03	Strenuous.	H, 63			
		H, 04	Tenedos.	H, 64	Duchess.		

Funnel Markings.

The following revised scheme of Funnel Markings of Destroyer Flotillas was officially notified to take effect from April 4th, 1925 :—

(*a*) Foremost funnel of leaders in Mediterranean and Atlantic Fleets will be marked with a 4ft. black band round the top.

(*b*) Divisional commanders will have a 2ft. band three feet from the top of the foremost funnel, as follows :—Atlantic Fleet, white ; Mediterranean Fleet, black.

(*c*) After funnel in all vessels will be marked with bands as follows :—Mediterranean Fleet— 1st Flotilla, one black ; 2nd Flotilla, two black ; 3rd Flotilla, three black ; 4th Flotilla, no mark.   Atlantic Fleet—5th Flotilla, one white ; 6th Flotilla, two white.

1 Admiralty Type.

7 Admiralty Large Design. (SCOTT type.)

CODRINGTON.

1930 *Photo, Abrahams, Devonport.*

Codrington.
Built by Swan-Hunter. Laid down, 1928, launched, August 7, 1929. Completed, June, 1930.

Displacement : 1520 tons standard. 2000 tons full load. Dimensions : 332 × 33¾ × 12¼ feet. Guns : 5—4.7 inch, 2—2 pdr. pom-pom 5 M.G. Tubes : 8—21 inch on quadruple mounts. Machinery : Geared Parsons turbines. 2 screws. Designed S.H.P. 39,000 = 35 kts. Boilers : Yarrow; working pressure 300 lbs. with superheaters. Oil fuel : about 500 tons. Complement.

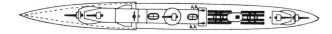

Note.—On Trials *Codrington* maintained a mean speed of 38 kts. for 4 hours, reaching 40 knots at times, during Trials. At no time was the machinery pressed in any way, in conformance with Admiralty instructions. If maximum power had been worked up, this ship would have achieved record figures.

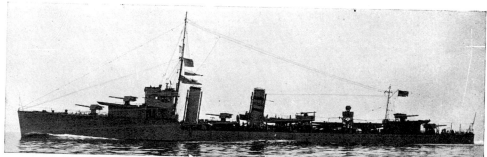

MACKAY.

Photo, Gieves, Ltd. (28th September, 1920).

5 *Cammell Laird :* **Bruce, Campbell, Douglas, Mackay** (ex *Claverhouse*), **Malcolm.**
2 *Hawthorn Leslie .* **Montrose, Stuart.**

Displacement : 1800 tons *normal,* up to 2053 tons on *deep load.* Dimensions : 320 (*p.p.*), 332½ (*o.a.*) × 31¾ × 12¼ feet (*mean*) draught. Guns : 5—4.7 inch B.L. (DIR. CON), 1—3 inch AA., 2—2 pdr. AA., 1 M.G., 4 Lewis. Tubes : 6—21 inch, in two triple mountings. Machinery : Parsons (all-geared) turbines in Cammell-Laird boats : Brown-Curtis in Hawthorn-Leslie boats. Designed S.H.P. 40,000 = 36.5 kts.* Boilers : Yarrow. Oil fuel : 504/401 tons. Complement, 183.
*On *trials,* light load draught ; on deep load, 31 kts. with same S.H.P.
General Notes.— Emergency War Programme boats. *War Losses : Scott* (Cammell Laird). *Cancelled* 1918 : *Barrington,* *Hughes* (both Cammell Laird).
To Distinguish.—By 4.7 inch guns in 5 positions. Deep chart-house and bridges ; thin funnels, equal in height. AA. gun platform well abaft 2nd funnel. Variations are 2 or 3 yards on foremast and small topmast to mainmast in one or two boats.

		Begun.	Launch.	Comp.			Begun.	Launch.	Comp.
Bruce ..	..	12/5/17	26/2/18	29 /5/18	Mackay	..	5/3/18	21/12/18	/6/19
Campbell	..	10/11/17	21/9/18	21/12/18	Malcolm	..	27/3/18	29/5/19	14/12/19
Douglas	..	30/6/17	8/6/18	30/8/18	Montrose	..	4/10/17	10/6/18	14/9/18
					Stuart ..	..	18/10/17	22/8/18	21/12/18

BRUCE

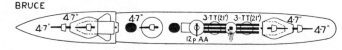

General Notes to all destroyer Plans (British).
Triple tubes are diagrammatically shown as if mounted side by side on one level : actually the centre tube is above and between the other two.

5 Thornycroft Type (Shakespeare class).

SPENSER.　　　　　　　　　　　　　　　　1920 *Photo, Seward, Weymouth.*

5 *Thornycroft* : **Broke** (ex-*Rooke*), **Keppel, Shakespeare, Spenser, Wallace.** *Normal* displacement : 1550 tons ; *full load*, 1750 tons. Dimensions : 318¼ (*p.p.*), 329 (*o.a.*) × 31 ft. 9 in. × 12⅓ feet (*mean*), 14¾ (*max.*) draught. Guns : 5—4.7 inch B.L. (DIR. CON.), 1—3 inch AA., 2—2 pdr. pom-pom. 1 M.G., 4 Lewis. Tubes : 6—21 inch in 2 triple deck mountings.

Machinery : Brown-Curtis all geared turbines. Designed S.H.P. 40,000=36 kts.§ 2 screws. Boilers : Thornycroft. Oil 550/250 tons (*Keppel*, 500/250). Complement, 183. §Light load on *trials* ; on deep load, same S.H.P. = 31 kts.

General Notes.—Built under War Emergency Programme. Appearance almost exactly same as *Bruce, Campbell,* &c., but these boats have the usual big, flat-sided Thornycroft funnels. No War Losses. *Cancelled* 1918 : *Saunders, Spragge. Broke* was completed at Pembroke Dockyard, *Keppel* at Portsmouth and Pembroke. Plans as for *Bruce* on preceding page. Standard displacement is 1480 tons.

		Begun.	Launch.	Comp.	Trials.	Cost.
Broke	... ...	10/18	23/4/20	13/12/24	35.6 (*mean*) 38 (*max*)	£409,394
Keppel	... ...	11/18	16/9/20	15/4/25	36 1　"	411,374
Shakespeare	... ...	10/16	7/7/17	10/17	38.74	
Spenser	... ...	10/16	22/9/17	12/17	37 76	
Wallace	... ...	8/17	26/10/18	2/19	37.72	

1 Kempenfelt Type (Grenville class).

SAUMAREZ.　　　　　　　　　　　1921 *Photo, Seward, Weymouth.*

1 *Cammell-Laird :* **Grenville.** 1670 tons. Dimensions : 315 (*p.p.*), 325 (*o.a.*)×31¾×11 feet (*mean*), 12¼ (*max.*) draught. Guns : 4—4 inch (DIR. CON.), 2—2 pdr. pom-pom. 1 M.G., 4 Lewis. Tubes : 4—21 inch in pairs. Machinery : Parsons turbines. 3 screws. Designed S.H.P. 36,000= 34 kts. Boilers : Yarrow. Oil : 515/416 tons. Complement, 140.

General Notes.—All Emergency War Programme. Same hull design as *Abdiel,* but have only three funnels and super-firing 4 inch gun forward. Built, 1915-1916.

War Losses.—*Hoste* (Cammell-Laird). *Removals.*—*Anzac* (Denny) presented to Australia, 1919. *Parker* and *Seymour* sold. *Saumarez* sold 1930.

		Begun.	Launch.	Comp.
Grenville	... ...	19/6/15	17/6/16	11/10/16
Saumarez	... ...	2/3/16	14/10/16	21/12/16

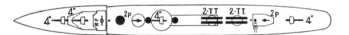

1 Kempenfelt Type (Minelayer).

ABDIEL.　　　　　　　　　　　　　　　　1922 *Photo.*

1 *Cammell-Laird :* **Abdiel.** 1670 tons. Dimensions, H.P., speed, as other 2 ships of this class above. Parsons turbines. Armament : 3—4 in., 1—2 pdr. 1 M.G., 4 Lewis. Tubes : none. This boat is a mine-layer carrying about 60—70 mines from fourth funnel to stern. Complement, 128. Laid down May, 1915 ; Launched Oct. 1915. Completed March, 1916. To be scrapped 1932.

"B" and "C" class "Leaders."

KEITH.　　　　　　　　　　　1931 *Photo, Favour of Messrs. Vickers-Armstrong.*

1 *Vickers-Armstrong* **Keith** (June, 1930). 1330 tons.

1 *White* **Kempenfelt** (Oct. 1931). 1330 tons.

1 *Portsmouth D.Y.* **DUNCAN** (　　　). 1390 tons.

1 To be Built 1931 Programme.

Although officially rated as "leaders," these vessels are only the "*Beagle*" design with a little extra staff accommodation.

8 "**B**" **Type** (**Beagle class**).
4 "**C**" **Type** (**Crusader class**).
8 "**D**" **Type** (**Defender class**).

8 Modified "A" Type (**Acasta class**).

ARROW.   1930 *Photo, favour of Messrs. Vickers-Armstrong.*

BRAZEN.

1931 *Photos, R. Perkins, Esq.*

ACTIVE.

1930 *Photo, Cribb.*

	⎧ 2 *Clydebank*: **Basilisk** ( ), **Beagle** (Sept. 26, 1930).
Estimates 1928-29	⎨ 2 *Hawthorn*: **Blanche** ( ), **Boadicia** (Sept. 23rd, 1930).
		2 *Palmers*: **Boreas** (July 18th, 1930), **Brasen** (July 25th, 1930).
	⎩ 2 *Swan Hunter*: **Brilliant** (Oct. 9th, 1930), **Bulldog** (Dec., 1930).
1929-30.	⎧ 2 *Portsmouth D.Y.*: **Crusader** (Oct., 1931), **Comet** (Oct., 1931).
	⎩ 2 *Vickers-Armstrong*: **Cygnet** ( ), **Crescent** ( ).
1930-31.	⎧ 2 *Vickers-Armstrong* **Defender** ( ), **Diamond** ( ).
		2 *Thornycroft*: **Daring** ( ), **Decoy** ( ).
		2 *Fairfield*: **Dainty** ( ), **Delight** ( ).
	⎩ 2 *Palmers*: **Diana** ( ), **Duchess** ( ).
1931-32.	8 To be Built.

General Notes.—Are similar to *Acasta* class from which they differ only in detail.

2 *Clydebank*: **Acasta** (Aug. 7th, 1929). **Achates** (Oct. 4th, 1929).
1 *Thornycroft*: **Acheron** (Mar. 18. 1930).
2 *Hawthorn Leslie*: **Active** (July 9th, 1929), **Antelope** (July 27th, 1929).
2 *Scotts*: **Anthony** (April 24th, 1929). **Ardent** (June 26th, 1929).
1 *Vickers-Armstrong*: **Arrow** (Aug. 22nd, 1929).
Displacement: 1330 tons.   Dimensions: 312 (*p.p.*) 323 (*o.a.*) × 32½ × 12 feet.   Guns: 4—4.7 inch, 2—2 pdr. pom-pom, 5 M.G.   Tubes: 8—21 inch on quadruple mounts   Machinery: Single reduction geared turbines.   2 screws. Designed S H.P. 34,000 = 35 kts.   Boilers: 3 Yarrow (working pressure 300 lbs.) with superheaters.   Oil fuel: 380 tons.   Complement 138.
General Notes.—All laid down 1928, under 1927-28 Estimates.   Completed 1930.   A very successful class, all having exceeded designed speed with ease.   Thus *Arrow* maintained 36.7 kts. with 34,119 H.P. for 6 hours, full power figures being those recorded at boiler capacity for this period.   No short period spurts were included in the trails. *Acheron* is fitted with special 500 lb. pressure boilers.   All have proved economical steamers, averaging ·81 lbs. (*Acheron* ·608 lbs.) fuel per S.H.P. per hour.

2 "A" Type.

AMAZON — 1927 *Photo, Messrs: Thornycroft (Builders).*

AMBUSCADE. — 1926 *Photo, Messrs. Yarrow (Builders).*

1 *Thornycroft:* **Amazon** (Jan. 27th, 1926). Displacement: 1352 tons. Dimensions: 311¾ × 31½ × 9 1/12 feet (*mean draught*).
1 *Yarrow:* **Ambuscade** (Jan. 15th, 1926). Displacement: 1173 tons. Dimensions: 307 × 31 × 8¼ feet (*mean draught*).

Guns: 4—4.7 inch, 2—2 pdr. pom-poms, 5 M.G. Tubes: 6—21 inch. in triple mounts. Machinery: Brown-Curtis turbines (all-geared type) H.P. and cruising; Parsons L.P. Boilers: By Builders: Designed S.H.P. 39,500 (*Amazon*). 33,000 (*Ambuscade*) = 37 kts. (made on trials). Superheated steam. Oil: *Amazon*, 433 tons; *Ambuscade*, 385 tons. Complement: 138.
Notes.—Built under 1924-25 Estimates. All-steel bridges, higher freeboard and improved cabin accommodation are principal features of this type, which has a larger radius of action than preceding classes. If necessary, induced ventilation can be supplied throughout the vessel, with a view to possible service in Tropics. *Ambuscade* laid down December 8th, 1924; *Amazon* in January, 1925. Both completed Sept., 1926. Cost: *Amazon*, £319,455; *Ambuscade*, £326,616.

14 "Admiralty Modified W."

VETERAN. — 1930 *Photo, Abrahams, Devonport.*

VERITY. — 1920 *Photo, Seward, Weymouth.*

7 BOATS, APPEARANCE AS ABOVE PHOTO :—

1 *Clydebank:* **Veteran.** 2 *Swan-Hunter:* **Whitshed, Wild Swan.**
4 *White:* **Witherington, Wivern, Wolverine, Worcester.**† (Completed by †Portsmouth D.Y.)

To distinguish.—Proportions of funnels reversed compared with other V's and W's. These boats have *thick* fore funnel and *thin* after funnel. No AA. guns abaft 2nd funnel. 2 pdr. pom-poms in echelon between funnels. White boats have plain S.L. tower without compass platform on fore side. *Witherington* and *Wivern*, only, have oval afterfunnel, built in sideways.

7 BOATS, APPEARANCE AS ABOVE PHOTO :—

1 *Beardmore:* **Vansittart.** 2 *Clydebank:* **Venomous** (ex *Venom*), **Verity.** 1 *Denny:* **Volunteer.**
1 *Fairfield:* **Wanderer.** 1 *Swan Hunter:* **Whitehall.** (Completed by Chatham D.Y.)
1 *Yarrow:* **Wren.** (Completed by Pembroke D.Y.)

To distinguish.—Difficult to distinguish from six tube V's. The short mainmast separates them from Admiralty W's. Only distinctive feature is the 2—2 pdr. AA. guns abaft after funnel, in echelon. *Vansittart, Wanderer,* have plain S.L. towers without compass platform on fore side. *Wren* has no caged caps to funnels and no compass platform forward of S.L. tower. *Volunteer* and *Whitehall,* no compass platform before S.L. tower.

WOLVERINE

WANDERER.

General Notes for both Types.

Displacement: 1120 tons *average* (1500 *full load*). Dimensions: 300 (*p.p.*), 312 (*o.a.*) × 29½ × 10⅝ feet (*mean*) draught. Guns: 4—4.7 inch (DIR. CON.), 2—2 pdr. pom-poms, 1 M.G., 4 Lewis. Tubes: 6—21 inch, in two triple mountings. Machinery: Turbines (all-geared type)—all Brown-Curtis, but *Whitehall*, Parsons. Designed S.H.P. 27,000 = 34 kts.* 2 screws. Boilers: Yarrow, except *White* boats with White-Forster. Oil: 374-353/324-318 tons; *Whitehall*, 368/318. Complement, 134.
*Light load draught on *trials*; on deep load 31 kts. with same S.H.P.
Notes.—Begun under War Emergency Programme, 1918, cost of completion of all comes under post-war Estimates. Differ from preceding V's in armament. Sometimes—but unofficially—referred to as "Repeat W Class." None of these boats were finished till 1919.

		Begun.	Launch.	Comp.
Veteran	.. ..	30/8/18	26/4/19	13/11/19
Whitshed	..	6/18	31/1/19	11/7/19
Wild Swan	..	7/18	17/5/19	14/11/19
Witherington	..	27/9/18	16/1/19	10/10/19
Wivern	..	19/8/18	16/4/19	23/12/19
Wolverine	..	8/10/18	17/7/19	27/7/20
Worcester	..	20/12/18	24/10/19	20/9/22

		Begun.	Launch.	Comp.
Vansittart	.. ..	1/7/18	17/4/19	5/11/19
Venomous	..	31/5/18	21/12/18	6/19
Verity	..	17/5/18	19/3/19	17/9/19
Volunteer	..	16/4/18	17/4/19	7/11/19
Wanderer	..	1918	1/5/19	18/9/19
Whitehall	..	6/18	11/9/19	9/7/24
Wren	..	6/18	11/11/19	2/23

19 Admiralty "W"

WARWICK.

1924 Photo, Abrahams.

2 *Beardmore :* **Wakeful, Watchman.***
2 *Denny :* **Walker,* Westcott.**
2 *Doxford :* **Walpole, Whitley.**
2 *Fairfield :* **Walrus, Wolfhound.**
2 *Hawthorn Leslie :* **Warwick,* Wessex.**
2 *Palmer :* **Waterhen, Wryneck.**
2 *Scott :* **Westminster, Windsor.**
1 *Stephen :* **Voyager.†**
2 *Swan Hunter :* **Whirlwind,* Wrestler.**
2 *White :* **Winchester, Winchelsea.**

Note.—*Vanquisher* and *Venturous*, though officially included in Admiralty "V" class on following page, are actually almost indistinguishable from Admiralty "W" type.

* Fitted as Mine Layers during War, but not so used now. Still have chutes at stern.

† *Voyager* has always had 6 tubes and is not an "Admiralty V" re-armed.

Displacement : 1100 tons.   Dimensions : 300 (*p.p.*), 312 (*o.a.*) × 29½ × 10 ft. 10 ins. (*mean*), 11¼ (*max.*) draught.   Guns : 4—4 inch (Mk. V Dir. Con.), 2—2 pdr. pom-poms, 1 M.G., 4 Lewis.   Torpedo tubes : 6—21 inch in two triple deck mountings.   Machinery : "All-Geared" turbines, Brown-Curtis in all except Palmer boats with Parsons. 2 screws. Designed S.H.P. 27,000 = 34 kts.*   Boilers : 3 Yarrow, except White boats with White-Forster. Oil : *about* 368/322 tons.   Complement, 134.

* Light load draught on *trials* ; on deep load at 1480 tons, 31 kts. with same S.H.P.

General Notes.—All Emergency War Programme. The Notes to the Admiralty V's also apply to these boats. No War Losses.

To distinguish.—From Improved W's : 3 inch AA. gun in bandstand abaft 2nd funnel ; from V's with 6 tubes : by higher mainmast ; from *Vampire* : by shorter foremast no extension to S.L. platform for standard compass, after mast stands away from after superstructure and is tall.

	Begun	Launch.	Comp.			Begun.	Launch.	Comp.
Wakeful	..	17/1/17	6/10/17	11/17	Waterhen	..	7/17	26/3/18	17/7/18
Watchman	..	17/1/17	2/12/17	1/18	Wryneck	..	7/17	13/5/18	11/18
Walker	..	26/3/17	29/11/17	12/2/18	Westminster	..	4/17	24/2/18	18/4/18
Westcott	..	30/3/17	14/2/18	12/4/18	Windsor	..	4/17	21/6/18	28/8/18
Walpole	..	5/17	12/2/18	7/8/18	Voyager	..	17/5/17	8/5/18	24/6/18
Whitley	..	6/17	13/4/18	10/18	Whirlwind	..	5/17	15/12/17	3/18
Walrus	..	2/17	27/12/17	8/3/18	Wrestler	..	7/17	25/2/18	15/5/18
Wolfhound	..	4/17	14/3/18	27/4/18	Winchester	..	12/6/17	1/2/18	29/4/18
Warwick	..	10/3/17	28/12/17	18/3/18	Winchelsea	..	24/5/17	15/12/17	15/3/18
Wessex	..	23/5/17	12/3/18	11/5/18					

(Plans as for "6 tube V's" *Vanessa, Vanity,* &c., on next page.)

2 Thornycroft "W"

WOOLSTON

1931 Photo, R. Perkins, Esq.

2 *Thornycroft :* **Wolsey, Woolston.**   1120 tons.   Dimensions : 300 (*p.p.*), 312 (*o.a.*) × 30ft. 7in. × 10¾ feet (*mean* draught).   Guns : 4—4 inch (Mk. V. Dir. Con.), 1—2 pdr. pom-pom, 1 M.G., 4 Lewis.   Tubes : 6—21 inch in two triple deck mountings.   Machinery : Brown-Curtis turbines (all-geared type).   2 screws.   Designed S.H.P. 30,000 = 35 kts.*   Thornycroft boilers.   Oil : 374/322 tons.   Complement, 134.

* Light load draught on *trials* ; on deep load at 1512 tons, 31 kts. with same S.H.P.

General Notes.—Emergency War Programme. Differ from other Admiralty W's in H.P., speed, and a few other particulars. No War Losses. Plans as " 6-tube V's" on next page.

To distinguish.—Big flat-sided after funnel. Fore funnel does not look so prominently raised, owing to extra height of after funnel. Hulls stand high out of water.

	Begun.	Launch.	Comp.	Trials.		Begun.	Launch.	Comp.	Trials.
Wolsey	3/17	16/3/18	14/5/18	36.64	Woolston	4/17	27/1/18	28/6/18	37.11

2 Thornycroft "Modified W" Type.

WISHART.

1921 Photo, Hopkins, Southsea.

2 *Thornycroft :* **Wishart, Witch.**   1140 tons (1550 *full load*).   Dimensions : 300 (*p.p.*), 312 (*o.a.*) × 30 ft. 7 in. × 10 feet. 11 ins.   Guns : 4—4.7 inch (Dir. Con.), 2—2 pdr. pom-poms, 1 M.G., 4 Lewis.   Torpedo tubes : 6—21 inch in two triples.   Machinery : Brown-Curtis turbines (all-geared type).   2 screws.   Boilers : 3 Thornycroft.   Designed S.H.P. 30,000 = 35 kts. (light load draught on *trials*) and 32 kts. (deep load).   Oil fuel : 374/322 tons.   Complement, 134.

General Notes.—Begun under Emergency War Programme   Differ from Admiralty "Modified W's" in dimensions, H.P., speed and a few other details.

To distinguish.—Big, flat-sided fore funnel, set well aft of bridges, both funnels nearly equal in height.   High mainmast.   These T.B.D. stand high out of water.

		Begun.	Launch.	Comp.
Wishart	..	6/18	18/7/19	6/20
Witch	..	6/18	11/11/19	3/24†

†*Witch* completed by Devonport D.Y.

(Plans generally as for *Wolverine* on preceding page.)

25 Admiralty "V."

VIVACIOUS.

1922 *Photo, Gieves, Ltd.*

2 Beardmore : **Vanessa, Vanity.**

1 Doxford : **Vega.**

2 Fairfield : **Vendetta, Venetia.**

1 Hawthorn Leslie : **Verdun.**

2 Stephen : **Vidette, Vesper.***

2 Swan Hunter : **Violent, Vimiera.**

2 White : **Vectis, Vampire.**

2 Yarrow : **Vivien, Vivacious.**

3 Denny : **Valorous,* Valkyrie, Venturous.**

1 Clydebank : **Vanquisher.**

2 Cammell-Laird : **Valhalla, Valentine.**

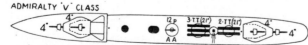

ADMIRALTY 'W' CLASS,
'V' LEADERS & SIX TUBE V's

All above boats have 6—21 inch tubes in 2 triple deck mountings (1920 alteration), except *Vivien*, whose tubes have been removed temporarily, for experimental purposes. Otherwise as General Notes.

To distinguish.—Identical now with " Admiralty W " boats, but have *short* mainmasts (except *Vanquisher. Vampire, Venturous, Valorous*, which have *high* mainmast, like "W" class, from which they are practically indistinguishable in appearance).

*Probably still retain minelaying chutes at stern.

VELOX

1925 *Photo, Abrahams, Devonport.*

1 Beardmore : **Vimy** (ex *Vancouver*)*

1 Doxford : **Velox.***

1 Hawthorn Leslie : **Versatile.***

1 White : **Vortigern.***

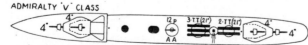

ADMIRALTY 'V' CLASS

All above have *five* 21 inch tubes in one triple (forward) and one double (after) deck mountings (1920 alteration). All fitted as Mine Layers during War, but not so used ; some retain chutes at stern. Otherwise as General Notes.

To distinguish.—The mixed T.T. mountings are special to these boats, and render them distinctive.

*5th Flotilla, Atlantic Fleet, fitted for Mine-laying.

VALHALLA.

1929 *Photo, Abrahams, Devonport.*

1 Clydebank : **Vanoc.**

ADMIRALTY 'V' CLASS

All excepting *Vanoc* are now fitted with triple tubes.

Vanoc has special arrangement of tubes for experimental purposes.

Special Note.—*Vampire, Valorous, Valhalla, Valkyrie, Valentine*, are fitted as Flotilla Leaders, having been originally designed and classed as such. Internal arrangements of these 5 differ from rest of class.

General Notes.

Displacements : 1090 tons (1300 tons normal Leaders being 1325 *normal*). (1480 *deep load*). Dimensions : 300 (*p.p.*), 312 (*o.a.*) × about 29½ × 10 ft. 10 in. (*mean*), 11¾ (*max.*) draught. Guns : 4—4 inch (Mk. V. DIR. CON.), 1—2 pdr. pompom. 1 M.G., 4 Lewis. Torpedo tubes : As noted above. Machinery : " All-Geared " turbines : Brown-Curtis in all, except Doxford, Swan-Hunter and Laird boats with Parsons. 2 screws. Designed S.H.P. 27,000 = 34 kts. (light load draught on *trials*) = 31 kts. (deep load draught). Boilers : 3 Yarrow in all, except White boats with White-Forster. Weight of machinery : 425 tons. Oil : 360/320 tons. Feed water : 20 tons+7 for drinking. Complement, 134. *Trials* : *Vivacious* 33.01, *Vivien* 36.79.

All Emergency War Programme. These boats are of remarkable size and power for Destroyers.

		Begun.	Launch.	Comp.			Begun.	Launch.	Comp.
Vimy	..	15/3/17	28/12/17	9/3/18	*Vendetta*	..	1916	3/9/17	17/10/17
Vanessa	..	16/5/17	16/3/18	27/4/18	*Venetia*	..	1917	29/10/17	19/12/17
Vanity	..	28/7/17	3/5/18	21/6/18	*Verdun*	..	13/1/17	21/8/17	3/11/17
Vanoc	..	20/9/16	14/6/17	8/17	*Versatile*	..	31/1/17	31/10/17	11/2/18
Vanquisher	..	27/9/16	18/8/17	10/17	*Vesper*	..	27/12/16	15/12/17	20/2/18
Venturous	..	9/10/16	21/9/17	29/11/17	*Vidette*	..	1/2/17	28/2/18	27/4/18
Vega ..	..	1916	1/9/17	12/17	*Violent*	..	1/16	1/9/17	11/17
Velox ..	..	1/17	17/11/17	1/4/18	*Vimiera*	..	10/16	22/6/17	10/17
Valentine	..	7/8/16	24/3/17	27/6/17	*Vectis* ..	..	7/12/16	4/9/17	5/12/17
Valhalla	..	8/8/16	22/5/17	31/7/17	*Vortigern*	..	17/1/16	15/10/17	25/1/18
Valkyrie	..	25/5/16	13/3/17	16/6/17§	*Vivacious*	..	7/16	3/11/17	12/17
Valorous	..	25/5/16	8/5/17	21/8/17	*Vivien*	..	7/16	16/2/18	28/5/18
Vampire	..	10/10/16	21/5/17	22/9/17					

War Losses.—*Vehement* (Denny). *Verulam* (Hawthorn Leslie) and *Vittoria* (Swan Hunter) lost 1919 in Baltic operations. §*Valkyrie* mined during war and had to be almost entirely rebuilt at Chatham D.Y.

34 Admiralty "S."

5 *Clydebank*: **Scimitar, Scotsman, Scout, Seafire, Searcher.**

6 *Denny*: **Senator, Sepoy, Seraph, Serapis, Serene, Sesame.**

2 *Doxford*: **Shamrock, Shikari.***

3 *Fairfield*: **Sirdar, Somme, Spindrift.**

4 *Hawthorn Leslie*: **Tenedos, Thanet, Thracian,**† **Turbulent.**

3 *Palmer*: **Steadfast, Sterling, Stormcloud.**

4 *Scott*: **Strenuous, Stronghold, Sturdy, Swallow.**

3 *Stephen*: **Sabre, Saladin, Sardonyx.**

1 *Swan Hunter*: **Sportive.**

3 *White*: **Tribune, Trojan, Trusty.**

*Completed by Chatham D.Y. 1924 and †by Sheerness D.Y. 1922. Rest completed 1918-19.

905 tons.   Dimensions: 265 (*p.p.*), 276 (*o.a.*) × 26¾ × 10⅝ feet (*mean*) draught. Guns: **3**—4 inch (Mk. IV Dir. Con. with 30° elevation), 1—2 pdr. pom-pom, 1 M G., 4 Lewis. Tubes: 4—21 inch in pairs.* (*See Notes*). Machinery: Turbines (all-geared type). Brown-Curtis (A.G.) in all except following:—Palmer boats, Parsons (A.G.); *Tilbury, Tintagel*, Parsons (A.G.). Designed S.H.P. 27,000 = 36 kts. 2 screws. 3 Yarrow boilers in all, except White boats with White-Forster. Oil: 301/254 tons. Complement, 98.

*Tara, has also 2—18 inch single T.T. to P. and S. under charthouse, for instructional purposes.

General Notes.—Emergency War Programme boats, but cost of completion of about 45 boats included in post-war Estimates. Design derived from "Admiralty Modified R" boats. Reported to be not quite so successful as the Admiralty R's. They are wet with sea on beam or bow: they ride well in head seas, but throw spray over bridges. Bows not strengthened for submarine attack by ramming. No War losses. *Saturn, Sycamore* (both Stephen) cancelled. *Stalwart, Success, Swordsman, Tattoo, Tasmania*, presented to Royal Australian Navy, 1918. *Stonehenge* wrecked, 1920. *Sikh* and *Spear* sold. *Tactician, Seabear, Simoon, Shark, Sparrowhawk, Splendid, Tilbury* sold 1930. *Trinidad, Tintagel, Seawolf, Scythe, Tara, Truant* sold 1931.

To distinguish.—Long fo'xle, sheered and slightly turtle-backed. Funnels about equal in height, the extra height of fore funnel not being very prominent. Wedge-shaped bridges built off fo'xle. Features in these boats which also appear in the Modified R types are:—Mounting of searchlight on after pair of tubes; pom-pom on platform just before mainmast; after 4 inch in bandstand; boats abeam of 2nd funnel. As the openings under forebridges can be screened in, they are not a reliable identification feature. *Shikari* has had W/T. deckhouse erected in place of gun between funnels and carries a much reduced armament. *Senator* and *Sepoy* have very big flat-sided funnels. *Truant* has had after gun removed. *Thanet* fitted with catapult for experimental purposes.

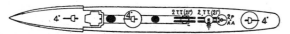

TILBURY.

1920 *Photo, J. Spartali, Esq., Smyrna.*

SPINDRIFT.

1924 *Photo, Abrahams.*

Sepoy.
Sterling.   } 3 of these
Serapis.   to be scrapped
Somme.   1932.

2 Thornycroft "V."

VISCOUNT.

Photo added 1923.

2 *Thornycroft:* **Viceroy,**† **Viscount.** 1120 tons. Dimensions : 300 (*p.p.*), 312 (*o.a.*) × 30′ 7″ × 10¾ feet (*mean*) 11¾ feet (*max.*) draught. Guns : **4**—4 inch (Mk. V DIR. CON.), **1**—2 pdr pom-pom, **1** M.G., **4** Lewis. Tubes : **6**—21 inch in 2 triple deck mountings. Machinery : Brown-Curtis (all-geared) turbines. 2 screws. Designed S.H.P. 30,000 = 35 kts.* Boilers : 3 Thornycroft. Oil fuel : 374/322 tons. Complement, 134.

* Light load draught on *trials* : on deep load at 1512 tons, 31 kts. with same S.H.P.

General Notes.—Emergency War Programme boats. Differ from Admiralty V design in dimensions, H.P. and speed. No War Losses.

To distinguish.—As Notes to *Wolsey* and *Woolston*, except in height of mainmast, which is *short*, in these two boats.

	Begun.	Launch.	Comp.	Trials.
Viscount	12/16	29/12/17	3/18	37.69
Viceroy	12/16	17/11/17	1/18	36.5

(Plans as "6 tube V's" on preceding page.)   † H.S. Sweeps.

9 "Admiralty R."

ROWENA. (Note stump W.T. mast.)   *1927 Photo, R. Perkins, Esq.*

3 *Clydebank :* **Restless, Rowena, Skate.**

1 *Fairfield :* **Tempest.**

2 *Harland & Wolff* (*Govan*) : **Salmon, Tetrarch.**

2 *Hawthorn Leslie :* **Thisbe, Thruster.**

1 *Swan Hunter :* **Torrid.**

Displacement : 900 tons. Length (*p.p.*), 265 feet (*o.a.* varies from 274 to 276 feet). Beam, 26¾ feet. *Mean* draught, 10¾ feet. *Max.* draughts, 11¾ to 15 feet. Guns : **3**—4 inch (DIR. CON.), **1**—2 pdr. pom-pom, **1** M.G., **4** Lewis. Torpedo tubes : **4**—21 inch in pairs. Machinery : Turbines—"all-geared" types. Clydebank, Fairfield, Harland & Wolff, Swan Hunter boats, Brown-Curtis A.G. turbines ; Hawthorn Leslie boats, Parsons A.G. turbines. Designed S.H.P. 27,000 = 36 kts. 2 screws in all. Boilers : 3 Yarrow or Modified Yarrow. Oil fuel : 301-285/258-243 tons. Complement, 98.

Appearance Notes.—*Skate, Restless,* mainmast for Poulsen W/T. *Salmon* has S.L. platform just abaft after funnel. *Rowena* has very short mainmast stepped abaft pom-pom platform and no after control. *Thisbe, Thruster* have no funnel caps. *Torrid* has had her forward 4 inch gun removed ; *Tetrarch* her after one, together with its platform. *Restless* has had tubes removed temporarily.

General Notes.—All Emergency War Programme boats. In Reserve or attached to Training Establishments. *Tetrarch* fitted for target towing, with towing winch in place of after 4 inch.

Engineering Notes.—Propeller revolutions, 350 ; about 3,000 R.P.M. in H.P., and 2,300 R.P.M. in L.P. Each set of turbines = one H.P. and one L.P. driving common gear wheel on propeller shaft. Cruising turbine replaced by extra stage in H.P. turbine which is by-passed at full speed, an arrangement which has worked very successfully. Boiler pressure, 250 lbs. per sq. in. Furnaces = 24,700 sq. ft. heating surfaces.

War Losses.—*Simoom* (Clydebank), *Recruit* (Doxford), *Tornado* (Stephen), *Torrent* (Swan Hunter), *Setter* (White).

Sold.—*Rigorous, Rob Roy, Rocket, Redoult, Skilful, Springbok, Sylph, Sarpedon, Sceptre, Sturgeon, Satyr, Sharpshooter, Tarpon, Telemachus, Redgauntlet, Stork, Radstock, Raider, Sorceress, Sable Tancred, Tenacious, Starfish, Romola, Tormentor.*

ADMIRALTY "R" CLASS

1 Yarrow "R." ("Later M.")

Photo, Gieves, Ltd. (22/6/20).

1 *Yarrow:* **Tyrant.** Displacement : 760 tons. Dimensions : 269¼ (*p.p.*), 271½ (*o.a.*) × 25¾ × 9 ft. 7 in. (*mean*), 10½ (*max.*) draught. Guns : **3**—4 inch (DIR. CON.), **1**—2 pdr. pom-pom, **1** M.G., 4 Lewis. Torpedo tubes : **4**—21 inch, in pairs. Machinery : Brown-Curtis turbines. 2 screws. Designed S.H.P. 23,000 = 36 kts. Boilers : 3 Yarrow. Oil fuel : 256-228/215-202 tons. Complement, 98.

General Notes.—Emergency War Programme. Has *no* geared turbines, nor is the after 4 inch in a bandstand. Accordingly, though officially styled "Yarrow R." more correctly and usually referred to as "Later M" type. *Relentless, Rival, Sybille, Sabrina* and *Truculent* disposed of 1926. *Tyrant* has had guns and tubes removed while attached to *Fisgard* training establishment.

War Losses.— *Strongbow, Surprise, Ullieswater* (all Yarrow).

	Begun.	Launch.	Comp.	Trials.*
Tyrant	3/16	19/5/17	7/17	37.37

*Displacement on *trial*, 1050 tons.

YARROW "M"

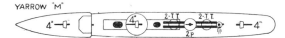

3 P-Boats (Patrol Boats.)

(All have foretopmast now.)   1919 *Photo, Robertson, Gourock.*

1 *Hamilton:* **Spey** (ex *P 38*) (1917).
2 *White (Cowes):* **P 40,** (1916), **P 59** (1917).

Displacement : 613 tons. Dimensions : 230 (*p.p.*), 244½ (*o.a.*) × 23¾ × 7 feet 11 inches. Guns : Designed to mount **2**—4 inch but guns mounted are **1**—4 inch and **1**—2 pdr. pom-pom. Tubes : Originally 2 single 14 inch, removed from old Torpedo Boats and fixed on quarters, but removed from nearly all boats and replaced by rails and 30 D.C. Machinery : Brown-Curtis or Parsons geared turbines. 2 screws. Yarrow boilers (White-Forster in *White* boats). Designed S.H.P. 3500 = 20 kts. Oil fuel : *normal* 50 tons, *max.* 93 tons. Complement, 56.

General Notes.—All built under Emergency War Programme. Were designed to relieve destroyers of patrol and escort work and submarine hunting. Outline scheme for these boats stipulated ; minimum size consistent with sea-keeping qualities, simplicity of construction, and adequate speed to run down submarines ; also shallow draught : low upperworks to reduce visibility ; and economy of fuel. Built of mild steel, but with hard steel stem for ramming submarines. Large rudder area and hull strongly cut up aft to give rapid turning. Proved very useful boats and an excellent anti-submarine type in all weathers. Could do 23 kts. when new. *Spey* so named when selected for Fishery Protection Duty, 1924.

2 P.C. Boats (Converted Patrol Boats).

DART.   1926 *Photo, Abrahams & Sons, Devonport.*

2 *White :* **P.C. 74** (1918). **Dart** (ex *P.C. 73*) (1918.
Dimensions : 694 tons : 233 (*p.p.*), 247 (*o.a.*) × 26¾ × 8 feet. Guns : **1**—4 inch, **2**—12 pdr. Torpedo tubes : removed. Carry 24-30 D.C. Machinery : Parsons or Brown-Curtis geared turbines. Boilers : White-Forster. 2 screws. Designed S.H.P. 3,500 = 20 kts. Oil : 164 tons *max.* Complement, 56.

General Notes.—Built under Emergency War Programme. Design as P-boats, but converted or modified while building, to act as Submarine Decoy Vessel or "Q-boat." The after 4 inch gun was hidden behind various forms of dummy deck loads, *e.g.*, bales or packing cases of merchandise, trusses of hay ; in a few boats it was located within a collapsible pantechnicon furniture van, or under a dummy boat built in folding sections. The 12 pdr. were behind lidded ports to port and starboard of chart house. It was expected that, on account of shallow draught, torpedoes fired by U-boats would under-run *P.C.*-boats. *Dart* so named on selection for Fishery Protection Duty, 1925.

SPEY.   1929 *Photo, Cozens & Co., Portsmouth.*

BRITISH NAVY—SUBMARINES.

53 (+ 6 *Building*) = **59** Submarines.

1 Minelayer.

Building.

1 *Vickers-Armstrong :* **Porpoise.** Armament : 1—4·7 inch gun. ? Tubes. 1930 Estimates.

3 To be Built under 1931–32 Programme.

1 Thames class.

Building.

1 *Contract built.* **Thames.** Dimensions : 345 × 28 × 13½ feet = 1760 tons surface. Armament : 1—4·7 inch gun. ? Tubes. 1929 Estimates.

4 Swordfish class.

Building.

`2 Chatham D.Y.:` **Swordfish, Sturgeon.** 1929 Estimates.

2 *Chatham D.Y.:* **Starfish, Seahorse.** 1930 Estimates.

Dimensions : 202½ × 24 × 10½ feet = 640 tons surface.

Armament : 1—3 inch AA. gun. ? Tubes.

4 "R" Type (Rainbow class).

REGULUS.

1930 Photo, Vickers-Armstrong.

REGULUS.

1931 Photo, R. Perkins, Esq.

1 *Chatham Dockyard:* **Rainbow.**

3 *Vickers-Armstrong:* **Regent, Regulus, Rover** (June, 1930).

Displacement : 1475/2015 tons.   Dimensions :   Armament : 1—4″ or 4·9″ gun, 8—21″ tubes (6 bow, 2 stern).
Designed H.P.

Laid down 1929 under 1928-29 Estimates: Two more boats *Royalist* (Beardmore) and *Rupert* (Lairds) cancelled in July, 1929.

5 "P" Type (Parthian class).

PERSEUS (mounting new model 4·9″ gun).

Photo, R. Perkins, Esq.

1930 Photo, Messrs. Vickers-Armstrong.

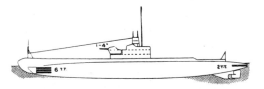

1 *Chatham:*   **Parthian** (June 22nd. 1929).
1 *Cammell Laird:*   **Phœnix** (Oct 3rd, 1929).
3 *Vickers-Armstrong:*   **Pandora** (*ex Python*) (Aug. 22nd, 1929),   **Perseus** (May 22nd, 1929),   **Proteus** (July 23rd, 1929).

Displacement: 1475/2040 tons.   Dimensions: 260 × 28 × 13½ ft.   Armament: 1—4 inch gun, 8—21 inch tubes (6 bow, 2 stern).   Designed H.P. $\frac{4400}{1350} = \frac{17\cdot5}{9}$ kts.

General Notes.—All laid down 1928 under 1927-28 Estimates.   Generally resemble "O" type, with higher surface speed and other improvements.   Completed during 1930.

Perseus armed with experimental 4·9″ gun which, if satisfactory, may be supplied to other classes.

Poseidon lost in collision June 9th, 1931.

1 " X " Class.

X 1 (June 16th, 1923) by Chatham Dockyard, provided under 1921-22 Navy Estimates. Understood that her design embodies various novel features derived from war experience, post-war experiments, and trials run with sundry types of surrendered German Submarines. Displacement : standard 2425, *normal* surface 2780 tons ; *submerged*, 3600 tons. Dimensions : 350 × 29¾ × 17 feet. Armament : **4**—5.2 inch, **2** M.G., and **6**—21 inch torpedo tubes. Diesel engines of 6000 H.P.=19.5 kts. Submerged, B.H.P. 2600=9 kts. Complement 110. Total cost, £941,794, or with alterations, £1,044,158.

Notes.—It is reported that X 1 is capable of remaining submerged for 2½ days, and that she has an exceptionally small turning circle. Designed for deep diving, and construction is therefore of exceptional strength. Gun positions appear to be armoured. Laid down 1/11/21; first trials run in Jan., 1924. Official commissioning date, 25 Sept., 1925.

Placed in Reserve 1930, at Chatham.

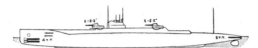

X 1.   1925 *Photo, Cribb, Southsea.*

X 1.   1925 *Photos, Cribb, Southsea.*

X 1.   1926 *Photo, Cribb, Southsea.*

9 "O" Class.

OBERON.

1927 *Photo, Cozens, Portsmouth.*

Chatham Dockyard : **Oberon (Ex O.1.** Sept. 24th, 1926) Displacement 1311/1805.

Armament : **1—4″,** 2 smaller, **8** 21″ tubes (6 bow, 2 stern). H.P. $\frac{2950}{1350} = \frac{15\cdot0}{9\cdot0}$ knots.

OSWALD.

1930 *Photo, Cribb.*

1 *Chatham Dockyard :* **Odin** (May 5th, 1928).

2 *Beardmore :* **Olympus** (Dec. 11th, 1928), **Orpheus** (Feb. 26th, 1929).

3 *Vickers-Armstrong :* **Osiris** (May 19th, 1928), **Oswald** (June 19th, 1928), **Otus** (Aug. 31st, 1928).

Displacement : 1475/2030 tons. Dimensions : 260×28×13½ feet draught. Armament : **1—4″** gun (in armoured position), **8**—21″ tubes (6 bow, 2 stern). Designed H.P. $\frac{4400}{1320} = \frac{17\cdot5}{9\cdot0}$ kts. Oil fuel : 200 tons.

2 *Vickers-Armstrong :* **Oxley** (ex-*AO* 1, June 30th, 1926), **Otway** (ex-*AO* 2, Sept. 7th, 1926). Both completed in 1927.

1354/1835 tons. Guns : **1**—4 inch in armoured position. Tubes : **6**—21 inch (bow), **2**—21 inch stern. H.P. $\frac{3000}{1350} = \frac{15.5}{9 \text{ kts}}$

Fuel : 200 tons. Built for the Royal Australian Navy and presented to the British Navy in 1931 as a measure of economy.

2 M Class.

M 3.

.1930 *Photo, R. Perkins, Esq.*

M. 3   M. 2

M 2. With hangar and crane fitted.

1928 *Photo, Cribb.*

M 2 ex *K 19* (Oct., 1918), by Vickers. **M 3** ex *K 20* (Oct., 1920), by Armstrong Whitworth.

Admiralty double-hulled type. Displacement : $\frac{1450}{1950}$ tons. Dimensions : 303 (*o.a.*) in *M* 3 and 296 (*o.a.*) in *M* 2 × 24½ × 15¾ feet. Guns : **1**—3 inch disappearing, 1 Lewis (2 in *M* 2). Tubes : **4**—18 inch bow. Machinery : 2 sets of 12-cyl. 4-cycle, solid injection, 1200 B.H.P. Vickers type. Oil fuel : 76 tons. Designed H.P. $\frac{2400}{1600} = \frac{15\cdot5}{9\cdot5}$ kts.

Gunnery Notes.—Both ships formerly carried one 12 inch Mk. XI, but these have been removed. *M* 2 employed experimentally to carry a seaplane stowed in a watertight hangar on a catapult. *M* 3 is fitted for minelaying experimentally. Number of mines carried varies as type and she has no fixed official stowage capacity. Now placed in material reserve.

General Notes.—Begun under War Emergency Programme, 1916, and completed 1920. Are said to be very handy boats both in dive and general control.

Cancelled.—*M 4* (ex *K 21*) by Armstrong.

Lost.—*M* 1 (ex *K 18*). By collision, 12/11/25.

L Classes.

(Shape of C.T. varies in these boats.)

L 52, L 53 as above photo of L 71, which no longer carries an after gun.   1920 *Photo, Gieves, Ltd.*

L 56. Deck before C.T. not raised.   1927 *Photo, Abrahams, Devonport.*

L Classes—*continued.*

L 25 Mine-laying Boat.   1921 *Photo, Abrahams, Devonport.*

L 20. (*L* 18, 21, 22, same *L* 33. No step in slope to stern).   1919 *Photo, Cribb, Southsea.*

6 L Class. (Third " L " series : "*L 50 Class*").

(All delivered by November, 1924.)

2 *Armstrong Whitworth :* **L 52** (1918), **L 53*** (1919).
1 *Denny :* **L 54**† (1919).
1 *Fairfield :* **L 56** (1919).
1 *Beardmore :* **L 69**§ (1918).
1 *Scotts :* **L 71** (1919).

* Completed by Chatham D.Y., 1924.
† Completed by Devonport D.Y., 1924.
§ Completed by Rosyth D.Y., 1923.

Admiralty saddle-tank type. Displacement: 845/1150 tons. Dimensions : 230½ (*p.p.*), 235 (*o.a.*) × 23½ × 13¼ feet. Guns : **1**—4 inch, **1** M.G. (*L* 52, *L* 53 have **2**—4 inch). Tubes : **6**—21 inch, all in bows. Machinery : 2 sets 12-cylinder solid-injection, Vickers type Diesel engines by Ruston & Hornsby, Willans & Robinson, Bellis & Morcom, Armstrong, Thornycroft. Oil : 78 tons. D.H.P. $\frac{2400}{1600} = \frac{17\cdot4}{10\cdot5}$ kts.

Notes.—All begun under Emergency War Programme, 1917. Equipment as Notes to *L* 9—33 on next page. Can be distinguished by the long C.T. (and two guns in *L* 52, 53). *L* 55 lost in the Baltic.

10 L Class. (Second series),

9 *Vickers :*   L 18, L 19, L 20, L 21, L 22, L 23*, L 25, L 26*, L 27* (1918-19).
1 *Swan Hunter :*   L 33 (1919).   * Completed by Dockyards.
Details as preceding boats.
Armaments : L 16, 18, 21, 22 =   **1**—4", **6** T.T. (2 beam).
L 19, 20, 26, 27, 33 = **1**—4", **4** T.T.
L 25 =   **1** M.G., **4** T.T., **16** mines.

Notes.—All begun under Emergency War Programme, 1916. Equipment of these boats is extensive, e.g., refrigerating machinery for storage batteries, gyro compass with repeaters, 3 periscopes (one for night work), directional hydrophones, &c. Breastwork revolves with gun. *L* 10 War loss. *L* 24 rammed off Portland, January, 1924. *L* 9 foundered in a typhoon at Hong Kong, August, 1923, but was salved the following month ; since placed on Disposal List.

L 11, 12, 14, 15, 16, 17 scrapped in 1931–32.

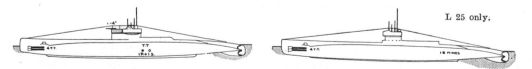

L 25 only.

Submarines—*continued.*

14 H Class.

1920 Photo, Gieves, Ltd.

H 23. (*H 24—32, H 48—50* same; *H 33, 34,* have flat-topped C.T.; and *H 43, 44* have right angled instead of curved after screen to C.T.)

7 *Vickers :* **H 23** (1918) **H 24** (1918), **H 27, H 28, H 30—32** (all 1918).

2 *Cammell Laird :* **H 33, H 34** (both 1918).   2 *Armstrong Whitworth :* **H 43, H 44** (both 1919).

3 *Beardmore :* **H 48, H 49, H 50** (all 1919).

Single-hull "Holland" (Electric Boat Co.) type modified by Admiralty. Displacement, 410/500 tons. Dimensions : 164¼ (*p.p.*), 170 (*o.a.*) × 15¾ × 11¼ feet. Tubes : 4—21 inch bow. Machinery : 2 sets of Diesel engines, 8 cylinder, 4-cycle, air-injection "H" type, developing 240 B.H.P. at 375 r.p.m., and built by Vickers, North British Diesel Co., Ruston & Hornsby, &c. Oil : 16 tons. D.H.P. $\frac{480}{320} = \frac{13·0}{10·5}$ Kts.

Notes.—All built under War Emergency Programme. Launching dates as above. First boat delivered January, 1918, and *H 44* last, in March, 1920. *H 29* sank in dock at Devonport, August, 1920, and placed on disposal list in consequence. *H 26, H 52* on disposal list, 1927; *H 22, H 25,* 1928. *H 47* sunk by collision with *L 12,* July, 1929.

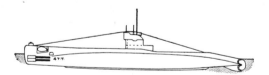

1 R Class.

R 4.   *1921 Photo, Gieves, Ltd.*

R 4 by Chatham D.Y.

Single hull type to Admiralty designs. Displacement : 385/500 tons. Dimensions : 163 (*o.a.*) × 15½ × 11 ft. 7 ins. Tubes : 6—18 inch bow. When in surface trim, 2 tubes *above water* and 4 *submerged.* Machinery : 1 set 8-cylinder 4-cycle air injection "H" type, developing 240 B.H.P. at 375 r.p.m. and built by Ruston & Hornsby, North British Diesel Engine Co. and Chatham D.Y. H.P.: 240/1200 = 9·5/15 Kts. Oil : 13 tons, but have an abnormal *submerged* endurance.

Notes.—Built under Emergency War Programme. These boats were produced as a "submarine destroyer of submarines," or Contra-Submarine Type. Their outstanding feature is that—unlike all other submarines in the world—they are faster below water than on the surface. Rudder is placed before propeller, and is small in area. Propellers close to surface. Steering on surface is very poor. It was intended that they should submerge and chase U-boats, and use their six bow tubes by salvo, specially big torpedo-compensating tanks with rapid flooding gear being placed in bows.

Miscellaneous.

NET LAYER.

GUARDIAN. (Chatham D.Y.). Laid down under 1930 Programme. Details of this ship are confidential, but the armament is officially stated to consist of 2—4 inch guns.

BOOM DEFENCE VESSEL.

MOORGATE. Building under 1930 Programme. Of an experimental type and to be armed with 1—4 inch gun. Dimensions : 98·8 × 25 × 7·6 feet = 260 tons displacement.

GUNNERY TRAINING SHIP.

IRON DUKE. ex-Battleship of 26,250 tons displacement. De-militarised under London Treaty, 1931–32 : Revolving parts of raised turrets B and Y; Conning tower; Belt armour and Torpedo Tubes removed. Speed reduced to 18 kts. Three foremost boilers to be mutilated.

Minelayers.

Notes.

The following are fitted for mine-laying duties.

Destroyers.—Vancouver, Velox, Versatile, Vortigern, Walker, Warwick, Watchman, Whirlwind, and *Vanoc,* retain mine-laying gear.

Flotilla Leader.—Abdiel is fitted for mine-laying.   Number of mines carried : 20 in Destroyers, 60 in *Abdiel.*

Submarines.—L 25, carries 16 mines.   *M 3* has also been equipped for mine-laying.

(SPECIAL " CRUISER-MINELAYER " TYPE—1 SHIP.)

ADVENTURE (18th June, 1924).

" Standard " displacement, 6,740 tons ; *normal* displacement, 7,260 tons. Complement.

Length $\begin{Bmatrix} p.p., & 500 \text{ feet} \\ o.a., & 520 \text{ feet} \end{Bmatrix}$ Beam, 59 feet, (over bulges) Draught $\begin{Bmatrix} mean, & 19\frac{1}{4} \text{ feet.} \\ max., & \text{ feet.} \end{Bmatrix}$

Armour :

Guns :
4—4.7 inch. A A.
4—3 pdr.
12 M.G.
No. of mines carried :
   320 of an improved pattern.

ADVENTURE.   1927 *Photo, Gieves, Ltd.*

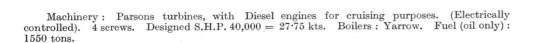

Machinery : Parsons turbines, with Diesel engines for cruising purposes. (Electrically controlled). 4 screws. Designed S.H.P. 40,000 = 27·75 kts. Boilers : Yarrow. Fuel (oil only) : 1550 tons.

General Notes.—Laid down under 1921-22 Estimates at Devonport Yard, 29th November, 1922 ; completed 1926, and commissioned May, 1927. Designed by Sir E. H. Tennyson d'Eyncourt as an experimental type, combining the characteristics of a minelayer with those of a light cruiser. The hull is flush-decked, with a marked sheer forward. The curious flat stern, without a counter, is a new departure for a minelayer. There are four large mine-dropping ports in it. Weight has been saved by the sacrifice of armament and ammunition supply, thus giving increased capacity for mines of a new and enlarged pattern. There are 2 pairs of derricks, abreast of bridge and mainmast respectively.

Gunnery Notes.—Was experimentally fitted with 8 pom-poms on a single mounting, with distant firing position, on forward shelter deck. Now removed. (1930). Reported that this AA weapon was an entire success and is to be adopted in the Fleet generally.

Engineering Notes.—The Diesel engines for cruising with electric drive are a novel feature, the results of which are understood to have encouraged the use of Diesel engines for propulsion of depot ship *Medway.* Diesel exhaust shaft is abaft second funnel. The turbine engines were built by Devonport Dockyard ; the Diesels by Vickers. Trials : S.H.P. 40,700 = 27.85 kts.

ADVENTURE.   *1927 Photo, Cribb.*

ADVENTURE.   *1927 Photo, Cribb.*

MELPOMENE.   *1921 Photo, Abrahams, Devonport.*

MEDUSA (ex-M 39), **MELPOMENE** (ex-M 31), (Workman Clark), **MINERVA** (ex-M 33), (Harland & Wolff). Launched and completed 1915. 535 tons. Complement, 52. Dimensions: 177 (*o.a.*) × 31 × 6¾ feet. Guns: None. Carry 52 mines. Designed H.P. 400 = 10 kts. Machinery: Triple expansion. 2 screws. Boilers: Yarrow. Oil fuel: 45 tons.

1921 Photo, Gieves, Ltd.

MEDEA (ex-M 22), (1915). Built by Sir Raylton Dixon & Co. 540 tons. Dimensions: 177 (*o.a.*) × 31 × 6 feet. Guns: None. Carries 44 mines. Machinery: Triple expansion engines and White-Forster boilers. I.H.P. 650 = 12 kts. 2 screws. Oil: 28 tons. Complement, 52.

Note.—Originally Small Monitors built under Emergency War Programme in about six months from laying of keels. Converted by Devonport D.Y. (*M* 31 and *M* 22) Pembroke D.Y. (*M* 29 and *M* 33) during 1922-25, and used for instructional purposes. Names conferred in place of numbers, 1 Dec., 1925.

VERNON (ex-**Strathcoe**.) (Hall, Russell, 1916, purchased)). 436 tons. 117¾ (*o.a.*) × 22 × 14 ft. 10 in. *max.* draught. No guns. Carries 24 mines. I.H.P. 430 = *about* 10 kts. Coal: 110 tons. Complement: 15.

Kate Lewis (Converted Trawler built by Cochrane, 1916, purchased). *About* 325 tons gross. Dimensions: 117¾ (*o.a.*) × 22 × 12 ft. 4 in. No guns. Carries 24 mines. I.H.P. 475 = 11 kts. Coal: 110 tons. Complement: 15.

Note.—Similar to *Vernon* in appearance, but has taller foremast and no raised forecastle.

Nightingale. (built at Portsmouth 1931). Displacement: 255 tons. Dimensions: 106 × 25·8 × 6·8 feet. H.P.: 400 = 10 kts. Fuel (coal): 15 tons. (Tender to *Vernon*).

NIGHTINGALE.   *1931 Photo, Cribb.*

VERNON.   *1921 Photo, Cribb, Southsea.*

BRIDGEWATER.   1929 *Photo, Abrahams, Devonport.*

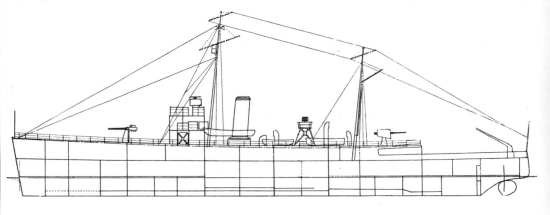

(SANDWICH CLASS—14 SHIPS.)

2 *Hawthorn Leslie :* **BRIDGEWATER** (Sept. 14th, 1928.), **SANDWICH** (Sept. 28th, 1928).

3 *Devonport Dockyard :* **HASTINGS, PENZANCE.** Laid down July, 1929. **FOWEY.** (November 4th, 1930). Completed, 1930.

2 *Swan Hunter :* **FOLKESTONE, SCARBOROUGH.** Laid down 1929. Completed 1930.

1 *Chatham Dockyard :* **SHOREHAM.** Laid down 1929. Completed 1930.

4 *Devonport Dockyard :* **BIDEFORD.** (April 1st, 1931). **FALMOUTH.** ( ). **MILFORD.** ( ). **WESTON-SUPER-MARE.** ( ).

2 *Chatham Dockyard :* **ROCHESTER.** (July 16, 1931). **DUNDEE.** ( ).

4 To be built under 1931 Programme.

Displacement : Standard 1040/1105 tons (about 1250 tons deep load). Dimensions : 250 (*p.p.*), (266 *o.a.*), × 34 × 8½ feet. (*mean*). Guns : **2**—4 inch AA, **2** M.G. Machinery : Parsons' impulse reaction turbines with single reduction gearing. 2 screws. 2 3-drum watertube boilers, pressure 250 lbs. Designed S.H.P. 2,000=16–16·5 kts. Oil : 275 tons. Designed for service in Far East and fitted for minesweeping. *Bridgewater* and *Sandwich* built under 1927–28 Estimates and both completed March, 1929. Under 1928–29 Estimates : *Hastings, Penzance, Folkestone* and *Scarborough.* Under 1929–30 Estimates : *Fowey, Shoreham, Bideford, Rochester.* Under 1930–31 Estimates : *Falmouth, Milford, Weston-super-Mare, Dundee.*

FOLKESTONE.   1930 *Photo, Cribb.*

Sloops.

HEATHER.   1923 *Photo, Seward, Weymouth.*

HAREBELL.   *Photo, Abrahams, Devonport, 12th Oct., 1921.*

BRYONY.   1921 *Photo, J. Spartali, Smyrna.*

ANCHUSA TYPE—(First 2 Ships)—and AUBRIETIA TYPE—(3rd Ship.)

HAREBELL (May, 1918), by Barclay, Curle. **BRYONY** (Oct., 1917), by Armstrong Whitworth. **HEATHER** (June, 1916) by Grangemouth Dockyard Co. " Q " Boat type of Convoy Sloop. *Displacement: 1345 tons. Completed Oct., 1916—June, 1918. *Dimensions : 250 (*p.p.*), 262¼ (*w.l.*)×35×11½-12 (*mean*), 12½-13⅔ (*max.*) feet draught. Guns : *Harebell*, 2—4 inch, 4—3 pdr. ; *Bryony*, 4—3 pdr., 1 M.G. ; *Heather*, 1—4 inch, 1—3 pdr. AA. Machinery : 4-cylinder triple expansion. Boilers : 2 cylindrical. 1 screw. Designed H.P. 2500=16.5 kts. Coal : 260 tons (316 tons in *Harebell*). Complement, 98 (118 in *Harebell*).

Note.—Chrysanthemum (for Fleet Target Service) transferred to another page. *Lychnis* (now renamed) transferred to Government of India. *Harebell* at present employed on Fishery Protection duties. *Heather* attached Anti-Submarine School. *Heather* 1250 tons. 277½ × 33½ × 13¼ feet.

(For Fleet Target Service.)

1924 *Photo, Corpl. E. Arnold, R.M.*

CHRYSANTHEMUM (Armstrong, Nov., 1917). Ex-Convoy Sloop of *Anchusa* type (*Flower* classes). 1345 tons. Dimensions : 262¼ (*w.l.*) × 35 × 11 feet. Guns : 2—3 pdr., 1 M.G. Machinery : 4-cylinder triple expansion. 1 screw. 2 cylindrical boilers. Designed I.H.P. 2500 = 16.5 kts. Coal : 260 tons *max.* Complement, 95.

CORNFLOWER.   *Photo, Dec., 1920, Com. M.P. Cooper, R.I.M.*

(ARABIS TYPE—7 SHIPS.)

CORNFLOWER (Mar., 1916), by Barclay, Curle. **GODETIA** (Jan., 1916), by Connell. **SNAPDRAGON** (Dec., 1915), by Ropner. **LUPIN** (May, 1916), by Simons. **VERBENA** (Blyth S.B. Co., Nov., 1915), **DELPHINIUM** (Napier & Miller, Dec., 1915), **ROSEMARY** (Richardson, Duck, Nov. 1915).

Displacement, 1175 tons (1373 tons *deep load*), but those refitted for service on Foreign Stations now displace up to 1500 tons *normal*, with a *mean* draught of 12-14 feet.

Completed Dec., 1915—June, 1916. Dimensions: $255\frac{1}{4}$ (*p.p.*), $267\frac{3}{4}$ (*o.a.*) × $33\frac{1}{2}$ × 11 (*mean*). $11\frac{1}{4}$-$11\frac{3}{4}$ *feet* (*max.* draught) for 1250 tons displacement. For present guns *v.* Table below. Designed I.H.P. 2000 = 16.5 kts. Machinery: 1 set 4-cylinder triple expansion. Boilers: 2 cylindrical. 1 screw. Coal: 130 tons *normal*, 260 tons *max.* = *about* 2000 miles at 15 kts. (*Lupin* is now oil-fired.) Complement, 98/118 for Foreign Service. Also see *General Notes.*

Snapdragon fitted for Fleet Target Duties. *Geranium* and *Marguerite* now R. Australian Navy. *Godetia* at present employed on Fishery Protection Duties.

GUNS CARRIED.†

		Cornflower	{2—4 inch {16 smaller
Delphinium, Verbena, Lupin	{2—4 inch* {4—3 pdr. AA. {2—2 pdr. pom-pom {2—4 inch. 13 smaller	Godetia	{1—4 inch {1—12 pdr.
		Rosemary	{1—4 inch {2—2 pdr. pom-pom

* In those refitted for Foreign Service, 4 inch are Mk. IV, with 30° elevation, with Light Directors.
† Some carry 8 to 10 Lewis guns in addition.

Cyclamen scrapped in 1931. *Cornflower, Snapdragon, Delphinium, Verbena,* to be scrapped in 1932.

SNAPDRAGON

(2 poles abaft second funnel for spreading W/T. aerials now removed.)   *Photo added,* 1925.

Note.—Is fitted with powerful towing engine and special kinema cabinet at stern for taking motion-pictures of fall of shot on and around target. It is reported that this addition to super-structure causes her to roll and reduces speed.

Minesweepers. (Details next page.)

(ACACIA TYPE.)

HELIOTROPE (Lobnitz, Sept., 1915).

DAHLIA (April, 1915), **FOXGLOVE** (Mar., 1915), both by Barclay, Curle. **DAFFODIL** (August, 1915), by Scotts S.B. Co. **LABURNUM** (June, 1915), by Connell & Co. **VERONICA** (Dunlop, Bremner, May, 1915).

All 1165 tons *standard*, 1269–1325 *full load*. Completed, May-Sept., 1915. Dimensions: 250 (*p.p.*), 262½ (*o.a.*) × 33 × 11 (*mean*), 11¼-12 feet (*max.* draught). For present guns, see Table on next page. Designed H.P. 1800 = 16.5 kts., but actually require about 2200 I.H.P. for this speed. Machinery: 1 set 4-cylinder triple expansion. Boilers: 2 cylindrical. 1 screw. Coal: 130 tons *normal*, 250 tons *max.* = *about* 2000 miles at 15 kts. Complement, 104. For *Mallow* of this type, see Royal Australian Navy.

GUNS CARRIED. (Several carry M.G. in addition.)

Foxglove	..	..	{ 2—4 inch { 4—3 pdr.	Heliotrope	..	..	..	.. { 1—4 inch { 2—2 pdr. pom-pom
Laburnum	..	..						
Magnolia, Veronica	..	{ 2—2 pdr. pom-pom	Dahlia ..	..	..	..	.. { 1—4 inch { 1—12 pdr.	
Daffodil	..	..	{ 2—4 inch { 4—3 pdr. AA.					

GENERAL NOTES, for Arabis and Acacia Types.

Single-screw Fleet Sweeping Vessels (Sloops), all built under Emergency War Programme. Originally planned that only 12 should be ordered, but the first series ordered December, 1914-January, 1915, comprised 24 ships. A further 48 were ordered between May and September, 1915. In all, 72 of these ships were built. To ensure rapid building, design was made as simple as possible; mercantile practice was resorted to and orders were distributed among firms which did not usually build war vessels up to 1914. Built under Lloyds survey, in about 25 weeks. Have triple hulls at bows to give extra protection against loss when working up mines. Not handy ships, as single screw gives a wide turning circle. Very lively ships, but can face any weather. Few can do more than 15 knots at sea. Some have been altered to burn oil fuel.

Magnolia scrapped in 1931. *Daffodil* to be scrapped in 1932.

TIVERTON.

1929 *Photo, Abrahams, Devonport.*

TEDWORTH.

1924 *Photo, Abrahams, Devonport.*

SUTTON.

1931 *Photo, Kestin, Weymouth.*

ALRESFORD.

1921 *Photo, Gieves, Ltd*

FERMOY.

1929 *Photo.*

(TWIN SCREW CLASS—29 SHIPS.)

4 Ailsa S.B. Co : **ABERDARE, ABINGDON** (a), **ALBURY** (b), **ALRESFORD,**
1 Ardrossan Co.: **BAGSHOT.**
2 Bow, McLachlan : **CARSTAIRS, CATERHAM.**
4 Clyde S.B. Co.: **DERBY** (a), **DUNDALK** (b), **DUNOON** (b), **FORRES** (b).
1 Dundee S.B. Co.: **FERMOY** (a).
1 Dunlop Bremner : **FAREHAM** (a).
2 Eltringhams : **HARROW** (a), **HUNTLY** (b).
1 Fairfield : **LYDD** (a).
1 Fleming & Ferguson : **MARAZION** (b).
3 Lobnitz : **PANGBOURNE, PETERSFIELD, ROSS** (b).
1 McMillan : **SUTTON** (a).
3 Murdoch & Murray : **SALTASH** (a), **SALTBURN** (a), **SELKIRK** (b).
1 Napier & Miller : **WIDNES.**
1 Chas. Rennoldson : **STOKE** (a).
3 Simons : **ELGIN** (b), **TEDWORTH, TIVERTON** (a).

All built under Emergency War Programme and launched between June, 1917 and Aug., 1919. Displacement, 710 tons ; *except Tedworth*, 660 tons. Dimensions : 220 (*p.p.*), 231 (*o.a.*) × 28 ft. 7¼ in. × 7½ ft. (*mean* draught). Machinery : Vertical triple expansion. 2 screws. Yarrow boilers. Designed I.H.P. 2200 = 16 kts. ; *except Tedworth*, 1800 = 14 kts. Coal : 185 tons = *about* 1500 miles at full speed (*Tedworth*, only 140 tons). Complement of all, 73. Guns : in Ships marked (a), 1—4 inch, 1—12 pdr. ; marked (b), 1—6 pdr. *Petersfield* has 1—4 inch, 4—3 pdr. ; *Tedworth*, 1—3 inch AA. ; and remainder carry no guns at present.

The majority of these ships are paid off and comprise the Reserve of mine-sweepers. *Tedworth* is tender to Gunnery and Diving Schools, Devonport. There are various minor variations in these ships, besides those illustrated above, *e.g.*, many have had gallows and sweeping gear removed, deck houses built aft, &c.

PETERSFIELD. (Very high topmasts.)

1924 *Photo, R. G. Strugnell, Esq.*

River Gunboats.

1 to be built under 1931 Programme.

TERN.   1928 *Photo, Lieut. P.B.A. Caruana, R.N.*

SEAMEW (1927), **TERN** (1927), both designed and built by Messrs. Yarrow & Co., Ltd. Displacement, 287 tons. Dimensions: 160 (*w.l.*), 167½ (*o.a.*) × 27 × 3 ft. 2¾ ins. draught. Guns: **2**—3 inch AA., **8** M.G. Machinery: Geared turbines. Boilers: Yarrow. Designed H.P. 1200 = 14 kts. Fuel: 50 tons oil.

GANNET (1927) & **PETEREL** (1927), both designed and built by Messrs. Yarrow & Co., Ltd. Displacement, 345 tons. Dimensions: 177 (*w.l.*), 184⅔ (*o.a.*) × 29 × 3 ft. 2½ ins. draught. Guns: **2**—3 inch AA., **8** M.G. Machinery: Geared turbines. Boilers: Yarrow. Designed H.P. 2120 = 16 kts. Fuel: 60 tons oil.

FALCON ( ) built by Messrs. Yarrow & Co., Ltd. Guns: **1**—3·7″ Howitzer. **2**—6 pdr., Hotchkiss. Dims: 150 × 28·8 × 4·9 ft. = 354 tons. displ. S.H.P. 2,250 = 15 Kts. Fuel = 84 tons. Oil.

CRICKET.   For description see next column.   1929 *Photo.*

River Gunboats—*continued.*

SCARAB.   *Photo added* 1925.

BEE (as flagship S.N.O., Yangtse River). *Photo by favour of R. G. Strugnell, Esq.* (TARANTULA similar, but has large crow's nest.)

APHIS.   1929 *Photo.*

APHIS (1915), **BEE** (1916), both by Ailsa Co.
CICALA (1915), **COCKCHAFER** (1915), **CRICKET** (1915) all by Barclay Curle.
GNAT (1915), **LADYBIRD** (1915), both by Lobnitz.
MANTIS (1915), **MOTH** (1915) both by Sunderland S.B. Co.
SCARAB (1915), **TARANTULA** (1915), both by Wood, Skinner and Co.

625 tons Compl. 54—65. Dimensions: 237½ (*o.a.*) × 36 × 4 feet. Guns: **2**—6in. (*Bee* **1** only), **1**—3in. AA., **1**—2 pdr. pom-pom (except *Aphis, Ladybird* and *Bee* which have **1**—12 pdr). **6** or **8** M.G. Machinery: Triple expansion. Twin screws in tunnels fitted with Messrs. Yarrow's patent balanced flap. Boilers: Yarrow. Designed H.P. 2000 = 14 kts. Fuel: 35 tons coal 54 tons oil. (*Moth,* 76 tons oil only). On Trials 18 knots was easily obtained.

Note.—Messrs Yarrow & Co., Ltd., were solely responsible for the design of these vessels, which were built under their supervision during the War.

River Gunboats—*continued.*

1929 *Photo.*

MOORHEN (1901). 180 tons. Dimensions: 165 × 24½ × 2¼ feet. Armament: **2**—6 pdr. and **8** M.G. Bullet-proof hull, &c. H.P. 670 = 13 kts. Complement, 35. Coal: 39—36 tons. Built by Yarrow & Co., Ltd., in sections, and re-erected in China. Now nearly worn out. *Widgeon* and *Teal* scrapped 1931.

Special Service Vessel.

1924 *Photo, Abrahams.*

TRIAD. S. N. O's Ship in Persian Gulf. (Caledon S.B. Co., 1909, purchased 1915). 2354 tons. Dimensions: 264 × 35 × 15¾ feet. Guns: **4**—3 pdr., Hotchkiss. I.H.P. 2235 = 14 kts. Coal: 480 tons.

1918 Photo, Abrahams, Devonport.

SANDHURST (ex S.S. *Manipur*, Harland & Wolff, purchased 1915 and converted by Workman, Clark). 11,500 tons. Dimensions : 470 (*p.p.*) 485 (*o.a.*) × 58 × 20 feet (*max. draught*). *Guns 4—4 inch, 1—3 inch AA. I.H.P. 3300 = 10.5 kts. Coal : 1475 tons. Complement, 258. Cyl. boilers.

* Also carries several additional 4 inch guns as spares for destroyers and 2—H.A. pom-poms on forecastle.

1921 Photo, Hopkins, Southsea.

GREENWICH (Dobson & Co., completed by Swan Hunter. Purchased 1915). 8100 tons. Dimensions : 390 (*p.p.*), 402 (*o.a.*) × 52 × 19⅔ feet (*max.* draught). Guns : 4—4 inch, 1—3 inch AA. I.H.P. 2500 = 11 kts. Coal : 960 tons. Complement, 244. Cyl. boilers.

AMBROSE.   1928 Photo, Cribb.

AMBROSE (Sir Raylton Dixon & Co., 1903, converted by Clyde S.B. Co., 1915. Purchased 1915). 6600 tons. Dimensions : 387¾ (*o.a.*) × 47½ × 20¾ feet. I.H.P. 6350 = 14½ kts. Coal : 540 tons. Complement, 238. Previously employed as Sub-marine Depot Ship.

Miscellaneous Depot Ship.

1919 Illustration.

ARK ROYAL (Blyth S.B. Co., 1914, purchased during construction 1914). 7080 tons. Dimensions : 352½ (*p.p.*), 366 (*o.a.*) × 50⅚ × 17½ feet (*mean*). Guns : 4—12 pdr., 4 M.G., 10 Lewis. I.H.P 3000 = 11 kts. Machinery : Vertical triple expansion. 1 screw. Boilers : Cylindrical. Oil : 500 tons. Complement, 139. Originally employed as an Aircraft Tender. Refitted 1920-21. Until lately, Depot Ship for Central Reserve of Minesweepers, and since used periodically by School of Naval Co-operation.

Submarine Depot Ships.

Notes.—Minesweeper **FERMOY** is attached to Portland Submarine Flotilla ; Minesweeper **ROSS** to Submarine School, Portsmouth ; and Minesweeper **MARAZION** to 4th Submarine Flotilla, China Station.

Under 1928-29 Estimates a Submarine Depot Ship was laid down at Chatham Dockyard, her machinery being ordered from J. Samuel White & Co., Ltd., of Cowes. She was to have been named *Maidstone*, but in July, 1929, the order for her construction was cancelled as a measure of economy.

1929 Photo, Abrahams, Devonport.

MEDWAY. (Vickers, July 19th, 1928). Laid down April, 1927, under 1926-27 Estimates, and completed in Sept., 1929. Displacement, 15,000 tons. Dimensions: 545 (*p.p.*), 580 (*o.a.*) × 85 × 23 feet. Guns : 2—4 inch, 4—4 inch AA. Has twin-screw double-acting 2 stroke M.A.N. Diesel engines, total H.P. 8000 = 16 kts. Oil : 530 tons own fuel + 1900 tons for submarines. Equipment includes a Foundry, Machine shop, Plate shop, Smithy, Torpedo shop, Plumber's shop, etc. Designed to mother 18 submarines.

Submarine Depot Ships—*continued.*

1920 *Photo, Lieut. T. B. McDonald, R.N.*

TITANIA (Clyde S.B. Co., 1915, purchased 1915). 5250 tons. Dimensions: 335 (*p.p.*) × 46¼ × 18 feet 5 ins. I.H.P. 3200 = 14.5 kts. Torpedo tubes: 2. Coal: 498 tons. Complement, 249. Cyl. boilers.

1931 *Photo, Kestin, Weymouth.*

Submarine Depot Ships—*continued.*

1920 *Photo, Abrahams, Devonport.*

LUCIA (Furness Withy & Co., 1907, ex German Prize, *Spreewald*,* converted by Clyde S.B. Co., 1916). 5805 tons. Dimensions: 367½ (*o.a.*) × 45 feet 2¼ ins. × 18⅝ feet. Guns: 2—3 pdr. AA. I.H.P. 2750 = 12·7 kts. Coal: 615 tons. Cyl. boilers. Complement, 262.

*Hamburg-America Liner, captured by H.M.S. *Berwick*, September, 1914.

ADAMANT.   1921 *Photo, Gieves, Ltd.*

(ALECTO has shorter topmasts and smaller bridge.)

ADAMANT and **ALECTO** (both Laird, 1911). 935 tons. Dimensions: 190 (*p.p.*), 212 (*o.a.*) × 32½ × 11 ft. 1 in. (*mean* draught). Guns: *Adamant*, 1—4 inch.* Designed H.P. 1400 = 14 kts. Coal: 180 tons. Complement, 76.

*Officially listed, but not always carried.

Submarine Depot Ships—*continued.*

1923 *Photo, R. Perkins, Esq.*

CYCLOPS (ex-*Indrabarah*, Sir Jas. Laing & Co., 1905). 11,300 tons. Dimensions: 460 (*p.p.*), 477 (*o.a.*) × 55 × 21 ft. 2 in. Guns: 2—4 inch (mounted in bows). Machinery: Triple expansion. Designed H.P. 3500 = 13 kts. Coal capacity: 1595 tons. Complement, 266.

Note.—Originally served as Repair Ship. Converted to present use by Chatham D.Y., 1922. Reboilered, 1929.

Repair Ships.

{1930, Messrs. Vickers-Armstrong.

RESOURCE. (Vickers, Nov. 27th, 1928), laid down, August, 1927, under 1926-27 Estimates. She was completed in Oct., 1929. Displacement, 13,500 tons. Dimensions : 500 (p.p.) × 83 × 20½ feet. Guns : 4—4 inch AA. 2 sets Parsons single reduction geared turbines. H.P. 7500 = 15 kts. 4 Yarrow 3 drum boilers, pressure 235 lbs. Auxiliary machinery is Diesel, electrically driven. Oil : 1100 tons + 350 tons for other vessels.

Royal Yacht.

VICTORIA AND ALBERT (1899). 4700 tons. Dimensions : 380 (p.p.) × 40 × 18 feet (mean draught). Guns : 2—6 pdr. (bronze). H.P. 11,800 = 20 kts. Belleville boilers. Coal : normal, 350 tons ; maximum, 2000 tons. Comp. 363.

Admiralty Yacht.

1920 Photo.

ENCHANTRESS (1903). 3470 tons. Dimensions : 320 × 40 × 15 feet. Guns : 4—3 pdr. H.P. 6400 = 18 kts. Yarrow boilers. Coal : 350 tons.

Oilers (R.F.A.)

Note :—
The first 22 of these Oil Tankers are at present under management.

BRITISH BEACON.　　Photo, Abrahams, Devonport (added 1927).

Oilers (R.F.A.)—continued.

BRITISH BEACON, BRITISH LANTERN (both Workman Clark, 1918), **BRITISH STAR** (Swan Hunter, 1917). 6891, 6897 and 6888 tons gross, respectively. Dimensions : 430 × 57 × 26¼ feet. Deadweight capacity : 9000 tons. Triple expansion engines and cylindrical boilers.

BRITISH LIGHT (Palmers, 1917). 6470 tons gross. Dimensions : 419½ × 54¼ × 26 feet. Deadweight capacity : 8000 tons. Triple expansion engines and cylindrical boilers.

WAR BAHADUR.　　Photo, Abrahams, Devonport (added 1927).

WAR KRISHNA.　　Photo, Abrahams, Devonport (added 1927).

WAR AFRIDI (R. Duncan & Co., 1920), **WAR BAHADUR** (1918), **WAR MEHTAR** (1920), (both Armstrong) ; **WAR BRAHMIN** (1920), **WAR DIWAN** (1919), **WAR PINDARI** (1920), all three Lithgows ; **WAR BHARATA** (1920), **WAR NAWAB** (1919), **WAR NIZAM** (1918), **WAR SUDRA** (1920), all four Palmers ; **WAR HINDOO** (Hamilton, 1919) ; **WAR KRISHNA** (Swan Hunter, 1919); **WAR PATHAN** (1919), **WAR SIRDAR** (1920), both Sir J. Laing & Sons ; **WAR SEPOY** (W. Gray & Co., 1919). 5518 to 5730 tons gross. Dimensions : 400 × 52¼ × 25⅔ feet. Deadweight capacities vary from 6300 tons (War Pindari) to 8100 tons (War Bahadur). Triple expansion engines and cylindrical boilers.

Oilers (R.F.A.)—continued.

1930 *Photo, R. Perkins, Esq.*

OLEANDER (Pembroke D.Y., 1922), **OLNA** (Devonport D.Y., 1921). 7045 and 7023 tons *gross*, respectively. Dimensions : 430 × 57 × 26¼ feet. Deadweight capacity : 10,000 tons. Triple expansion engines and cylindrical boilers.
Note.—*Olna* used for experiments with Oertz rudder, 1929.

DELPHINULA. *Photo added 1927, by courtesy of Messrs. Armstrong.*

DELPHINULA (ex-*Buyo Maru*, Armstrong, 1908). 4990 tons *gross*. Dimensions : 385 × 50½ × 24⅔ feet. Deadweight capacity : 6600 tons. Triple expansion engines and cylindrical boilers.

LEAF Type.   *Photo added* 1927

Oilers (R.F.A.)—continued.

APPLELEAF (ex-*Texol*) (Workman Clark), **CHERRYLEAF** (Sir R. Dixon & Co.), **PLUMLEAF** (ex-*Trinol*) (Swan Hunter),**BRAMBLELEAF** (Russell & Co.),**ORANGELEAF** (J. L. Thompson & Sons), **PEARLEAF** (W. Gray & Co.). All launched 1917. Displacement, 11,628 tons (from 5891 to 5927 tons *gross*). Dimensions : 405 × 54½ × 27½ feet. Triple expansion engines and cylindrical boilers. I.H.P. 6750 = 14 kts. Deadweight capacity : First three, 5400 tons ; second three, 5000 tons.

DREDGOL (Simons, 1918). 7589 tons. Dimensions : 326 × 54½ × 18¾ feet. I.H.P. 2500 = 11 kts. Own oil : 360 tons. Cylindrical boilers. Deadweight capacity : 4000 tons.

SERBOL.   1920 *Photo, Gieves, Ltd.*

FRANCOL (Earles S.B. Co.), **MONTENOL** (W. Gray), **SERBOL** (Caledon S.B. Co.). All details as *Belgol* below, but of different appearance. All launched 1917.

SLAVOL.   1920 *Photo, Abrahams, Devonport.*

BELGOL (Irvine's S.B. & D.D. Co.), **CELEROL** (Short Bros.), **FORTOL** (McMillan), **PRESTOL** (Napier & Miller), **RAPIDOL** (W. Gray), **SLAVOL** (Greenock D.Y. Co.). All launched 1917. 5049 tons. Dimensions : 335 × 41½ × 20½ feet. I.H.P. 3375 = 14 kts. Own oil : 300 tons. Cylindrical boilers. Complement, 39. Deadweight capacity : 2000 tons.

Oilers (R.F.A.)—continued.

EBONOL.   1921 *Photo, Seward, Weymouth.*

BIRCHOL, BOXOL (Barclay, Curle), **EBONOL** (Clyde S.B. Co.), **ELDEROL, ELMOL** (Swan Hunter), **LARCHOL, LIMOL** (Lobnitz), **HICKOROL** (McMillan). All launched 1917. 2200 tons. Dimensions : 220 × 34⅔ × 13¼ feet. Triple expansion engines and cylindrical boilers. I.H.P. 700 = 9 kts. Own oil : 40 tons. Complement, 19. Deadweight capacity : 1000 tons.

DISTOL (W. Dobson & Co.), **PHILOL, SCOTOL** (Tyne Iron S. B. Co.), **KIMMEROL, VISCOL** (Craig, Taylor). All launched 1916. 2200 tons. Dimensions : 220 × 34⅔ × 12½ feet. I.H.P. 700 = 9 kts. Own oil : 40 tons. Cylindrical boilers. Complement, 19. Deadweight capacity : 1000 tons.

TREFOIL (Pembroke, 1913). 4500 tons. Dimensions : 280 × 39 × 18¼ feet. 2 sets 6-cylinder 2-cycle Diesel engines. B.H.P. 1500 = 12 kts. Deadweight capacity : 2000 tons. Own oil : 200 tons.

1921 *Photo, Abrahams, Devonport.*

TURMOIL (Pembroke, 1917). 4484 tons. Similar to *Trefoil*, above, but with reciprocating engines. Draught : 22 feet. I.H.P. 1800.

1920 *Photo, Coates, Harwich.*

MIXOL (Caledon S. B. & Eng. Co., 1916). **THERMOL** (Greenock D.Y. Co., 1916). 4326 tons. Dimensions : 270 × 38½ × 20¼ feet. I.H.P. 1200 = 11 kts. Oil : 150 tons. Deadweight capacity : 2000 tons.

Oilers (R.F.A.)—*continued.*

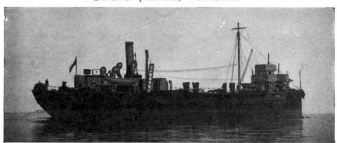

CAROL. 1921 *Photo, Seward, Weymouth.*

ATTENDANT (Chatham, 1913), **CAROL** (Devonport, 1913). 2178 tons. Dimensions : 200 × 34 × 13 feet. I.H.P. 450 = 8 kts. Coal : 60 tons. Deadweight capacity, 1000 tons.

BURMA (Greenock D.Y. Co., 1911). 4116 tons. Dimensions : 270 × 36½ × 18 feet. H.P. 1200 = 11 kts. Deadweight capacity, 2000 tons oil fuel. Own fuel : 210 tons.

PETROLEUM. *Photo, Abrahams, Devonport (added 1927).*

PETROLEUM (Swan, Hunter, 1903). 9700 tons. Dimensions : 370 × 48⅔ × 24 feet. H.P. 2000 = 13 kts. Own oil : 426 tons. Deadweight capacity, 6000 tons.

KHARKI (Irvine S. B. & Eng. Co., 1900). 1465 tons. Dimensions : 185 × 29 × 12 feet. H.P. 775 = 13 kts. Fuel : 90 tons. Deadweight capacity, 680 tons.

Note.—Oiler *Ruthenia* is now fuel storage hulk at Singapore.

Petrol Carriers.

PETROBUS. 1920 *Photo, G. Dott, Esq.*

PETROBUS, PETRELLA, (Dunlop, Bremner, 1918). 1024 tons. Dimensions : 164 × 28 × 11½ feet. I.H.P. 500 = 9-10 kts. Deadweight capacity : 300 tons. Own oil : 50 tons. Cylindrical boilers. Complement, 16.

Water Carrier.

PETRONEL.—As *Petrobus, Petrella,* just above.

Distilling Vessel & Store Carrier (R.F.A.).

1920 *Photo, Abrahams, Devonport.*

BACCHUS (Hamilton & Co., 1915, purchased 1915). About 3500 tons. Dimensions : 295 × 44 × 12½ feet. I.H.P. ? = ? kts. Coal : 873 tons. 2000 tons capacity.

Fleet Supply Ship.

PERTHSHIRE. 1927 *Photo, Cassar, Malta.*

PERTHSHIRE (Hawthorn Leslie, 1893). 9336 tons. 5865 tons *gross.* Dimensions : 420 × 54 × 29 feet. I.H.P. 3400 = 11 kts. Cargo capacity, 3400 tons. Own fuel : 300 tons.

Store Carriers.

ARGO (J. Shearer & Sons, Ltd., 1906). Tonnage : 854 *gross.* Capacity : 1250 tons. Dimensions : 198 × 30 × 11¾ feet. I.H.P. 1000.

BISON. Tonnage : 760 (displacement). I.H.P. 500.

ISLEFORD (Ardrossan D.D. Co., 1913). Tonnage : 414 (*gross*). Dimensions : 149⅔ × 25½ × 10 feet. Oil engines. I.H.P. 450. 1 screw.

JOHN EVELYN. Tonnage : 435 *gross.* I.H.P. 500.

*JOYCE.
*LUCY.
*MARCHWOOD.
Tonnage: 140 (displacement). Dimensions: 81½ × 16½ × 8 feet. I.H.P. 280 = 8 kts.

UPNOR. Tonnage : 600 (displacement). I.H.P. 300.

* Also fitted for towing.

Hospital Ship (R.F.A.)

MAINE (ex P. S. N. Co. liner *Panama*, built by Fairfield, 1902, purchased 1920 for conversion). Displacement : 10,100 tons (4035 tons *net*, 6599 tons *gross*). Dimensions : 401 ft. 2 in. × 58 ft. 4 in. × 23 ft. 7 in. I.H.P. 4000 = 13 kts. Triple expansion engines. 2 double-ended and 2 single-ended boilers. Coal : 1300 tons.

Surveying Vessels.

ORMONDE. (HERALD similar ; IROQUOIS has shorter funnel). 1924 *Photo, Abrahams, Devonport.*

IROQUOIS (Barclay, Curle, 1918), **ORMONDE** (1918), **HERALD** (ex *Merry Hampton*, 1918), both by Blyth S.B. Co. Converted Minesweepers of "24" (Racehorse) class. 1320 tons. Dimensions : 276½ × 35 × 12 feet. Guns : 1—3 pdr. I.H.P. 2500 = 17 kts. Coal : 260 tons. Cylindrical Boilers.

Note.—All converted by Devonport D.Y., 1922-23. Sister ship *Moresby* has been transferred to R. Australian Navy 1925.

Surveying Vessels—*continued.*

KELLETT. *1924 Photo, Abrahams, Devonport.*

BEAUFORT (1919), by Ailsa S.B. Co. **FITZROY** (1919), **FLINDERS** (1919), both by Lobnitz & Co. **KELLETT** (1919), by Simons & Co. Converted Twin Screw Mine-sweepers of "Hunt Class." 800 tons. Dimensions: 231 (*o.a.*) × 28 ft. 7¼ in. × 7½ feet. Guns: 1—3 pdr. I.H.P. 2200 = 16 kts. Machinery: Vertical triple expansion. 2 screws. Boilers: Babcock or Yarrow. Coal: 185 tons. Complement, 88.

Note.—**Protea**, of this type, transferred to S. Africa, 1921.

1924 Photo, Abrahams, Devonport.

ENDEAVOUR (Fairfield, 1912). 1280 tons. Dimensions: 241¼ (*o.a.*) × 34 ft. 2 in. × 11¾ feet. Guns: 1—3 pdr., 1 M.G. H.P. 1100 = 13 kts. Coal: 220 tons. Complement, 140. Specially built for Hydrographic Duties.

Target Service Ship.

CENTURION. *1928 Photo, C. Cozens.*

CENTURION (Devonport D.Y., Nov. 18th, 1911). Ex-battleship, converted for service as wireless controlled Target Ship in replacement of *Agamemnon* by Chatham D.Y., 1926-27, at a cost of £358,088. Displacement, 23,000 tons. Dimensions: 589½ (*w.l.*) × 89 × 30⅝ feet (*max.* draught). Guns: Rendered ineffective on conversion or removed. Machinery: Parsons turbines. Boilers: 18 Yarrow. Designed H.P. 27,000 = 21 kts. Coal: 3150 tons, plus 850 tons oil. Begun under 1910 Estimates, completed 1913, and removed from Effective List in 1926, under conditions of Washington Treaty.

Note.—Other vessels employed in connection with Target Service include Sloops **CHRYSANTHEMUM** and **SNAP-DRAGON**; Submarine **L 6**; Trawlers **MOY** and **OUSE**; Fleet Tugs **ST. CYRUS, ST. FAGAN, ST. ISSEY** and **ST. MARTIN**—all described and illustrated on other pages, under their respective classes.

1 Whaler.

1925 Photo, Abrahams, Weymouth.

CACHALOT, Emergency War Programme. Built 1915, by Smiths Dock Co. 336 tons. (237 tons *gross*.) Dimensions: 139¾ × 25 × 6½ feet. Guns: 1—12 pdr. (not mounted at present). H.P. 1000 = 12-13 kts. Coal: 60 tons. Complement, 26.

15 Trawlers.

(See also *Vernon* and *Kate Lewis*, listed under Minesweepers).

Note.—Those marked * are rated as "Fishery Protection Gunboats" have black topped funnels, and carry 1—12 pdr. *Pembroke* has same armament, plus 2—3 pdr. *Colne* has bowsprit and bow walk.

"MERSEY" TYPE. *1926 Photo, Abrahams & Sons, Devonport.*

EXCELLENT. *1928 Photo, C. Cozens.*

Blackwater(ex-*William Inwood*). **James Ludford.**
***Boyne** (ex-*William Jones*). **Moy** (ex-*Alexander Hills*).
***Cherwell** (ex-*James Jones*). **Ouse** (ex-*Andrew King*).
***Colne** (ex-*Isaac Chant*). **Pembroke** (ex-*Stour, ex-Daniel*
***Doon** (ex-*Fraser Evans*). *Fearall*)
Excellent (ex-*Nith, ex-Andrew Jewer*).

All belong to "Mersey" type (designed by Messrs. Cochrane & Sons, Ltd., Selby, 1917-18). All built by Messrs. Cochrane except *Colne* and *James Ludford*, by Lobnitz. Displacement: 665 tons (324 tons *gross*). Dimensions: 138¼ (*p.p.*) × 23¾ × 13½ feet. Triple expansion engines. 1 boiler. I.H.P. 550 = 11 kts. Coal: 204 tons. *Boyne, Cherwell,* are R.N.R. mine-sweeping instructional vessels; *Moy, Ouse,* are on Fleet Target Service.

Trawlers.—*continued.*

"DEE" TYPE.　　　*1926 Photo, Gieves, Ltd., Portsmouth.*

Dee (ex-*T* 16, ex-*Battleaxe*).　　*Kennet* (ex-*T* 17, ex-*Iceaxe*).

Garry (ex-*T* 13, ex-*Goldaxe*).　　*Liffey* (ex-*T* 14, ex-*Stoneaxe*).

Ex-Russian Trawlers, designed and built by Smiths Dock Co., Ltd., 1916. Displacement: about 500 tons. (292 tons *gross*). Dimensions: 130 (*p.p.*) × 23½ × 13½ feet. I.H.P. 490 = 10.5 kts. Coal: 140 tons.

ROBERT CLOUGHTON (1917). "Castle" type, designed by Smiths Dock Co., Ltd., and built by Bow, McLachlan & Co., Ltd., 547 tons. (273 tons *gross*.) Dimensions: 125 (*p.p.*) × 22½ × 12½ feet. I.H.P. 480 = 10.5 kts. Coal: 164 tons.

---

29 Drifters.

(All built of steel except those marked with an asterisk, which are believed to be wood. Those marked † are on Fleet Auxiliary List).

†*Anticyclone.*	*Landfall.*
Billow.	*Leeward.*
Cascade.	†*Loraine.*
Cloud.	*Lunar Bow.*
Cold Snap.	*Mist.*
Crescent Moon.	*Noontide.*
Ebbtide (ex-*C.D. 1*).	†*Onyx* (ex-*C.D. 82*).
Eddy.	*Seabreeze.*
Fiery Cross.	*Sheen.*
Flicker.	*Shower.*
Fumarole.	*Sundown.*
†*Glitter.*	*Sunset.*
Halo.	*Whirlpool.*
Harmattan.	
Horizon.	
Indian Summer.	

Displace 199 tons (except ex-*C.D.* type, 150 tons). Dimensions: 87 × 19¾ × 9½ feet. I.H.P. 270 = 9 kts. Guns: Usually 1—6 pdr. or 3 pdr. Coal: 31-39 tons.

Note.—Cascade lent to Air Ministry, 1928.

---

18 Fleet Tugs.

ROYSTERER.　　　*1929 Photo, N. T. Tangye, Esq.*

4 ROLLCALL TYPE.

RESOLVE, RESPOND (both by Ayrshire D.Y. Co.), **RETORT** (Day, Summers & Co.), **ROYSTERER** (Thornycroft.) Built 1918-19. About 825 tons *gross*. Dimensions: 175 × 34 × 17 (*maximum* draught). 2 screws. I.H.P. 2,500 = 14 kts.

1929 Photo, N. T. Tangye, Esq.
(Some have black-topped funnels; are mostly differentiated by funnel bands).

15 "RESCUE" TYPE (SAINT CLASS).

ST. ABBS, ST. BLAZEY, ST. BREOCK, ST. CLEARS, ST. CYRUS, ST. DAY, ST. DOGMAEL, ST. FAGAN, ST. ISSEY, ST. JUST, ST. MARTIN, ST. MELLONS, ST. MONANCE, ST. OMAR. Built by various yards, 1918-19. About 425 tons *gross*. Dimensions: 135 × 30 × 11½ feet (*maximum* draught), 1 screw. I.H.P. 1,250 = 12 kts. Coal: 240 tons.

Note.—St. Cyrus, St. Fagan, St. Issey, St. Martin, employed for Target Towing, others on Fleet Auxiliary List. Another of this type, Toia (ex St. Boniface) transferred to New Zealand.

ROYAL AUSTRALIAN NAVY.

TORPEDO CRAFT.

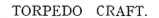

Tasmania *class* (5).

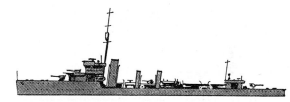

Anzac.

CRUISERS, SLOOPS & MISCELLANEOUS.

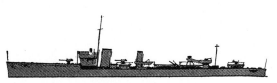

Albatross.

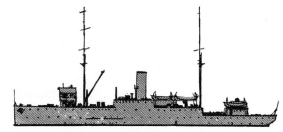

Penguin.

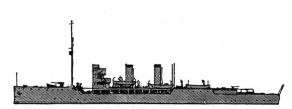

Marguerite.

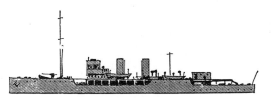

Geranium.

Mallow.

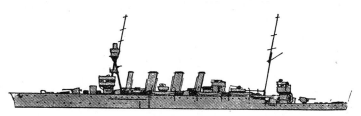

Brisbane.

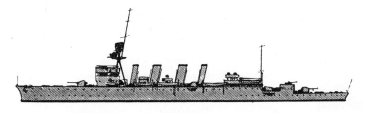

Adelaide.

Australia, Canberra.

Seagoing Ships in Commission, 1931 (excluding Harbour Training Service).

Cruisers : **AUSTRALIA** (flagship), **CANBERRA**.

Seaplane Carrier : **ALBATROSS**.

Depôt and Repair Ship : **PENGUIN**.

Destroyer : **TATTOO**.

Surveying Vessel : **MORESBY**.

Australian Naval Board.

Commander-in-Chief: Rt. Hon. Baron Stonehaven, P.C., G.C.M.G., D.S.O.

President: Minister of State for Defence, Hon. Albert E. Green, M.P.

1st Naval Member: Rear-Admiral G. F. Hyde, C.V.O., C.B.E.

2nd Naval Member: Captain H. J. Feakes, R.A.N.

Finance and Civil Member: Mr. T. J. Thomas, O.B.E.

Secretary: Hon. Paymaster Commander G. L. Macandie, C.B.E.

Commanding Australian Squadron.

Rear-Admiral : ?

Liason Officer, London : Mr. T. Trumble.

AUSTRALIA (17th March, 1927), **CANBERRA** (31st May, 1927).

"Standard" displacement, 10,000 tons. (13,630 *deep load*). Complement, 679. (710 as flagship).

Length (*p.p.*), 590 feet (*o.a.*), 630 feet. Beam, 68⅓ feet. Draught, 16¼ feet (*mean*.)

Guns :
8—8 inch, 50 cal.
4—4 inch AA.
4—3 pdr.
4—2 pdr pom-poms.
4 Machine, 8 Lewis
Torpedo tubes :
8—21 inch in quadruple mountings.

Armour :
4″ Deck ....
2″—1½″ Gun Houses
3″ C.T.
Bulges ....

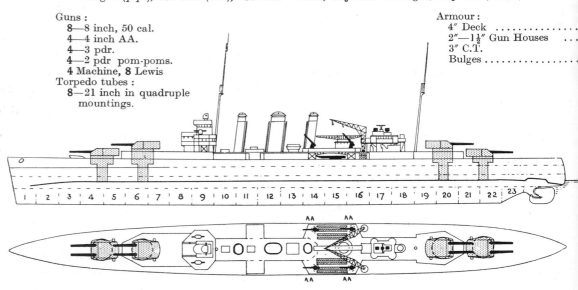

AUSTRALIA.   1928 *Photo, Abrahams & Sons, Devonport.*

Machinery : Brown-Curtis geared turbines. 4 screws. Designe[d]
S.H.P. 80,000 = 31.5 kts. Boilers : 8 Yarrow. Oil fuel : 3400 ton[s]
Radius at full speed, 2,300 miles ; at economical speed (11—14 kts.[)]
10,400 miles.

General Notes.—Sisters to *Kent* class, in British Navy Section. Designed
Sir E. H. Tennyson d'Eyncourt. Laid down by John Brown & Co., Ltd[.]
Clydebank, in 1925, and completed in April and July, 1928, respectivel[y]
(See also detailed notes under British *Kent* class, which apply to these tw[o]
ships.)

ADELAIDE.　　　　　　　　　　　1924 *Photo, W. W. Stewart, Esq.*

ADELAIDE (July, 1918).

Laid down at Sydney, Jan., 1915. Completed, Aug., 1922.

Displacement, 5560 tons. Complement, 470.

Length (*o.a.*), 462⅔ feet. Beam, 49⅚ feet. Draught, 15⅚ feet (*mean*), 17¾—19 (*max.*).

Guns (Dir. Con.):
　9—6 inch, 50 cal.
　1—3 inch AA.
　4—3 pdr.
　2 M.G., 8 Lewis.
Torpedo tubes (21 inch) :
　2 *submerged* (broadside).

Armour :
　2″ Deck (on slopes).
　3″ (on sides) amidships.
　1½″ (on sides) fore and aft.

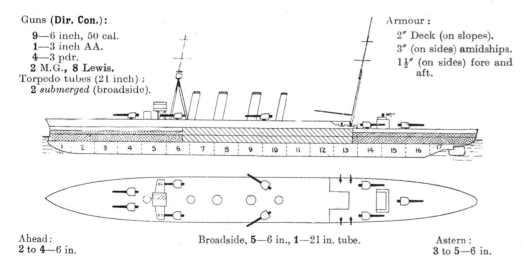

Ahead :
2 to 4—6 in.

Broadside, **5**—6 in., **1**—21 in. tube.

Astern :
3 to 5—6 in.

Machinery : Parsons turbines. Boilers : Yarrow, ⅓ oil, ⅔ coal burning. Designed S.H.P. 25,000 = 25 kts. Coal : *normal,*　　tons ; *maximum,* 860 tons. Oil fuel : 550 tons. 2 screws.

Notes.—Laid down at Cockatoo Navy Yard, Sydney, in 1915. Cost £1,271,782 to build.

Gunnery Notes.—Electric Ammunition Hoists, dredger type. Reported 6 inch guns have up to 40° elevation.

Torpedo Notes.—7 Torpedoes carried. 4 Searchlights.

1926 *Photo, Cribb, Southsea.*

BRISBANE (30th Sept., 1915).

Laid down at Sydney, Jan., 1913. Completed Nov., 1916.

Displacement, 5400 tons. Complement, 391.

Length (*p.p.*), 430 feet. Beam, 49⅚ feet. { Mean draught, 15¾ feet } Length (*over all*), 457 feet.
　　　　　　　　　　　　　　　　　{ Max.　　,,　　17¾—18½ feet. }

Guns (Dir. Con.):
　8—6 inch, 50 cal.
　1—3 inch anti-aircraft.
　4—3 pdr.
　2 M.G.
　8 Lewis.
Torpedo tubes (21 inch) :
　2 broadside (*submerged*).

Armour (Hadfield) :
　2″ Deck (on slopes).
　3″ (on sides).

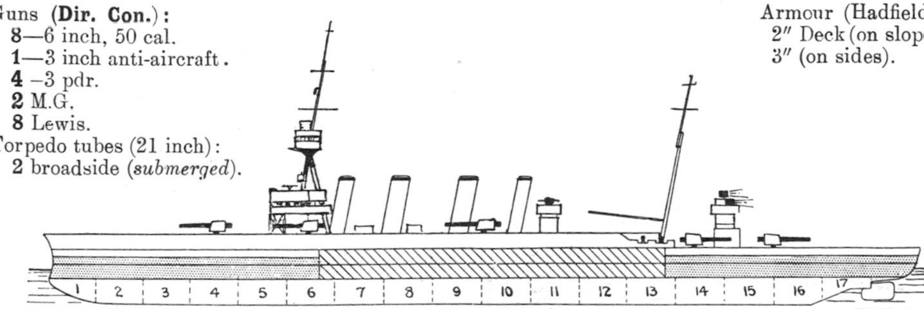

Ahead :
3—6 in.

Astern :
3—6 in.

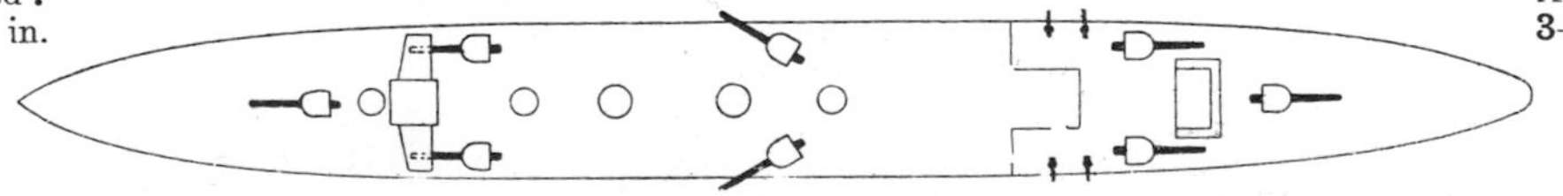

Broadside : **5**—6 in., **1**—21 in. torpedo tube.

Machinery : Parsons turbine. 4 screws. Boilers : Yarrow. Designed H.P. 22,000, (*n.d.*) 25,000 *f.d.* = 25·5 kts. Coal : *normal,* 750 tons, *maximum,* 1196 coal+260 oil.

Gunnery Notes.—Electric ammunition hoists. *Torpedo Notes.*—7 torpedoes carried. 4 searchlights.

Armour Notes.—Internal protection by longitudinal and transverse bulkheads. Double bottom extends over magazine and machinery spaces.

Engineering Notes.—500 r.p.m.=full power. Boilers: 3 drum small tube type. Uniflux condensers.

Note.—*Brisbane* refitted, 1926-28. Sister ships *Melbourne* and *Sydney* removed from effective list, 1928.

ALBATROSS (Feb. 21st, 1928).

Standard Displacement 6000 ⎫
Normal   ,,   6500 ⎬ tons.   Complement 450.
Full load   ,, over 7000 ⎭

Length (p.p.) 422 ft., (o.a.) 443¾ ft.
Beam, 58 ft., (60⅚ ft. extreme).   Draught, 16¼ ft.

Guns :
    4—4.7 inch AA.
    2—2 pdr. pom-pom AA.

Accommodation for 9 seaplanes.   (At present 6 Fairey
    machines are carried).

ALBATROSS.

1929 *Photo.*

Machinery : Parsons geared turbines.   2 screws.   Designed H.P. 12,000 = 20 kts.   Boilers : 4 Yarrow.
Oil fuel 997 tons.

General Notes.—Laid down at Cockatoo Yard, Sydney, in April, 1926, and completed at end of 1928.
Cost £1,200,000 complete with armament and equipment.   Trials, Dec., 1928, gave 22.5 kts. *maximum*
with 12,910 H.P.   Officially described as a "Seaplane Carrier."

ALBATROSS.

1929 *Photo.*

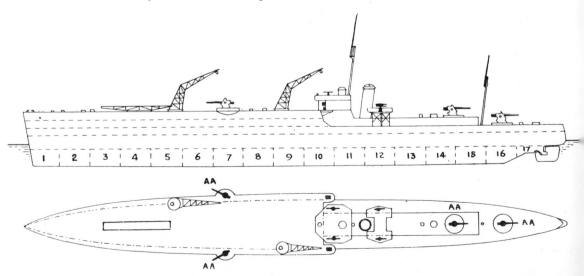

92

Fleet Sweeping Vessels (Sloops).

GERANIUM.   *R.A.N. Official Photo, 1922.*

MARGUERITE.   *Photo added 1926.*

GERANIUM (Greenock Dockyard Co. Begun Aug., 1915; launched 8th Nov., 1915; completed March, 1916). **MARGUERITE** (Dunlop Bremner. Begun July, 1915; launched 23rd Nov., 1915; completed Jan., 1916). Fleet Sweeping Vessels (Sloops) of *Arabis* type. 1250 tons. Dimensions: $255\frac{1}{4}$ (p.p.), $267\frac{3}{4}$ (o.a.) × $33\frac{1}{2}$ × 11 feet (*mean*), $11\frac{3}{4}$ (*max.* draught). Guns: 1—4·7 inch, 2—3 pdr. AA. in *Geranium*, 1—4 inch, 2—3 pdr. in *Marguerite*. Designed I.H.P. 2000=16·5 kts. Trials; *Geranium*, 2312=17; *Marguerite*, 2309=16·1. Machinery: boilers, screws, as *Mallow*. Coal: 270 tons *Geranium*, 256 tons *Marguerite*=2050 miles at 15 kts. Complement, 79. Built under Emergency War Programme; presented to Australian Navy, 1919. *Geranium* has recently been employed on surveying work.

(Appearance as Silhouette).

MALLOW (Barclay Curle. Launched 13th July, 1915; completed Sept., 1916.) Fleet Sweeping Vessel (Sloop) of *Acacia* type. 1200 tons. Dimensions: 250 (p.p.), $262\frac{1}{2}$ (o.a.) × 33 × 11 feet (*mean*), $11\frac{1}{4}$ (*max.* load). Guns: 1—12 pdr. (12 cwt.), 1—3 pdr. I.H.P. 1800=16·5 kts. Trials: 2328=16·3 kts. Machinery: 1 set triple expansion inverted and 2 cylindrical boilers. Coal: 250 tons=2000 miles at 15 kts. Complement, 77. Built under Emergency War Programme; presented to the Australian Navy, 1919.

Flotilla Leader

1920 *Photo, Abrahams, Devonport.*

1 *Denny :* **Anzac.** 1,666 tons. Dimensions : 315 ft. (p.p.), 325 ft. (o.a.) × 31 ft. 10 in. × 12 ft. $1\frac{1}{2}$ in. (*max.* draught aft). Guns : 4—4 inch, 2—2 pdr. pom-poms, 1 M.G., 4 Lewis. Torpedo tubes : 4—21 inch in 2 rev. deck mountings. Machinery : Brown-Curtis turbines. 3 screws. Boilers : Yarrow small tube. Designed S.H.P. 36,000 = 34 kts. Oil, 416/515 tons = *about* 2500 miles at 15 kts. Complement, 122. Begun January 31st, 1916. Launched January 11th, 1917. Completed April 24th, 1917. Begun under Emergency War Programme and presented to Australia, 1919. Sister to *Grenville* of British Navy.

5 Destroyers.

TASMANIA.   *R.A.N. Official Photograph, 1922.*

2 *Beardmore :* **Tasmania, Tattoo.**   1 *Doxford :* **Success.**   1 *Scott :* **Swordsman.**
1 *Swan Hunter :* **Stalwart.**
1075 tons. Dimensions : 265 (p.p.), 276 (o.a., *Success* 277) × $26\frac{1}{4}$ × $10\frac{5}{8}$ feet (*mean*) draught. Armament : 3—4 inch (Mk. IV with 30° elevation DIR. CON.), 1—2 pdr. pom-pom, 1 M.G., 4 Lewis. 4—21 inch tubes in two twin deck mountings, 1—24 inch searchlight controlled in unison with guns. Machinery : Brown-Curtis all-geared turbines. 2 screws. Boilers : 3 Yarrow small tube. Designed S.H.P. 27,000 = 36 kts. Fuel (oil only) : 254/301 tons = *about* 2000 miles at 15 kts. Complement, 90.

Notes.—Built under Emergency War Programme 1918-19 and presented to Australian Navy, 1919. For any further notes, refer to description of " Admiralty S Class " in British Navy Section.

Depot and Repair Ship.

R.A.N. Official Photo, 1922.

PENGUIN (ex-*Platypus*) (J. Brown, Clydebank. Begun Sept. 2nd, 1914; launched Oct. 28th, 1916; completed Mar., 1917.) 3476 tons. Dimensions: 310 (*w.l.*), 325 (*o.a.*) × 44 × 15⅔ feet. (*max.* draught). Guns: *nil.* I.H.P. 2650 = 15½ kts. Two sets triple expansion reciprocating engines and 4 cylindrical return-tube boilers. 2 screws. Coal: 450 tons. Complement, 357. Serves as Destroyer Depot Ship and Fleet Repair Ship.

Surveying Vessel.

Appearance similar to *Ormonde*, in British Navy section.

MORESBY (ex-*Silvio*, Barclay, Curle & Co., 1918). Ex-Minesweeper of " 24 " (*Racehorse*) class, converted by Pembroke D.Y., 1924-25. 1320 tons. Dimensions: 276½ (*o.a.*) × 35 × 12 feet. Guns: 1—3 pdr. I.H.P. 2500 = 17 kts. Cylindrical boilers. Coal: 260 tons.

Miscellaneous.

MOMBAH. (1921). Floating Coal Depot Vessel. Dimensions: 315 × 50 × 23.

CERBERUS (ex-*Kooranga*). Motor vessel. 61 tons. H.P. 200. 1 screw. Guns: 2—4 inch, 2—12 pdr., 4—3 pdr. Serves as tender to Flinders Naval Depot, Waterport.

ROYAL INDIAN MARINE.

Flag Officer Commanding and Director R.I.M. : Rear-Admiral H. T. Walwyn, C.B., D.S.O.

Flags.—Vessels of R.I.M., fly red pennant as Page 8, Admiralty Flag Book. Director R.I.M. when afloat flies broad red pennant, charged with a Cross in gold, and in first canton a lion rampant.

Special Note.

The Government of India has decided to complete the reconstruction of the R.I.M. in accordance with the recommendations of the Departmental Committee of 1925, but the force will not have the right to be called the Royal Indian Navy. It will, however, become a combatant force and will assume the functions and serve under the conditions which were originally intended for the Royal Indian Navy.

Sloops.

HINDUSTAN.

1930 *Photo, favour of Messrs. Swan Hunter.*

HINDUSTAN. Swan, Hunter & Wigham Richardson. Laid down 1929, launched May 12th, 1930 and completed trials in October 1930. Dimensions: 296 (*o.a.*) × 35 × 8½ft. Displ.: 1150 tons. Guns: 2—4 inch and 4—3 pdrs. Machinery: Parsons impulse reaction Turbines with single reduction gearing: 2 screws. 2 3-drum W.T. Boilers: 250 lbs. pressure. S.H.P. 2000=16·5 kts. Oil: ? tons. The internal arrangements have been designed with special care, making the ship most suitable for the Tropics, and the ventilation has been very carefully planned. The refrigerating plant is of the electrically driven CO_2 type. Is a slightly enlarged edition of "Sandwich" class.

Sloops.

1925 *Photo, Commander M. P. Cooper, R.I.M.*

CORNWALLIS (ex *Lychnis*) Hamilton, August, 1917. Convoy Sloop of *Anchusa* series, 1290 tons. Dimensions: 255¼ (*p.p.*), 266¼ (*w.l.*), 277¾ (*o.a.*) × 35 × 14⅛ feet. Guns: 3—4 inch, 2—2 pdr. pom-poms. Machinery: 4-cyl. triple expansion vertical. Boilers: 2 cylindrical. 1 screw. Designed H.P. 2500 = 15 kts. Coal: 260 tons. Complement, 140.

Note.—*Cornwallis* sold to Indian Government by the Admiralty, September 1921. Sister ship *Elphinstone* wrecked, Jan. 1925.

Minesweeping Sloops.

1920 *Photo, by courtesy of the Director-General of Stores, India House.*

LAWRENCE (ex-*Despatch Vessel*, launched by Messrs. Beardmore, July 30th, 1919, completed December 27th, 1919). 1412 tons (1225 tons standard). Dimensions : 225 (*p.p.*), 248½ (*o.a.*) × 34 × 8¾ feet (*light*), 12 feet (*max.*) draught. Complement, 97. Guns : 2—4 inch, 1—2 pdr. pom-pom. All-geared turbines. 2 screws. 2 Babcock boilers. S.H.P. 1900 = 15 kts. Oil : *normal*, 144 tons ; *max.*, 153 tons. Designed by Sir Wm. Biles & Co.

1920 *Photo, by courtesy of the Director-General of Stores, India House.*

CLIVE (launched by Messrs. Beardmore, December 10th, 1919, completed April 20th, 1920). 2100 tons (2050 tons standard). Dimensions : 240 (*p.p.*), 270⅔ (*o.a.*) × 38½ × 10½ feet (*light*), 14 feet (*max.*) draught. Complement, 111. Guns : 2—4 inch, 2—2 pdr. pom-poms. All-geared turbines. 2 screws. 2 Babcock & Wilcox boilers. S.H.P. 1700 = 14½ kts. Oil : 179 tons *normal*, and 199 tons *max.* Designed by Sir Wm. Biles & Co.

Surveying Ships.

1921 *Photo, Mr. Pallett, Chief Writer, R.N.*

INVESTIGATOR (Vickers, 1907). 1355 tons. (1172 tons standard). Dimensions : 204 × 33 × 13 feet. I.H.P. 1550 = 13 kts. 1 set triple expansion engines and 1 M-Return tube boiler. Coal : 172 tons. No guns. Complement, 110.

Note.—Length given above is between perpendiculars. Overall length is 232¼ or with bowsprit, 241¼ feet.

PALINURUS.   1921 *Photo, Mr. Pallett, Chief Writer, R.N.*

PALINURUS (Cammell Laird, 1907). 538 tons (444 tons standard). Dimensions : 140 × 24 × 10 feet (*max.* draught). 1 set triple expansion engines. 1 M-Return tube boiler. I.H.P. 475 = 11.25 kts. Coal : 64 tons. No guns. Complement, 45.

Patrol Boats.

1924 Photo, by courtesy of the Director, R.I.M.

PATHAN (ex P.C. 69). Workman, Clark. (1918). 832 tons (695 tons standard). Dimensions : 247½ × 26¾ × 9 feet. Turbines : S.H.P. 3,500 = 20 kts. Oil, 164 tons. Guns : 1—4 in., 2—12 pdrs.

BALUCHI (ex P.C. 55). Barclay, Curle. (1917). 755 tons (682 tons standard). Dimensions : 248½ × 25½ × 9 1/12 feet. Turbines : S.H.P., 3,500 = 20 kts. Oil, 134 tons. Guns : 1—4 in., 2—12 pdrs.

Depot Ship.

DALHOUSIE (Greenock, 1886). 1960 tons. Dimensions : 239½ × 36 × 15⅔ feet. (Machinery removed.) Guns : 4—3 pdr., 1—2 pdr. pom-pom. Fitted out as Depot Ship for the Royal Indian Navy, at Bombay.

Minesweeping Trawlers.
BOMBAY, CALCUTTA, COLOMBO, KIDDERPORE, MADRAS, SEALDAH

(1918-19). 588 tons, except *Bombay*, 590 tons. H.P. 480 = 10 kts. Guns : 1—12 pdr. *Bombay* oil fuel, others coal.

Trawler (used as Lighthouse Tender).

SALSETTE. Similar to *Bombay*. No armament at present.

NEWFOUNDLAND.

Transport.

Photo added 1929, by courtesy of Builders.

CARIBOU (Nieuwe Waterweg Scheepsbouw Maatschappij, Rotterdam, 1925). 2222 tons *gross*. Dimensions : 266 × 41¼ × 18¼ feet draught. Armament nil. I.H.P. 2800 = 14 kts. Machinery : Triple expansion. 1 screw. 2 S.E. boilers, working pressure 200 lbs. Coal : 411 tons. Complement, 51. Accommodation also provided for 243 passengers or troops. Strengthened for ice navigation.

14 Patrol Vessels, etc.

(Under control of Ministry of Finance and Customs.)

KYLE (Swan, Hunter, 1913). 1055 tons *gross*. Dimensions : 220 × 32¼ × 17¾ feet.

PORTIA, PROSPERO (1904). 978 tons *gross*. Dimensions : 204¾ × 31⅛ × 16 feet.

MEIGLE (ex-*Solway*, 1881). 836 tons *gross*. Dimensions : 220 × 30 × — feet.

SAGONA (1912). 808 tons *gross*. Dimensions : 175 × 28¼ × 13½ feet.

GLENCOE (1899). 767 tons *gross*. Dimensions : 208 × 30 × 17 feet.

ARGYLE, CLYDE, HOME (1900). 439 tons *gross*. Dimensions : 154½ × 25 × 14 feet.

MALAKOFF, SEBASTOPOL, SENEFF (1918). Ex-patrol boats of French " Victoire " type. 784 tons.

PRIESTMAN (1910). Steam grab hopper. 291 tons *gross*.

DAISY (1912). 248 tons *gross*. (Displacement, 510 tons.)

Note.—Sloop *Lobelia* (replaced by *Caribou*), Patrol Vessels, *Watchful* and *Petrel* appear to have been disposed of.

DOMINION OF CANADA.

Chief of the Naval Staff under Minister of National Defence : Commodore Walter Hose, C.B.E., R.C.N.

Personnel : R.C.N., Officers, 70 ; Men, 500. R.C.N.R., 70 and 430, R.C.N.V.R., 70 and 830. *Uniforms :* As British Navy.

RECOGNITION SILHOUETTES.

Scale : 1 inch = 160 feet.

Government Vessels :—

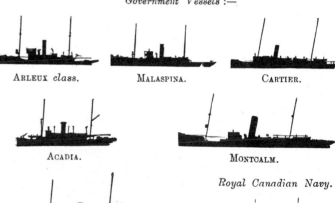

ARLEUX *class.*   MALASPINA.   CARTIER.

ACADIA.   MONTCALM.

Royal Canadian Navy.

LADY GREY.   ARMENTIERES *class* (4).

SKEENA, SAGUENAY.

CHAMPLAIN, VANCOUVER.

2 "Skeena" class.

1931 Photo, by favour of Messrs. Thornycroft.

SAGUENAY (July 12, 1930) and **SKEENA** (October 10, 1930), were ordered in January, 1929, from Messrs. Thornycroft. Cost about £670,000, with armament. Displacement, 1320 tons. Dimensions: 322 × 32¼ × 12 feet. H.P. 34,000 = 35 kts. Machinery: Single reduction geared turbines. 3 Thornycroft boilers, with superheaters. Oil fuel: 380 tons. Complement: 138.

These ships exceeded 37 knots on trials with ease, and their running was marked by almost complete absence of vibration. Similar to British A class, but specially strengthened to withstand ice pressure.

2 "Thornycroft S" class.

CHAMPLAIN.   *1928 Photo, C. Cozens.*

2 *Thornycroft* "S." **CHAMPLAIN** (ex-*Torbay*), **VANCOUVER** (ex-*Toreador*). 1075 tons. Dimensions: 266¾ (p.p.) 275¾ (o.a.) × 27 ft. 5¼ in × 11 feet. Guns: 3—4 inch, 1—2 pdr. pom-pom, 1 M.G., 4 Lewis: Torpedo tubes: 4—21 inch in two twin deck mountings. Machinery: Brown-Curtis turbines and 3 Yarrow boilers (built by Thornycroft). 2 screws. S.H.P. 29,000 = 36 kts. Oil: 306/248 tons. Complement 90. Transferred to Canada 1928, to replace worn-out *Patriot* and *Patrician,* and are employed for Training R.C.N.V.R. on Atlantic and Pacific Coasts respectively.

	Begun	Launch.	Comp.	Trials
Champlain	11/17	6/3/19	17/7/19	} 36·4
Vancouver	11/17	7/12/18	4/19	

3 Minesweeping Trawlers.

(A = Atlantic, P = Pacific.)

(P) *Armentieres,*		Steel. Built 1918.
(A) *Festubert,*		357 tons gross, 136 tons net register. Dimensions: 130 × 25 × 14 feet.
(A) *Ypres,*		Guns: 1—12 pdr., Q.F. 12 cwt.
		Speed: 10 kts. Complement, 18.

Department of Marine and Fisheries.

With the exception of *Malaspina*, all guns dismounted and removed to store.

Services ships were engaged on, 1924, are abbreviated thus:—

FP–A:—Fisheries Protection, Atlantic.

FP–P:—Fisheries Protection, Pacific.

HS–A:—Hydrographic Survey, Atlantic.

HS–P:—Hydrographic Survey, Pacific.

HS–GL:—Hydrographic Survey, Great Lakes.

ACADIA (1913). Steel 439 tons (net registered). Dimensions: 170 × 33.7 × 19.1 feet. H.P. 1200 = 12 kts. Guns: 1—4 inch Q.F., 2—12 pdr. Q.F. 12 cwt. Coal: 260 tons. Complement, 42. **(HS–A.)**

ARANMORE (1890). Iron. 502 tons (net registered). Dimensions: 241.5 × 34.8 × 15.7 feet. H.P. 1500 = 13 kts. Coal: 200 tons.

ARLEUX (FP–A), ARRAS (FP–P). Steel trawlers, both built 1918. 136 tons net. Dimensions: 130 × 25 × 13 feet. Guns: 1—12 pdr. Q.F. 12 cwt. Speed: 10 kts. Complement, 18.

BAYFIELD (1889). Steel. 114 tons net. Dimensions: 140 × 24 × 10.5 feet. Speed: 11 kts. Coal: 100 tons. Complement, 25. **(HS–GL).**

BELLECHASSE (1912). 216 tons net. Dimensions: 142.2 × 27 × 12 feet. H.P. 1000 = 15 kts. Coal: 24 tons.

BRADBURY (1915). Steel. 500 tons. Dimensions: 151 × 27¼ × 8 feet. Speed: kts. Complement, 13. (*Fisheries Patrol, Lake Winnipeg*).

CARTIER (1910). Steel. 234 tons net. Dimensions: 164 × 29 × 13 feet. Guns: 3—12 pdr. 12 cwt. Q.F. H.P. 830 = 12 kts. Coal: 150 tons. Complement, 34. **(HS–A.)**

DOLLARD (1913). Steel. 323 tons (net registered). Dimensions: 178 × 31.9 × 15.3 feet. H.P. 1000 = 11 kts. Coal: 100 tons.

DRUID (1902). 193 tons net. Dimensions: 160 × 30 × 12.5 feet. H.P. 800 = 13 kts. Coal: 100 tons.

ESTEVAN (1912). 607 tons net. Dimensions: 212 × 38 × 15.3 feet. H.P. 1500 = 12½ kts. Coal: 350 tons.

FISPA (1913). 25 tons net. Dimensions: 82 × 14 × 5¾ feet. Complement, 7.

Government Vessels (continued).

Department of Marine and Fisheries (continued) :—

GIVENCHY (FP-P). Steel trawler, built 1918. 136 tons net. Dimensions: 130 × 25 × 14 feet. Guns: **1**—12 pdr. Q.F. 12 cwt. Speed: 10 kts. Complement, 18.

GRENVILLE (1915). 232 tons *net*. Dimensions: 155 × 30.9 × 10.9 feet. H.P. 900 = 11.5 kts. Coal: 100 tons.

GULNARE (1893). Steel. 1 screw. 500 tons. Dimensions: 137 × 20.5 × 12 feet. Speed: 10 kts. Coal: 65 tons. Complement, 34. (*Tidal Survey—Atlantic.*)

LADY GREY (1906). 439 tons *net*. Dimensions: 170 × 32 × 15.9 feet. H.P. 2300 = 14 kts. Coal: 200 tons.

LADY LAURIER (1902). 1970 tons. Dimensions: 214.9 × 34.2 × 17.2 feet. H.P. 1800 = 13 kts. Coal: 175 tons.

LAURENTIAN. 155 tons *net*. Dimensions: 149 × 24 × 11 feet. H.P. 520 = 11 kts.

ILLOOET (1908). Steel. 760 tons. Dimensions: 163 × 27 × 13 feet. H.P. 900 = 11¾ kts. Coal: 140 tons. (HS-P.)

LOOS (FP-A.). Steel trawler, built 1918. 136 tons net. Dimensions: 130 × 25 × 14 feet. Guns: **1**—12 pdr. Q.F. 12 cwt. Speed: 10 kts. Complement, 18.

MALASPINA (1913). Steel. 1 screw. 850 tons. Dimensions: 160 × 26.5 × 14.5 feet. Guns: **1**—6 pdr. Q.F. Hotchkiss. H.P. 1350 = 14½ kts. Coal: 200 tons. Complement, 40 (FP–P.)

MARFISH (1912). 83.4 × 18.5 × 9 feet. Gross tonnage, 115.76. Registered tonnage, 78.72. N.H.P., 19.5. Complement, 7.

MONTCALM (1904). Steel. 586 tons *net*. Dimensions: 245 × 40.6 × 15.7 feet. H.P. 3600 = 14 kts. Coal: 425 tons.

NEWINGTON (1889). 76 tons *net*. Dimensions: 115.3 × 21 × 11.5 feet. H.P. 600 = 10 kts. Coal: 85 tons.

RESTLESS (1906). Wood. 205 tons. Dimensions: 271 × 17 × 9 feet. Speed: 8½ kts. Complement, 8. (HS-P.)

STANLEY (1888). 395 tons *net*. Dimensions: 207.8 × 32 × 17.9 feet. H.P. 300 = 15½ kts. Coal: 250 tons.

Department of Customs :—

MARGARET (Thornycroft, 1913). 950 tons. Guns: 2—6 pdr. Designed H.P. 2000 = 15½ kts. *max.* speed. Coal: 200 tons. Strengthened for ice navigation.

Note.—A new 17 kt. vessel of this type was ordered from Canadian Vickers Ltd., August, 1928.

UNION OF SOUTH AFRICA.

Officer Commanding South African Naval Service (under Department of Defence) : Commander R. F. U. P. Fitzgerald, R.N.

Surveying Vessel.

1920 *Photo, Abrahams, Devonport.*

PROTEA (ex-*Crozier*), built by Messrs. Simons, Renfrew, Scotland. Launched July 1st, 1919; completed August 28th, 1919. Taken over from H.M. Navy, 1921. Converted Twin Screw Mine-Sweeper of "Later Hunt" type. Displacement: 800 tons. Dimensions: 231 (*o.a.*) × 28 ft. 7¼ in. × 7½ feet. Guns: **1**—3 pdr. Machinery (by Simons): Vertical triple expansion. Boilers: Yarrow. 2 screws. I.H.P. 2200 = 16 kts. Coal: 185 tons. Complement, 88.

Minesweeping Trawlers.

Immortelle (ex-*Eden*)   (ex-*Thomas Johns*) } Both launched 1918. "Mersey type," taken over from H.M. Navy, 1921.
Sonneblom (ex *Foyle*)   (ex-*John Edmund*) } 325 tons. *gross*. Dimensions: 138½ × 23½ × 12¾ feet. Speed: 10.5 kts.

Oceangoing Tugs.

T. S. McEwen (Bow, McLachlan & Co., Ltd., Paisley, 1925). 793 tons *gross*. Dimensions: 160 × 34½ × 15⅝ feet. H.P. 3400 = 15 kts. Watertube boilers. 2 screws.

Sir David Hunter (Ferguson Bros., Port Glasgow, 1915). 621 tons gross. Dimensions: 160 × 32 × 15 feet. H.P. 2300 = 13 kts. 2 screws.

(Some smaller Tugs also exist.)

DOMINION OF NEW ZEALAND.

Naval Board.

President : The Minister of Defence, the Hon. Thos. M. Wilford.

First Naval Member : Commodore Geoffrey Blake, C.B., D.S.O., R.N.

Second Naval Member* and Chief Staff Officer : Captain J. S. G. Fraser, D.S.O., R.N.

Naval Secretary† : Paymaster Commander J. T. V. Webster, D.S.O., R.N.

*Until such time as Commodore vacates command of H.M.S. *Dunedin* or other ship relieving her.

†Secretary to Commodore is also Secretary to Naval Board.

RECOGNITION SILHOUETTES.

DIOMEDE (note turret)

DUNEDIN.

NUCULA.

DIOMEDE. (Note forward gunhouse.) (Now has gaff on mainmast instead of foremast, and a 4″ on blast screen aft.) *Photo added 1923.*

Oiler.

NUCULA.   1927 *Photo, Nautical Photo Agency.*

NUCULA (ex-*Soyo Maru*, ex-*Hermione*) (Armstrong, 1906). 4614 tons *gross*. Dimensions: 370 × 48½ × 24¼ feet. I.H.P. 2400 = 10.5 kts. Deadweight capacity: 6000 tons.

DIOMEDE (29th April, 1919). **DUNEDIN** (19th Nov., 1918).

Displacement: 4765 and 4650 tons respectively. Complement: 450/469.

Dimensions: 472½ (o.a.), 46½ × 14¼ feet (*mean*), 16½ (*max*).

Guns:
6—6 inch, 50 cal. (**Dir.Con.**)
3—4 inch AA.
4—3 pdr.
2—2 pdr. pom-poms.
2 M.G.
8 Lewis.
Torpedo tubes (21 inch)
12 in 4 triple deck mountings.

Armour:
1″ Upper Deck (amidships) ...
3″ Side (amidships) ....
2″, 1¾″, 1½″ Side
(bow and stern) ....
1″ Deck over Rudder ....

Ahead:
2—6in.

Astern:
2—6 in.

Machinery: *Diomede* has Parsons and *Dunedin* Brown-Curtis geared turbines. Yarrow boilers in both. Designed S.H.P. 40,000 = 29 kts. *Trials*: 41,268 = 29.19. Oil fuel: *normal*, 300 tons; *max.*, 1060 tons. Begun under Emergency War Programme, *Diomede* by Vickers, June, 1918, and *Dunedin* by Armstrong, Nov., 1917, and completed 24th April, 1922, by Portsmouth D.Y., and Oct., 1919, respectively. Machinery by Vickers and Hawthorn, respectively. Transferred to New Zealand, 1924—25.

DUNEDIN.   1921 *Photo, Seward.*

Training Ship (ex-Cruiser).
PHILOMEL (Aug., 1890). 2575 tons. Complement, 222. Dimensions (o.a.): 278×41×16⅝ (*max.*) feet. Armament: 1—6 inch, 1—4 inch, 2—12 pdr. Torpedo Tubes: Nil. Armour: 2½″ Deck. Designed H.P. 7500 = 19 kts. (*f.d.*). Coal: 450 tons. Serves as Training and Depot Ship at Auckland.

Minesweeping Trawler.
WAKAKURA (ex-*T.R.*1). "Castle" type, similar to ROBERT CLOUGHTON, in British Navy section.

Fleet Tug.
TOIA (ex-*St. Boniface*, ex-*St. Fergus*). Details as "Saint" class, at end of British Navy Section.

Note.—Sloops **LABURNUM** and **VERONICA** are under control of the Admiralty while on this station for duty in the islands of the S. Pacific.

ARGENTINE FLEET.

Revised by courtesy of the Ministry of Marine, 1931.

Flags.

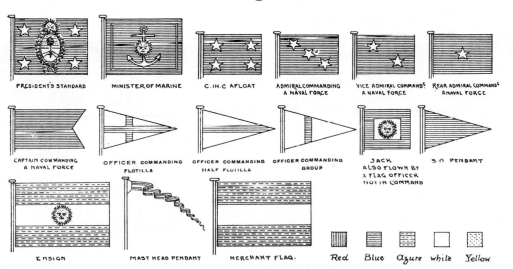

Insignia of Rank.

(As amended December 19th, 1923.)

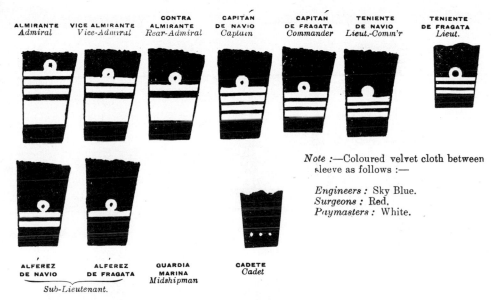

Note :—Coloured velvet cloth between sleeve as follows :—

Engineers : Sky Blue.
Surgeons : Red.
Paymasters : White.

Nota-tion.	Nominal Calibre.		Maker.	Length in Calibres.	Muzzle Velocity.	Weight A.P. Projectile.	*Max.*penetration against K.C. with capped A.P. at	
							5000 yards.	3000 yards.
	inches.	c/m.		calibres.	ft. secs.	lbs.	inches.	inches.
HEAVY	12	30·5	B	50	2900	870	19	23
MEDIUM	10	25·4	A	40	2207	500	7	9½
	9·4	24	K	35	{ 2300 } { 2133 }	352	4½	6
	8	20·3	A	45	2660	210	6½	9
	8	20·3	A	40	2550	210	3	5
	7·5	19	A	52	3116	200	...	...
LIGHT	6	15	B	50	2600	105	...	8¼
	6	15	A	45	2500	100	3	4½
	6	15	A	40	2200	100	3	3¾
	4·7	12	A	45	2570	45	...	2¾
	4·7	12	A	40	2230	45	...	...
	4	10·16	B	50	2996	30	...	...

In the Maker's column A = Armstrong ; B = Bethlehem ; K = Krupp.
The above details of Argentine Naval Ordnance have been officially revised.

Arsenals.

(1) **BUENOS AIRES.** Dry docks : (Eastern) 590½ × 65½ × 25 feet, and (Western) 492 × 65½ × 25 feet. There is also a small private dock at San Fernando, 17 miles above the city.

(2) **PUERTO BELGRANO** (Bahia Blanca). Dry docks : (1) 657 × 84 × 32½ ft., (2) 683 × 114 × 43 ft.

(3) **RIO SANTIAGO.** Dock, 672 × 114 × 36 feet. Two floating docks : (1) 1500 tons lift ; (2) 300 tons lift.

Mercantile Marine.

(From " Lloyd's Register," 1931 figures.)
Total gross tonnage, 327,980 tons, including 1 vessel of 16 kts. or over.

General Notes.

Personnel : about 12,000 all ranks.   *Reserve* : about 4,500.   *Special reserve* : 18,000 conscriptos.
Minister of Marine : Vice Almirante Carlos Daireaux.
Chief of Naval Staff : Cap. de Navio Aureliano Rey.
Chief of Naval Commission (Europe) : Cap. de Navio Pedro Gully.
Naval Attaché (London) : Cap. de Navio Dalmiro Sáenz.

INDEPENDENCIA.
LIBERTAD.

ALMIRANTE BROWN.
25 DE MAYO.

ROSARIO.
PARANA.

PRESIDENTE SARMIENTO.

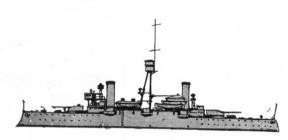

GENERAL BELGRANO. PUEYRREDON.
SAN MARTIN.

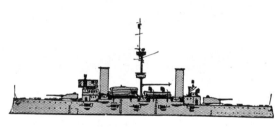

GARIBALDI.

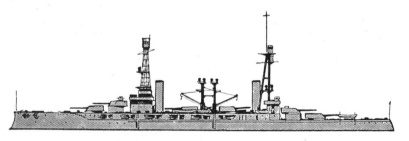

MORENO.
RIVADAVIA.

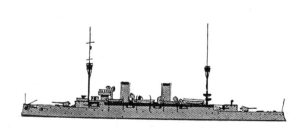

BUENOS AIRES.

5 MENDOZA *Class.*

CORDOBA.   CATAMARCA. } t.b.d.
LA PLATA. JUJUY.

M 1—9
(*Despatch Vessels*).

RIVADAVIA (26 Aug., 1911) & MORENO (23 Sept., 1911).

Normal displacement, 27,940 tons. *Full load*, 30,600 tons. Complement, 1215.

Length (*w.l.*), 577½ feet. Beam, 95 feet. *Max.* load draught, 28 feet. Length (*over all*), 585 feet.

Guns (Bethlehem):
12—12 inch, 50 cal. } **Dir.**
12—6 inch, 50 cal. } **Con.**
4—3 inch AA.
4—3 pdr.
6 M.G.
(4 landing).

Torpedo tubes (21 inch):
2 *submerged*
(broadside).

Armour (Krupp):
11″—8″ Belt (amidships) {
5″ Belt (bow) N.C.............
4″ Belt (stern) N.C. ....
3″ Deck (slopes) ....
9″—8″ Side above belt..
12″—9″ Big gun turrets ..
6″ Secondary battery (N.C.)
12″ Conning Tower (forward)
9″ Do.   (aft.)
Total weight: 7600 tons.

Machinery : Curtis geared turbines. 3 screws. S.H.P. 45,000 = 23 kts.
Boilers : 18 Babcock (converted to oil burning, 1924-25). Oil : 3,600 tons.
Nominal radius : 3930 miles at full speed, 8500 miles at 10 kts.

New Construction.

The current Naval Programme, approved by Parliament in Sept., 1926, involves the expenditure of 75,000,000 gold pesos (£15,000,000) over the ten years 1927-1936. In addition to the extension of present dockyard facilities on the River Plate and at Puerto Belgrano, and the opening of a new yard at Mar del Plata, the construction of the following vessels to replace obsolete tonnage is provided for :—

3 Cruisers.	1 Aircraft Tender.
6 Flotilla Leaders.	2 Surveying Vessels.
6 Submarines.	

These ships are to absorb over £5,000,000 of the sum voted.

1926 Photo, Fore River Yard (Builders).

Gunnery Notes.—Heights of barbettes over normal draught w.l. : No. 1, 29½ feet ; No. 2, 37½ feet ; Nos. 3 and 4 (echelon), and No. 5, 29 feet ; No. 6, 20 feet ; 6 inch guns, 19½ feet above w.l. Arcs of fire : end barbettes, Nos. 1 and 6, 270° ; Nos. 2 and 5 (super-firing), 300° ; Nos. 3 and 4 (echelon) 180° own beam and 100° far beam. R.F. on heads of derrick posts. Director controls (U.S.) type installed during 1924—25 refits. Rates of fire are reported to be : 12 inch, 2 rounds a minute ; 6 inch, 8 ; 4 inch, 12.

Armour Notes.—Main belt is 8 feet deep, 4½ feet above water-line and 3½ feet below same at normal draught. It is 240 feet long, but 11″ section is only 2 feet deep from top edge of belt, and then tapers to 5″ on lower (under-water) edge. Belt under end barbettes is 10″ tapering to 5″ as main belt. Upper belt 400 feet long, 9″ lower edge, 8″ top edge, 6″ battery above this. Funnel bases, 1½″ nickel steel for 15 feet above deck. Protective decks, 1½″ upper, 3″ lower. Two Director stations behind upper belt at bases of C.T. communication tubes. Barbettes : bases are 9″ where exposed. Shields to these : 12″ port-plate, 9″ sides, 11″ back, 3″ roof.

Anti-Torpedo Defence.—3″ longitudinal wing bulkheads in way of machinery and magazine spaces. ½″ nickel steel flats under magazines, boilers, and engine rooms. Total weight, 680 tons (included in 7,600 tons total weight of armour given above). 12—38-inch searchlights.

General Notes :—Built under 1908 Programme. Large refits in U.S.A., 1924—25.

Electric Engineering Notes.—Electric installation at 220 volts.

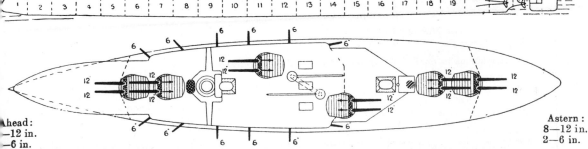

Ahead :
4—12 in.
4—6 in.

Astern :
8—12 in.
2—6 in.

Broadside : 12—12 in., 6—6 in.

103

Name	Builder	Machinery	Laid down	Completed	Trials	Boilers	Best recent speed
Rivadavia Moreno	Fore River Co. N.Y. Ship-building	Fore River Co.	May, '10 July, '10	Dec., 1914 Mar. 1915	39,750 = 22·5	Babcock Babcock	

ARMOURED CRUISERS.

BELGRANO.
(On completion of reconstruction).

1930 *Photo, favour of Capt. M. Mille, R.S.N.*

BELGRANO.

1930 *Photo, courtesy of Ministry of Marine.*

GARIBALDI.
(Training ship).

1918 *Photo, courtesy of Ministry of Marine.*

GARIBALDI (1895) by Ansaldo, Sestri Ponente.

Displacement : 6,457 tons (normal).   Dimensions : 328 (*o.a.*)×59·7×23·5 feet.

Guns :	Armour : (Harvey)	Machinery : 2 sets T. Exp.
2—10″	Belt 6″–3″	Boilers : 8 cylindrical.
10—6″	Deck 1½″–2″	H.P. : 13000=18 kts.
6—4·7″	Lower deck side 6″	Coal : 400/1137 tons.
4—6 pdr.	Battery 6″	Radius : 5,000 miles at 10 kts.
	Barbettes 6″	
	Gunhouses 3″	
	C.T. 6″	

BELGRANO (July, 1897), Orlando, Leghorn.

SAN MARTIN (1896), Orlando, Leghorn.

PUEYRREDON (1897), Ansaldo.

Displacement : 6,100 tons (normal).   Dimensions : 328×59·7×23·5 feet.

Guns : *Belgrano* : 2—10″
8—6″
4—6 pdr.

Pueyrredon : 2—10″
8—4·7″
4—6 pdr.
1—37 mm. AA.

San Martin : 4—8″
6—4·7″

Armour as in *Garibaldi*. (*Pueyrredon* has Terni armour).

Machinery as in *Garibaldi*. *Pueyrredon* has Belleville boilers. All to be converted to oil fuel and have main deck battery removed, tripod mast fitted and Director firing installed. *Belgrano* completed 1930 by Odero.   *San Martin* and *Pueyrredon* are being taken in hand at Buenos Aires and Puerto Belgrano respectively. *Garibaldi* as yet unaltered.

Note.—These ships belong to one of the most successful designs for small armoured cruisers ever produced, and are the first of a series of 10 ships of which the Japanese *Nisshin* and *Kasuga* are the last.

VEINTICINCO DE MAYO.

1931 *Photo.*

ALMIRANTE BROWN.

1931 *Photo, favour of Count C. de Grave Sells.*

VEINTICINCO DE MAYO.

1930 *Photo, by favour of Count C. de Grave Sells.*

ALMIRANTE BROWN (Aug. 25th, 1929). **VEINTICINCO DE MAYO** (Aug. 11th, 1929).
"Standard" displacement, 6800 tons. (*Full load about* 8600 tons.) Complement, 600.

Length, 533¼ feet. Beam, 58 feet. Draught, 16¼ feet.

Guns :
  6—7.5 inch, 52 cal.
  12—3.9 inch, 47 cal. AA.
  6—40 m/m. pom-poms.
Torpedo tubes (21 inch) :
  6 *above water* (in triple
     mountings). 21 inch.

Armour :
  1″ Deck   ....
  1.96″ Gun Houses ....
  2.36″ C.T.   ....

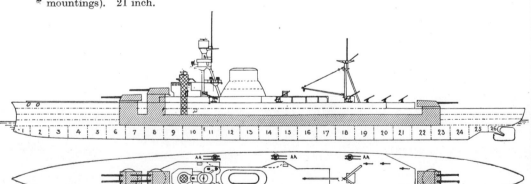

Machinery : Geared Parsons turbines. 6 Yarrow boilers. S.H.P. 85,000 = 32 kts. Oil fuel :
  1800 tons. 2 screws.
General Notes.—Both laid down 1927, *25 de Mayo* by Orlando at Leghorn, *Alm. Brown* by Odero at Sestri Ponente.
  To cost £1,225,000 each. A third Cruiser of this type is projected.
Gunnery Notes—AA. guns are in twin mountings similar to those in Italian *Trento* type. Proposed alternative plans
  included a Triple Turret fore and aft with a thick pole foremast.

1926 *Photo, T. de N. Mateo Mille, R.S.N.*

BUENOS AIRES (Armstrong, 1895). Displacement 4600 tons. Sheathed and coppered. Complement
375.   Length (*o.a.*), 403½ feet. Beam, 47⅛ feet. *Maximum* draught, 19 feet. Guns (Armstrong):
4—6 inch, 45 cal., **8**—4·7 inch, 45 cal., **4**—47 mm. Torpedo tubes : removed. Armour
(steel) : 5″ Deck (amidships), 5″ Engine hatches, 4½″ Gun shields, 3″ Hoists to guns, 6″ Conning
tower (Harvey). Machinery : 2 sets vertical 4-cylinder (2 low-pressure cylinders). 2 screws.
Boilers : 4 double-ended and 4 single-ended. Designed H.P. 13,000 = 23 kts.; 17,000 = 24 kts.
Coal : *normal* 400 tons ; *maximum* 1000 tons. Endurance : 5000 miles at 10 kts.

Coast Defence Battleships.

INDEPENDENCIA.   1918 *Photo, by courtesy of the Ministry of Marine*

INDEPENDENCIA (1891), **LIBERTAD** (1890). Both built by Laird's, Birkenhead. Displacement, 2595 tons. Complement, 196. Length (*p.p.*), 240 feet. Beam, 43 feet. *Max.* draught, 13 feet. Guns: **2**—9·4 inch, 35 cal. (Krupp), **4**—4·7 inch, 40 cal. (Armstrong), **4**—3 pdr. Armour (compound): 8″ Belt (amidships), 2″ Deck (flat on belt), 8″ Bulkhead (forward), 6″ Bulkhead (aft), 8″ Barbettes and bases, 5″ Shields to big guns (fronts), 4″ Conning tower. Machinery: Compound vertical. 2 screws. Boilers: 4 double cylindrical. Designed H.P. 3000 = 13 kts. Oil fuel: 170 tons. (Converted to burn oil, 1925-27, *Libertad* re-instated from Non-effective List for that purpose.)

Training Ship.

PRESIDENTE SARMIENTO (1898). Built at Birkenhead. 2850 tons. Complement 294. Dimensions: $251\frac{5}{12} \times 43\frac{1}{4} \times 23\frac{1}{4}$. Guns: **3**—4·7 inch, 45 cal.; **1**—4 inch, **2**—6 pdr., **2**—3 pdr. Torpedo tubes: **3** *above water*. Designed H.P. 2800=15 kts. Coal: 330 tons. Boilers: 1 Niclausse, 1 Yarrow, 2 cylindrical single-ended.

Notes.—Sheathed and coppered. Has accommodation for 400 boys. Refitted by builders, 1926.

5 + 1 (projected) Flotilla Leaders.

MENDOZA.   1929 *Photo, by courtesy of Builders.*

Plan by courtesy of Messrs. J. Samuel White & Co., Ltd.

3 White: **Mendoza** (July 18th, 1928), **Tucuman** (Oct. 16th, 1928) and **La Rioja** (Jan. 26th, 1929). All laid down in June, 1927 for completion in June, 1929. Displacement, (*normal*) 1520 tons; (*full load*) 2300 tons. Complement, 160. Dimensions: $332\frac{1}{4}$ (*w.l.*), 335 (*o.a.*) × $31\frac{3}{4}$ × $12\frac{1}{3}$ feet. Guns (Vickers-Armstrong): **5**—4·7 inch, **1**—3 inch AA., 2 pom-pom. Torpedo tubes: **6**—21 inch, in triple deck mountings. 2 sets Parsons turbines, with single reduction gearing. Steam supplied at 250 lbs. from 4—3 drum water-tube boilers. Designed speed, 36 kts. 38 kts. maintained for 6 hours on trials by *Mendoza* and *Tucuman*; *La Rioja* touched 39.4 kts. without running machinery in excess of designed power.

JUAN DE GARAY.   1928 *Photo, Capt. Don Mateo Mille, R. Sp. N.*

Cervantes (ex-*Churruca*, Cadiz, June 26th, 1925), **Juan de Garay** (ex-*Alcala Galiano*, Cartagena, Nov. 3rd, 1925). Purchased from Spanish Government, 1927. Displacement, 1650 tons *normal* (1800 tons *full load*). Dimensions: 320 × $31\frac{1}{4}$ × $10\frac{1}{4}$ feet. Guns: **5**—4·7 inch, **1**—14 pdr. AA. Torpedo tubes: **6**=21 inch, in triple deck mountings. 2 D.C. carried. Machinery: 2 sets Parsons geared turbines. S.H.P. 42,000 = 36 kts. Oil fuel: 540 tons. Radius of action: 4500 miles at 14 kts.

Note.—Design generally resembles that of British *Scott* class. The acquisition of a third vessel of this type is understood to have been authorised, to complete programme.

4 Destroyers.

No	Type	Date	Displacement tons	H.P.	Max. speed kts.	Fuel	Complement	T. tubes	Max. draug't feet
2	*Cordoba* (S)	'10-'12	950	20,000	32	200 tons oil	99	4	8
2	*Catamarca* (K)	'10-'12	950	20,000	32	220 tons oil	99	4	8½

K=Krupp. S=Schichau.

CORDOBA, as altered.   1931 *Photo, Official.*

2 (*German*) type: **Cordoba** (Schichau, Nov. 1910), **La Plata** (Germania, Jan., 1911). 1000 tons. 295 × 29½ × 7¾ feet.
Armament: **3**—4 in. (Beth.), **2**—37 mm. AA. **4**—21 inch. tubes. 1 D.C. Thrower. Curtis (A.E.G.) turbines. Boilers:
5 Schulz-Thornycroft, altered to burn oil. Designed S.H.P. 28,000=26·5 kts. Oil: 200 tons. Endurance: 2700 miles at
15 kts., 715 miles at full speed. Trials (*max.*): *Cordoba*, 34·2; *La Plata*, 34·7.

2 (*German*) type: **Catamarca** (Schichau, Jan., 1911), **Jujuy** (Germania, March, 1911). 997 tons. 288⅝ × 7¼ × 28 feet.
Armament: **3**—4 inch (Beth.), **2**—37 mm. AA., **4**—21 inch tubes. 1 D.C. Thrower. Curtis (A.E.G.) turbines. Boilers:
Schulz-Thornycroft, altered to burn oil. Designed S.H.P. 28,000=27·2 kts. Oil: 220 tons. Endurance: 3000 miles at
15 kts., 800 miles at full speed.

Appearance Note.—*Cordoba* and *La Plata* have ram bow.

3 Submarines.

Building.

3 *Cavallini* type; **Salta, Santa Fé,** (July, 19, 1931), **Santiago del Estero.** Ordered from Cantiere Navale
Franco Tosi, Taranto, Oct., 1927. Displacement $\frac{775}{920}$ tons. H.P. 3000=17.5 kts., on surface. Submerged speed 9 kts.
Armament: **1**—4 inch, **1**—37 mm. AA. guns, **8**—21 inch tubes. To cost £206,000 each, fully equipped. General design
resembles Italian *Mameli* tpye.

3 Surveying Vessels.

1928 *Photo, by courtesy of Messrs. R. & W. Hawthorn, Leslie & Co., Ltd.*

SAN JUAN (Sept. 27th, 1927). **SAN LUIS** (Oct. 26th, 1927). Both built by Hawthorn,
Leslie & Co., Ltd., Hebburn-on-Tyne. Delivered Feb. 1928. Displacement, 970 tons.
Dimensions: 207 (*o.a.*) × 33 × 11 feet draught. Complement, 92. Guns : Nil. Machinery:
Single shaft Hawthorn-Werkspoor Diesel engine. B.H.P. 700 = 12 kts. 1 screw. 1 single
ended Scotch boiler to supply steam to auxiliary machinery. Oil fuel 85 tons. Radius
of action : 4000 nautical miles.

ALFEREZ MACKINLAY (Netherlands, 1914). 783 tons. Dimensions : 193¾ × 28¼ × 13 feet.
Guns : Nil. H.P. 520 = 10 kts. Used as Lighthouse Inspection Vessel.

MISCELLANEOUS.

Despatch Vessels. *(Rastreadores).*

M.7.　　1930 *Photo, by courtesy of Ministry of Marine.*

M1, M2, M3, M4, M5, M6, M7, M8, M9, (Germany, 1916-19). These are ex-German Minesweepers of the "M" type, purchased by the Argentine Government in 1922 for use as Despatch Vessels. Displacements vary from 350 to 508 tons. Dimensions : 182 (*w.l.*), 192 (*o.a.*) × 23½ × 7½ feet (*max.*). Engines : 2 sets vertical triple expansion. Boilers : 2 Schulz water-tube. I.H.P. 1800 = 16 kts. Coal : 550 tons.

Armoured River Gunboats.

Official Photo, 1918.

PARANA (April, 1908) & **ROSARIO** (July, 1908). Both built by Armstrong. Displacement, 1055 tons. Complement, 142. Length, 329⅔ feet. Beam, 32⅔ feet. Draught, 7₁₅ feet. Guns : 2—6 inch Howitzers, 6—12 pdr., 2—37 mm. AA., 2 landing. Armour : 3″ Belt (amidships), 1½″—1″ Deck, 3″ Conning tower. H.P. 1600 = 15 kts. 2 Yarrow boilers. 2 screws. Coal : 120 tons. *Nominal* radius, 2400 miles at 10½ kts.

Note.—These two vessels are remarkable in that their main armament consists of howitzers, 13 calibres in length.

River Police Craft. *(Policia fluvial).*

SAYHUEQUE (1901), built by Rennie Forrest. 145 tons. Dimensions : 125 × 25 × 2¾ feet. H.P. 185 = 9 kts.

Oil Tanker *(rated as Transport).*

MINISTRO EZCURRA (Grangemouth Dockyard Co., Grangemouth, 1914). 2600 tons. Dimensions : 250 × 40 × 18¾ feet. H.P. 1243 = 10½ kts.

Transports *(Transportes).*

(Tonnage given is gross in each case.)

CHACO (ex-*Rio Claro*, 1923), **PAMPA** (ex-*Rio Bueno*, 1923) (both built by Danziger Werft, Danzig). 1100 tons. Dimensions : 273 × 37 × 24 feet. H.P. 1500 = 11 kts.

AMERICA (ex-*Lake Hector*, 1920). 2686 tons. Dimensions : 262 × 43½ × 24 feet. H.P. 1520 = 9.5 kts.

Transports—*continued.*

BAHIA BLANCA (Reiherstieg, Hamburg, 1911, taken over during War, 1914-18). 9349 tons. Dimensions : 489 × 59 × 27½ feet. H.P. 4200 = 12.5 kts.

VICENTE FIDEL LOPEZ (Earles, 1906). 507 tons. Dimensions : 164 × 26 × 11½ feet. H.P. 480 = 9.3 kts.

PRIMERO DE MAYO (Howaldt, 1893). 925 tons. Dimensions : 197 × 29½ × 14 feet. H.P. 650 = 11 kts.

Tugs *(Remolcadores).*

TOBA.　　1928 *Photo, by courtesy of Builders.*

MATACO (Jan. 24th, 1928), **TOBA** (Dec. 23rd, 1927). Both built by Hawthorn Leslie. (Completed March, 1928). 339 tons *gross*. Dimensions : 130½ (*p.p.*), 137 (*w.l.*) × 28½ × 13½ feet. H.P. 1100 = 12 kts. 2 screws. Oil fuel.

AZOPARDO (ex-*Barstow*, Bethlehem Co., 1919). 437 tons *gross*. Dimensions : 164 × 27½ × 14 feet. H.P. 1800 = 14 kts.

ONA, QUERANDI (Thornycroft, 1913). 345 tons *gross*. Dimensions : 130 × 28 × 12 feet. H.P. 1200 = 12 kts.

ALBANIA.

Ensign

Commander of the National Defence

Mercantile Marine

General X. H. Aranitasi

Pendant   *field = red device = black*

The following particulars of the vessels which form the nucleus of the new Albanian Navy have been officially supplied.

4 Motor Boats : TIRANE, SARANDA, DURRES, VLORE.

Displacement : 46 tons.   Length : 80 feet.   Motors : 450 B.H.P. = 17 kts.   Guns : 1—3″/40 cal., 2 M.G.   Built at Venice (Svan), 1926.

2 Gunboats (ex-German) : SKENDERBEG, SHQIPNIA.

Displacement : 230 tons.   Length : 140 feet.   2 engines : 600 H.P. = 12 kts.   Guns : 1—2·3″.

BELGIUM.

Flags.

Black ▪

Yellow ▫

Red ▥

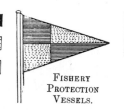

FISHERY PROTECTION VESSELS.

OTHER STATE-OWNED SHIPS.

Uniforms.

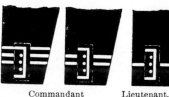

Commandant de 1e Classe.

Lieutenant. de 2e Classe.

The National Flag is also used as Ensign for both State and Mercantile vessels.

Mercantile Marine.

(From "Lloyd's Register" 1931).   Total gross tonnage, 547,470 including 9 vessels of 16 kts. or over.

Sloop (*Aviso*).

ZINNIA.   1920 *Photo, Abrahams, Devonport.*

ZINNIA (ex-British "Flower" class Sloop *Zinnia*, launched August, 1915, by Messrs. Swan, Hunter & Wigham Richardson, Wallsend. Purchased for Belgian Navy, June, 1920). 1200 tons. Dimensions : 250 (*p.p.*), 262½ (*o.a.*) × 33 × 11 (*mean*) × 11¾ feet (*max.* draught). Guns : 1 M.G. on AA. mounting. Designed I.H.P. 1400 = 17 kts., but actually requires *about* 2000 I.H.P. for this speed. 1 set, triple expansion engines. Boilers : 2 cylindrical. 1 screw. Coal : 130 tons *normal* ; 250 tons *max.* = *about* 2000 miles at 15 kts. Complement (as British ship), 77. Employed on Fisheries Protection duties.

BULGARIAN DANUBE FLOTILLA.

BRAZILIAN FLEET.

Officially revised by courtesy of the Chief of the Naval Staff, 1929.

Note.—Under the Treaty of Peace, Bulgaria is only allowed to maintain four fast Patrol Boats and six Vedette Boats on the Danube, for Police and Preventive Duties. This Force is organised on a civilian basis and is under the direction of the Ministry of Commerce.

Note that the red of the flag is crimson.

IIIIII = Red.   ⬜ = White.   ▨ = Green.   ⋮⋮⋮ = Yellow.

Flags.

Jack : A white flag with a green saltire and superimposed over all the Cross of St. George.

Minister of War and Marine :—Lieut.-General Ivan Velkoff.

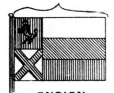

ENSIGN

MERCANTILE

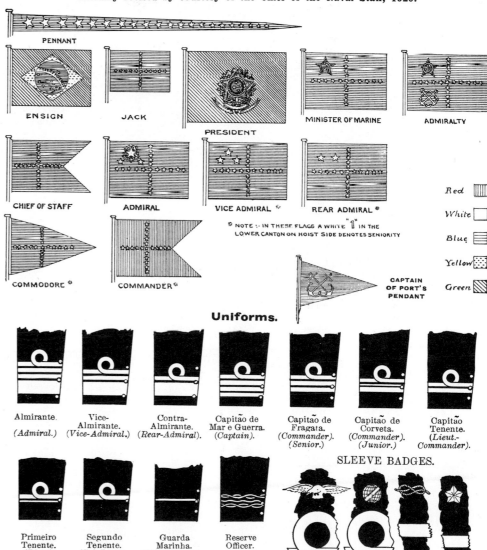

Red IIII

White ⬜

Blue ☰

Yellow ⋮⋮

Green ▨

* NOTE :— IN THESE FLAGS A WHITE "I" IN THE LOWER CANTON ON HOIST SIDE DENOTES SENIORITY

Uniforms.

Almirante. *(Admiral.)*	Vice-Almirante. *(Vice-Admiral.)*	Contra-Almirante. *(Rear-Admiral).*	Capitão de Mar e Guerra. *(Captain).*	Capitão de Fragata. *(Commander). (Senior.)*	Capitão de Corveta. *(Commander). (Junior.)*	Capitão Tenente. *(Lieut.-Commander).*

SLEEVE BADGES.

Primeiro Tenente. *(Lieut).*	Segundo Tenente. *(Sub-Lieut).*	Guarda Marinha. *(Midshipman).*	Reserve Officer.

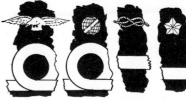

Aviation.   Engineers.   Harbour Master.   Honorary Rank.

Patrol Boats.

SILHOUETTE.

4 *Creusot boa* : **Smyeli, Khrabry, Derzki, Strogi** (built in sections in France ; reassembled at Varna, 1907-8). 100 tons. Dimensions : 126½×13¼×8¾ feet. Armament : **3**—3 pdr. Torpedo tubes removed. Designed H.P. 2000 =26 kts. 1 screw. Du Temple boilers. Coal, 27 tons. Civilian complement, 23.

Motor Vedette Boats.

Minior, Vzrif, Capitan Minkoff, Conductor Dokizanoff. No particulars available. **Nos. 1, 2** (ex French *C 27, C 80,* purchased 1922). 77 tons. 3 sets of 220 B.H.P. standard petrol motors, totalling 660 B.H.P.=17 kts. Petrol : 9 tons. Endurance : 700 miles at 10 kts. Guns : **2**—6 pdr. Complement, 26.

River Patrol Boats (on Danube).

Botef, Levski. 12 tons. Armed with spar torpedoes. **Tzar Arsen, Tzar Simeon.** No particulars available.

All have three buttons towards back of sleeves and across stripes. Deck, Engineer and Aviation Branches all have curl. Other branches have not.

Caps :--As British Navy.
Minister of Marine :—Rear-Admiral A.S. Pinto da Luz.
Chief of Naval Staff :—Vice-Admiral José Maria Penido.
Naval Attaché, London :—Commander José Maria Neiva.

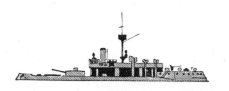

PERNAMBUCO.

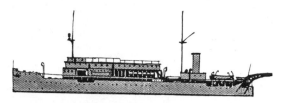

CEARA (S/M. Depot Ship).
(Double hulls at stern.)

FLORIANO.

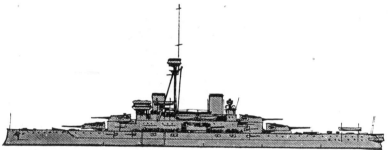

MINAS GERAES class (2 ships).

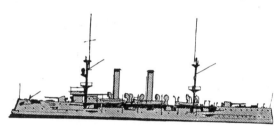

BARROSO.

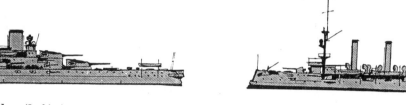

BAHIA class (2 ships).

Guns in Service.*

Nota-tion.	Calibre.		Length in calibres	Weight of A.P. shell.	Muzzle Velocity.	Max. penetration A.P. capped at K.C. at		Danger Space against average ships at			Service rounds per minute
						5000 yards.	3000 yards.	10,000 yards.	5000 yards.	3000 yards.	
	inch.	c/m.	cals.	lbs.	ft. secs.	inch.	inch.				
HEAVY	12	30·5	45	850	2800	...	...	...	...	...	2
MEDIUM	9·4	24	45	380	2700	9	11½	...	...	...	3
LIGHT	6	15	40	100	2500	4	5	65	200	420	6
	6	15	50	100	2640	4¼	5½	72	240	460	6
	4·7	12	40	45	2150	..	..	...	...	...	8
	4·7	12	50	45	2630	...	...	...	...	...	8
	4	10	50								

* **Note.**=These particulars of the Brazilian Naval Ordnance must be regarded as only approximate, though they have been officially corrected.

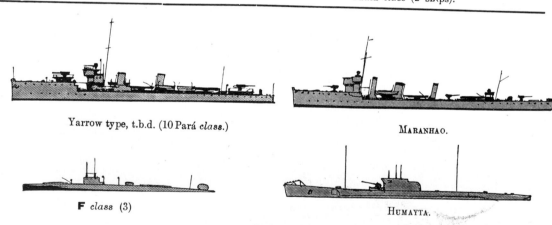

Yarrow type, t.b.d. (10 Pará class.)

MARANHAO.

F class (3)

HUMAYTA.

Mercantile Marine.

(From "Lloyd's Register" 1931 figures.)
Total gross tonnage, 498 789.

(MINAS GERAES CLASS—2 SHIPS.)

MINAS GERAES (Sept., 1908), **SÃO PAULO** (April, 1909).

Normal displacement 19,200 tons.　*Full load* 21,200 tons.　Complement, 850.

Length (*waterline*) 533 feet ; (*p.p.*), 500 feet.　Beam, 83 feet.　*Max.* load draught, 25 feet.　Length (*over all*), 543 feet.

Guns (Armstrong) :
　12—12 inch, 45 cal. } **Dir. Con.**
　22—4·7 inch, 50 cal. }
　2—3 inch, 50 cal. AA:
　　(U.S. Navy).
　8—3 pdr.
　4 M.G.
Torpedo tubes :
　Dropping gear for boats and
　carry torpedoes for this
　purpose.
Note to Plans :—Revised 1921.

Armour (Krupp) :
　9″ Belt ....
　6″—4″ Belt (bow) N.C. ..
　6″—4″ Belt (aft) N.C......
　Decks as notes ....
　9″—6″ Upper belt.........
　9″ & 3″ Bulkheads.........
　9″ Battery (main deck) ...
　9″—8″ Turrets (K.C.).... .
　12″ Conning tower (fore) .
　9″ Conning tower (aft) ...
　8″—3″ Com. Tubes........
　1½″ Torp. Pro. Bulkh'd...

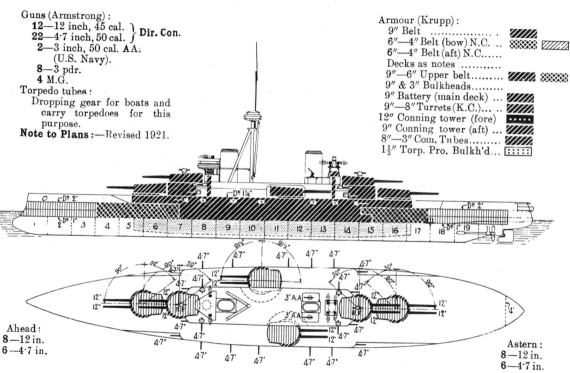

Ahead :
8—12 in.
6—4·7 in.

Astern :
8—12 in.
6—4·7 in.

Broadside : **10—12 in., 11—4·7 in.**

Machinery : 2 sets triple expansion.　**2 screws.**　Designed S.H.P. 23,500 = 21 kts. *f.d.*　Boilers : 18 Babcock.　Coal : *normal* 800 tons ; *maximum* 2360 tons + 350 tons oil.　Endurance : about 3600 miles at 19 kts., and about 8000 miles at 10 kts.

Gunnery Notes.—Complete modern standard Sperry-Ford, U.S.N. fire control installation, fitted at New York Navy Yard.　Arcs of fire : as plans.　Main deck, 4·7 inch, 100° ; 4·7 inch in superstructure casemates, 100°, those above, 121½°. 3 pdr. guns can be transferred to landing mountings.

Engineering Notes.—66 revs. = about 10 kts ; 126 = 20 kts. ; 148 about 21·5 kts.　Heating surface, 55,370 sq. ft.　Grate area, 1808 sq. ft.　On refit in U.S. Navy Yards, boilers adapted to burn oil.

Armour Notes.—Main belt 22½ ft. deep, 5 ft. of this being below waterline.　Decks are thus :—1¼″ upper deck, 2″ main, 1″ middle, 1″ lower.　Area of upper and middle decks roughly bounded by all gun positions ; main and lower decks at ends outside gun positions.　Barbette bases 3″ within belt.　Bulkheads 9″ down to main deck, 3″ to middle deck.　4″ Bulkhead across stern.

113

SÃO PAULO.

Photo, Cribb (added 1925).

Searchlight Notes : 6 U.S. Navy type, positions as plan and profile.

Name.	Builder.	Machinery.	Laid down.	Completed.	Trials.		Boilers.	Refit.
					30 hour at ⅕	Full power		
M. Geraes	Armstrong*	Vickers *	1907	Jan.'10	16,177 = 19·13	25,519 = 21·2	Babcock	1919.
S. Paulo	Vickers*	Vickers *	1907	July '10	16,067 = 19·85	25,517 = 21·2	Babcock	1921.

General Notes.—Both ships were somewhat over normal displacement on trials.　Built under 1907 Naval Programme. The third ship of this programme was *Rio de Janeiro*, sold to Turkey as *Sultan Osman Birindijieh*, and requisitioned for British Navy, Aug. 1914, as H.M.S. *Agincourt.*

* *Note.*—*São Paulo* underwent large refit at New York Navy Yard from May 1917–1919, it being expected that she might join British Grand Fleet.　A large amount of material was sent out from England for this purpose.　During 1919, she served with U.S. Atlantic Fleet for exercise at Guantanamo Bay. *Minas Geraes* has also been refitted at New York Navy Yard, at a cost of about two million pounds. She received inter-communication Wireless-telephony sets.　These ships are at present the best in the Brazilian Navy.　They are officially stated to be in a most efficient condition.

(1908) Cruisers (*Cruzadores*).

BAHIA (as altered).   1926 *Official Photo.*

BAHIA (Jan., 1909) & RIO GRANDE DO SUL (April, 1909).

Normal displacement 3150 tons.   Complement 400.

Length, { (*p.p.*), 380 feet. } Beam, 39 feet. *Mean* draught, 13 feet. 7½ ins.
         { (*o.a.*). 401½ ,, }

Guns :   Armour :
  10—4·7 inch, 50 cal.   1½″ Deck................... ..
    (Armstrong)   3″ Conning tower ....
  4—3 inch, 50 cal. AA.
    (U.S.)
  4—3 pdr. saluting.
  Torpedo tubes (21 in. Bliss) :
    4 *above water*, in twin
    mountings.

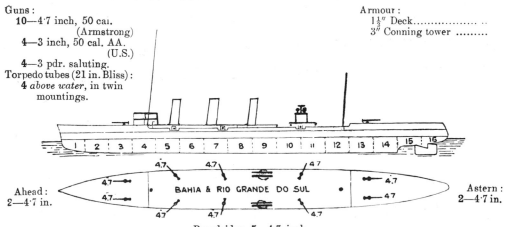

Ahead :   Astern :
2—4·7 in.   BAHIA & RIO GRANDE DO SUL   2—4·7 in.

Broadside : 5—4·7 inch.

Machinery : 3 Brown-Curtis geared turbines. 3 screws. Boilers : 6 Thornycroft oil-burning.
S.H.P. 22,000 = 27 kts. 1926 *Trials* : Bahia, 23,000=28.6. Oil fuel : 640 tons. Endurance :
about 2400 miles at 24 kts., 3092 miles at 18 kts., 6600 miles at 10 kts.

Gunnery Notes.—Fire control originally consisted of voice tube from control stations to bridge and to plotting rooms
  on second deck—thence to battery. 1 R.F. and 2 S.L., 1 S.L. over Chart house and 1 on after S.L. platform.
  These arrangements have been improved, and Director system is now being installed.

General Notes.—Built by Armstrong ; engined by Vickers ; both begun 1908 (under 1907 Naval Programme) and
  completed 1910. Completely refitted 1925-26, by Companhia Nacional de Navegação Costeira, Rio, new engines
  and boilers (to burn oil fuel) being installed by Messrs. Thornycroft. Heating Surface, 26,027 sq. ft.

(1896) Coast Defence Vessel (*Encouraçado*)

1919 *Photo, Commr. B. D. Holberton, R.N.*

FLORIANO (1899), built at La Seyne. Displacement, 3162 tons. Complement, 200. **Length**
(*p.p.*), 267½ feet. Beam, 48 feet. *Max.* draught, 13¼ feet. Guns : 2—9·4 in., 45 cal. ; 4—4·7 in.,
50 cal. Armour (Harvey-nickel) : 13¾″ Belt (amidships), 4″ Belt (ends), 1½″ Deck (reinforcing belt),
8″ Turrets, 3″ Casemates, 5″ Conning tower. Machinery : 2 sets triple expansion. 2 screws.
Boilers : (1912), Babcock. Designed H.P. 3400=15 kts. Coal : 246 tons. Radius of action :
2500 miles at 10 kts. Refitted 1924-1925. Sister ship *Deodoro*, sold to Mexico.

(1895) Cruiser.

1919 *Photo, Commr. B. D. Holberton, R.N.*

BARROSO (Armstrong, 1896). 3450 tons (sheathed and coppered). Comp. 375. Dimensions (*p.p.*):
330×43¾×16⅝ feet. Guns (Armstrong) : 6—6 in., 50 cal. ; 4—4·7 in., 50 cal. ; 4—6 pdr. Armour :
3½″ Deck (amidships). Machinery : 2 sets 3-cyl. triple expansion. 2 screws. Boilers : cylindrical.
Designed H.P. *forced* 7500=20.5 kts. Coal : *normal* 450 tons ; *maximum* about 850 tons.
Endurance : 6500 miles at 10 kts. Refitted 1916-17. Only improvised voice pipes for fire control.

11 Destroyers.

4 Submarines.

Photo added 1923.

HUMAYTA.   1929 *Photo, Capitan Mateo Mille, R. Sp. N.*

1 *Thornycroft* type. **Maranhão** (ex H.M.S. *Porpoise*, 1913). Displacement: 934 tons. Dimensions: 265¼ × 26¼ × 9¼ (*minimum*), 10¼ (*maximum*) draft. Guns: **3** 4 inch, **1**—2 pdr. Tubes: **4**—21 inch, in pairs. Designed H.P. 22,500 = 31 kts. Machinery: Parsons' turbines. Thornycroft boilers. Oil: 250 tons. Complement, 100.

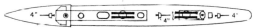

Note.—Reported to have lost greatly in speed. Employed as Stokers' Training Ship at present.

1 *Ansaldo* type: **Humayta.** Ansaldo San Giorgio Co., Spezia, April, 1927. Displacement: 1450 tons *surface*, 1884 tons *submerged*. Dimensions: 284½ × 25½ × 14 feet. Fiat type Diesel engines. Designed H.P. $\frac{4900}{2200} = \frac{18\cdot5}{10}$ kts. Armament: **1**—4 inch, 4 M.G., **6**—21 inch tubes. Tube aft for minelaying (16 mines carried). Similar in general design to Italian *Balilla* type (*vide* notes in Italian Section for further details). Ordered in 1926 and completed in 1927, but not delivered in Brazilian waters until two years later. Reported destroyed by internal explosion, 1931.

1918 *Photo.*

1917 *Photo, by favour of Ansalão San Giorgio Co.*

•10 *Yarrow* type: **Amazonas, Matto Grosso, Piauhy, Pará** (all launched 1908), **Rio Grande do Norte, Parahyba, Alagoas, Santa Catharina** (all launched 1909), **Parana, Sergipe** (both launched 1910). Displacement 560 tons. Dimensions: 240 × 23¼ × (*Mean* draught) 7⅝ feet. Armament: **2**—4 inch, **4**—3 pdrs., **2**—18 in. tubes. Designed H.P. 8000 = 27 kts. Machinery: 2 sets triple expansion reciprocating. 2 double-ended Yarrow boilers. Majority of these boats retubed 1917-18. Coal; 140 tons. Nominal radius: 1600 miles at 15 kts. On acceptance trials with 6563 to 8877 H.P. they made 27·1 to 28·7 kts. No effective means of controlling fire of guns or torpedo tubes. Complement, 75.

Note :—The numbers on after funnel are thus : 1, *Amazonas* ; 2, *Para* ; 3, *Piauhy* ; 4, *R. G. do Norte* ; 5, *Parahyta* ; 6, *Alagoas* ; 7, *Sergipe* ; 8, *Parana* ; 9, *S. Catherina* ; 10, *Matto Grosso*.

* In bad condition. These boats are continually under repair, 5 being kept in commission and 5 in reserve under refit.

3 *Laurenti-Fiat* type : **F 5, F 3, F I** (Spezia, 1913-14). Built by Fiat-San Giorgio Co. Dimensions : 150 × 13·8 × 9 8 to 12 feet draught. Displacement : 250 tons *on surface*, 305 tons *submerged*. Machinery : 2 sets 350 H.P. 6-cylinder, 2-cycle Fiat Diesel engines *on surface* = 700 H.P. 2 sets 250 H.P. electric motors + batteries = 500 H.P. *submerged*. Speeds : (maximum) 13½ kts. *on surface*, 8 to 8½ kts. *submerged*. Radii of action : *on surface* about 800 miles at full speed, 1600 miles at 8½ kts ; when *submerged*, 18 miles at full speed, or 100 miles at 4 kts. Torpedo tubes : **2**—18 inch in bows. Complement about 20.

Submarine Carrier, Depot, Docking and Salvage Ship.
(Also serves as Training Ship for submarine service.)

1917 *Photo, by courtesy of the Fiat San-Giorgio Co.*

CEARÁ (Spezia, 1915). Length (*p.p.*) 328 feet. Beam, 52 feet. Draught and displacement (with all stores) vary thus : (*a*) with dock empty and dock-gate closed 4100 tons at 14 feet draught ; (*b*) with dock-gate open and dock flooded to float submarine in, 4130 tons at 17½ feet ; (*c*) with gate closed and submarine docked, 4560 tons at 15 feet ; (*d*) with gate closed and submarine under hydraulic pressure test in dock, 6460 tons at 20¼ feet ; (*e*) with dock empty and gate closed, and when raising submarines by double cranes at stern, 4615 tons at 15 feet. Machinery : 2 sets 6-cylinder, 2-cycle Fiat-Diesel engines. 4100 B.H.P. = 14 kts. Fuel : 400 tons (own bunkers) + tons for submarines (sufficient fuel carried to fill tanks of six submarines four times). Radius of action : 4000 miles at 10 kts. Guns : 4—4 inch, 2 smaller. Built by Fiat-San Giorgio Co. Completed 1916.

Note.—This ship has been specially designed and completely equipped to serve as a depot ship, salvage ship, and floating dock for a flotilla of 6 submarines. There is a central, circular caisson dock 216½ feet long (to dock submarines up to 198 feet length and 23¼ feet beam) between the double hulls, and two salvage cranes at stern for raising 400 tons deadweight. Equipment for service to submarines includes two 150 Kw. charging dynamos, two electric-driven and one steam-driven 75-150 atmos. air compressors, refrigerating plant, workshops, powerful pumps to empty dock in 2 hours, &c. ; carries spare batteries, torpedoes. stores, &c., for 6 submarines.

Fleet Collier.

1920 *Photo, Gieves, Ltd.*

BELMONTE (ex-German S.S. *Valesia*, Rostock, 1912). 5227 tons *gross.* Dimensions : 364¾×51× ? feet. Guns : 4—4·7 in., 6—6 pdr. H.P. 2700 = 12 kts. Can take about 6500 tons as cargo.
Note.—Above ship seized in Brazilian port, 1917, after declaration of war against Germany.

Oiler.

NOVAES DE ABREU (Rotterdam, 1918). Displacement, 500 tons. Dimensions : 134½ × 23 × 12 feet *mean* draught. H.P. 400 = 10 kts. Oil : 400 tons.

River Craft.

1916 *Photo, Abrahams.*

PERNAMBUCO (1909-10, River Monitor, built at Rio). 470 tons. Dimensions : 146×24×5¼ feet. H.P., 800 = 11 kts. Coal : 45 tons. Guns : 3—4·7 inch, 10 machine. Armour : 6·6″–4″ belt, 4″ deck, 3½″ conning tower, 6″ turret. 2 screws. Took 20 years to build.

MISSOES (Yarrow, 1904). 110 tons. Dimensions : 120 × 20 × 2 feet. Armament : 1—3·4 inch (15 pdr.) howitzer, 1—6 pdr., 4 maxims. H.P., 300 = 11 kts. Complement, 30.

TEFFÉ (1890-92, refitted 1917). River Gunboat of 33 tons. Dimensions : 90 (*p.p.*)×15×5 feet. Guns : 1—3 pdr., 2 M.G. H.P. = 11 kts. Coal : 7 tons.

OYAPOCK (—). Despatch Vessel of 195 tons, 14 kts. speed. Guns : 1—3 pdr.

AJURICABA (Ross & Duncan, Glasgow, 1923). 120 tons. Dimensions : 125×18×9 feet. Coal : 35 tons. Guns : 4 M.G.

AMAPA (1917). 320 tons. Dimensions : 118×23×19 feet. Guns : 2—6 pdr., 4 M.G. Speed, 15 kts.

Officially revised by courtesy of the Jefe del Estado Mayor General de Marina, Santiago, 1931.

Flags.

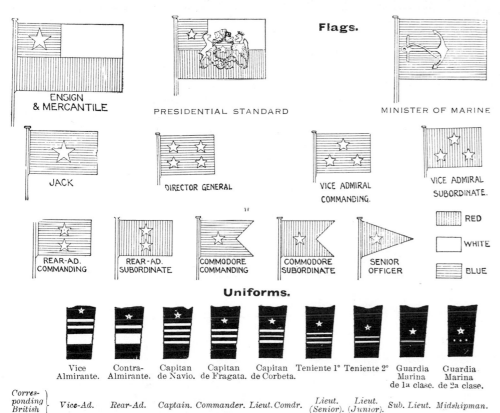

ENSIGN & MERCANTILE

PRESIDENTIAL STANDARD

MINISTER OF MARINE

JACK

DIRECTOR GENERAL

VICE ADMIRAL COMMANDING.

VICE ADMIRAL SUBORDINATE.

RED
WHITE
BLUE

REAR-AD. COMMANDING

REAR-AD. SUBORDINATE

COMMODORE COMMANDING

COMMODORE SUBORDINATE

SENIOR OFFICER

Uniforms.

Vice Almirante. / Contra-Almirante. / Capitan de Navio. / Capitan de Fragata. / Capitan de Corbeta. / Teniente 1° / Teniente 2° / Guardia Marina de la clase. / Guardia Marina de 2a clase.

Corresponding British or U.S. } Vice-Ad. / Rear-Ad. / Captain. / Commander. / Lieut. Comdr. / Lieut. (Senior). / Lieut. (Junior). / Sub. Lieut. / Midshipman.

Other Branches the same with colours as follows:—Engineers (blue), Paymasters (white), Doctors (red), Chaplains (purple)

Minister of Marine : Vice-Admiral Hipólito Marchant.
Chief of Naval Commission (London) : Rear-Admiral Felipe Wiegard.
Naval and Air Attaché (London).
Personnel : About 8000, all ranks.

Special Note.

There are several Officers of the Royal Navy as *Technical Advisers*. The Senior Officer is Captain W. L. Jackson, R.N.

Naval Bases.

TALCAHUANO. Two dry docks, 614 × 87 × 30½ feet and 800 × 116 × 36 feet respectively. One small floating dock, 216 × 42 × 15 feet. Gunnery, Torpedo, Submarine, and other Training Establishments here.

VALPARAISO. One small steel floating dock privately owned, 314 × 65 × 21 feet (4500 tons capacity). Naval Academy for training of executive and Engineering branches here, also schools for Communications, Coast Artillery, Navigation, etc.

There is also a small steel floating dock at Mejillones.

Naval Ordnance. (All details unofficial.)

	Type*	Calibre.		Length. (cals.)	Weight of Gun. (tons.)	Weight of Proj. (lbs.)	Weight of Charge. (lbs.)	M.V. (ft-secs.)	M.E. (ft. tons.)	Max. R.P.M.
		Inches.	Cm.							
HEAVY	A	14″	35·6	45	85	1585	324	2500	..	2
MEDIUM	C	9·4″	24	36	24	374	198	2230	12,421	..
	A	8″	20·3	45	18·5	210	44	2650	10,226	4
	A	8″	20·3	40	15	..	..	2582	..	..
	A	6″	15·2	50	8¾	100	31	3000	6240	9
	A	6′	15·2	40	6⅔ cwt.	100	18·3	2500	4334	8
	A	4·7″	12	50	63½	45	10¾	2953	2721	12
	A	4·7″	12	45	53	45	8	2552	2110	10
	C	4·7″	12	45	..	..	..	..	..	..
LIGHT	A	4″	10·2	..	..	..	..	..	..	..

* A = Armstrong ; C = Schneider-Canet.

14 inch, 45 cal., in *Alm. Latorre.*
9.4 inch, 36 cal., in *C. Prat.*
8 inch, 40 cal., in *O'Higgins, B. Encalada.*

6 inch, 50 cal., in *Alm. Latorre* and *Chacabuco.*
6 inch, 40 cal., in *O'Higgins, B. Encalada.*
4.7 inch in *Alm. Riveros* class (3).
4.7 inch in *C. Prat, Chacabuco, G. Baquedano*
4 inch in *Alm. Lynch* class (2) and *Alm. Riveros* class (3).

Torpedoes : 21 inch (heater), and 18 inch. **Mines :** Similar to British pattern.

Organization, 1931.

Main Squadron : *O'Higgins, Serrano, Orella, Riquelme, Hyatt, Aldea, Videla, Araucano, O'Brien, Thompson, Simpson, Fresia, Rancagua.*
Training Division : *Lynch, Condell, Uribe, Williams, Gualcolda, Tegualda, Rucumilla, Guale, Quidora* and *Colocolo.*

Mercantile Marine.

(From "Lloyd's Register" 1931 figures). Total *gross* tonnage, 193,131.
including 2 ships of 16 kts. and over.

RECOGNITION SILHOUETTES.

Leucoton, Elicura, Orompello.

General Baquedano.
(*Training Ship.*)

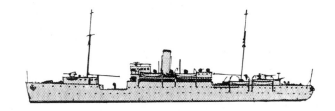

Araucano.

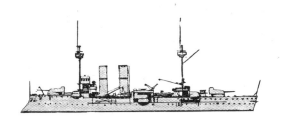

Capitan Prat.

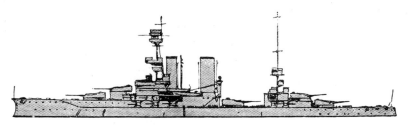

Almirante Latorre.

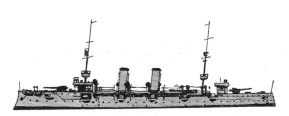

Chacabuco.

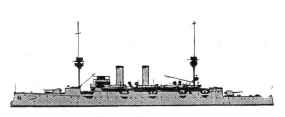

Blanco Encalada.

General O'Higgins.

TORPEDO CRAFT.

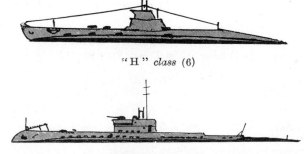

"H" *class* (6)

Serrano *class* (6).

Lynch *class* (5)
(With slight modifications between individual ships).

O'Brien *class* (3)

ALMIRANTE LATORRE (ex British *Canada*, ex Chilean *Almirante Latorre*, Nov., 1913.)   Displacement, 28,000 tons (about 32,000 *full load*).   Complement, 1176.

Length (*p.p.*), 625 feet.   (*o.a.*), 661 feet.   Beam, 103 feet.   { Mean draught, 28½ feet. }
{ Max.   „   30   „ }

Guns (Armstrong) :
  10—14 inch, 45 cal. } **Dir. Con.**
  14—6 inch 50 cal. }
  4—4 inch (anti-aircraft)
  4—3 pdr.
  (2 landing)
  4 M.G.
Torpedo tubes (21 inch) :
  4 *submerged*.

Armour :
  1″ Shelter (over case-
    mates)
  1″ Fo'xle (over battery)
  1½″ Upper (outside
    battery)
  1½″ Main (aft)
  1″ Protective
  2″ (forward) } lower
  4″ (aft) ... }
Torpedo Protec. :
  2″—1½″ Bulkheads
    (mags., &c.) Sections
    6–8, 15, 19–21 on plans.

Armour :
  10″ Lower belt ......
  7″ Middle belt ......
  4½″ Upper belt ....
  6″- 4″ Belt (ends)
  4½″, 1″ B'lkh'ds (f. & a.)
  6″ Batteries ....
  10″ Barbettes ....
  10½″-9″ Gunhouses
  3″ C.T. base*........
  11″ C.T. (6″—3″ hood)..
  6″ Fore com. tube ...
  6″ Torpedo C.T. ......
  6″ Aft com. tube .....

*Not shown on plans.

1931 *Photo, R. Perkins.*

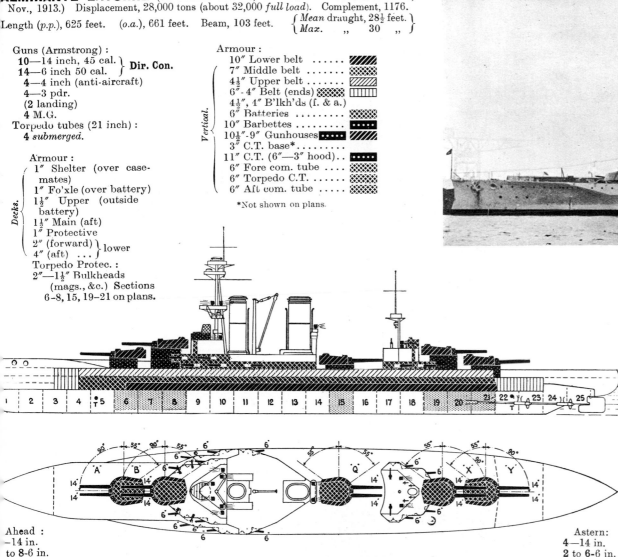

Ahead :
—14 in.
to 8–6 in.

Astern:
4—14 in.
2 to 6-6 in.

Broadside : **10—14 in., 7—6 in., 2—21 in. tubes.**

Machinery : Turbine, 4-shaft : (L.P.) Parsons ; (H.P.) Parsons.   Boilers : 21 Yarrow.
Designed H.P. 37,000 = 22.75 kts.   Oil :   tons.   Endurance : 4400 miles at 10 kts.

Gunnery Notes.—14-inch have a range only limited by max. visibility.   Originally had 16—6 inch, but the 2—6 inch on upper deck, abeam of after funnel, were removed and ports plated over.   Reason for removal was because guns were only a few feet from muzzle of " Q " turret 14-inch guns on extreme bearing and were damaged by blast.

Armour Notes.—Barbettes, 6″ and 4″ as they descend behind belts.

Searchlights.—8—24″ and 2—20″ (signalling) Harrison lamp type burners.

Aircraft Notes.—Anti-aircraft guns on after superstructure.

1931 *Photo, R. Perkins.*

General Notes.—Laid down for Chile by Armstrong, in Nov. 1911, as the *Valparaiso*, her name being altered afterwards to *Almirante Latorre*.   Purchased for British Navy on outbreak of War and re-named *Canada*. Completed Sept. 1915.   Additional protection, &c., added during War is said to have raised her *normal* displacement to over 30,000 tons.   First designed with secondary battery of 22—4.7 inch, and 2 masts abeam aft.   Re-purchased by Chile, April, 1920.   Her sister ship, *Almirante Cochrane*, was purchased and taken over for British Navy in 1917, re-named *Eagle*, and modified for service as an Aircraft Carrier. (See British Navy Section).   Arrived at Devonport in summer of 1929 to be refitted in the dockyard under a special contract with new machinery supplied by Vickers-Armstrong, Ltd.   Bulges fitted, and masts and bridgework underwent slight modifications.   The main topmast was raised to 60 feet, and controls fitted at the ends of the upper bridge : searchlights removed from bridge ; new turbines and oil fuel only installed. She returned to Chile early in 1931.   A catapult is to be mounted on the quarterdeck.

(1888) Coast Defence Battleship.

(Temporarily in use as Submarine Depôt Ship).

1919 Copyright photo, G. Allan, Valparaiso.

CAPITAN PRAT (La Seyne, 1890). *Reconstructed* 1909. 6902 tons (sheathed and coppered). Complement 500. Length (*p.p.*), 328 feet. Beam, 60⅔ feet. *Maximum* draught, 22⅝ feet. Guns (Canet): 4—9·4 inch, 36 cal., 8—4·7 inch, 45 cal., 8—6 pdr., 1—3 pdr., 1—1 pdr. Torpedo tubes (18 inch): 2 *above water*. Armour (Creusot): 12″ Belt (amidships), 3″ Deck (flat on belt), 10½″ Barbettes, 2″ Barbette hoods, 4″ Redoubt (amidships), 2″ Small turrets. Machinery: 2 sets horizontal triple expansion. 2 screws. Boilers: new in 1909, 12 Babcock. H.P. 12,000=18 kts. (about 16 to 18 kts. now). Coal: *normal* 400 tons; *maximum* 775 tons=*circa* 4650 miles at 10 kts. *Prat* was the first ship to have electrically manœuvred turrets.

(1896) Armoured Cruiser

1920 Photo, T. de N. M. Mille, R.S.N.

GENERAL O'HIGGINS (Armstrong, 1897). 8500 tons. Sheathed and coppered. Complement 700. Length (*p.p.*), 412 feet. Beam, 62¾ feet. *Max.* draught, 22 feet. Guns (Armstrong): 4—8 inch, 40 cal. 10—6 inch, 40 cal., 13—12 pdr. (1 field), 4 M.G. Torpedo tubes (18 inch): 2 *submerged*. Armour (Harvey-nickel): 7″-5″ Belt (amidships), 2″ Deck (slopes), 7½″ Port plates to 8 inch gun turrets, 6″ Hoists to these, 6″ Gun houses to 6in. guns, 6″ Casemates (6), 9″ Conning tower. Machinery: 2 sets triple expansion. 2 screws. Boilers: 30 Belleville (in 3 groups). Designed H.P. *natural* 10,000=19 kts.; *forced* 16,000=21·5 kts. (still steams very well and can do 21 kts. now). Coal: *normal* 700 tons; *maximum* 1200 tons. Endurance: (*a*) 2250 miles at 20 kts., (*b*) 6000 miles at 10 kts. Large re-fit 1928—29.

(1897) Protected Cruiser.

1919 Copyright photo, G. Allan, Valparaiso.

CHACABUCO (Armstrong, 1898, purchased 1902). 4500 tons. Complement 400. Length (*p.p.*), 360 feet. Beam, 46½ feet. *Maximum* draught, 17 feet. Guns (Armstrong): 2—6 inch, 50 cal. 10—4·7 inch, 40 cal., 5—12 pdr., 1—3 pdr. Armour (Harvey-nickel): 4½″ Deck (amidships), 1¾″ Deck (ends), 4½″ Fronts to 6 in. gun shields, 2½″ Sides to 6 in. gun shields, 2½″ Shields to 4·7 in. guns, 5″ Conning tower. Boilers, cylindrical. I.H.P. 15,500=24 kts. *forced*. Still steams well, and can do 23 kts. now. 2 screws. Coal: *normal* 300 tons; *maximum* 1028 tons. Electric training and elevating gear to 6 inch guns. Laid down at Elswick, 1897, as a speculation. Completed 1902, and purchased by Chile.

(1893) Protected Cruiser.

1919 Copyright photo, G. Allan, Valparaiso.

BLANCO ENCALADA (Armstrong, 1893). 4420 tons (sheathed and coppered). Complement 427. Length (*p.p.*), 370 feet Beam, 46½ feet. *Maximum* draught, 19½ feet. Armament: **2**—8 inch, 40 cal., **10**—6 inch, 40 cal., **5**—12 pdr., **1**—1 pdr., **2** Maxims. Armour: 4″ Deck, 6″ Shields to 8″ guns, 6″ Conning tower. Boilers: cylindrical (retubed 1908-9). Designed H.P. *forced* 14,500= 22·75 kts. (about 21·5 kts. now.) Coal: *maximum* 850 tons. Endurance: 5000 miles at 10 kts. Refitted, 1920, at Talcahuano.

Note.—Laid down Sept., 1892, launched a year later, and completed April, 1894.

Sloop (and Training Ship).

1919 Copyright photo, G. Allan, Valparaiso.

GENERAL BAQUEDANO (1898). 2500 tons, sheathed and coppered. Armed with **4**—4·7 inch 40 cal., **4**—6 pdr. I.H.P. 1500 = 13·75 kts. Belleville boilers (renewed 1924). Coal: 300 tons. Built by Armstrong, Whitworth & Co. Ltd. (Refitted 1923-24).

121

7 (+ 4 building or completing) Destroyers.

No.	Type	Date	Displacement	H.P.	Max. speed	Fuel	Complement	T. tubes	Max. draug't
			tons.		kts.	tons			feet
6	Serrano (T).	Bldg.	1430	28,000	35	320 oil	130	6	12⅔
3	Alm. Riveros (W)*	'11-'15	1730†	30,000	31·5t†	403 coal, 83 oil	205	4	11⅜
2	Alm. Lynch (W)	'11-'14	1730	30,000	31t	427 coal, 80 oil	160	6	11

(T)=Thornycroft. (W)=White. (t)=Turbines.

*When in British Navy 1914-20, these three boats were rated as Flotilla Leaders. The two *Alm. Lynch* boats, being of much the same design, can also be rated as Leaders.
†*Average* figures. For individual details, see below.

SERRANO.

1928 Photo, by favour of Builders.

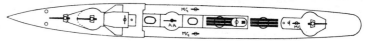

(Plan by courtesy of Messrs. John I. Thornycroft & Co. Ltd.)

6 Serrano Class.

6 *Thornycroft* type. **Serrano** (Jan. 25th, 1928), **Orella** (March 8th, 1928), **Riquelme** (May 28th, 1928), **Hyatt** (July 21st, 1928), **Aldea** (Nov. 29th, 1928), **Videla** (Oct. 16th, 1928). All laid down June-July, 1927. "Standard" displacement, 1090 tons ; *full load*, 1430 tons. Dimensions : 288¼ (*p.p.*), 300 (*o.a.*) × 29 × 12⅔ feet (*maximum* draught). Guns : **3**—4.7 inch, **1**—3 inch AA., **3** M.G. **2** D.C. Throwers. Tubes : **6**—21 inch, in triple deck mountings. Machinery : Geared turbines (Brown-Curtis h.p. and cruising, Parsons l.p.). Boilers : 3 Thornycroft. S.H.P. 28,000 = 35 kts. Oil fuel : 320 tons. 2 screws. Provision made for carrying mines. Complement, 130. *Notes.*—These destroyers will have exceptionally good accommodation for vessels of their size, and are adapted for service in a wide range of climates. The contract, amounting to about £1,750,000, was awarded to Messrs. Thornycroft after intensive competition with many other yards British and Foreign. It is the largest foreign naval contract placed with a British yard since the War. These vessels are named after naval officers who distinguished themselves at the battle of Iquique. Plating is galvanised throughout, and the heavy hull scantlings reduce the stresses to even less than those allowed by British Admiralty practice. All this class have exceeded their contract speed on trials.

5 Almirante Class. (Next page).

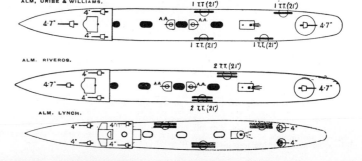

ALM. WILLIAMS.   *1923 Photo, Abrahams.*

(*Uribe* has upper bridge of same width as lower, and has paravane fitting forward.)

3 *White*: **Almirante Williams** (ex British *Botha*; ex Chilean *Almirante Williams Rebolledo*, 1911), 1742 tons; **Almirante Uribe** (ex British *Broke*; ex Chilean *Almirante Goni*, 1913), 1704 tons: **Almirante Riveros** (ex British *Faulknor*; ex Chilean *Almirante Simpson*, 1913), 1694 tons. Dimensions: $331\frac{1}{4} \times 32\frac{1}{2} \times 11$ ft. 7 in. Armament: 2—4·7 inch*, 2—4 inch*, 2—2 pdr. pom-poms. 4—21 inch tubes.† Designed H.P. 30,000=31 kts. in *Almirante Williams*, = 32 kts. in *Almirante Uribe* and *Almirante Riveros*. Machinery: Turbines. Boilers: White-Forster. 3 screws. Fuel: (*max.*) 403 coal + 83 oil. Complement, 205.

Note.—Another of the class, British *Tipperary*, ex Chilean *Almirante Riveros*, sunk in Battle of Jutland. The above three boats purchased August, 1914, on outbreak of war, from Chile. Re-armed by British Navy 1918-19, and re-purchased by Chile, April, 1920.

* Possibly controlled by British Navy type Light Directors.
†Tubes mounted in pairs in *Almirante Riveros*; singly mounted in *Almirante Uribe* and *Almirante Williams*.

*ALM. CONDELL (centre), ALM. LYNCH (behind).   *Copyright photo, G. Allan, Valparaiso.*
(Now have shorter mainmast than shown above.)

2 *White*: **Almirante Lynch** (1912), **Al. Condell** (1913). Dimensions: $320 \times 32\frac{1}{2} \times 11$ feet. *Normal* displacement: 1730 tons. *Full load*: 1850 tons. Armament: 6—4 inch, 4 M.G., 6—18 inch tubes. Designed H.P. 30,000=31 kts. Turbines: Parsons. Boilers: White-Forster. 3 screws. Fuel: 427 tons coal + 80 tons oil = 2750 miles at 15 kts. Trials: *Al. Lynch*, 31·8 kts. (6 hours); *Al. Condell*, 33·4 kts. Complement, 160.

**Note to Illustrations.*—Fore funnels of *Lynch* and *Condell* now raised. All these vessels now have first letter of name painted on bow for identification purposes, *e.g.*, W = *Williams*, L = *Lynch*, etc.

Submarines.

1930 Photo, Courtesy of Messrs. Vickers-Armstrong.

3 *Vickers-Armstrong*: **Capitan O'Brien** (October 2nd, 1928), **Capitan Thompson, Almirante Simpson,** (both Jan. 15th, 1929). Displacement $\frac{1540}{2020}$ tons. Dimensions: $260 \times 28 \times 13\frac{1}{4}$ feet draught. H.P. $\frac{2750}{1300} = \frac{9}{15}$ kts. Fuel: 200 tons. Guns: 1—4·7 inch. Tubes 8—21 inch. (6 bow, 2 stern). Of same general design as British "O" type. Built at Barrow-in-Furness, 1928-29.

H 2.   *1919 Copyright photo, G. Allan, Valparaiso.*

6 *Holland*: **H 1, H 2, H 3, H 4, H 5, H 6** (Fore River Co., U.S.A., 1915-17). Displacements: $\frac{364}{435}$ tons. Dimensions: $150\frac{1}{4} \times 15\frac{3}{4} \times 12\frac{1}{2}$ feet. H.P. $\frac{480}{320} = \frac{12.75}{10.25}$ kts. Machinery: *for surface* 2 sets 240 H.P. Nelseco Diesel engines. Endurance: 2800 miles at 11 kts. *on surface*; 30 miles at 5 kts. *submerged*. Oil: $17\frac{1}{2}$ tons. Torpedo tubes: 4—18 inch (bow). Complement 22.

Notes.—These boats were originally *H 13* and *H 16—20* of the British *H 11—20* group of submarines, built by the Fore River Co., U.S.A., during 1915. The Admiralty intended to take them over and equip them with torpedo tubes at the Canadian Vickers Co. Yard at Montreal—provided that these boats could legally be delivered in an unarmed state. The U.S. Government decided the submarines could not leave any U.S. port, so long as the United States remained neutral, and all the boats were interned at Boston. They were released on the U.S. declaration of war, 1917. With the approval of the U.S. authorities, the above six boats were ceded to Chile by Great Britain, in part payment for the Chilean warships building in British yards in August, 1914, and appropriated for the British Navy.

Submarine Depot Ship.

1930 Photo, favour of builders.

ARAUCANO. Laid down by Vickers-Armstrong, Ltd., at Barrow, 1st March, 1929. Displacement : 9000 tons. Dimensions : 390 × 55 × feet draught. Guns : 2—4.7 inch, 2— AA. S.H.P. 2500 = 13 kts. Machinery : Parsons geared turbines. 1 screw. Coal : 670 tons. Has accommodation for 585, including crews of attached submarines. To be completed March, 1930.

Oilers.

RANCAGUA
1930 Photo.

MAIPO, RANCAGUA. Laid down by Vickers-Armstrong, Ltd., on the Tyne, March, 1929. Displacement : 7715 tons (3800 tons *gross*). Complement : 54. Dimensions : 365 × 49¾ × 22½ feet draught. Guns : 2—4.7 inch. I.H.P. 4800 = 15 kts. Machinery : Triple expansion. 2 screws. 4 S.E. boilers. Oil fuel : 725 tons. Completed in March, 1930.

Note.—Old Ironclads, *Almirante Cochrane* (1874) and *Huascar* (1865), still exist at Talcahuano, being used as Depôt Ships.

Coastguard Vessels (*Escampavias*).

ELICURA.   *1931 Photo. Official.*

LEUCOTON (1919), built by Sandvikens Skeppsdocka Co., Helsingfors ; **ELICURA** (1919) and **OROMPELLO** (1919), both built by Maskin och Brobyggnads Co., Helsingfors. All four completed 1919. 530 tons. Length (*o.a.*), 172·6 feet. Beam, 24·6 feet. *Maximum* draught, 11 feet. Guns : 2—3 inch. I.H.P. 1400 = 14½ kts. speed. 2 sets triple expansion engines. 2 screws. Boilers : 3 cylindrical. Coal capacity : *Leucoton* 56 tons ; *Elicura* and *Orompello*, 65 tons. Complement, 42. Refitted by Messrs. J. Samuel White & Co., Cowes, 1920.

MICALVI (ex-*Bostonlincs*, ex-*Bragi*) (Ostsee Werft, Stettin, 1925). Displacement 850 tons. (612 tons *gross*). Dimensions : 181½ × 28¾ × 11 feet. Triple expansion engines. I.H.P. 380 = 9.5 kts.

AGUILA (1906). 820 tons. Speed 10 kts.

YELCHO (1906). 280 tons. Speed : 12 kts.

Lighthouse Tender **CONDOR.** Iron and wood. Built in Marseilles, 1889. Large refits 1927. Displacement : 145 tons. Dimensions : 102 × 18⅔ × 9 feet. Speed : 9 kts. Coal : 20 tons.

Fleet Tugs.

SIBBALD.   *1931 Photo. Official.*

SIBBALD (1916) built in Scotland. Displacement : 1,100 tons. Dimensions : 141 × 28¾ × 11 feet. *Maximum* speed : 12 kts. Coal capacity : 145 tons.

SOBENES.   *1931 Photo. Official.*

SOBENES, CABRALES (1929), **COLOCOLO, GALVARINO** and **JANEQUEO** (1930) built by Bow McLachlan. Displacement : 760 tons. Dimensions : 126½ × 27 × 12 feet (*mean*). *Maximum* speed : 11 kts. Coal capacity : 130 tons.

CHINESE FLEET.

Officially revised at the Chinese Admiralty, Nanking, 1931, by courtesy of the Vice-Minister of the Navy, who has also furnished most of the photos dated 1929—1931.

Uniforms.

Admiral. Vice-Admiral. Rear-Admiral. Commodore. Captain. Commander. Lieut.-Comm'r. Lieut. Sub-Lieut. 1st Class. Sub-Lieut. 2nd Class.

Colour between stripes :—*Engineers* (none) ; *Surgeons*, red ; *Paymasters*, white ; *Ship Constructor*, purple ; *Navigating Officers*, light indigo blue ; *Ordnance*, Pink; *Wireless*, Mauve ; *Bandmasters*, Green ; *Judge Advocates*, Grey; *Aviation*, (none). Gold Eagle replaces emblem above stripe. All these branches *without* the curl or emblem over top stripe.

Minister of the Navy :—Admiral Yan-Shu-Chuan.   *Vice-Minister of the Navy* :—Vice-Admiral S. K. Chen.

Special Note.—In July, 1929, it was requested by the Chinese Government that the services of a British Naval Mission should be lent to reorganise the Fleet. A new programme comprising 3 Cruisers, 4 Destroyers, and 2 Submarines is proposed.

Flags.

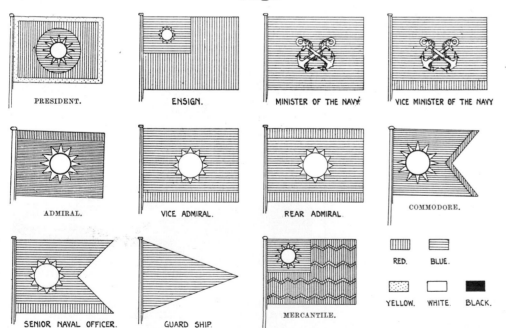

PRESIDENT.   ENSIGN.   MINISTER OF THE NAVY.   VICE MINISTER OF THE NAVY

ADMIRAL.   VICE ADMIRAL.   REAR ADMIRAL.   COMMODORE.

SENIOR NAVAL OFFICER.   GUARD SHIP.   MERCANTILE.

RED.   BLUE.   YELLOW.   WHITE.   BLACK.

Mercantile Marine.

(From "Lloyd's Register" 1931 figures). Total *Gross* Tonnage, 333,256

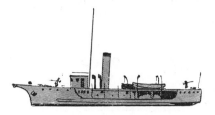

KUNG SHENG.

HAI OU HAI FU.

HAI HUNG.

T.B. 1, 3.

YUNG SHENG.
YE SHENG.
CHEN SHENG.

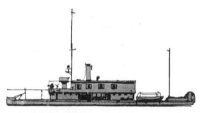

KIANG KUN.

CHIEN TIEN.

T.B. 7, 8, 9, 10.

SHUN SHENG.

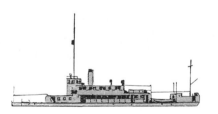

KIANG HSI.

FU AN.

T.B. 2, 4.

WEI SHENG.
TEH SHENG.

LI CHIEH.

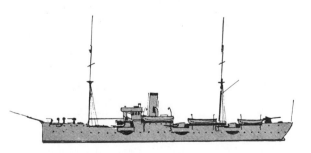

TUNG CHI.

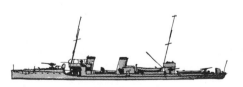

CHIEN KANG TUNG AN.
YU CHANG.

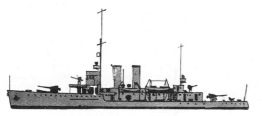

HSIEN NIN.   MING CHUN.

LI SUI.

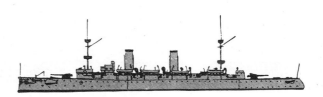

HAI CHI.

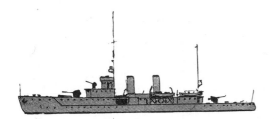

YUNG SUI.

YUNG CHIEN.   YUNG CHI.

HAI YUNG.   HAI CHU.   HAI SHEN.

YAT SEN.

YUNG FENG.   YUNG HSIANG.

YING SWEI.   CHAO HO.

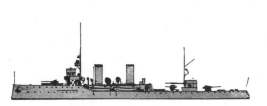

TA TUNG.   TZE CHION.

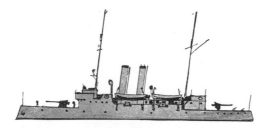

KIANG CHEN *class.*
CHU CHIEN *class* (with prominent
forebridge).

FEI YING.

126

1910 Protected Cruisers.

YING SWEI.

1929 *Official Photo.*

YING SWEI (July, 1911) & CHAO HO (Oct., 1911).

Normal displacement, 2460 tons; *full load* { *Ying Swei* : 2,750 tons. / *Chao Ho* : 2,600 tons. } Complement, 334.

Ying Swei : Length (*p.p.*), 330 feet, (*o.a.*) 346 feet. Beam, 39½ feet. *Max.* load draught, 14 feet 11 ins.
Chao Ho :   „   320 „   „   39 „   „   „   14 „

Guns (*see Notes*) :
2—6 inch, 50 cal.
4—4 inch, 50 cal.
2—3 inch, 50 cal.
6—3 pdr.
2—2 pdr. AA.
2—1 pdr.
Torpedo tubes (18 inch) :
2 *above water.*

Armour :
3″ Deck (amidships)
1½″ Deck (ends) ...
3″ Conning tower
„ Gun shields......

Ahead :
1—6 in.
2—4 in.

Astern :
1—6 in.
2—4 in.

CHAO HO.

Broadside : 2—6 in., 2—4 in.

Machinery : Parsons turbine. Boilers : see notes. 4 screws. Designed H.P. 6000 = 20 kts. Coal : *normal* : 220 tons ; *maximum* : 550 tons. Oil : 50 tons in *Ying Swei*, 100 tons in *Chao Ho.* Endurance : about 4500—5000 miles at 10 kts., and about 2900 miles at 18 kts.
Gunnery Notes.—Vickers models in *Ying Swei* ; Armstrong in *Chao Ho.*
General Note :—Both ships employed as seagoing training vessels.

Name	Builder	Machinery	Laid down	Completed	Trials (light) ⅘ths	Full power	Boilers
Ying Swei	Vickers-Armstrong	Vickers	1910	1912	5394 = 20·7	8797 = 22·23	White-F. + cyl.
Chao Ho		Hawthorn	1910	1912	...	8622 = 22·12	6 Yarrow

1897-8 Protected Cruisers.

1929 *Official Photo*

HAI YUNG (1897), HAI CHOU (1897) and HAI SHEN (1898).
Displacement, 2950 metric tons. Complement, 326-343. Length (*p.p.*) 314 feet, (*o.a.*) 328 feet. Beam, 40¾ feet. *Maximum* draught, 19 feet. Guns (Krupp): 3—6 inch, 40 cal., 8—4·1 inch, 40 cal., 4—3 pdr., 4—1 pdr., 1—2 pdr. AA. Torpedo tubes (14 inch): 1 bow (submerged). Armour : 2¾″ Deck (amidships), 1½″ deck (ends), 2″ gun shields, 1½″ conning tower. Designed H.P. 7,500 = 19 kts. 8 cylindrical boilers. Coal : *normal* 200-220 tons ; *maximum* 500-580 tons. All three ships built by Vulkan Co., Stettin. Speed now reduced to 10 knots or less in all except *Hai Chou*, refitted 1928.

Photo, Symonds & Co.

HAI CHI (Armstrong, 1898).
Displacement, 4,300 tons. Complement, 431. Length (*p.p.*), 424 feet. Beam, 46⅚ feet. *Mean* draught, 16¾ feet ; *max.* 19 feet. Guns (Armstrong): 2—8 inch, 45 cal., 10—4·7 inch, 45 cal., 12—3 pdr., 4—1 pdr., 6 machine. Torpedo tubes (18 inch): 5 *above water.* Armour (Harvey): 5″ Deck (amidships), 1½″ deck (ends), 4½″ gun shields, 4″ ammunition hoists, 6″ conning tower. Designed H.P.: 17,000 (*f.d.*) = 24 kts. Boilers : 12 cylindrical. Coal : *normal* 400 tons, *maximum* 990 tons. (Refitted, 1927.)

1931 Light Cruiser.

1931 *Photo: Official*

YAT SEN (1930). Displacement, 1,650 tons. Dimensions : 275 (*o.a.*), 252 (*p.p.*) × 34 × 11 feet. Complement, 173. Guns : **1**—6 inch, **1**—5·5 inch, **4**—3 inch A.A., **2**—3 pdr., **4** M.G. Speed = 20 kts. Coal : **?** tons.

1895 Cruiser (Training Ship).

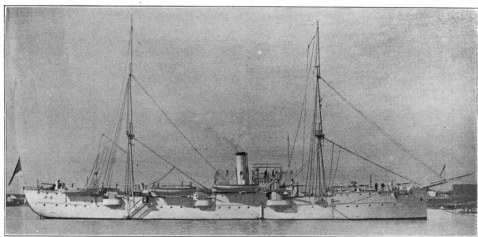

1929 *Official Photo.*

TUNG CHI (1895). Steel. 1900 tons. Dimensions : 252 × 34 × 16 feet. Guns : **2**—6 inch, **5**—4 inch, **3**—6 pdr., **8**—1 pdr. H.P. 1600 = 10.5 kts. 1 screw. Complement, 335. Built as a cruiser at Foochow, 1892-96, and later appropriated for training purposes.

T ZE C HION   1931 *Photo: Official.*

T A T UNG .   1931 *Photo: Official.*

TZE CHION (ex *Chien Wei*) (1902) and **TA TUNG** (ex *Chien An*) (1900). Displacement, 900 tons. Dimensions : 260 × 27 × 11 feet. Complement, 150. Guns : **2**—4·7 inch, **1**—3 inch, **2**— 6 pdr., **1**—2 mm. A.A., **6** M.G. Torpedo tubes : **2** *above water* (may have been removed). Armour : 1″ belt and deck (amidships). Designed H.P. 6000 = 20 kts. 2 screws. Coal : 180 tons. Built at Foochow under direction of M. Doyère, who was responsible for design. Engines built by F. & Ch. de la Mediterranée, Le Havre. Guns are Schneider-Canet. Completely re-built : 1930-31.

1929 *Official Photo.*

YUNG SUI. (1929). Built by Kiangnan Dock Co., Shanghai. Displacement, 650 tons. Complement, 100. Dimensions : 225 × 30 × 6 feet. H.P. 4000 = 18.5 kts. Guns : **1**—6 inch, **1**—4.7 inch, **3**—3 inch AA., **4**—6 pdr., **1**—1 pdr. pom-pom, **4** M.G.

1929 *Official Photo.*

HSIEN NIN (Kiangnan Dock Co., Shanghai, Aug. 16, 1928). Displacement, 418 tons. Complement, 115. Dimensions : 170 (*p.p.*), 180 (*o.a.*) × 24 × 6½ feet. H.P. 2500 = 17 kts. Guns : **1**—4.7 inch, **1**—4 inch, **3**—6 pdr., **5** M.G. Cost : $300,000.

Official Photo.

MING CHUN (1929). Displacement, 550 tons. Complement, 115. Dimensions : 196¾ × 26 × 6 feet (*mean*). H.P. 2200 = 17.3 kts. Guns : **1**—4.7 inch, **1**—4 inch, **1**—3 inch, **2**—6 pdr., **1**—1 pdr. pom-pom, **4** M.G.

YUNG CHIEN.   1929 *Official Photo*

YUNG CHIEN, YUNG CHI (Built 1915, by Kiangnan Dock Co., Shanghai). 860 tons. Dimensions : 205 (*p.p.*), 215½ (*o.a.*) × 29½ × 11½ feet. Guns : **1**—4 inch, **1**—3 inch, **4**—3 pdr., **2**—1 pdr., **1**—2 pdr. AA. Designed H.P. 1350 = 13 kts. Coal : 150 tons. Complement, 105.

YUNG-FENG.　　　　1921 *Photo, Rear-Admiral Ngen-Tao.*

YUNG HSIANG.　　　　1928 *Photo.*

YUNG FENG, YUNG HSIANG (Kawasaki Co., Kobé, Japan, 1912—13). 830 tons. Dimensions : 205 (*p.p.*) × 29½ × 8 feet. Guns : **1**—4·1 inch, **1**—3 inch, **4**—3 pdr., **2**—1 pdr.　H.P. 1350 = 13·5 kts. Coal : 190 tons. 2 screws. Complement, 105. 1 inch steel protective deck.

CHU TUNG.　　　　1929 *Official Photo.*

CHU KUAN.　　　　1929 *Photo.*

CHU YEW.　　　　1929 *Official Photo.*

CHU CHIEN.　　CHU TAI.　　CHU YU.
CHU KUAN.　　CHU TUNG.　　CHU YEW.
(For description see next column.)

130

All built by Kawasaki Yard, Kobé, 1906-07. 740 tons. (*Chu Yew*, 745 tons.) Complement, 123-135. Dimensions : 200 × 30 × 8 feet. Armament : **2**—4.7 inch, **2**—3 inch, **3**—6 pdr., **1**—2 pdr. AA., **2** M.G. (*Chu Yew* has **5**—9 pdr., **4**—1 pdr., **1**—1 pdr. AA. in place of latter 3 items.) Machinery : 2 sets vertical triple expansion. 2 screws. Boilers : Water-tube. Designed H.P. 1350 = 11 kts. (*Chu Yew*, 12 kts.). Coal : 150 tons.

Note.—Several of these vessels have been fitted with additional protection for gun crews. Speed in some cases is only about 9 kts. now.

KIANG CHEN.　　　　1929 *Photo.*

KIANG YUAN.　　　　1929 *Official Photo.*

KIANG CHEN　　　　KIANG LI
KIANG HENG　　　　KIANG YUAN

All built by Kawasaki Yard, Kobé, 1906-07. 550 tons. Complement, 106-123. Dimensions : 170 (*p.p.*), 180 (*o.a.*) × 28 × 7 feet. Armament : **1**—4.7 inch (bow), **1**—3 inch (aft), **4**—3 pdr., **4**—Maxims. Machinery : 2 sets vertical triple expansion. 2 screws. Boilers : Water-tube. Designed H.P. 950 = 13 kts. (reduced to 10 kts. in some). Coal : 113 tons.

Destroyers.

All Photographs below furnished 1929 by courtesy of Vice-Minister of the Navy.

1929 Official Photo.

3 *Schichau* type : **Chien Kang, Tung An, Yu Chang** (1912), 390 tons. Dimensions : 198 (*p.p.*), 208 (*o.a.*) × 21¾ × 10 feet. Armament : **2**—3 inch, **4**—2 pdr., **2**—18 inch tubes. Designed H.P. 6000 = 32 kts. Coal, 80 tons. Complement, 83.

First called *Fu Po, Fei Hung* and *Chang Feng* but names were altered by Yuan Shih Kai.

1929 Official Photo.

Fei Ying (July, 1895). Displacement 850 tons. Dimensions : 210 × 30 × 11 feet. Complement, 145. Guns (Krupp) : **2**—4·1 inch, **6**—3 pdr., **4** M.G., **3** tubes (1 bow, 2 broadside, *above water*). Designed H.P. 5500 = 22 kts. Boilers : Yarrow. Coal : 170 tons. Built at Stettin, and originally classed as a Torpedo Gunboat.

Torpedo Boats.

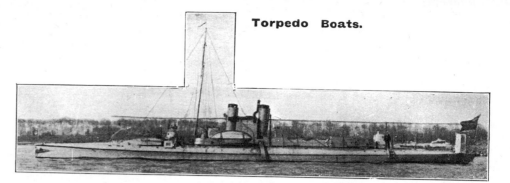

1929 Official Photo.

4 *Kawasaki-Normand* type : **Hu Peng** or **No. 7, Hu Oah** or **No. 8, Hu Ying** or **No. 9, Hu Chun** or **No. 10** (Kobe, Japan, 1907-8). 96 tons. Dimensions : 135 × 15½ × 7½ feet. Armament : **1**—3 pdr., **1**—1 pdr., **3**—14 inch tubes (1 bow *above water* and 2 deck). Designed H.P. 1200 = 23 kts. Coal, 28 tons *normal*. Complement : 41. Some can only do about 13 kts. now.

1929 Official Photo.

2 *Vulcan* type : **Su*** or **No. 4, Chen*** or **No. 2** (1895). 90 tons. 144 × 17 × 8 feet. Armament : *Su*, **3**—1 pdr. ; *Chen*, **2**—1 pdr. ; both **2** M.G. and **2**—14 inch torpedo tubes. H.P. 700 = 18 kts. (now reduced to 10 kts.). Complement, 40.

* These two T.B. sometimes have suffix *Ting* (Boat) or *Tzu* (meaningless) added to their names.

2 *Schichau* type : **Lieh*** or **No. 3** (1897), **Chang*** or **No. 1** (1895). 62 tons. 130 × 16 × 7 feet. Armament : **2**—1 pdr., **2** M.G., **3**—14 inch torpedo tubes. H.P. 600 = 16 kts. (now about 14 kts.) Complement 40.

* These two T.B. sometimes have suffix *Ting* (Boat) or *Tzu* (meaningless) added to their names.

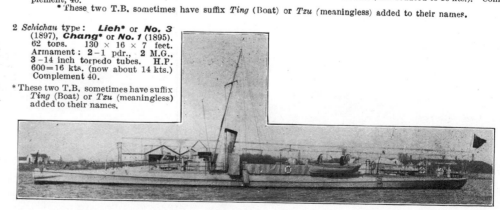

1929 Official Photo.

K

1921 *Photo, Rear-Admiral Ngen Tao.*

WU FENG (Tsingtao, 1912). 200 tons. Dimensions : 124 × 20 × 7 feet. H.P. 300 = 10 kts. Guns : **4**—3 pdr. Complement, 46.

1929 *Official Photo.*

YE SHENG (1911). Displacement, 350 tons. Complement, 37. Dimensions : 120½ × 20½ × 11 ft. H.P. 500 = 10 kts. Guns : **1**—9 pdr., **1**—6 pdr., **2** M.G.

1930 *Official Photo.*

SHUN SHENG (1911). Displacement, 380 tons. Complement, 67. Dimensions : 146 × 24½ × 6 feet. H.P. 500 = 10·7 kts. Guns : **1**—8 c.m., **1**—7·5 c.m., **2**—3·7 m.m. **4** M.G.

1929 *Official Photo.*

YUNG SHENG (1928). *Normal* displacement, 300 tons. Complement, 42. Dimensions : 125 × 21 × 7 feet. H.P. 500 = 10 kts. Guns : **1**—3 inch, **1**—6 pdr., **2** M.G.

1930 *Official Photo.*

WEI SHENG, TEH SHENG (1922). Displacement, 932 tons. Complement, 93. Dimensions : 205½ × 31 × 8 feet. H.P. 3300 = 16 kts. Guns : **1**—4.7 inch, **1**—3 inch, **4** M.G.

Note.—Both have been converted into Aircraft Tenders and carry 2 Seaplanes.

KUNG SHENG   1930 *Official Photo.*

JEN SHENG   1931 *Official Photo.*

KUNG SHENG (ex Chin Tien) (1911). **JEN SHENG** (1931). Complement, 47. Dimensions : 120 × 21 × 7·5 feet. Displacement 300 tons. H.P. 500 = 10 kts. Guns : **1**—8 c.m., **1**—6 pdr. **2** M.G.

HAI KU.   1929 *Official Photo.*

HAI HUNG.   1929 *Photo.*

HAI KU (1919), **HAI HUNG** (1916-17), both built by Fu-Chau Dockyard. Shallow-draught Gunboats of **190 tons.** Dimensions : 112×18×8½ feet. Guns : 2—2 pdr., 2 machine. H.P. 300 = 9 kts. Oil fuel : 20 tons. Complement, 35—31.

                                    1929 *Photo.*

KIANG KUN (Vulkan, 1912). Displacement, 140 tons. Dimensions : 146 (*p.p.*) × 26 × 2 feet. H.P. 500 = 10 kts. Boilers : 2 Schulz. Coal : 30 tons. Guns : 1—3.4 (22 pdr.) howitzer, 1—1 pdr., 4 M.G. Complement, 48.

HAI FU.   1929 *Official Photo.*

HAI OU, HAI FU (both built by Kiangnan Dock Co., Shanghai, 1916-17). 150 tons. Dimensions : 105 (*p.p.*), 109 (*o.a.*)× 17 × 7¾ feet. Guns : 2—1 pdr., 2 machine. H.P. 250 = 9.5 kts. speed (now about 7.5 kts.). Oil fuel : 35 tons. Complement 35.

                                    1929 *Official Photo.*

CHEN SHENG (1899). Displacement, 275 tons. Complement, 42. Dimensions : 120 × 20 × 7 feet. H.P. 400 = 10 kts. Guns : 1—6 pdr., 1—3 pdr., 2 M.G.

                                    1929 *Official Photo.*

CHIEN TIEN ex-*Kung Sheng* (1922). *Normal* displacement, 279 tons. Complement, 53. Dimensions : 145 × 20½ × 7 feet. H.P. 200 = 8.5 kts. Guns : 1—3 inch, 1—6 pdr., 2 M.G. (Surveying Service).

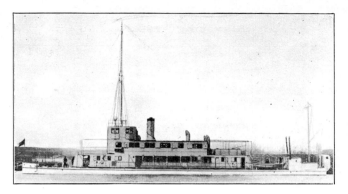

                                    1929 *Official Photo.*

KIANG HSI (Krupp, 1911). Displacement : 150 tons. Dimensions : 144 × 25 × 3 feet. H.P. 450 = 9 kts. Boilers : 2 Schulz. Coal : 35 tons. Guns : 1—3.4 inch howitzer, 1—1 pdr., 4 M.G. Complement, 58.

LI CHIEH (ex-German *Vaterland*, Elbing, 1903. Interned in China, 1914, and taken over for Chinese Navy about 1917). 266 tons. Dimensions : 177·6×26·7×2·7 feet. Guns : 2—6 pdr., 3 M.G. Armour : 2″ on waterline, 2″ C.T. I.H.P. 1300=14 kts. Boilers : 4 Schulz. Coal : 95 tons. Complement, 45.

LI SUI (ex-German *Otter*, Tecklenborg, 1909. Interned at Nankin, August, 1914, and taken over for Chinese Navy, 1917). 170 tons. Dimensions : 158×26·3×2 feet. Guns : 1—3·4 inch (22 pdr.) howitzer, 1—4 pdr., 2 M.G. I.H.P. 1300=13 kts. Boilers : 2 Schulz. Coal : 75 tons. Complement, 45.

CHINA—Surveying Vessels and Transports

Surveying Vessels.

1929 *Official Photo.*

KAN LU. (ex-*Atalanta* ex-*Lorena*). 1903 Leith. Displacement, 2132 tons. Dimensions: 300 × 33⅓ × 18 feet. Guns: 2—3 inch. Diesels, B.H.P. 1500 = 12·75 K.B. Oil = 300 tons. Bought 1925.

1929 *Official Photo.*

KING SING. Displacement, 140 tons. Dimensions: 108 × 18 × 7 feet. Guns: 2—37 m.m., 2 M.G. Speed = 10 kts.

1929 *Official Photo.*

CHIN YUN (1872). Displacement, 130 tons. Dimensions: 108 × 17 × 8 feet. H.P. 480 = 9 kts. Guns: 2 M.G. Complement, 118.

LIEN CHING (Shanghai, 1910). 500 tons. Dimensions: 150 (*p.p.*), 173 (*o.a.*) × 25 × 10 feet (*mean*). I.H.P. 800 = 12 kts. Cylindrical boilers fitted with Howden's f.d. Coal: 95 tons. Guns: 4—3 pdr., 2 M.G. Complement, 91.

Transports.

CHING AN (1906). Displacement, 4000 tons. Dimensions: 272 × 40 × 17¾ feet. H.P. 1160 = 11 kts. Guns: 2—6 pdr. Complement, 235.

TIN AN (1901). Displacement, 2011 tons. Dimensions: 230 × 33 × 18 feet. H.P. 918 = 11 kts. Complement, 70.

Transports—*continued*

HWA AN (1899). Displacement, 10,573 tons. Dimensions: 414 × 46 × 24⅙ feet. H.P. 5000 = 11 kts. Guns: 2—3 pdr. Complement, 136.

PU AN (1896). Displacement, 4600 tons. Dimensions: 393 × 45 × 25 feet. H.P. 6500 = 15 kts. Guns: 1—3 inch. Complement, 137.

FU AN. Built by Fu-Chau D.Y., 1894. Displacement: 1700 tons. Dimensions: 250 × 38 × 18 feet. Guns: 2—6 pdr., 2—1 pdr. I.H.P. 1600 = 10 kts. speed. Coal: 170 tons. Complement, 105.

COLOMBIA.

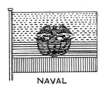

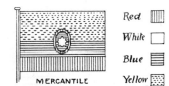

NAVAL   MERCANTILE

Red ▦
White ☐
Blue ▤
Yellow ▧

Gunboat.

Photo wanted.

CHERCINTO (1896). 643 tons. Dimensions: 185 (*p.p.*) × 31 × 12 feet. Guns: not known. Designed H.P. 400 = about 12 kts.

River Gunboats.

CARTAGENA, SANTA MARTA, BARRANQUILLA. (1930)

Dimensions: 137′ 9″ × 23′ 6″ × 2′ 7″ (41·9 × 7·16 × ·8 m). Guns: 1—75 mm., 4 M.G. Machinery: 2 semi-Diesel Gardner engines each 300 B.H.P. at 290 revs. Speed = 15·5 kts. 2 screws working in tunnels.

Notes.—These three vessels crossed the Atlantic under their own power without mishap, making the voyage from the Clyde to the Magdalena in 24 days with only one stop (St. Vincent). They represent an extraordinarily efficient type of shallow draft gunboat, incorporating many improvements on previous types. The designed speed has been exceeded on trial and is very high for this type of craft. Hull is of galvanised steel, and machinery spaces, cabins and magazines are of bullet proof plating. Ventilation and refrigerating plant designed to secure excellent habitability.

Photo wanted.

ESPERANZA (1897), **GENERAL NERINO** (1895), both built at Perth Amboy, U.S.A. Stern-wheelers of 400 tons. Dimensions: 140 (*p.p.*) × 9 × 3 feet. Guns: 3 M.G. Designed H.P. 430 — 15 kts. No other details known.

Coastguard Patrol Vessels.

PICHINCHA, CARABOBO, BOYACA.   1927 *Builders' Photo, by courtesy of M. Le Masson.*

BOYACA (July 8th, 1925), **CARABOBO** (August 8th, 1925), **PICHINCHA** (Sept. 5th, 1925). All built by Soc. Anon. des Chantiers et Ateliers de St. Nazaire (Penhoët), at Rouen. Dimensions: 100 × 20 × 8½ feet. Triple expansion engines and oil-burning water-tube boilers by Messrs. Thornycroft. Speed: 13 kts.

M. L. (*Motor Launches*).

Cauca (1913). 50 tons. Dimensions: 110 × 17 × 4 feet. Guns: Not known. Speed, 12 kts.

Guarda Costas 1, 2, 3, 4 (Yarrow, 1913). 20 tons. Dimensions: 80 × 12½ × 3½ feet. Guns: 1—1 pdr. H.P. 160 = 12 kts. Fuel: 1800 galls. petrol = 2400 miles at 10 kts.

Old Transport *Bogota* is still in service.

CUBA.

A Government dockyard is projected in Havana Bay, near the Tiscornia. To have a 4000 ton Floating Dock. Naval Academy at Mariel to be transferred to vicinity of Dockyard.

Private Docks: At Havana, private floating dock (U.S. and Cuban Allied Works Engineering Corp.) 360 × 66 × 17½ feet (5600 tons); also Havana Marine Co. has a slipway 3,000 tons capacity.

Minister of War and Navy: Dr. Rafael Iturralde.

Personnel: Officers, Line 65; Engineers 49, Paymasters 8, Surgeons 8, Judge-Advocates 2 = 132. Men 1050.

Mercantile Marine.

(From "Lloyd's Register" 1931 figures.) Total *gross* tonnage, 45,721.

Flags.

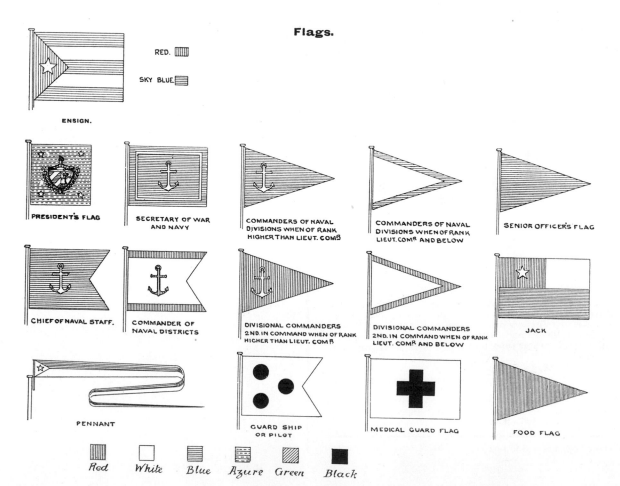

RED.

SKY BLUE.

ENSIGN.

PRESIDENT'S FLAG

SECRETARY OF WAR AND NAVY

COMMANDERS OF NAVAL DIVISIONS WHEN OF RANK HIGHER THAN LIEUT. COMR

COMMANDERS OF NAVAL DIVISIONS WHEN OF RANK LIEUT. COMR AND BELOW

SENIOR OFFICER'S FLAG

CHIEF OF NAVAL STAFF.

COMMANDER OF NAVAL DISTRICTS

DIVISIONAL COMMANDERS 2ND. IN COMMAND WHEN OF RANK HIGHER THAN LIEUT. COMR

DIVISIONAL COMMANDERS 2ND. IN COMMAND WHEN OF RANK LIEUT. COMR AND BELOW

JACK

PENNANT

GUARD SHIP OR PILOT

MEDICAL GUARD FLAG

FOOD FLAG

Red   White   Blue   Azure   Green   Black

Uniforms.

Insignia of Rank on Sleeves—Executives

CAPITAN DE NAVIO

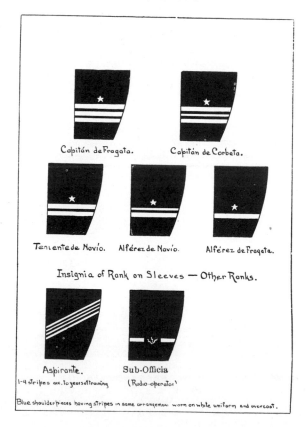

Capitán de Fragata.   Capitán de Corbeta.

Teniente de Navío.   Alférez de Navío.   Alférez de Fragata.

Insignia of Rank on Sleeves — Other Ranks.

Aspirante.   Sub-Oficia
1-4 stripes acc. to years of training   (Radio-operator)

Blue shoulderpieces having stripes in same arrangement worn on white uniform and overcoat.

New Construction.

The following programme has been recommended, to involve an expenditure of 7,220,000 pesos, spread over a period of ten years:—

1 cruiser of 4,500—5,000 tons.
1 ,,   ,, 2,500 tons.
8 gunboats of 900 tons.
8 ,,   ,, 200 tons.

Cruisers.

CUBA (Cramp, Philadelphia, 10th August, 1911). 2055 tons. Dimensions: (*p.p.*) 260 × 39 × 14 feet. Armament: **2**—4 inch, **6**—3 inch, **4**—6 pdr., **4**—3 pdr., **2** machine. H.P. 6000 = 18 kts. Babcock boilers. Coal: 250 tons.

(*Training Ship*).

PATRIA (Cramp, Philadelphia, 10th August, 1911). 1200 tons. Dimensions: 200 (*p.p.*) × 36 × 13 feet. Guns: **2**—3 inch (Bethlehem), **4**—6 pdr., **4**—3 pdr., I.H.P. 4000 = 16 kts. Babcock boilers. Coal: 150 tons.

Gunboats.

1921 *Photo, by courtesy of Captain J. Morales Coello.*

HABANA (1912) and **PINAR DEL RIO** (1912). Both wooden vessels of 80 tons, built at Havana. Dimensions: 100 × 18 × 6 feet. Guns: **1**—1 pdr. I.H.P. 200 = 12 kts. 1 screw. Coal: 20 tons.

Gunboats—*continued*.

DIEZ DE OCTUBRE (J. Samuel White, Cowes, 1911), **VEINTE Y CUATRO DE FEBRERO** (J. Samuel White, Cowes, 1911). 218 tons. Dimensions: 110 × 20 × 8 feet. Guns: **3**—3 pdr. Speed: 12 kts. Coal: 50 tons.

1921 *Photo, by courtesy of Captain J. Morales Coello.*

BAIRE (Klawitter Yd., Danzig, 1906). 500 tons. Dimensions: 196 × 23 × 9 feet. Guns: **4**—3 inch, **2**—3 pdr. H.P. 1200 = 14 kts. Babcock boilers. Coal: 120 tons. (Used as Presidential Yacht).

Naval Transport.

1925 *Photo, by courtesy of Captain J. Morales Coello.*

MAXIMO GOMEZ (ex-German s.s. *Constantia*, built by Barclay, Curle & Co., Glasgow, 1890). Acquired 1923. 3026 tons *gross*. 339½ × 41¾ × 26¼ feet. H.P. 1600 = 11 kts. Guns: **4**—3 inch, **2**—3 pdr.

Coast Guard Patrol Vessels.

MATANZAS (1912), **VILLAS** (1912). Details as *Habana* and *Pinar del Rio*; differ in appearance.

ENRIQUE VILLUENDAS (Chester. U.S.A., 1899). 178 tons. 132 × 20 × 9 feet. Guns: **2**—3 pdr. I.H.P. 600 = 16 kts. Coal: 55 tons.

ALFREDO (Seabury, New York, 1896). Wood. 40 tons. Dimensions: 60 × 12 × 6 feet. Guns: **1**—1 pdr. Speed: 11 kts.

YARA (Middlesborough, 1895). 449 tons. 155 × 26 × 13 feet. Guns: **2**—6 pdr., **2**—3 pdr. I.H.P. 600 = 12 kts. Coal: 150 tons.

MACEO (ex-Spanish gunboat, 1896). Wood. 35 tons. Dimensions: 75 × 10 × 5½ feet. Guns: **1**—1 pdr. Speed, 10 kts. Coal: 8 tons.

VEINTE DE MAYO (Glasgow, 1895). 203 tons. 141 × 18·5 × 10·5 feet. Guns: **2**—3 pdr., **2**—1 pdr. I.H.P. 500 = 12 kts. Coal: 50 tons.

As Illustration for " SC-boats," U.S. Navy Section.

No. 1 (ex U.S. *SC 274*, Mare Island, Navy Yd.). **Nos. 2—4** (ex U.S. *SC 302, 311, 312*, Puget Sound, Navy Yd.). All built 1917-18. About 77 tons. Dimensions: 105 (*w.l.*) × 14¾ × 5½ feet. Guns: **1**—3 inch (23 cal.), **2** Colt M.G. B.H.P. 660 = 16¾ to 18 kts.† Fuel: 2400 gallons petrol. Engines: 3 sets Standard motors.† Wooden hulls.

Note.

All 4 now employed for Coastguard duties, but on account of scarcity and high cost of fuel, are only used in emergency when high speed is required.

† Plans worked out for replacing motors by small boilers and reciprocating engine.

CZECHO SLOVAKIAN NAVY.

Compiled 1931 from material furnished by courtesy of the Minister of Defence.

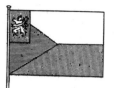

National.

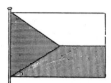

Ensign.

Administration.

Minister of Defence : Dr. Viskovsky.
Chief of the Naval Staff :
Naval Military Attaché in London : Major-General Stephen Andreas.
The Danube flotilla is under the control of the Engineer in Chief.
Principal Base == Gratislava.
Principal Private Establishment, the Skodavy Závody Lodenice (late Hungarian M.F.T.R.).

Ranks.

Colonel	= Plukovnik	Captain	=	Kapetan
Lt.-Colonel	= Podplukovnik	Lieut.	==	Nadporućnik
Major	= Major	Sub.-Lt.	=	Podaćnik
Sen. Captain	= Stabný Kapetan			

Uniform Cap	=	same as Army
Crew	=	Naval cap
Defence Estimates, 1931–32	=	kc. 1,715,000,000
Personnel	=	circa 400 men
Colour of ships	=	light grey

Future Construction.

1932–33. 2 ships of *Massaryk* type and some motor launches.

Mercantile Marine.

On the Danube	=	82,100 tons.
On the Elbe	=	20,000 tons.
At Sea	=	4,850 tons.
(Seaports	=	Hamburg and Stettin.)

Patrol Boats.

PRESIDENT MASSARYK (1930). Displacement : 200 tons. Complement : 50. Dimensions : $150 \times 20 \times \cdot 5$ feet. Guns : 4—3 inch A.A., 10 M.G. Machinery : 2 sets turbines. D.H.P. 1,600 = 16·8 kts. Oil : 45 tons. 2 more of this type are to be built.

Armoured Motor Launches.

O.M.d. 1, O.M.d. 2. Displacement : 17 tons. Complement : 23. Length : 80·6 feet. Guns : 2—3 inch, 2 M.G. H.P. 240 = 20 kts.

Patrol Boats—*continued.*

O.M.h. 4, O.M.h. 5. Displacement : 14 tons. Complement : 15. Armed with 1 or 2 machine guns.

Guard Boats.

8 **O.M.s. 11, 12, 13, 14, 15, 18, 19, 20.** Displacement : 7 tons. Complement : 11. H.P. 45 = 16 kts. Guns : 2 M.G.

Motor Tugs.

10 **O.M.v. 21 to 30.** Displacement : 10/14 tons. Complement : 9. H.P. 130. Guns : 1 M.G.

Naval Air Service includes 6 Seaplanes (Smolik type) stationed in the Bocche di Cattaro and at Divulja, the Yugo-Slavian flying station.

ROYAL DANISH NAVY.

General Notes—DENMARK

(Officially revised by Ministry of Marine, 1931).

Flags.

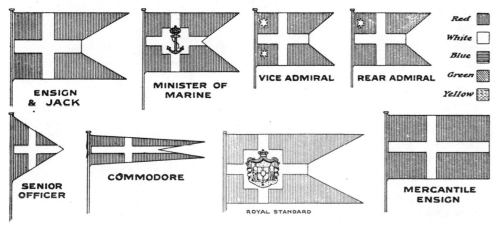

ENSIGN & JACK

MINISTER OF MARINE

VICE ADMIRAL

REAR ADMIRAL

SENIOR OFFICER

COMMODORE

ROYAL STANDARD

MERCANTILE ENSIGN

Red / White / Blue / Green / Yellow

Note.—Division flag pennant, otherwise as commodore.

Naval Guns. (Officially revised, 1927.)

Bore:		Length in Calibres.	Make and Date of Model.		Weight of Gun	Weight of Projectile.	Muzzle Velocity.	Mounted in :
ins.	cm.				metric tons.	lbs.	ft.-secs.	
9·4	24	43	Bofors	M. '06	24·5	352	2690	P. Skram
9·4	24	43	Bofors	M. '01	24·3	353	2690	O. Fischer
9·4	24	40	Canct	M. '96	22·9	353	2395	H. Trolle
5·9	15	45	Bofors	M. '20	6·1	101	2740	Niels Iuel
5·9	15	50	Bofors	M. '06	7·5	112	2723	P. Skram
5·9	15	43	Bofors	M '96/'01	5·5	112	2313	O. Fischer, H. Trolle
4·7	12	40	Krupp	M. '90	2·3	44	2395	Fylla

Torpedoes:—45 c/m. heater type in nearly all vessels.

Insignia of Rank on Sleeves.

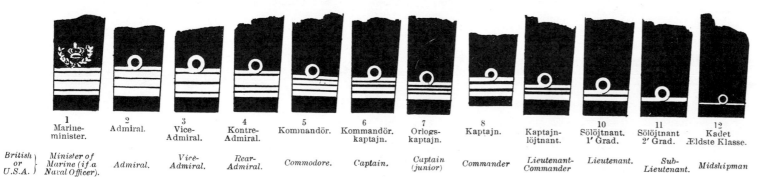

| 1 Marine-minister. | 2 Admiral. | 3 Vice-Admiral. | 4 Kontre-Admiral. | 5 Kommandör. | 6 Kommandör-kaptajn. | 7 Orlogs-kaptajn. | 8 Kaptajn. | Kaptajn-löjtnant. | 10 Sölöjtnant. 1' Grad. | 11 Sölöjtnant 2' Grad. | 12 Kadet Ældste Klasse. |

British or U.S.A. } Minister of Marine (if a Naval Officer). | Admiral. | Vice-Admiral. | Rear-Admiral. | Commodore. | Captain. | Captain (junior) | Commander | Lieutenant-Commander | Lieutenant. | Sub-Lieutenant. | Midshipman

The broad stripes in ranks 1—4 are 2·8 cm. wide.
The narrow „ „ 6, 7, 9 & 12 are 0·7 cm. wide.
The other stripes are 1·4 cm. wide. Distance between stripes is 0·7 cm.

Other ranks with special insignia are: Direktor for Marineministeriet (Director-General, Ministry of Marine). Uniform as Rear-Admiral, but with a golden crown inside curl.

Chef for Admiralitet Uniform as Commodore, but with a golden crown inside curl, and sword belt as flag officer.

Personnel: About 4000, all ranks.
Oversea Possessions: Greenland, Faröes Islands.
Minister of Defence: L. Rasmussen.
Director-General, Ministry of Marine:
Admiral H. Rechnitzer.

Mercantile Marine.
From "Lloyd's Register" 1931.
Total gross Tonnage, 1,157,479, including 5
Ships of 16 Kts. and over.

Note to pages following this

All displacements given in metric tons. Where measurement of length is not stated, it can be taken as between perpendiculars (*p.p.*). All draughts *max. load aft*, unless otherwise stated.
Displacements have all been altered to "Standard" calculation.

139

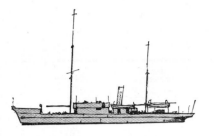

MARSTRAND. WILLEMOËS.

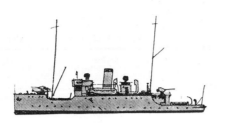

H. GERNER.

NIELS JUEL.

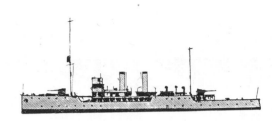

FYLLA.

ISLAND FALK.

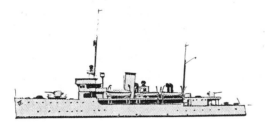

HVIDBJORNEN.

PEDR SKRAM *class*.

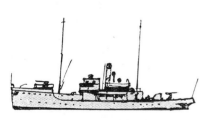

DIANA.

LOSSEN.

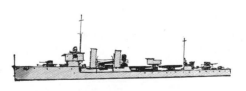

"T" *Class* T.b

"O" *Class* T.b.

BESKYTTEREN.

"N" *Class* T.b.

"P" *Class* T.b.

"R" & "S" *Classes* T.b.

NIELS IUEL (July, 1918.)

Displacement, { *Standard*, 3400 tons. / *full load*, 4320 tons. }   Complement, 310.

Length { (*p.p.*), 285½ feet. / (*w.l.*), —— feet. / (*o.a.*), 295¼ feet. }   Beam, 53½ feet.   Draught { *mean* 15¾ feet. / *full load*, aft., 16½ feet.

Guns (Bofors) :
10—5·9 inch, 45 cal.
4—6 pdr. (anti-aircraft).*
Torpedo tubes (17·7 inch heater) :
2 *submerged* (broadside).
*2 Mounted abaft funnel.
2 Mounted below bridge, abaft C.T.

Armour (Krupp) :
7¾″ ⎫
7¼″ ⎬ Side (amidships   d - e)
7″ ⎭
6″ Side (forward & aft.
     a - d and e - h)
6½″ Bulkheads (forward and aft.)
—″ Uptake to funnel ..
6¾″ Conning Tower ......
4″ Tubes to C.T. ....
1¾″ Gun shields (½″ at sides) ....
2¼″ Deck....................
2½″ Deck (forward) ......

Machinery : Triple expansion. 2 screws. Boilers : 4 Yarrow (2 coal and 2 oil fired). Designed H.P. 5500=16 kts. Fuel : 250 tons coal + 240 tons oil. Endurance : about 5000 miles at 10 kts. Laid down Feb., 1914 ; first commissioned 23rd May, 1923, and now used as sea-going training ship for midshipmen.

1926 Photo, Lieut.-Com. Steen Steensen, R.D.N.

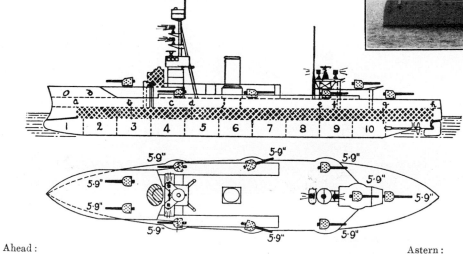

5·9″ 5·9″ 5·9″
5·9″   5·9″   5·9″
5·9″   5·9″   5·9″
5·9″

Ahead :   **Astern :**
4—5·9 in.   Broadside : **6**—5·9 in., **1**—18 in. T.T.   **4**—5·9 in.

Notes.

(a) *Gunnery* : The afterpart of conning tower contains an armoured range-finder, length about 9 feet. There is also another R.F. of same base length on after superstructure between the searchlights, and the 14 pdr. AA. guns have a small R.F. on centre-line, between them. 5·9 inch guns elevate to 30°, and are reported to range up to 18,000 metres.

(b) *General* : Below foretop, the side tripod legs project in front of the centre leg, not joining in flush with the centre leg as in ordinary tripods. The searchlight platforms on foremast are set on the side tripod legs, at an angle of 45 degrees from right ahead. The starboard platform is about 15 feet lower than the port one. The boats are all carried on davits, even steamboats, and there is no main derrick or other lifting appliance.

(c) *Torpedo* : All four S.L. are 36 inch.

     1925 Photo Lieut.-Com. Steen Steensen, R.D.N.

PEDER SKRAM (1908), OLFERT FISCHER (1903), HERLUF TROLLE (1899).

(All built at Copenhagen Dockyard.)

Standard dislacement,—3,400–3,500 tons. Complement, 270.

Length (*p.p.*) 275 feet. Beam, 51 feet. Draught, 16½ feet.

(**H. TROLLE** slightly smaller.)

Guns :—

   2—9·4 inch, 43 cal.
   4—5·9 inch, 50 cal.
   6 or 8—14 pdr.
   2—14 pdr. AA.
   2—1 pdr.

Torpedo Tubes see Notes below.

Armour (*see Notes*) :
   7″ Side (amidships) ...
   4″ Side (aft) ... ...
   3″ Deck (forward) ...
   [Deck flat on belt.]
   7″ Turrets ... ...
   6″ Casemates (KNC)...
   7″ Bulkhead ... ...
   7″ Conning tower ...

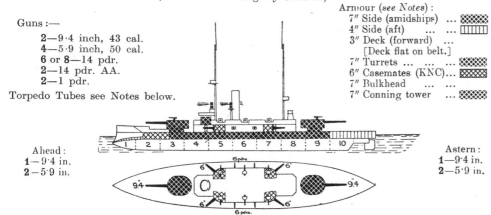

Ahead :
1—9·4 in.
2—5·9 in.

Astern :
1—9·4 in.
2—5·9 in.

OLFERT FISCHER.   1928 *Photo, Lt. Com. Steen Steensen, R.D.N.*

Machinery : 2 sets, triple expansion, 2 screws. All are fitted with 6 Thornycroft boilers. Coal (*maximum*) : 255 tons in *O. Fischer* and *P. Skram*; 245 tons in *H. Trolle.*

Gunnery Notes.—Bofors 1906 models in *P. Skram*; Bofors 1903 models in *O. Fischer.* In *H. Trolle* 9·4 inch are Canet 1896 model, and 5·9 inch are Bofors 1896 model.

Armour Notes.—Krupp armour in *P. Skram*, Creusot in other ships. Belt is 7 feet deep, 3½ feet above, and 3½ feet below water-line. It stops 20 feet from bow. Armoured deck is 3 feet above water-line.

Torpedo Notes.—All tubes 18 inch and submerged : 1 bow, 1 stern, 2 broadside in *P. Skram*, 1 bow and 2 broadside in *O. Fischer* and *H. Trolle.*

Engineering Notes.—Trial : 4,400 to 5,400 = 16 kts. Endurance is about 2000 miles at 10 kts. and 1050 miles at 14¾ kts.

OLFERT FISCHER.   1928 *Photo, Lieut. Com. Steensen, R.D.N.*

Funnel Band :—*Fischer* none.
                 Trolle 1 red.
                 Skram 2 red.

PEDER SKRAM.   H. TROLLE.   *Photo added* 1930.

Sloops.

Officially rated as a Fishery Inspection Vessel.   1929 *Photo, Lieut.-Com. R. Steen Steensen, R.D.N.*

HVIDBJORNEN (Copenhagen Dockyard, 1929). Displacement 915 tons. Complement 58. Dimensions: $156\frac{3}{4} \times 32 \times 13$ feet (*mean* draught). Guns: **2**—3·4 inch. S.H.P. 1800=14·5 kts. 2 boilers (1 Babcock, 1 Thornycroft). **Oil**: 140 tons. Radius: 3300 miles at 12 kts. On service in Greenland waters.

1930 *Photo, Lieut.-Com. S. Steensen, R.D.N.*

(*Used as Fishery Cruiser*).

FYLLA (ex-British Fleet Sweeping Vessel *Asphodel*, launched December, 1915, by Messrs. D. & W. Henderson, Glasgow. Sold to Danish Navy, June, 1920, refitted at Copenhagen D.Y.). Displacement: **1245 tons** (standard). Dimensions: $255\frac{1}{4}$ (*p.p.*), $267\frac{3}{4}$ (*o.a.*) $\times 33\frac{1}{2} \times 11$ (*mean*) 15 feet (*max.* draught). Guns: **2**—4·7 inch, **2**—6 pdr. Designed I.H.P. 1400=17 kts., but actually requires about 2400 H.P. for this speed. Machinery: 1 set triple expansion, 1 screw. Boilers: 2 cylindrical. Coal: 130 tons *normal*; 260 tons *max.*=about 2000 miles at 15 kts. Complement: 75.

HVIDBJORNEN.   1931 *Photo, Lieut.-Com. Steen Steensen, R.D.N.*

26 Torpedo Boats. *(Torpedobaade)*

("Improved Ormen" class, single screw; next three classes twin screw; last class single screw).

No.	Class	Date.	Displacement	H.P.	Max speed	Fuel	Complement	T. tubes	Max. draug't
			tons		kts.	tons			feet
6	*Dragen* (Ny)	'29—'30	285		28			8	
10	*Improved Ormen* (Ny)	'15—'19	93	2000	24·3	15 tons coal	22	2*	9
3	*Hvalrossen* (Ny)	1913	160	3500	26	29 tons coal	30	1	7
3	*Söridderen* (Y)	1911	230	5000	27·5	80 tons coal	33	5	6¼
3	*Tumleren* (S)	1911	250	5000	27·0	„ „	33	5	7¼
1	*R 1* (No)	1907	89	2100	24·5	11 tons coal	21	3	8¼

(Ny) = Navy type.   (S) = Schichau type.   (Y) = Yarrow type.   (No) = Normand type.
* Also have two depth charge tubes.

Note.—In 1930 all Danish Torpedo Boats were numbered as follows:—

No.	Name	No.	Name	No.	Name	No.	Name.
R 5	Sælen	S 5	Havhesien	P 3	Sværdfisken	O 1	Söridderen
R 4	Havkatten	S 4	Söhunden	P 2	Delfinen	C 3	Spækhuggeren
R 3	Nordkaperen	S 3	Söloven	P 1	Hvalrossen	C 2	Vindhunden
R 2	Makrelen	S 2	Stören	O 3	Söulven	C 1	Tumleren
S 6	Narhvalen	S 1	Springeren	O 2	Flyvefisken	R 1	Ormen

T1--Dragen.   T2--Hvalen.   T3--Laxen.

6 "T" Class.

DRAGEN.   *1930 Photo, Lieut.-Com. R. Steen Steensen, R.D.N.*

6 boats: **Dragen** (Dec., 1929), **Glenten** (   ), **Högen** (   ), **Hvalen**, **Laxen** (both 1930), **Örnen** (   ), all by Copenhagen D.Y.   Displacement 285 tons.   Dimensions:—198·7 × 19·5 × 7·6 feet. Armament: **2—14 pdr., 2—20 MM. AA., 8—18 inch tubes** (2 in bow and 2 triples).

Torpedo Boats—*continued.*

4 "R" Class.

1922 Photo. Lieut.-Com. R. S. Steensen, R.D.N.

4 *Improved Ormen* class: **Havkatten R4, Saelen R5,** (both launched 1919), **Makrelen R2, Nordkaperen R3,** (all launched 1917).   All by Copenhagen D.Y.   Dimensions: 126·3 (o.a) × 13·9 × 8·8 feet *normal draught* (9 feet *full load* draught).   Armament: **2—6 pdr., 30 cal.** (anti-aircraft), **2—18 inch tubes** (one bow, one deck, both *above water*), and two depth charge tubes.

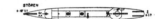

6 "S" Class.

SÖLÖVEN.   *1930 Photo, Lieut.-Com. R. S. Steensen, R.D.N.*

6 *Improved Ormen* class (similar to above): **Springeren (S1), Stören (S2), Söloven (S3), Söhunden (S4), Havhesien (S5), Narhvalen (S6).**   (All by Copenhagen D.Y., launched 1916–17).   Guns: **2—6 pdr. AA.**, tubes **1—18″** in bow.   After tube removed and replaced by mine-sweeping gear.

3 "P" Class.

HVALROSSEN. (*Hvalrossen* has only raised fore funnel).   *1922 Photo, Lieut.-Com. S. Steensen, R.D.N.*

3 *Hvalrossen* type: **Delfinen, P 2, Hvalrossen, P 1, Sværdfisken, P 3,** (all 1913), built at Copenhagen Dockyard.   Dimensions: 148¼×17×7 feet.   Armament: **1**—14 pdr. (aft)., **1**—8 mm. AA.   **4**—18 inch tubes.

Note.—In sketch annexed, twin tube should be shown as *astern* of single ones.

3 "O" Class.

SÖULVEN.   *1927 Photo, Lieut.-Com. Steen Steensen, R.D.N.*

3 *Yarrow* type: **Söridderen, O 1, Söulven, O 3, Flyvefisken, O 2,** (all 1911). First built by Yarrow, others by Burmeister & Wain, Copenhagen.   Dimensions: 181¼×18×6¼ feet.   Armament: **2**—14 pdr., **1**—8 mm. AA.   **5**—18 inch tubes.   There are 10 w.t. compartments.   On trial did 5300 I.H.P.=28·2 *max.* Curtis turbines in *Söridderen.*   Yarrow boilers in all.

SÖRIDDEREN and TUMLEREN classes.

3 "N" Class.

VINDHUNDEN.   *1917 Photo, Ebbesen, Aarhus.*

3 *Schichau* type: **Tumleren, N 1, Vindhunden, N 2, Spækhuggeren, N 3** (all 1911). First by Schichau, others by Copenhagen Dockyard.   Dimensions: 184·9 (o.a.)×19·1×7·3 feet.   Armament: **2**—14 pdr., **1**—8 mm. AA. **5**—18 inch tubes.   Turbine engines and Normand boilers in all.

1 "R" Class.

ÖRMEN.   *1927 Photo, Lieut.-Com. Steen Steensen, R.D.N.*

1 *Normand* type: **R 1** (ex Örmen), (Copenhagen D.Y. 1907).   124·7 (o.a.) × 13·9 × 8·5 feet.   Armament: **2**—1 pdr., **1**—18 inch tube (bow, *above water*). **2**—18 inch amidships.   Cruising speed is 12 kts.

Note—Officially classed as "Watch duty Torpedo Boat."

13 Submarines (*Undervandsbaade*).

Note.—Danish Submarines numbered thus for identification purposes: *Havfruen* A2 ——, *Najaden* A6 ——, *Nymfen* A7 ——, *Aegir* B8 ——, *Ran* B9 ——, *Triton* B10 ——, *Neptun* B11 ——, *Galathea* B12——, *Rota* C1 ——, *Bellona* C2 ——, *Flora* C3 ——, *Daphne* D1, *Dryaden* D2.

DRYADEN.   1928 *Photo, Lieut.-Com. R. Steen Steensen, R.D.N.*

2 *Navy* type: **Daphne** (Dec., 1925), **Dryaden** (June 3, 1926). Built at Copenhagen D.Y. Burmeister & Wain 6-cylinder, 4-cycle Diesel engines of 1000 B.H.P. = 14 kts. *on surface.* Motors of 650 H.P. = 9 kts. *submerged.* Dimensions: *About* 160×15×9 feet. Displacement $\frac{300}{387}$ tons. Armament: **1**—14 pdr. AA. gun, **4** bow and **2** stern 18 inches tubes. *Daphne* completed 1926, *Dryaden* 1927. Complement, 20.

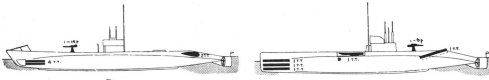

DAPHNE.   FLORA.

FLORA.   1927 *Photo, Lieut.-Com. R. Steen Steensen R.D.N.*

3 *Navy* type: **Bellona** (1919), **Flora** (1920), and **Rota** (1918). All built at Copenhagen D.Y. Burmeister & Wain 6-cylinder, 3-cycle Diesel engines. Dimensions: 155·7+14·4×8·8 feet. Displacement $\frac{300}{365}$ tons. Armament: **1**—6 pdr. anti-aircraft gun; **4**—18 inch torpedo tubes: 3 bow, 1 stern. *Rota* has one deck tube in addition abaft C.T. Complement, 17.

NEPTUN.   1923 *Photo, Lieut.-Com. Steensen, R.D.N.*

5 *Holland* type: **Aegir** (1914), **Galathea** (1916), **Neptun** (1915), **Ran** (1915), **Triton** (1915), all built at Copenhagen D.Y. Diesel motors. Dimensions: 133¼×12+8 feet. Displacement $\frac{177}{169}$ tons. Armament: **3**—18 inch torpedo tubes, 2 bow, 1 stern. These boats are an enlarged and slightly improved *Havmanden* design. Complement, 11.

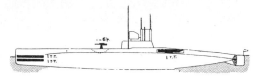

AEGIR CLASS.

NAJADEN.   1923 *Photo, Lieut.-Com. Steensen, R.D.N.*

3 *Holland* type: **Havfruen** (1912), built by Whitehead & Co., Fiume, and **Najaden** (1913), **Nymfen** (1914) both built at Copenhagen D.Y. 1 set 6-cyl. Diesel engines. Dimensions: 118 × 11·9 × 8 feet. Displacement $\frac{250}{270}$ tons. **2**—18 inch torpedo tubes in bows. Guns: **2**—8 m/m. AA. Complement, 11.

Note.—A11 at present in Reserve.

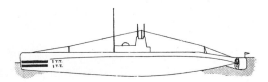

Submarine Depôt and Repair Ship.

HENRIK GERNER.   1928 *Photo.*

HENRIK GERNER (1927). Displacement, 750 tons. 160 × 27 × 8 feet. Guns: **2**—14 pdr. 2 Burmeister & Wain 6-cylinder, 4-cycle Diesel engines of 900 combined B.H.P. = 13·2 kts. Oil: 45 tons. Complement, 40. Fitted for minelaying.

Mine Ship (*Mineskib*).

Photo, Ministry of Defence (added 1921).

LOSSEN (1910). 600 tons. Complement, 53. 149·3 (*p.p.*) × 28 × 9·5 feet. Guns: **2**—14 pdrs. I.H.P. 900 = 13 kts. Coal: 20 tons. 175 mines carried.

Mining Craft (*Minekraner.*)

1920 *Photo, Lieut.-Com. Steensen, R.D.N.*

MINEKRAN V * (1917), **MINEKRAN VI** † (1919), both built at Copenhagen D.Y. 186 tons. Dimensions: 88·5 (*p.p.*) × 20·7 × 6·6 feet (*mean* draught). Guns: **2**—1 pdr. Machinery: in each, 2 sets of Bergsund surface-ignition, heavy-oil motors and electric drive. B.H.P. 290 = 10 kts. Complement, 26. Carry 60 mines.

In Danish * *V = Fem*; † *VI = Seks*

Surveying Ships (*Opmaalingsskibe*).

WILLEMOËS.   1925 *Photo, Lieut. R. Steen Steensen, R.D.N.*

MARSTRAND, 170 tons, **WILLEMOËS,** 160 tons. (Both built 1861, re-built 1896). 114 × 17·5 × 6·4 feet (*mean* draught). Both launched 1861. Complements, 28 to 39. I.H.P. 250 = 11 kts. Guns: **2** machine. *Marstrand* was completely refitted, 1922-23.

1930 *Photo, Lieut.-Com. R. Steen Steensen, R.D.N.*

DAMPBAAD A (ex *Minekran I*) (1896). 110 tons. Dimensions: 72·2 × 16·4 × 6·6 feet. Guns: **2** machine. Speed: 8 kts. Complement, 18.

Torpedo Transport (*Torpedo Transportbaad*).

1920 *Photo, Lieut.-Com. R. S. Steensen, R.D.N.*

SLEIPNER (1882) 80 tons. 73 × 14·8 × 5·9 feet (*mean* draught). Guns: none. I.H.P. 110 = 9 kts.

Royal Yachts (*Kongeskib*).

1925 Photo, by courtesy of the Navy Dept.

DANNEBROG (1879). 1100 tons. 235 (*p.p.*) × 26·8 × 10·4 feet. Guns: **2** M.G. I.H.P. 940 = 13 kts. Complement, 56.

New Royal Yacht

New Royal Yacht.—Dimensions: 244·3 × 32·9 × ? feet. Displacement: 1,200 tons. H.P. 1,300 = 14 kts. 2 Diesel engines. Building by Burmeister and Wain.

Fishery Patrol Vessels (*Fiskerriinspektiouskibe*).

For Sloops *Fylla*, and *Hvidbjornen* used on this service, see an earlier page.

1921 Photo, Lieut. R. S. Steensen, R.D.N.

ISLANDS FALK (Elsinore 1906). 775 tons. Complement, 63. 170·6 (*p.p.*), 183·6 (*o.a.*) × 29·3 × 14·7 feet. Guns: **2**—6 pdr., **2**—3 pdr. I.H.P. 1100 = 11·7 kts. (*f.d.*) Cruising speed is 9 kts. Reboilered 1921. Employed on North Sea Fisheries. Now has short Topmasts.

1920 Photo, Lieut. Steensen, R.D.N.

DIANA (Holland, 1916). 260 tons. 116·5 (*p.p.*), 124·8 (*o.a.*) × 21·5 × 8·8 feet. Guns: **2**—3 pdr. I.H.P. 400 = 11·5 kts. Complement, 27.

Fishery Patrol Vessels—*continued*.

1921 Photo, Lieut. R. S. Steensen, R.D.N.
(*Fishery Cruiser, Faröes Islands*).

BESKYTTEREN (1900). 447 tons. Comp. 73. 134 (*p.p.*), 142·5 (*o.a.*) × 24·8 × 11·5 feet. Guns: **1**—6 pdr., **2**—3 pdr. I.H.P. 620 = 12·5 kts. (*f.d.*). Cruising speed is 9 kts. Re-boilered 1920. Serves as parent ship for Aircraft and T.S. for Cadets and Boys.

Tender.

FENRIS.   *1926 Photo, Lieut. R. S. Steensen, R.D.N.*

FENRIS (Holland, 1915). 190 tons. 86·4 (*p.p.*) × 20·7 × 9·2 feet. Guns: **2**—3 pdr. I.H.P. 420 = 12 kts. Complement, 18. Employed as Tug and Squadron Tender.

(Officially revised by courtesy of the Chief of the Naval Staff, Tallinn,
by courtesy of Chief of Naval Staff, 1931.)

Naval Uniforms.

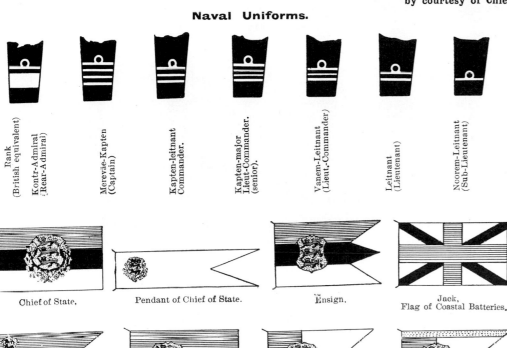

| Rank (British equivalent) | Kontr-Admiral (Rear-Admiral) | Merevãe-Kapten (Captain) | Kapten-leitnant Commander. | Kapten-major Lieut-Commander. (senior). | Vanem-Leitnant (Lieut-Commander) | Leitnant (Lieutenant) | Noorem-Leitnant (Sub-Lieutenant) |

Chief of State.

Pendant of Chief of State.

Ensign.

Jack, Flag of Coastal Batteries.

 Auxiliary Craft. (Ensign.)

 Minister of War.

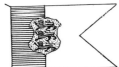 R. Admiral.

C. in C.

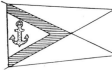 Chief of Naval Forces (If not Admiral).

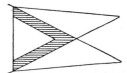 Chief of Division.

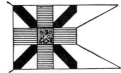 Chief of Coastal Batteries

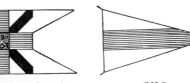 S.N.O.

Masthead Pendant.

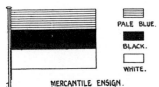

PALE BLUE.

BLACK.

WHITE.

MERCANTILE ENSIGN.

Commander-in-Chief of Fleet and Coast Defence : Rear-Admiral H. Salza.
Chief of Naval Staff : Commander V. Grenz.
Naval Officers and Men : 1600
Colour of Ships : Grey.
Mercantile Marine ("Lloyd's Register" 1931) : Total *gross* tonnage, 93,397.

2 Destroyers. (*Miini Ristlejad.*)

(Both captured by British Cruisers and Destroyers in the Baltic, in Dec., 1918, and transferred to Estonian Navy.)

1929 *Official Photo.*

Lennuk (ex-Russian *Avtroil*). Launched at Tallinn by Reval Shipbuilding Co., 1915, completed 1917. Displacement : 1800 tons. Dimensions : 344½ × 31¼ × 10½ feet. Guns : 5—4 inch, 60 cal., 1—3 inch AA., 2—57 m/m., 1—2 pdr. Pom-pom, 2 M.G. Torpedo tubes : 9—18 inch, in 3 triple deck mountings. Designed to carry and lay 80 mines. Designed S.H.P. 32,700 = 32 kts. A.E.G. Curtis turbines. Oil fuel : 400 tons = 2400 miles at 15 kts. Complement, 125.
Note.—This vessel was built to the design of Chantiers et Ateliers Augustin Normand, Le Havre.

1929 *Official Photo.*

Vambola (ex-Russian *Spartak*, ex-*Mikluha Maklai*). Launched by Putilov Works, Petrograd, 1915, and completed 1918. Displacement : 1585 tons. Dimensions : 314¾ × 30½ × 10 feet. Guns : 4—4 inch, 60 cal., 1—2 pdr. Pom-pom, 2 M.G. Torpedo tubes : 9—18 inch, in 3 triple deck mountings. Designed to carry and lay 80 mines. Designed S.H.P. 30,000 = 32 kts. A.E.G. Curtis turbines. Oil fuel : 400 tons = 2500 miles at 15 kts. Complement, 115.

Torpedo Boat.

1929 *Official Photo.*

Sulev (ex-German *A*32).   Built at Elbing, 1916.   (Sunk off Estonian Coast, October, 1917, salved and refitted 1923.)   Displacement, 228 tons.   Dimensions : 165½ × 17½ × 6 feet.   Guns : **2**—3 inch, 50 cal.   Torpedo tubes : **2**—18 inch, in double deck mounting.   Can carry 10 mines.   Designed S.H.P. 3500 = 26 kts.   Oil : 50 tons = 975 miles at 20 kts.   Complement, 35.

Gunboats.   (*Suurtiiki Laevad*).

1929 *Official Photo*

MARDUS.   Refitted 1921.   80 tons.   Dimensions : 90 × 21 × 7 feet.   Guns : **2**—3 inch, 50 cal., 2 M.G.   Designed H.P. 225 = 11 kts.   Complement, 25.   In Reserve.

Gunboats *—continued.*

1929 *Official Photo.*

LAENE (1915).   400 tons.   Dimensions : 129 × 20 × 11½ feet.   Guns : **1**—57 m/m.   Designed H.P. 350 = 12 kts.   Coal : 80 tons.   Complement, 25.

1929 *Official Photo.*

*TARTU.   Paddle vessel.   Refitted 1919.   108 tons.   Dimensions : 128½ × 17½ × 2¾ feet.   Guns : **2**—47 m/m., 2 M.G.   Designed H.P. 120 = 11 kts.   Complement, 20.

*Stationed in Peipus Lake.

Gunboats—*continued.*

1929 *Official Photo.*

*AHTI. Built 1908, refitted 1919. 144 tons. Dimensions : 90½ × 16½ × 6 feet. Guns : 2—47 m/m., 2 M.G. Designed H.P. 220 = 10 kts. Complement, 17.

**Stationed in Peipus Lake.

Minelayers.

RISTNA.   1929 *Official Photo.*

RISTNA (1908), **SUUROP** (1907). Paddle Vessels. Refitted 1927. 500 tons. Dimensions : 198½ × 49½ (over paddle boxes) × 6½ feet. Guns : 1—3 inch, 50 cal., 1—1 pdr. Pom-Pom. Designed H.P. 750 = 12.5 kts. Complement, 40. Also fitted for use as Minesweepers.

Minelayers—*continued.*

KALEV (ex-Russian *M.8*), **OLEV** (ex-Russian *M.10*) (1914). 50 tons. Dimensions : 68½ × 15 × 4 feet. Guns : 1—57 m/m. Engines : 2 sets of petrol motors. Designed H.P. 80 = 9 kts. Complement, 10.

Minesweeper.

(See also *Ristna* and *Suurop*, in preceding column.)

1929 *Official Photo.*

TAHKONA (1919). 45 tons. Dimensions : 57½ × 10½ × 55 feet. Designed H.P. 150 = 12 kts. Complement, 8.

Coastguard Vessels.

KÕU. Refitted 1928. 100 tons. Dimensions : 87 × 17½ × 8½ feet. Guns : 1—50 m/m., 2 M.G. Designed H.P. 350 = 12 kts. Complement, 18.

1929 *Official Photo.*

ERILANE. Built 1915, refitted 1919. 25 tons. Dimensions : 53 × 10 × 5 feet. 1 M.G. Designed H.P. 50 = 10 kts.

Coastguard Vessels—*continued.*

1929 *Official Photo.*

M.P.5. (1909). 9 tons. Dimensions : 50 × 11½ × 5½ feet. 1 M.G. Designed H.P. 50 = 9 kts. Complement, 8.

Naval Tugs and Tenders.

1929 *Official Photo.*

KOMPASS (1918). 300 tons. Dimensions : 143 × 21 × 12 feet. Designed H.P. 220 = 9 kts. Complement, 20. Fitted for cable laying.

Naval Tugs and Tenders—*continued.*

JAAN POSKA. 250 tons. Dimensions: 101 × 21 × 9½ feet. H.P. 600 = 11 kts. Complement, 15. Commissioned in 1929 as a Tug-icebreaker.

SAKALA. 40 tons. Dimensions : 62 × 11 × 6½ feet. Designed H.P. 40 = 8 kts. Complement, 6.

M.P.10. 24 tons. Dimensions : 55½ × 9½ × 3½ feet. Designed H.P. 100 = 13.5 kts. Complement, 6.

1929 *Official Photo.*

M.P.8., M.P.14., M.P.23. (1909). 12 tons. Dimensions : 53 × 13 × 6 feet. Designed H.P. 55 = 9 kts. Complement, 6.

Icebreakers.

SUUR TÕLL (ex-*Vainamoinen*) (4800 tons), **TASUJA** (1100 tons), and **JÜRI VILMS** (200 tons), are in peace-time all under the control of the Government Shipping Department.

ECUADOR.

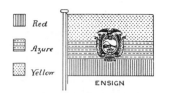
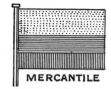

▦ Red		
▤ Azure	ENSIGN	MERCANTILE
▦ Yellow		

Flag Notes : The upper half of flag is corn yellow ; the lower half is equally divided into two stripes, the upper one of pale blue and the lower one of red. The emblem in the centre of the flag differs from that of the Colombian Flag.

Gunboats.

1918 *Photo, G. Chambers, Esq.*

LIBERTADOR BOLIVAR (ex *Alm. Simpson*, 1896, purchased from Chile, 1907). Displacement 750 tons. Length, 240 feet. Beam, 27½ feet. *Maximum* draught, 10½ feet. Guns (Armstrong): 4—3 pdr., **2** Maxims. Torpedo tubes (18 inch): **3** *above water.* Armour (Harvey): 1″ Belt, 4½″ Gun shields, 1″ Hood to steering gear, 1″ Bulkheads. Machinery : 2 sets triple expansion. 2 screws. Boilers : 4 Normand. Designed I.H.P. *forced* 4500 = 21·5 kts. Coal : 100 tons. Built by Laird.

1918 *Photo, G. Chambers, Esq.*

COTOPAXI (1884). 300 tons. 135 (*p.p.*) × 21 × 9 feet. Guns : 2—3 pdr. small Q.F. I.H.P. 175. *Max.* speed, 10½ kts.

A:—Coastguard and Fisheries Administration.
Patrol Vessels.

1930 *Photo, Swan, Hunter.*

EL AMIRA FAWZIA (Swan, Hunter, July 8th, 1929). 2,640 tons. Dimensions: 275 × 38 × 23½ feet. Machinery: Triple expansion. H.P. 2,750 = 15 kts. 2 screws. 2 S.E. boilers (working pressure, 180 lbs.). Oil fuel. Fitted as transport for 400 men and 40 horses. Normally employed on coasting service carrying passengers.

EL AMIR FAROUQ (Hawthorn Leslie, 1926). 947 tons *gross*. Dimensions: 247 × 34 × 12½ feet draught. Guns: Not known. Machinery: Triple expansion. 2 screws. I.H.P. 2,000 = 18 kts. Oil fuel.

RACHIB (*ex*-British "P" class Patrol Boat, 1917). Displacement, 613 tons. Dimensions: 230 (*p.p.*), 244½ (*o.a.*) × 23¾ × 7 feet *max.* draught. Guns: 1—12 pdr., 1 S.L. Parsons geared turbines. S.H.P. 3560 = 22 kts. Complement, 40.

1930 *Photo, Swan, Hunter.*

MABAHISS—Built by Swan Hunter and completed 1930. Employed on research work. Dimensions: 138 × 23½ × 13½. Displacement ? tons. Machinery: Triple expansion. 650 H.P. Speed: 11 kts.

ABDUL MONEIM (Clydebank, 1902). 610 tons. Dimensions: 177 (*p.p.*) × 28 × 12¼ feet *max.* draught. Guns: none. 1 S.L. Machinery: Triple expansion. I.H.P. 850 = 13.5 kts. Complement, 44.

B:—Ports and Lighthouses Administration.
Transport (*ex*-Sloop).

SOLLUM.   1927 *Photo, Lieut-Com. R. H. Mandley, R.N.*

SOLLUM (*ex*-British Sloop *Syringa*, of *Anchusa* class, built by Workman, Clark & Co., 1917). Displacement, 1290 tons. Dimensions: 255¼ (*p.p.*), 262¼ (*o.a.*) × 35 × 12 feet. No guns. Designed H.P. 2500 = 16 kts. 1 screw. Coal: 260 tons. Many alterations have been effected at considerable cost to fit this vessel for accommodation of Government officials on visits of inspection, etc., to Mediterranean coast.

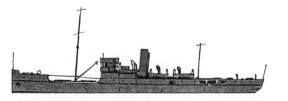

Inspection Vessels and Store Carriers.

NAFTIS (1905). 325 tons *net*. Dimensions : $187\frac{3}{4}$ (*p.p.*) × $30\frac{1}{2} \times 7\frac{1}{4}$ feet.

MONAGAM (1904). 87 tons *net*. Dimensions : 118 (*p.p.*) × $19\frac{3}{4} \times 8\frac{2}{3}$ feet.

Note.—There are also a large number of Harbour Craft, Tugs, etc., for which space cannot be afforded.

Lighthouse Tender.

AÏDA (A. & Ch. de la Loire, Nantes, 1911). 1428 tons *gross*. Dimensions : $246\frac{1}{3} \times 31\frac{3}{4} \times 13\frac{1}{2}$ feet draught. I.H.P. 1300 = 15 kts. 1 screw. Serves in Red Sea.

C:—Royal Yacht.

MAHROUSSA. 1927 *Photo, Cribb.*

MAHROUSSA. Iron. Built by Samuda Bros., Poplar, 1865. Reconstructed by A. & J. Inglis, Glasgow, 1905, and since re-fitted at Portsmouth Dockyard. Displacement : 4561 tons. Dimensions : 400 (*p.p.*), 420 (*w.l.*), $477\frac{5}{6}$ (*o.a.*) × $42\frac{3}{4} \times 17\frac{1}{4}$ feet draught. Machinery : 3 Parsons turbines. Boilers (new 1905) : 5 main and 1 auxiliary Inglis multitubular. 3 screws. S.H.P. 5500 = 16 kts. Oil : 346 tons. Complement, 164.

FINNISH FLEET.

Revised 1931 by courtesy of Commander A. Raninen, Finnish Navy.

Uniforms.

(a) = Finnish Rank ; (b) = British Rank.

ould be
ee thin
tripes
d no
rs be-
e lion.

(a) Amiraali.
(b) Admiral.

(a) Vara-Amiraali.
(b) Vice-Admiral.

(a) Kontra-Amiraali.
(b) Rear-Admiral.

(a) Kommodori.
(b) Commodore.

(a) Komentaja.
(b) Captain.

(a) Komentaja-Kapteeni.
(b) Commander.

(a) Kapteeni-Luutnantti.
(b) Lieut-Conmr.

(a) Luutnantti.
(b) Lieutenant.

(a) Alihutnantti.
(b) Sub-Lieut.

The figure over top stripe is the Lion of the Finnish Arms, as enlarged sketch reproduced herewith.   Colour of cloth between stripes :—

Engineers : red ; *Paymasters :* silver stripes and *no* Lion badge ; *Surgeons :* white ; *Army officers in Naval service :* green.   *Reserve* officers have *no* Lion badges.

Wireless.

Marconi Western Electric and Telefunken systems used.

Colour of Ships.

Grey.

Mercantile Marine.

Total *Gross* Tonnage, 649,036.

Flags :—

NATIONAL FLAG

ENSIGN

MERCANTILE

MARINE DEPARTMENT

PRESIDENT'S STANDARD

PRESIDENT'S PENNANT

MINISTER OF WAR

COMMANDER IN CHIEF

INSPECTOR OF COAST DEFENCE

COMMANDER-IN-CHIEF OF FLEET

COMMANDER OF A FLOTILLA

COMMANDER OF HALF FLOTILLA

CAPTAIN OF PORT.

PENNANT

NOTE:- THE LION IN THE FLAGS IS SIMILAR TO THAT SHOWN ENLARGED FOR THE UNIFORMS. IN THE FLAGS THERE ARE 9 CONVENTIONAL ROSES DISPOSED ABOUT THE LION.

Red   White   Blue   Yellow

SVEABORG.

HÄMEENMAA.
UUSIMAA.

KARJALA.
TURUNMAA.

TORPEDO CRAFT.

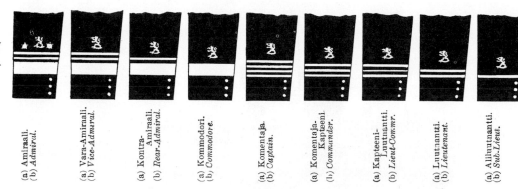

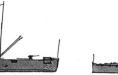

VÄINÄMÖINEN.   ILMARINEN.

M1

S5   Same appearance but (a) Foremast stepped *abaft* fore bridge.
(b) *No* high ventilator before third funnel.

S1.

KLAS HORN.
MATTI KURKI.

Coast Defence Ships.

Patrol Vessels.

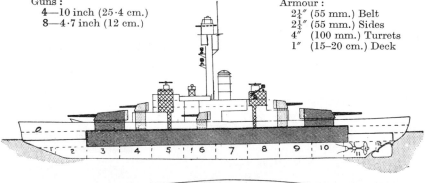

VÄINÄMÖINEN (Dec., 1930). **ILMARINEN** (July 9th, 1931).
Both at A. B. Crichton-Vulcan, Abo.
Displacement, 4,000 tons. Complement,

Length.	Beam.	Draught.

Guns :
    4—10 inch (25·4 cm.)
    8—4·7 inch (12 cm.)

Armour :
    2¼″ (55 mm.) Belt
    2¼″ (55 mm.) Sides
    4″ (100 mm.) Turrets
    1″ (15—20 cm.) Deck

Ahead :
2—10 in.
6—4·7 in.

Astern :
2—10 in.
6—4·7 in.

Broadside : **4**—10 in., **6**—4·7 in.
Machinery : Diesel electric drive. Leonard system. D.H.P.   =16 kts. 2 Screws. Fuel :
tons.
Laid down Aug.-Sept., 1929. To be delivered in 1932 and 1933.

1924 *Photo, Commdr. Raninen.*

KARJALA (ex-Russian *Filin*), **TURUNMAA** (ex-Russian *Orlan*), built by Crichton A/B, Åbo.
Ordered by late Imperial Russian Government, 1914. Launched, 1918. Displacement : 342 tons.
Complement, 48. Length, (*p.p.*) 154 feet, (*o.a.*) 164½ feet. Beam, 22½ feet. Designed load draught,
7½ feet. Guns : **2**—11 pdr., **3** M.G. Machinery : 2 sets triple expansion. Boilers : Yarrow.
Designed I.H.P. 1150=15 kts. Coal capacity *about* 50 tons.

Notes.—" Borowski type " Patrol Vessels and generally sisters to Polish *M. Pilsudski* and *Gen. Haller*. *Turunmaa* is
employed as Cadets' Training Ship.

2 Patrol Boats.

1921 *Official Photo.*

MATTI KURKI (ex-Russian *Posadnik*), **KLAS HORN** (ex-Russian *Voevoda*), both built by Schichau, Elbing, 1892. Displacement: 420 tons. Complement, 62. Length, (*p.p.*) 187¾ feet. Beam, 23 feet. Draught, 10¼ feet. Guns: 2—3·9 inch, 2—3 pdr. Hotchkiss, 3 M.G. Machinery: 1 set triple expansion. Boilers: Locomotive type. Designed H.P. 3300 = 20 kts. Best present speed about 16 to 17 kts. Coal: about 80 tons. Can carry 50 mines each.

Notes.—Built for late Imperial Russian Navy as Torpedo Craft but re-rated as Patrol Vessels. On the outbreak of the Russian Revolution they were abandoned by their crews at Finnish Ports and taken over for the Finnish Navy.

2 Torpedo Boats.

S 1

1924 *Photo, Commdr. Raninen.*

S 5

1921 *Official Photo.*

Yarrow type : **S1** (ex-Russian *Ryani*, 1899). **S5** (ex-Russian *Podvishni*, 1901). Displacements : S 1, 250 tons; S 5, 270 tons. Lengths, (*p.p.*) 180 feet for S 1 and 190 feet for S 5. Beam, 18½ feet. Draughts, *about* 5¼ feet *mean.* and 7½ feet *max.* Guns: 2—11 pdr. and 3 M.G. Torpedo tubes : 1—17.7 inch. As Russian craft, were fitted to carry and lay 14 or 18 mines. Machinery : 2 sets triple expansion. Boilers : 4 Yarrow. Designed I.H.P. 3800 = 27 kts. Coal : 72 tons. Sister boat, S 2 foundered in heavy weather, Oct., 1925.

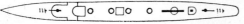

3 Submarines.

VETCHINEN.

1930 *Photo, favour of " Flottes de Combat."*

3 boats : **Vetchinen** (1930), **Vesipiisi** (1930), **Iku-Turso** (1931). Ordered 1926 from the Crichton-Vulcan Yard at Turku, Abo, the first keel being laid in Sept., 1926, other two early in 1927. Displacement : 493/716 tons. Dimensions : 164 (*o.a.*) × 19½ × feet. H.P. 1060/—. Speed, 14/8. Radius : 1,500/75 miles. Complement : 25. Torpedo Tubes : 4—21 inch (533 m/m). Guns : 1—76 m/m, 1—20 m/m. To be capable of diving to 40 fathoms. Diesels made by A. B. Atlas Diesel Co., Stockholm. Construction of *Vetchinen* delayed by nearly a year owing to strikes.

1 Submarine.

Building.

1 boat : **Saukko** (1930). Laid down 1929 by the Sandvikens Skeppsdocka Co. of Helsingfors. Should have been delivered in 1928, but construction delayed by strikes. Displacement : 99/ tons. H.P. 200/ . Speed : 9/5¾ kts. Radius : 375/45 miles. Complement : 11. Torpedo Tubes : 2—18 inch (450 m/m). Guns : 1—13 m/m.

FINLAND

Mine Sweepers.

1924 *Photo, Commdr. Raninen.*

T.2 (1916) and **RAUTU** (ex Russian *Murman*, 1917). Displacement: 240 tons. Complement, 32. Dimensions: 143 (*p.p.*) × 20 × — feet. Guns: **1**—11 pdr., **2** M.G. Machinery: **2** sets triple expansion. Designed H.P. 550 = 14 kts. Coal: 30 tons.

1921 *Official Photo.*

18 "A-boats": Numbered between *A.11—A.53*. Fitted as Mine Sweepers. Displacement: 9 tons. Complement, 8. Dimensions: 50 (*p.p.*) × 11½ × — feet. Engines: Petrol motor. Designed H.P. 50 = 9 kts. All still in service, 1927.

Minelayers.

HÄMEENMAA.   1924 *Photo, Commdr. Raninen.*

UUSIMAA (ex *Beo*, 1918), **HÄMEENMAA** (ex *Wulf*, 1918). Displacement: 400 tons. Complement, 32. Dimensions: 160 (*p.p.*) × 24 × 10 feet. Guns: **2**—3·9 in., **1**—37 m/m. AA., **2** M.G. Machinery: **2** sets triple expansion. Designed H.P. 1000 = 15 kts. Coal: 100 tons.

1924 *Photo, Commdr. Raninen.*

M.1. (ex *Voin*, Kolomna, 1916.) Displacement, 776 tons. Complement, 41. Dimensions: 151 (*p.p.*) × 26½ × 7½ feet. Guns: **2**—3 pdr. Machinery: **1** set triple expansion. Designed H.P. 800 = 12 kts. Coal: 50 tons.

Minelayers—*continued.*

1925 *Photo, Commdr. Raninen, F.N.*

SVEABORG (Maskin & Bro. A/B. Helsingfors, 1905). Displacement, 780 tons. Complement, 36. Dimensions: 143½ × 20 × 8¼ feet. Guns: Nil. Designed H.P. 300 = 10 kts. Coal: 30 tons. Carries 60 mines.

Motor Launches.

M.T.3—M.T.5 (1928). Usual Thornycroft 55 ft. type. Armament: **2**—18 inch torpedoes, **2** Lewis guns, **2** D.C. Speed: 40 kts. 2 more of this type have been built in Finland, one at Burgaa, one at Abo.

1924 *Photo, Commdr. Raninen.*

M.T.V. 1 and **M.T.V. 2** (ex *M.A.S. 220* and *221.*) Built for Royal Italian Navy by Flli. Orlando in 1917, and purchased 1920. 12 tons. Dimensions: 52½ × — × 3¼ feet. Guns: **2** M.G. on high-angle mounts. Torpedoes: **2**—17·7 inch carried in dropping gears on each beam. Machinery: **2** sets petrol motors. B.H.P. 500 = 26·5 kts.

Icebreakers.

The Government Icebreakers **JAAKARHU, SAMPO, TARMO, VOIMA** and **MURTAJA** would be available for naval use in wartime, but are no longer listed here, as they are under the control of the Board of Navigation.

NOTE.—The following pages, descriptive of the French Navy, have been inspected and approved by the Ministry of Marine, Paris, 1931, though the Ministry of Marine accepts no responsibility for the accuracy of any of the statements made in "Fighting Ships" as regards the French Navy.

Minister of Marine—Monsieur Charles Dumont.

Naval Attaché (London)—Capitaine de Vaisseau Yves Donval.

Asst. Naval Attaché—Capitaine de Corvette (Constructive Branch) André Bron.

„ „ „ (*Aéronautique*)—Lieut. de Vaisseau L.M.P. A. Sala.

Navy Estimates.

1931. Frcs. 2,799,830,314.

Personnel.

3,880 Officers, 53,750 Men.

Flags.

Drawings prepared 1924 from information furnished by courtesy of the Ministry of Marine, Paris.

Presidential Flag: Initials of the President worked in Gold letters on central (white) stripe of the Ensign, the letters and their dimensions being chosen by M. le Président.

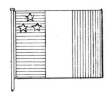

Pavillon du Président de la République.

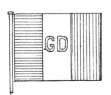

Ensign & Jack (Minister of Marine).

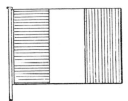

Maréchal de France.

Vice-Amiral Chef d' Etat Major Général ou Inspecteur Général des Forces Maritimes.

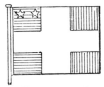

Autres Vice-Amiraux, et Généraux de Division en Mission Officielle, ou pourvus d'un Commandement en Chef.

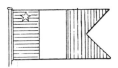

Contre-Amiral et Général de Brigade en Mission Officielle.

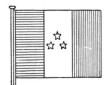

Capitaine de Vaisseau Chef de Division (independant ou en sous ordre).

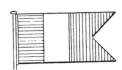

Capitaine de Vaisseau Comm't un groupe de bâtiments; ou Major-Général ou Commandant la Marine.

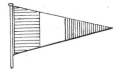

Capitaine de Frégate ou de Corvette, Comm't un groupe de bâtiments ou Commandant la Marine.

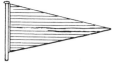

Comm't supérieur temporaire de tout grade.

Rouge *Blanc* *Bleu*

hydravions

Uniforms.

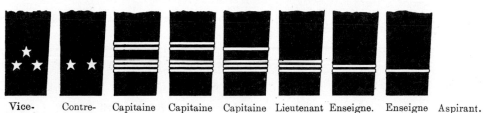

Vice-Amiral.	Contre-Amiral.	Capitaine de vaisseau.	Capitaine de frégate.	Capitaine de corvette.	Lieutenant de vaisseau.	Enseigne.	Enseigne 2e classe.	Aspirant.

Corresponding to British—

| Vice-Ad. | Rear-Ad. | Captain. | Commander. | Lieut. Comm'der. | Lieut. | Lieut. (junior.) | Sub-Lieut. | Midshipman. |

Capitaine de Vaisseau, Chef de Division, has one star above the stripes.

Only three of the Capitaine de frégate's stripes are gold: the second and fourth are silver.

Aspirant golden stripe with two light blue patches.

Epaulettes with parade uniform are of the usual sort, *except that*—

    A Vice-Admiral's epaulettes have the usual anchor and 3 stars.

    A Rear-Admiral's „ „ „ „ „ 2 „

Caps are similar to British Navy in shape but badge differs, being more like Italian and there are stripes right round corresponding to rank. The cocked hat carries the tri-colour.

Torpedoes. (Details official).

Whitehead pattern, made at Toulon Torpedo Factory; also at St. Tropez, where Whitehead marks are built by the Société Française de Torpilles Whitehead.

Date.	French Designation.	Diameter.	Length.		Charge.	Pressure in chamber.	Maximum range.
		inches.	feet.	ins.	lbs.	lbs. per sq. in.	
1919	55 c/m (D)	21·7	27'	"	551	2420	15,000
1919	55 c/m. (V)	21·7	21'	7"	551	2200	4375
1912	45 c/m *long*	18	22'	2"	317	2420	8000
1911	45 c/m *short*	18	17'	3"	317	2140	1000
1909	45 c/m *cold*	18	16'	8"	317	2140	2000

Notes.—All fitted with gyros. There are also other recent models of the *55 c/m.* torpedo.

Mines.

9 marks in use up to 1914, but present types understood to include mainly 120 and 200 kilo. types for laying by S/M; 360-kilo. Sautter-Harlé spherical and 700-kilo. Breguet spherical types. Paravanes British marks.

General Notes.

COLOUR OF SHIPS: *Big ships.*—Grey all over, but some have grey-green or greenish-brown turrets, or black barbette shields.

    Destroyers, etc.—Light grey; Flotilla Leaders and Destroyers, also Submarines of *Requin* class, bear distinguishing numbers instead of letters as formerly.

    Submarines.—Sea green or light grey.

EFFECTIVE LIFE OF SHIPS: Fixed in 1923 as—Battleships and Aircraft Carriers, 20 years; Cruisers, 17 years; Torpedo Craft, 15 years; Submarines, 12 years.—all reckoned from date of first commissioning for trials.

Washington Treaty standard has been adopted for regulation of displacements.

Mercantile Marine.

(From "Lloyd's Register," 1931 figures.)

Total gross tonnage, 3,566,227 including 29 vessels of 16 knots and over.

NAVAL ORDNANCE.

Naval Ordnance (converted from official 1919 Table furnished by courtesy of the Ministry of Marine and officially revised in 1927).

	13.4		12		9.4	8	7.6			6.5			6.1	5.5			5.1		3.9	
Calibre (ins.)	**13.4**		**12**		**9.4**	**8**	**7.6**			**6.5**			**6.1**	**5.5**			**5.1**		**3.9**	
Do. (c/m)	34		30.5		24	20.3	19			16			15.5	13·8			13		10	
Mark	1912	1912	1906-10	1906	1902-6	1924	1902	1893-6	1893	'93-'96M	1893-6	1893	1920	1923	1910	1893	1924	1919	1917	'91 &'93
Length (calibres)	45	45	45	45	49.5	50	50	40	40	45	45	45	50	40	55	45	40	40	—	45
Weight of Gun (English tons)	65.33		54.7	54.7	29.1	20.4	14.9	12.5	10.2	7.96	7.96	6.52	8.72	4.05	5.17	4.01	3.42	4.34	1.54	1.67
Weight of Shell (capped) in lbs.	A.P. 1190.5	Capped 1256.6	922.3	960.4	487.2	271.4	199	199	199	121	121	121	123.5	88.2	80.5	84	70.5	70.5	29.7	35.5
Weight of Charge (lbs.)	330.7	337.3	267.4	282.2	148.1	116.8	84	74.5	49.2	45.6	43.7	28.9	43.2	19.8	22.7	16	17	17	8.16	8.16
Max. Pressure (lbs.)	59,525	57,320	57,320	57,320	57,320	46,000	59,083	61,739	47,400	47,400	61,739	44,092	42,900	35,500	55,155	53,706	34,500	34,500	5,291	5,291
Muzzle-Velocity (ft.-secs.)	2624.7	2605	2559	2559	2625	2936	3117	2756	2526	2953	2838	2527	2854	2297	2723	2395	2408	2408	2362	2329
Remaining Velocity at 21,872 yds. / 20,000 m.	..	1309	..	..	..		..	..	..	..	..	..	..	..	..	..	..	..	..	..
Remaining Velocity at 16,404 yds. / 15,000 m.	1178	1462	..	..	1102		..	..	..	..	..	..	..	..	..	..	..	..	..	..
Remaining Velocity at 10,936 yds. / 10,000 m.	1473	1762	1529	1529	1348		1106	1010	992	928	918	922	..	..	860	905	..	..	879	856
Remaining Velocity at 5468 yds. / 5000 m.	1640	2162	1992	1992	1896		1860	1571	1447	1417	1351	1257	..	..	1230	1168	..	..	1115	1033
Angle of descent at 20,000 m.	..	25° 10″	..	..	..		..	..	..	..	..	..	..	..	..	..	..	..	..	..
Angle of descent at 15,000 m.	21° 10″	14° 50″	..	..	25° 50″		..	..	..	..	..	..	..	..	..	..	..	..	..	..
Angle of descent at 10,000 m.	9° 30″	7° 35″	9° 25″	9° 25″	11° 10″		14° 10″	18° 10″	20° 50″	23° 20″	24° 30″	26° 30″	..	..	27° 30″	28° 40″	..	..	30° 20″	34° 10″
Angle of descent at 5000 m.	3° 10″	2° 53″	3° 14″	3° 14″	3° 20″		3° 10″	4° 10″	5°	4° 20″	5° 10″	6° 20″	..	..	6° 10″	7° 20″	..	..	8° 10″	9° 20″

A new 90 m/m. (3.5 inch) Anti-aircraft gun has been introduced. A 1929 model 5.1 inch has been mounted in latest destroyers.

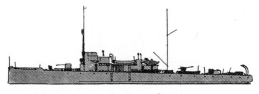

DILIGENTE
ENGAGEANTE (Dummy funnel) } (Minesweepers).
SURVEILLANTE (Yacht stern)

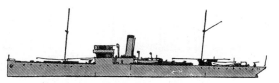

DOUDART DE LAGRÉE (River Gunboat).

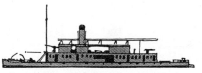

VILLE D'YS (Despatch Vessel).

DUNKERQUE class (Despatch Vessels).

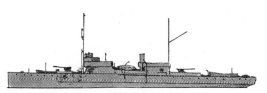

VAILLANTE class (Minesweepers).

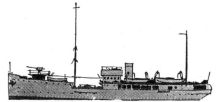

ARGUS, VIGILANTE (River Gunboats).

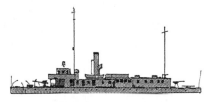

LA PÉROUSE type (Surveying Vessels).

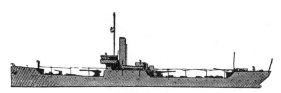

ARRAS class (Despatch Vessel).

TROUPIER (Patrol Boat).

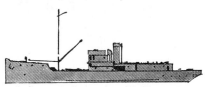

ALIDADE type (Surveying Vessel).

J. COEUR & CHAMPLAIN (Transports).

DUBOURDIEU class (5) (Gunboats).

GRANIT
MEULIÈRE
MICA } (Minesweepers).
PORPHYRE
QUARTZ

PASSEREAU, FAUVETTE (Patrol Vessels).

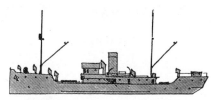

COËTLOGON class (Transports).

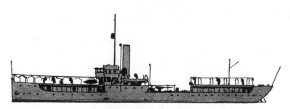

VITREY-LE-FRANÇOIS.

RECOGNITION SILHOUETTES

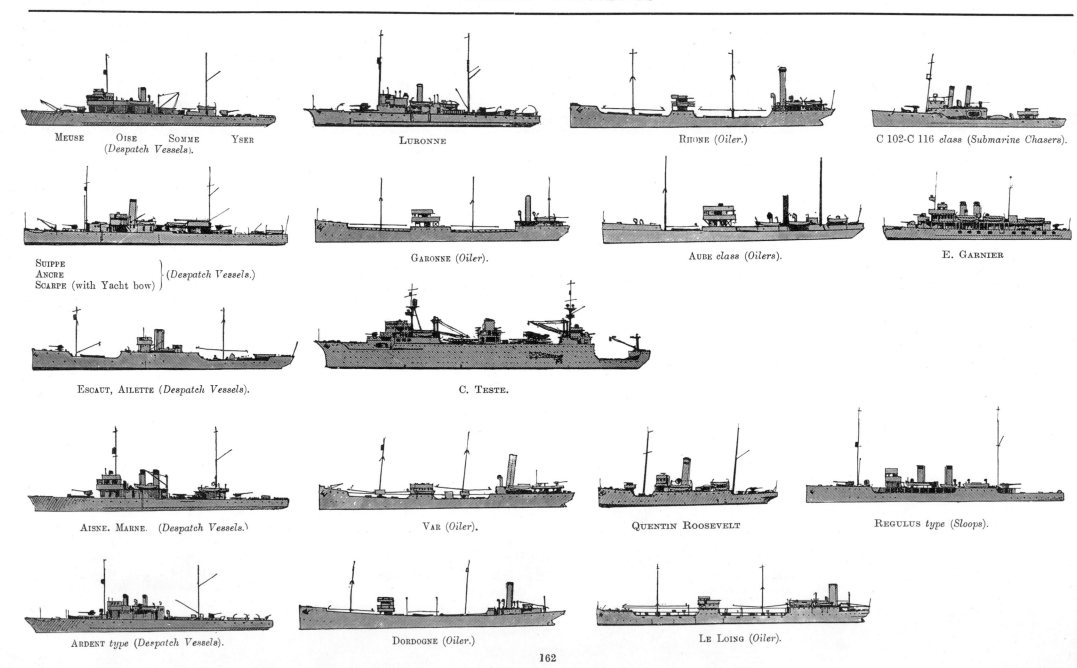

MEUSE OISE SOMME YSER
(Despatch Vessels).

LURONNE

RHONE (Oiler.)

C 102-C 116 class (Submarine Chasers).

SUIPPE
ANCRE
SCARPE (with Yacht bow) } (Despatch Vessels.)

GARONNE (Oiler).

AUBE class (Oilers).

E. GARNIER

ESCAUT, AILETTE (Despatch Vessels).

C. TESTE.

AISNE. MARNE. (Despatch Vessels.)

VAR (Oiler).

QUENTIN ROOSEVELT

REGULUS type (Sloops).

ARDENT type (Despatch Vessels).

DORDOGNE (Oiler.)

LE LOING (Oiler).

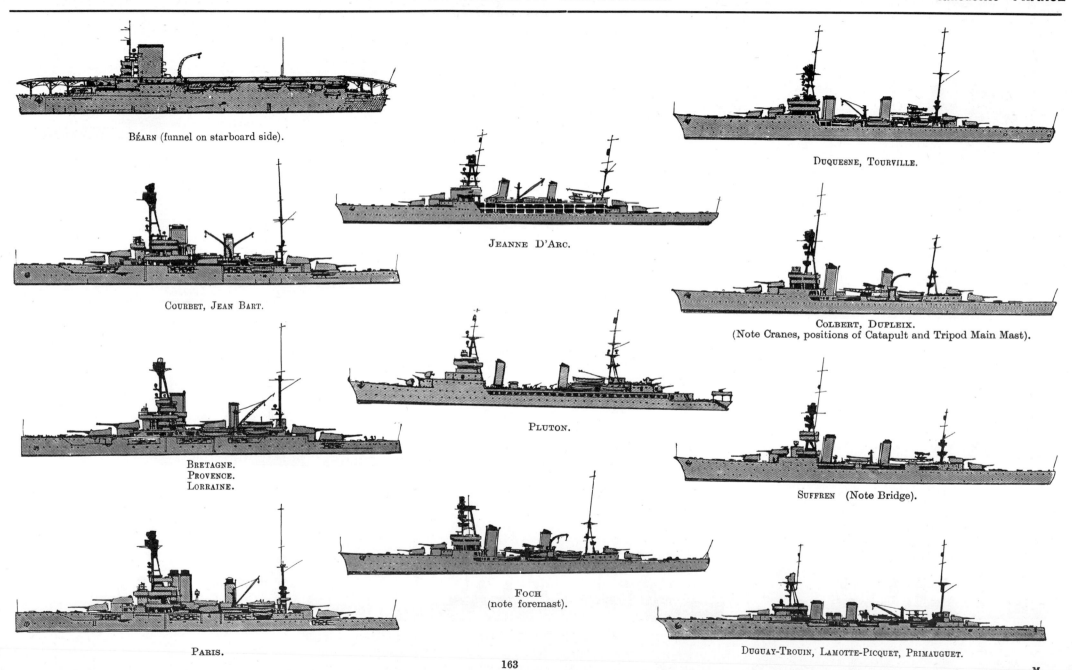

BÉARN (funnel on starboard side).

DUQUESNE, TOURVILLE.

JEANNE D'ARC.

COURBET, JEAN BART.

COLBERT, DUPLEIX.
(Note Cranes, positions of Catapult and Tripod Main Mast).

BRETAGNE.
PROVENCE.
LORRAINE.

PLUTON.

SUFFREN (Note Bridge).

PARIS.

FOCH
(note foremast).

DUGUAY-TROUIN, LAMOTTE-PICQUET, PRIMAUGUET.

M

CASTOR.

POLLUX.

BOUGAINVILLE Class.

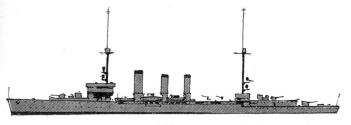

VULOAIN (*Repair Ship*.)

MULHOUSE.

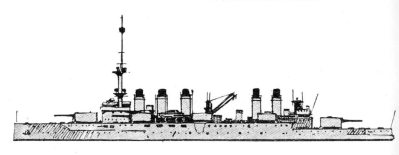

VOLTAIRE.

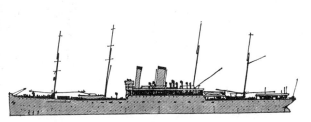

METZ.

THIONVILLE.
(additional tubes now replace AA. aft.)

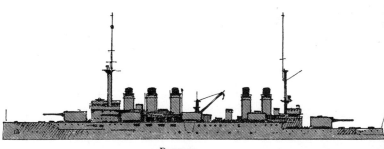

DIDEROT.

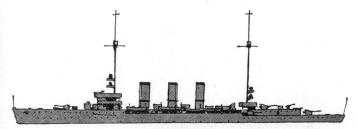

STRASBOURG.

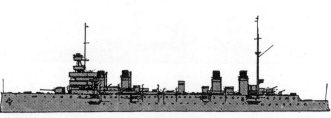

GUEYDON.

WALDECK-ROUSSEAU.

DELAGE, RAGEOT DE LA TOUCHE.

AVENTURIER, INTRÉPIDE.

GUÉPARD type.

CHASTANG, DELIGNY, MAZARÉ, VESCO.

SIMOUN type.

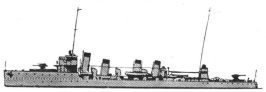
MAT. LEBLANC.

P. DURAND.

CHACAL type (Leaders).

OPINIÂTRE, TÉMÉRAIRE.

BORY type.
(Funnel heights and spacing vary.)

BUINO.

ALGÉRIEN type.

ENSEIGNE ROUX, MEC.-PR. LESTIN.

AM. SÉNÈS, Leader.

C. LUCAS.

ENS. GABOLDE.

SUBMARINES.—

Amazone II, Armide.

Bellone *type*.

Halbronn.

Daphné.

Fulton, Joessel.

Siréne *type*.

M. Callot.

P. Chailley.

V. Réveille.

Redoubtable *class*.

Dupuy de Lôme, Sané, Lagrange, Laplace,
Regnault, Romazzotti,

J. Roulier *type*.

Turquoise *class*.

R. Audry.

Gustave Zédé,   Néréïde.

Requin *class*.

P. Marrast.

H. Fournier, O'Byrne.

J. Corre, Carissan, Trinité-Schillemans.

Surcouf.

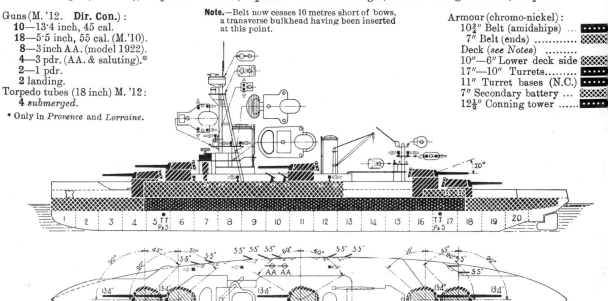

BRETAGNE (April, 1913), **LORRAINE** (September, 1913), **PROVENCE** (April, 1913).
Standard displacement, 22,189 tons. Complement, 1109 (+ 57 as Flagship.)
Length (*waterline*), 541⅓ feet. Beam, 88½ feet. *Maximum* draught, 29 feet. Length *over all*, 544½ feet.

Guns (M. '12. **Dir. Con.**) :
10—13·4 inch, 45 cal.
18—5·5 inch, 55 cal. (M.'10).
8—3 inch A.A. (model 1922).
4—3 pdr. (A.A. & saluting).*
2—1 pdr.
2 landing.
Torpedo tubes (18 inch) M. '12:
4 submerged.

* Only in *Provence* and *Lorraine*.

Note.—Belt now ceases 10 metres short of bows,
a transverse bulkhead having been inserted
at this point.

Armour (chromo-nickel) :
10¾″ Belt (amidships) ...
7″ Belt (ends) ....
Deck (*see* Notes) ....
10″–6″ Lower deck side
17″–10″ Turrets........
11″ Turret bases (N.C.)
7″ Secondary battery ...
12½″ Conning tower ......

Ahead :
4—13·4 in.

Astern:
4—13·4 in.
4—5·5 in.

Broadside: **10**—13·4 in., **9**—5·5 in.

Machinery : Parsons turbine. 4 screws. Boilers : see *Notes*. Designed H.P. 29,000 = 20 kts.
Coal : *normal* 900 tons ; *maximum* 2680 tons. Also **300** tons oil.
Gunnery Notes.—Carry 100 rounds per gun for 13·4 inch and 275 per gun for the 5·5 inch. Janney electro-hydraulic
mountings to big guns. Special cooling for magazines—temperature 77° Fahr. Magazines can be completely flooded
inside ten minutes. Height of guns above l.w.l.: 1st turret, 30¼ feet ; 2nd, 37¾ feet ; 3rd, 33¼ feet ; 4th, 28¼ feet ; 5th,
21⅓ feet. Arcs of training : Nos. 1 and 5, 270° ; Nos. 2 & 4, 280° ; No. 3, 120° either beam. Arcs of secondary guns : 120°.
Big gun elevation increased from 18° to 23°: max range = 23,000 metres.
Torpedo Notes.—8—36″ and 2—30″ searchlights. 4—200 k.w. dynamos. Torpedoes : 24 carried. Also 30 blockade mines.
Armour Notes.—Turrets of maximum thickness at ports, instead of uniform thickness as in *J. Bart* type. According
to the 1917 Edition of "Flottes de Combat," the barbette shields are not of uniform design. Those for the end
barbettes are 13·4″ thick, for the super-firing barbettes 9¾″ thick and for the central barbette 15¾″ thick. The double
bottom is carried to the under side of protective deck. Main belt is 13¼ feet wide, 5⁷⁄₁₂ feet below and 7¾ above
l.w.l. Battery 197 feet long with 7 in. bulkheads. Protective decks : lower 2″ slopes, 1¾″ flat. Upper, 1¾″ flat on
top of belt.
Engineering Notes.—Boilers : *Bretagne*, 24 Niclausse ; *Lorraine*, 24 Belleville ; *Provence*, 18 Guyot du Temple. Grate area :
Bretagne, 2,090 sq. feet ; *Lorraine*, 2,030 sq. feet ; *Provence*, 1,492 sq. feet. Heating surface : *Bretagne*, 64,660 sq. feet ;
Lorraine, 63,700 sq. feet ; *Provence*, 62,585 sq. feet. Pressure, 256 lbs. per sq. in. 300 turbine r.p.m. 2,700 tons coal in
13 bunkers, 300 tons oil in 4 tanks. Endurance : 4,700 miles at 10 kts. 2,800 at 18⅓ kts.

Name	Builder	Machinery	Laid down	Com- pleted	Trials	Turbines	Boilers	Best recent speed
Bretagne	Brest	La Seyne	July '12	Sept.'15		Parsons	Niclausse	⎫
Lorraine	S. Nazaire (Pen.)	S. Nazaire (Pen.)	Nov.'12	July '16	21·4 kts.	Parsons	Belleville	⎬ 20.5
Provence	Lorient	La Seyne	June '12	June'15		Parsons	D.T.Guyot	⎭

General Notes.—B., L. and P. belong to the 1912 programme, one of them being a replace ship for the *Liberté*, blown
up September, 1911. Estimated cost, £2,908,000 per ship=£126 per ton. *Lorraine* taken in hand for extensive
refit at Brest, Sept., 1929 and is being converted to oil-burning. *Bretagne* undergoing similar alterations at La Seyne.

*Unofficial.

LORRAINE. (Now high main Topmast and no fore Topmast). 1928 *Photo, W. A. Fuller, Esq.*

1912 FRENCH BATTLESHIPS.

BRETAGNE.

1930 *Photo.*

PROVENCE.

1930 *Photo, R. Perkins, Esq.*

PROVENCE.

Oct., 1927 *Photo, Dussau (added* 1928).

168

COURBET (Sept., 1911), **JEAN BART** (Sept., 1911), **PARIS** (Sept., 1912).

Standard displacement, W.D.= 22,189 tons. *Full load*, 25,850 tons. Complement, 1108.
Length (p.p.), 541⅓ feet. Beam, 88½ feet. *Maximum* draught, 29 feet. Length *over all*, 544½ feet.

Guns (M. '06—10) :
12—12 inch, 45 cal. } Dir.
22—5·5 inch, 55 cal. (M. '10). } Con.
4—3 inch AA. (M. 1922).
4—3 pdr. (may be AA.)
11—3 pdr. (*Courbet*)
2—1 pdr.
2—landing.
Torpedo tubes (18 inch) :
4 *submerged.*

Armour : (Chromo-nickel) :
11¾″ Belt (amidships)......
7″ Belt (bow) (N.C.) ...
7″ Belt (aft) (N.C.) ......
2¾″ Deck ....
10″—6″ Lower deck side
12½″ Turrets (N.C.) ......
11″ Turret bases (N.C.)...
7″ Secondary battery ...
11¾″ Conning tower (N.C.)

PARIS.

1929 Photo, M. Bar, Toulon.

Name	Builder	Machinery	Laid down	Completed	Trials Full power	Boilers	Best recent speed
J. Bart	Brest	F.&C. de la Méd	Nov., '10	June '13	= 22 04	Belleville	20
Courbet	Lorient	St. N'z're (Ch. de l'Atlantique)	Sept., '10	Sept. '13	= 20·81	Belleville & Du Temple	20
Paris	La Seyne	F.&C. de la Méd	Nov., '11	Aug. '14	35,610 = 21·6	Belleville	20·5

General Notes—Designed by M. Lyasse. Construction very fine and highly finished in details. Average cost about £2,475,000. The heavy weight of deep 7″ belt at ends made them pitch in a head sea, hence modification noted against plans above. On the other hand, *J. Bart* was twice torpedoed in the bows by an Austrian submarine and her heavy bow belt contributed largely to her survival. *France*, of this class, foundered in Quiberon Bay, Aug., 1922. All this class have been reconstructed, 1928–1929. *Courbet* has been completely reboilered at La Seyne (1929) with ex-Normandie type boilers, and is now gunnery training-ship instead of *Ernest Renan.*

Ahead :
8—12 in.
6—5·5 in.

Astern :
8—12 in.
10—5·5 in.

Broadside : **10—12 in., 11—5·5 in.**

Machinery : Parsons turbine. 4 screws. 24 Boilers : Belleville or Du Temple (see notes). Designed H.P. 28,000 = 20 kts. Coal : *normal*, 906 tons ; *maximum* 2452 tons. ; also 450 tons oil (two boiler rooms are fitted for oil burning). *Endurance —— at 10 kts., 2700 at 18¾ kts.

Armour Notes—Belt, 13¼ feet wide ; 7¾ feet of it above water, 5½ feet of it below. For about 325 feet it is 10¾″. Upper belt, 7″ thick forms redoubt for secondary battery. The 4—5·5 inch aft. are in casemates. Prot. decks : 2¾″ curved from lower edge of belt to l.w.l. level. Above that a flat 1¾″ deck from end to end on top of main belt. Above again is a 1¼″ splinter deck against aerial attack. Conning tower is in three stories. 10¾″ communication tube. Two armoured fire control stations on top.

**Gunnery Notes.*—Amidship 12 inch 180°, the centre line turrets 270° each. The 5·5 inch 120°. Elevation of guns reported increased to give range of 24,000 metres. Height of guns above water : Turrets (1) 30½ feet, (2) 37¾ (amidships) 25 feet, (5) 28½ feet, (6) 21⅓ feet ; upper deck battery, 5·5 inch, 21⅓ feet ; main deck, 5·5 inch aft, 11⅔ feet. Ammunition carried : 100 for each 12 in., 275 for each 5·5 inch, 300 for each 3 pdr. Westinghouse refrigerators in magazines. 77°F.

**Torpedo Notes.*—8 searchlights (36 inch), also 2—30 inch. Carries 12 torpedoes and 30 blockade mines.

**Engineering Notes.*—Pressure : 256 lbs. outer shafts : H.P. turbines ; inner, L.P. Condensers (2) : 32,076 sq. feet cooling surface. Turbines : 300 r.p.m. Belleville oil fuel system.

* Unofficial.

COURBET. (*Jean Bart* similar, but goose neck cranes.)

1930 Photo, Bar.

DANTON CLASS.— 3 SHIPS.

DIDEROT (April, 1909), **CONDORCET** (April, 1909), and **VOLTAIRE** (Jan., 1909).

Standard displacement, 17,597 tons.   Complement, 923.

Length (*w.l.*), 475¾ feet.   Beam, 84⅔ feet.   *Mean* draught, 27 feet.   *Max.* draught, 28⅔ feet.
Length (*over all*), 481 feet.

Guns :
  4—12 inch, 45 cal. (M '06).
  12—9·4 inch, 49·5 cal.
  (M '02-'06).
  *12—3 (none on board *Condorcet*).
  2—3 in. A.A. (on 9·4 inch turrets).
  4—3 pdr. (*Condorcet*).
  2—3 pdr. (landing).
  2—1 pdr.
Torpedo tubes (M'04, 18 inch) :
  2 *submerged* (broadside).

  (See also notes.)

Armour :
  10½" Belt (amidships) … ……
  6" Belt (ends) ………………
  3" Deck (flat on upper belt) …
  3" Deck (below belt) …………
  9"—6" Lower deck side. ……
  2½" Upper belt (bow) …………
  12½" Turrets (big guns) (N.C.)
  11" Turret bases (N.C.)
  8¾" Secondary turrets (6) (N.C.)
  12" Conning tower (N.C.) ……
  Total weight about 4800 tons.

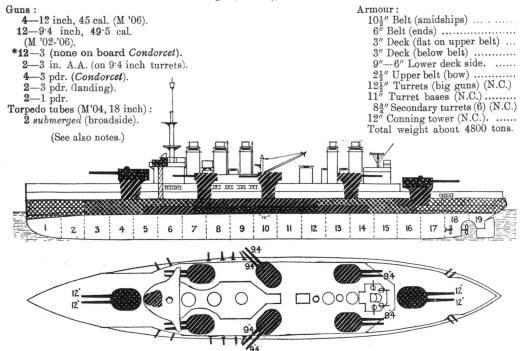

VOLTAIRE.   (*Condorcet* similar.)   1925 *Photo, by courtesy of the Ministry of Marine.*

Machinery : Parsons turbine. 4 screws. Boilers : 26 Belleville or Niclausse (large tubes). Designed
H.P. 22,500 = 19·25 kts. Coal : *normal* 965 tons : *maximum* 2100 tons. Endurance : *nominally*, 3750 miles
at 10 kts., 2300 at 18½ kts. (See note below.)

Name.	Builder.	Machinery.	Laid down	Completed.	Trials. 24 hrs.	Trials. 10 hrs.	Trials. 5 hrs.	Boilers	Best recent speed.
Diderot	St. Nazaire	St. Nazaire	Oct. '07	Sept.,'11	=18·4	=19·48	=19·9	Niclausse	
Condorcet	St. Nazaire	St. Nazaire	Aug. '07	June '11	=18·02	=19·31	=19·7	Niclausse	14-16
Voltaire	La Seyne	F. & Ch., Médit.	July,'07	Aug. '11	=18·60	=19·78	=20·66	Belleville	

DIDEROT.   1930 *Photo, by M. Bar.*

General Notes.—Average cost, £2,190,000 each. They are not very successful ships, and consume large quantities of
coal at cruising speed. Some have lateral anti-torpedo "caissons" along hull below waterline. *Danton* of this
class lost during War. *Voltaire* twice torpedoed by U-boat during 1918 and repaired. Designed by M. Lhomme.
Vergniaud condemned 1921, and expended as a target for aircraft bombs. *Condorcet* and *Voltaire* refitted, 1923-24,
Diderot 1925, extra under-water protection being given at some sacrifice of speed. All three are now employed
as sea-going training ships. *Condorcet*, being attached to Torpedo School, carries several extra deck torpedo tubes
for practice purposes and no 3" gun battery.

BÉARN (F. & Ch. de la Mediterranée, La Seyne).

Laid down January, 1914, as a battleship of the "*Normandie*" class. Launched April, 1920, construction having been suspended during the war; re-designed as a Fleet Carrier and conversion begun at La Seyne in August, 1923. Finally completed May, 1927.

Standard displacement: 22,146 tons; 25,000 tons *full load*.

Dimensions: 576 (*w.l.*), 560 (*p.p.*) feet × 89 feet × 26 feet. (Extreme beam is 102 feet.)

Complement, 875.

Guns :
8—6.1 inch.
6—14 pdr. AA.
8—3 pdr. AA.
12 M.G.
Tubes :
4—21.7 inch.

Armour :
1″ Main deck ....
1—2¾″ Lower deck ....
1″ Flight deck ....
3¼″ Side armour to 6½ feet below w.l.

BÉARN, (fore end of flight deck now curved down).

1927 *Photo, Marius Bar, Toulon.*

Total designed H.P. 39,000 = 21 kts. Fitted with 2 turbines on inner shafts (for main propulsion), = 24,000 S.H.P. and 2 sets reciprocating engines on outer shafts (for cruising and manœuvring purposes only) = 15,000 I.H.P. This machinery was originally ordered for *Normandie.* 12 Du Temple-Normand small tube boilers. 4 screws. Oil fuel: 2,160 tons. Radius: 6,000 miles at 10 kts. Is capable of accommodating over 40 planes.

At a height of 51 feet from the waterline is the flight deck, 600 feet long. An external gangway at a level 3 ft. 9 in. lower allows personnel to move about clear of the flight deck. Underneath the flight deck is the central hangar, in which are housed 5 torpedo planes, 5 reconnaissance planes, and 7 fighter planes (part of the total of 40 carried). Under this hangar again, are workshops for assembling and repairs, and for accommodation of partially equipped planes. The hangar and workshops can be divided into two portions, by means of asbestos curtains.

Hangar and workshops are equipped with overhead transporter cranes for the rapid manipulation of heavy weights, and a special type of derrick (12 tons capacity, 33 feet radius) is fitted on the starboard side of ship, abaft funnel.

Planes are carried up to flight deck by means of three electric lifts, the smallest being 27 × 40 feet and the largest 50 × 50 feet. On a lift, forward, is a charthouse which by this means can be raised above or dropped below flight deck.

A catapult, of the compressed air type, about 65 feet in length, is mounted on a turntable ; it can throw off a plane at a speed of about 47 m.p.h.

Smoke is diluted with cold air to avoid eddies in surrounding atmosphere.

Other items of equipment comprise a special hot water service for filling radiators of seaplanes, and a pneumatic distributing system for conveying their fuel.

Stores carried include 3530 cubic ft. of petrol, under inert gas, and 530 cubic feet of oil.

It has been stated that owing to lack of space on flight deck, only about one fourth of the total number of planes carried can be employed simultaneously.

Trials.—On trial a speed of barely 20 kts. was reached with over 40,000 H.P.

1928 *Photo, W. A. Fuller, Esq.*
BÉARN, showing lift opening up.

BÉARN, bow view.

1927 *Photo, M. Bar.*

AIRCRAFT TENDER. (*Transport d'Aviation.*)

BÉARN.

Note alteration to flight deck at bows.

1927 *Photo, Marius Bar, Toulon.*

1930 *Photo, M. Bar.*

BÉARN.

1928 *Photo, R. Perkins, Esq.*

1931 *Photo, Bar, Toulon.*

COMMANDANT TESTE. (April 12th, 1929).

Standard Displacement, 10,000 tons. Length, 512¾ feet (*p.p.*), 558 feet (*o.a.*). Beam, 71½ feet (88½ feet, extreme). Draught, 23½ feet. Complement, 649.

Guns :
   12—3.9 inch AA.
   8—3 pdr. AA.
   12 M.G.

Armour :
   2″ (H.T.?) side at waterline and a
   1½″ protective deck over engine and boiler spaces.

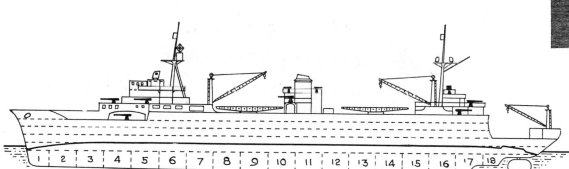

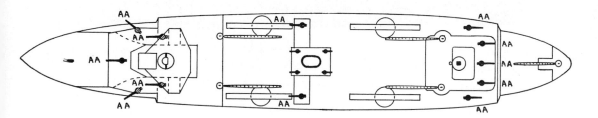

Machinery : 2 Schneider-Zoelly geared turbines. 2 screws. 4 Small tube boilers (mixed firing). S.H.P. 21,000 = 20.5 kts. Radius of action : 6000 miles at 10 kts. Fuel :— Oil 290, coal 720 tons.

Notes.—This vessel is intended to act as a tender to *Béarn*, and as a reserve from which aircraft supplies can be drawn by cruisers which carry planes. Authorised under 1926 Programme, she was ordered in May, 1927, from the Sociétie d'Exploitation des Chantiers de la Gironde, Bordeaux (a subsidiary of the Schneider group). She will ultimately mount 4 catapults.

Special Note.—The small transports *Hamelin* and *A. de Courcy* (described elsewhere) are now fitted as Aircraft Tenders their official rating being " Ravitailleurs d'Aviation."

COMMANDANT TESTE. (guns not mounted).

1931 *Photo, Bar, Toulon.*

Commandant Teste, running trials without guns aboard.

1931 *Photo, Official.*

1930 *Photo.*

WALDECK-ROUSSEAU (March, 1908).

Standard displacement, 12,017 tons.   Complement, 892.

Length (*waterline*), 515 feet.   Beam, 70⅔ feet.   *Max.* draught, 27½ feet.   Length *over all*, 521⅓ feet.

Guns--(M. '02) :

14—7·6 inch, 50 cal.
8 - 3 inch plus 2 A A.
10—9 pdr.
2—3 pdr.
2—1 pdr. or M.G.

Torpedo tubes (18 inch) :
2 *submerged*
(over Section 4).

Armour :

6¾″ Belt (amidship)
3″ Belt (ends)
6″ Bulkhead (aft) ...
2½″ Deck (slopes)
6″ Turrets (N.C.) ...
5″ Turret bases ...
6″ Casemates (4) ...
10″ Conning tower ...
(*Total weight 3400 tons*).

Ahead :
6—7·6 in.

Astern :
6—7·6 in.

Broadside : **9—7·6 in.**

Machinery : 3 sets vertical triple expansion.   3 screws.   Boilers (large tube) : *See Notes.*   Designed H.P.
36,000 = 23 kts.   Coal : *normal* 1,242 tons ; *maximum* 1,900 tons.   *Nominal endurance* : 6560 miles at 10 kts.
2 seaplanes added to equipment, 1923.   *E. Quinet* Lost Jan. 1930.

Name	Builder	Machinery	Laid down	Completed	Trials : 30 boilers 10 hours	Full power 3 hours	Boilers	Best recent speed
W. Rousseau	Lorient Yard		June,'06	1911		35,286=23·1	42 Niclausse	20

Will terminate her career as flagship of Far Eastern Forces.

GUEYDON.   (Note alterations to mast and bridgework.)   1927 *Photo, M. Bar, Toulon.*

(*Sea-going Gunnery Training Ship.*)

GUEYDON (September, 1899).   Displacement : 8320 tons.   Length (*waterline*), 452¾ feet.   Beam,
63⅔ feet.   *Max.* draught, 25 feet.   Length (*over all*), 459 feet.   Guns : 8—5.5 inch, 4—3
inch AA., 12—40 m/m., 4—37 m/m,   Armour (Harvey Nickel) : 6″ Belt (ends), 3″ Forecastle,
2″—1″, ¾″ Decks, 3″—2¼″ Lower deck side, 7¾″ Casemates (8), 6¼″ Conning tower.   Machinery :
2 sets vertical triple expansion.   3 screws.   Boilers : 20 Niclausse.   Designed H.P. 19,600 =
21 kts.   Coal : *normal* 1030 tons, *maximum* 1650 tons.   Begun at Lorient, 1898 ; completed,
1902.   Complement, 487.   Reconstructed, with tripod mast and other modifications, 1926.

ERNEST RENAN   } Disarmed 1930.   Now floating barracks at Toulon.
JULES MICHELET

CONDE, Disarmed and now floating barracks at Lorient.

MONTCALM, Disarmed and now floating barracks at Brest (3rd and 4th funnels cut down).

1931 CRUISERS 1932

La GALISSONNIÈRE   **JEAN-de-VIENNE.**

C. D. E. F.

Displacement, 7,500 tons.

Length.   Beam.   Draught.

Guns :
9—6·1 inch.

The design for these ships is still under consideration.   That most favoured includes three turrets, two forward and one aft, each mounting three guns. The secondary armament of three twin 4″ guns disposed as in the Italian *Condottieri* class.   A certain amount of protection is to be included and a high speed—36 knots nominal—allowed for.

The first two belong to the 1930–31 Programme : the other four to the 1931–32 Programme.

(Algerie Class **1.**)
ALGERIE, (Brest, Dec., 1931).
Standard Displacement, 10,000 tons.   Complement,

Length,   Beam,   Draught,

Guns : 8—8″ (new model). (**Dir. Con.**)

12—4″ AA.

8—37 mm.

Torpedo tubes :

6—21 inch in triples.

Armour :

Belt—6 inch.

1931 Illustration.

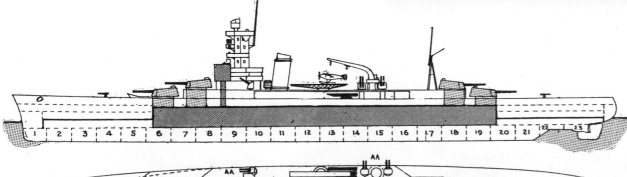

Machinery : 4 Ratean geared Turbines   Boilers : 8 Guyot.

D.H.P. 80,000=31–32 kts.   Fuel :   tons.

General Notes.—Laid down on December 1st, 1930 at Brest. The design constitutes a distinct departure from the "Tin-clad" vogue, and is to be more along the lines of a modern edition of the armoured cruiser of thirty years ago, being a reply to the Italian *Zara* type. A novel distribution of internal armour is to be introduced giving special anti-aerial and torpedo protection, while the big guns and hoists are to be adequately armoured instead of being mounted in gunhouses made up of thin plating with unarmoured hoists. Speed will undergo some reduction, but the ships are not likely to suffer any real loss of military qualities on this account. A new model 8″ gun is to be introduced in this class, firing improved shells and having a greater range than the present model.

FOCH

1931, *Official Photo.*

1931, *Official Photo.*

SUFFREN CLASS—4 SHIPS.

SUFFREN.

1930 *Photo.*

SUFFREN (May 3rd, 1927).   **COLBERT** (April 20th, 1928).

FOCH (April 24th, 1929).   **DUPLEIX** (October 9th, 1930).

Standard Displacement, 9,938 tons.   Complement, 605.

Length (*p.p.*), 607 feet, (*o.a.*), 617 feet.   Beam, 65 feet.   Draught, 20 feet.

Guns :

8—8″ (Dir. Con.)
8—3·5″ AA. (3″ in *Suffren*)
8—37 m/m Q.F.
Torpedo Tubes :
6—21″ (in triples above water)
2 Catapults.
3 Seaplanes.

Armour :

Has a patch of thin armour over engine and boiler spaces, with 17 W.T. bulkheads carried right up to upper deck. Coal bunkers arranged to give extra protection. Fitted with external bulges.

Machinery : 4 Rateau geared turbines.   Boilers : 9 Guyot (8 main and 1 auxiliary).   Designed : S.H.P. 90,000=33 kts.   3 screws.   Fuel : oil, tons.   Coal : tons.   Auxiliary equipment driven through 3 Diesel (Renault type) with dynamos.   Radius :

Name	Builder	Machinery	Laid down	Completed	Trials
Suffren	Brest	A. & C. de	May, 1926	Dec., 1928	98,300=33·7
Colbert	,,	Bretagne	June, 1927	Sept., 1929	101,800=33·9
Foch	,,	in all	June, 1928	1930	119,000—34.1
Dupleix	,,		Oct., 1929	1931	

Are able to steam at 29 knots with half-power.

Cost : *Suffren*, 144 million. *Colbert*, 147 million francs.
  Foch, 156 million. *Dupleix*, 167 million francs.
General Notes.—Are modified editions of *Tourville* class in which about two knots has been sacrificed in order to gain better protection. They differ in detail as regards appearance, *Dupleix* being similar to *Colbert*. At full speed *Foch* proved very successful, (compare with *Lamotte-Picquet*) due to modified bow and stern lines.

COLBERT. (Note position of catapult, bridgework, cranes, and after mast.)

1930 *Photo.*

Dupleix similar, but with s.l. on foremast mounted on a single platform.

DUQUESNE. (with fore control top). 1930 *Photo.*

TOURVILLE. *Photo added 1930, W. W. Stewart, Esq.*

SUFFREN. 1930 *Photo, courtesy of the Ministry of Marine.*

1924 CRUISERS.

(TOURVILLE CLASSES—2 SHIPS).

DUQUESNE (Dec. 17th, 1925), **TOURVILLE** (Aug. 24th, 1926).   Standard displacement, 10,000 tons (11,900 tons deep lead).   Complement, 605.   Length (*p.p.*), 607 feet; (*o.a.*), 626½;   Beam, 63 feet.   Draught, 20⅔ feet.

TOURVILLE (without control top).

1928 *Photo, by courtesy of Ministry of Marine.*

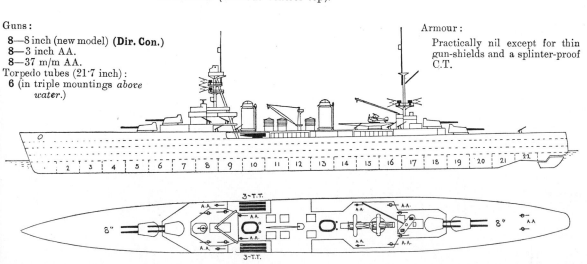

Guns:
  8—8 inch (new model) **(Dir. Con.)**
  8—3 inch AA.
  8—37 m/m AA.
Torpedo tubes (21·7 inch):
  6 (in triple mountings *above water*.)

Armour:
  Practically nil except for thin gun-shields and a splinter-proof C.T.

Machinery: 4 Rateau geared turbines.   Boilers: 9 Guyot (8 main and 1 auxiliary).   Designed S.H.P., 120,000 = 34.5 kts.   4 screws.   Oil: 1800 tons.   Radius: 5,000 miles at 15 kts.; 700 at full speed.

Duquesne and *Tourville* equipped with 2 scouting seaplanes and a launching catapult.

Name	Builder	Machinery	Laid down	Completed	Trials
Tourville	Lorient	A. & C. de	14 April, 1925	1928	130,000 = 36.15
Duquesne	Brest	Bretagne	30 Oct., 1924	1928	135,000 = 35.3

General Note.—Above ships are practically enlarged copies of *Duguay-Trouin* design, with an improved form of hull and heavier armament.

Engineering Notes.—Boiler and engine rooms are arranged alternately, and not in two separate groups, as suggested in plans appearing elsewhere.   *Tourville's* trial speed of over 36 kts. was obtained while running on normal Displacement.   Auxiliaries driven through 3 Diesels (Renault Type) with dynamo.

JEANNE D'ARC (Feb. 14th, 1930.)

Standard Displacement, 6,496 tons.   Dimensions, $525 \times 57\frac{1}{2} \times 17\frac{3}{4}$ feet.

Complement : 505

1931 *Official Photo.*

Guns :
   8—6·1″.
   4—3″ AA.
   2—37 m/m.
Tubes :
   2—21·7 inch.
Seaplanes : 2.

Armour : Nil.

Protective deck and light plating to gun-houses and conning tower.

Machinery Note.—Auxiliary driven through 4 groups of 200 k. watts (steam) when at sea, and 2 Diesels (Renault type) of 120 k. watts.

Fuel consumption :—
   14·5 kts.=145 kilos p.m. (154 estimated).
   20 ,, =257 ,, ,, (318 ,,).

3 hours' full power : 39,000 H.P.=27·84 kts.
19 kts. maintained with cruising turbines only.

Ahead **4**—6·1″.   Broadside 8—6·1″.   Astern **4**—6·1″.

Machinery : Penhoët, Parsons turbines. 4 screws. Designed H.P. 32,500=25·5 kts.
Oil : 14,000. Radius, 5,000 miles at cruising speed (14–15 kts.). Boilers : 4 Penhoët.

General Notes.—Designed to carry two catapults as shown in plan, but these have been discarded and she will now have seaplane stowage amidships only. Will accommodate 156 midshipmen and cadets and 20 instructional officers, in addition to ordinary complement. Authorised under 1927 Programme and laid down at Penhoët Yard, St. Nazaire in 1928. Completed in 1931.

DUGUAY-TROUIN.

1927 *Official Photo.*

LAMOTTE PICQUET.

1930 *Photo.*

DUGUAY-TROUIN

1927 *Photo "Fighting Ships."*

DUGUAY-TROUIN.

1928 *Photo, W. A. Fuller Esq.*

1922 CRUISERS.

(DUGUAY-TROUIN CLASS—3 SHIPS.)

DUGUAY-TROUIN (14th Aug., 1923), **LAMOTTE-PICQUET** (21st March, 1924),
PRIMAUGUET (21st May, 1924.)

Standard displacement, 7,249 tons. Normal displacement, 7,880 tons. (*Full load*, 9,350.) Complement, 577
Length (*p.p*) 575 feet, (*o.a.*) 604 feet. Beam, 56¼ feet. Draught, 17¼ feet *mean*; 20 feet *maximum* at full load.

PRIMAUGUET.   1930 *Photo.*

Guns:—
  8—6·1 inch, 55 cal. (**Dir. Con.**)
  4—3 inch AA.
  2—3 pdr. (saluting).
  1—1 pdr. (landing).
  4 Machine.
Torpedo tubes (21·7 inch) :
  12 (in triple mountings)
    above water.

Armour :
  Practically nil, except
  for thin gunshields,
  splinter-proof C.T.,
  and double armoured
  deck.

Machinery : 4 Parsons geared turbines. Boilers : 8 Guyot. Designed S.H.P. 100,000 = 34 kts. 4 screws. Oil : 500 tons *normal*, 1500 tons *maximum*. Radius : 880 miles at 34 kts. ; 1290 at 30 ; 3000 at 20 ; 4500 at 15. Each vessel carries 2 scouting type seaplanes, and a launching catapult (abaft after turret). Depth charges carried.

Gunnery Notes.—6.1 inch guns are a new model with ballistic powers superior to old marks of 7.6 inch. Range reported to be 23,000 metres, elevation 35°. Reason for adoption of this calibre is said to have been its uniformity with Army type 6.1 inch, simplifying munition supply, more particularly of gas and incendiary shells. Gunhouses are reported to be gas-tight, and to have a special method of ventilation by forced draught.

Engineering Notes.—Trial results tabulated are averages of 6 hours with full complement of fuel and stores. *Maximum* speed for 1 hour, 34.5 kts. All three ships maintained 30 kts. for 24 hours' continuous steaming at half power with full load, and have proved very economical. Excellent sea-keeping qualities. Heating surface, 13,209 sq. feet.

Torpedo Notes.—24 torpedoes carried (12 in tubes, 12 in magazine). In addition, 4—17.7 inch torpedoes are carried for picket boats.

Name.	Builder.	Machinery.	Laid down.	Completed.	Trials. (6 hours)	
Duguay-Trouin	Brest	F. & C. de la Méd.	4 Aug., '22	Aug., 1925	116,235 = 33·6	
Primauguet	Brest	A. & C. de la Loire	10 Aug.,'23	Nov., 1925	116,849 = 33·06	
Lamotte-Picquet	Lorient	C. & A. de St. Nazaire (Penhoët).	17 Jan., '23	Dec., 1925	115,100 = 33·04	

General Notes.—Completion dates given above do not represent actual passing into service, but merely dates of beginning trials. These ships have shown excellent sea-going qualities.

EMILE BERTIN, (PENHOËT, ST. NAZAIRE.   ).

Displacement : 5,886 Tons.   Complement ———.   Dims :   ×   ×

Guns :
6—5·5 inch.
 —37 mm. H.A.
 —M.G.

Machinery :   S.H.P.   Kts.   Fuel :   Boilers.

Notes.—Authorised under the 1933 Programme. Laid down 1930. To be completed in 1933. The triple mounting makes
  its first appearance in the French Navy in this ship. She is a development of the *Pluton* but the cruiser characteristics are not so much subordinated to those of the mine-layer.

1928 MINELAYING CRUISER.

PLUTON (April 10th, 1929).
Standard Displacement, 4,850 tons. Complement, 406. Length, 472½ feet. Beam, 51 feet.
Draught, 17 feet.

PLUTON.

1931, *Official Photo*.

Guns :
 4—5.5 inch.
 10—37 m/m. AA.
 12 M.G.

Armour : Nil.

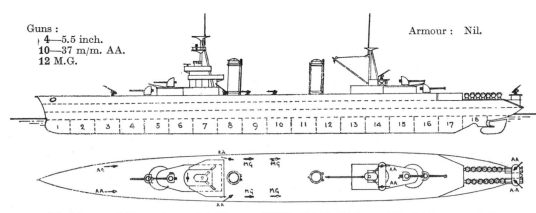

Machinery : 2 Breguet geared turbines. S.H.P. 57,000 = 30 kts. Oil = 1,200 tons. Boilers :
4 small tube.

Note.—Authorised under 1925 Programme, and laid down at Lorient Dockyard in April, 1928, comple ed April, 1931.
Trials : H.P., 56,000 = 30·6 kts.

186

1914 (ex-German) Cruiser.

METZ.

1922 *Photo.*

METZ (ex-German *Königsberg*, December, 1915).

Standard displacement, 5,264 tons (6,142 *full load*).   Complement, 438.

Length (*w.l.*) 489 feet, (*p.p.*) 478¼ feet.   Beam, 47 feet.   *Designed* draught, 16½ feet *mean*; at *full load* maximum is 21 feet.

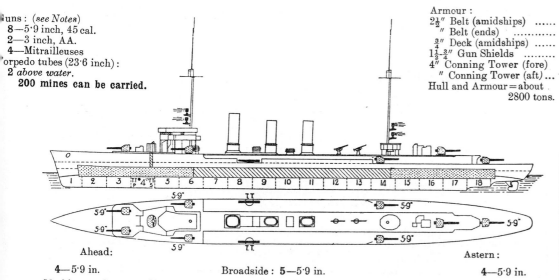

Guns : (*see Notes*)	Armour :
8—5·9 inch, 45 cal.	2½″ Belt (amidships) ......
2—3 inch, AA.	″ Belt (ends) ....
4—Mitrailleuses	¾″ Deck (amidships) ......
Torpedo tubes (23·6 inch) :	1½–¾″ Gun Shields ....
2 *above water*.	4″ Conning Tower (fore)
200 mines can be carried.	″ Conning Tower (aft) ...
	Hull and Armour = about 2800 tons.

Ahead:

4—5·9 in.   Broadside : 5—5·9 in.

Astern :

4—5·9 in.

Machinery : German "Marine type" turbines. 4 screws. Boilers : 14 Schulz-Thornycroft in 5 rooms; 8 mixed burning, 6 oil only. Designed H.P. 36,000 = 27·5 kts. Coal : *normal*, 500 tons ; *maximum*, 1276 tons (+475 tons oil fuel). German authorities give radius as 1162 at 27 kts., 4875 at 10 kts.

Gunnery Notes.—Magazines immediately below protective deck and crowns come above w.l.

General Notes.—Was begun as *Ersatz Gazelle*, of German 1914-15 Programme. Built and engined by Weser Co., Bremen. Begun 1914, completed August, 1914. Surrendered at Cherbourg, 1920, and added to French Navy, September, 1920. Belt 3′ 11″ below *w.l.* and 6′ 10″ above. Freeboard at bow 26′ 6″, 13′ 3″ at stern. Machinery and engineering stores about 1320 tons. The French consider her a good and dry seaboat, but burns an enormous amount of coal. Reported to be good for about 22-23 kts. continuous sea speed. Now in reserve.

1912 (ex-German) Cruiser.

1922 *Photo*, Dussau.

STRASBOURG (ex-German *Regensburg*, April, 1914).

Standard displacement, 4,723 tons (5,511 *full load*).   Complement, 420.

Length (*w.l.*), 456 feet.   Beam, 45 feet.   Draught, 16 feet *mean*, 17 feet *max*.

Guns (German) :		Armour (Krupp):
7—5·9 inch (45 cal.)		4″ Belt (amidships) ....
1—3 inch, AA.	**Correction to Plan.**	2½″ Belt (ends) ....
4 machine.	*Only 1 gun is now mounted forward instead of a pair as shown below.*	2″ Deck (amidships) ....
Torpedo tubes (19·7 inch German) :		4″ C.T. ....
4 *above water*.		
Mines :		
Fitted to carry 120.		

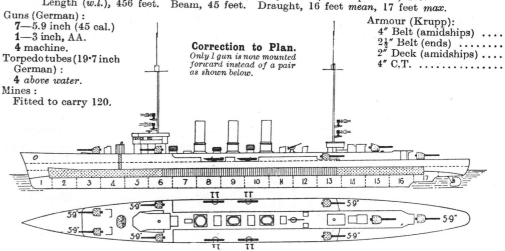

Machinery : German "Marine type" turbines. 4 screws. Boilers : 14 Schulz-Thornycroft. Designed S.H.P. 32,000 = 27.25 kts. Coal : *normal*, 470 tons ; *maximum*, 1170 tons. Oil : 430 tons. Endurance : 4466 miles at 11 kts. : 918 miles at 25.5 kts.

Notes.—Begun under German 1912 Programme as *Ersatz Irene*, by Weser Co., Bremen. Completed late in 1914. Surrendered at Cherbourg, June, 1920. Armaments mounted in this ship, when in German Navy, were (*a*) 12— 4·1 inch, 1914-15, (*b*) 2—5·9 inch, 8—4·1 inch, about 1915-17, (*c*) 7—5·9 inch, at end of war. Has done 26 kts. on trials, after refit (March, 1925) but is only good for about 22-23 kts. at sea now. Now in reserve.

THIONVILLE.   *1930 Photo, M. Bar, Toulon.*

THIONVILLE (ex-Austrian *Novara*, Feb., 1913).
(Classed as *Contre-Torpilleur*.)

Standard displacement, 2922 metric tons.   Complement, 318, as Torpedo Training Ship, 425.

Length (*w.l.*), $410\frac{3}{4}$ feet.   Beam, 42 feet.   *Mean* draught, 15 feet.   Length *over all*, $428\frac{1}{2}$ feet.

Guns (French) :
9—3·9 inch (M. 1917)
1—3 inch A.A.
Torpedo tubes (French 21 inch) :
4 *above water*.
(As Torpedo School.)

Armour (steel) :
$2\frac{1}{2}''$ Belt (amidships)
2″ Bulkheads ....
$\frac{3}{4}''$ Deck................

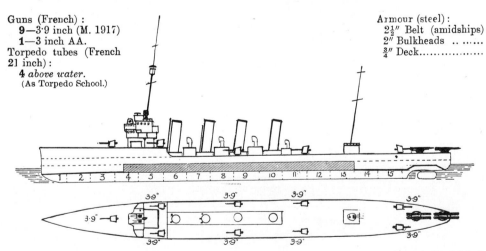

Ahead :
2—3·9 inch.
     Broadside : 4—3·9 inch, 5—18 inch torpedo tubes.
Astern : 2—3·9 inch.
3—18 inch T.T.

Machinery : A.E.G. (Curtis) turbine (*see Notes*).   4 screws.   Boilers: 16 Yarrow, modified by Indret. Designed H.P. 25,000=27 kts.   Coal : *normal,* 450 tons ; *maximum,* 650 tons.   Nominal radius of action : 860 miles at 27 kts., 1600 miles at 24 kts. (actually less).

Notes.—Built for Austro-Hungarian Navy at Fiume ; engined by Ganz-Danubius Co.   Begun February, 1912, completed October, 1914.   Interned at Cattaro, Nov., 1918.   Towed to Bizerta, 1920, *Thionville* foundered near Brindisi while on passage, but she was refloated. Refitted at Cherbourg D.Y., 1921. *Venezia* (ex-*Saida*) and *Brindisi* (ex-*Helgoland*) of this class added to Italian Navy.   Attached to Torpedo School, Toulon, for long distance running, and officially rated as Contre-Torpilleur. Best recent speed, 26 kts.

MULHOUSE.   *1925 Photo, by courtesy of the Ministry of Marine.*

MULHOUSE (ex-German *Stralsund*) (Nov., 1911).
Standard displacement, 4527 tons ; 5100 tons, *full load.* Complement, 453.
Length (*w.l.*), $446\frac{1}{5}$ feet.   Beam, 43·6 feet.   *Mean* draught, $16\frac{3}{4}$ feet.

Guns (German) :
7—5·9 inch, 45 cal.
2—3 inch A.A.
4—3 pdr.
2 machine.
Torpedo tubes
(19·7 in. German) :
2 *above water.*
Carries 120 mines.

Armour :
$3\frac{1}{3}''$ Belt (amidships)
$2\frac{1}{4}''$ Belt (ends)......
2″ Deck (amidships)
4″ Conning tower...

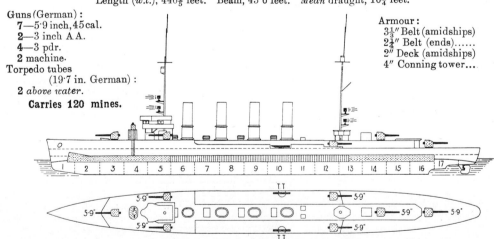

Machinery : Turbine.   4 screws.   Boilers : 16 Schulz-Thornycroft (re-tubed 1925). Designed H.P. : 24,200 = 26·75 kts.   Coal : *normal* 750 tons ; *max.* 1100 tons.   Radius : 5850 miles at 12 kts.   Oil : 140 tons.
Armour Notes.—Belt is very narrow, and at full load practically submerged.
Engineering Notes.—4 boilers are oil burning.

Name	Builder	Machinery	Laid down	Completed	Trials (mean)		Turbines	Best speed
					6 hours	Best hour		
Mulhouse	Weser, Bremen	Weser	Ap. '10	June '12	27,032 = 26·9	35,515 = 28·27	Bergmann	22

Begun under German 1910 Programme. *Magdeburg* of this class sunk 1914 in the Baltic. *Breslau* mined and sunk off Imbros, 1918.   Sister ship *Taranto* added to Italian Navy, 1920.   They were very fast ships, but vibrated greatly over 22 kts.   Proved bad sea boats on first trials, and large bilge-keels were fitted to lessen rolling.   All were heavily forced on trials.   Very lightly built, extensive use being made of steel castings and aluminium.   Engine-rooms very cramped.   Double-bottom shallow, and only carried up amidships to under side of protective deck. Above protective deck are coal-bunkers, about 12 feet wide. *Mulhouse* surrendered at Cherbourg and added to French Navy, Sept., 1920. Refitted at Brest, 1925, but is not considered good for much more service. Now in reserve.

1 Experimental Type.

1931–32 PROGRAMME.

Displacement, 2,600 tons.
Speed 42 knots.
To be laid down in 1932.

1 Experimental Type.

Displacement 1600 tons.
To be laid down in 1932.

6 Improved Aigle Class.

1930 PROGRAMME.

Le Fantasque	Lorient.
L'Andacieux	
Le Malin	La Seyne.
Le Terrible	Ch. France.
Le Triomphant	Ch. Loire.
L'Indomptable	La Seyne.

All commenced during 1930.

Displacement: 2,500 tons.
Dimensions:
S.H.P. 70,000 = 36 kts.
Guns: 5—5·5 inch, 1—3 inch AA., 4—37 m/m, 4 D.C. throwers.
Tubes: 8—21·7 inch. (2 quadruples).
Machinery: 2 sets geared turbines.
Boilers: 4 small tube.

VAUBAN.

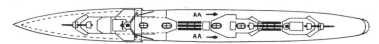

1931 *Photo, M. Bar.*

BISON.

1931 *Photo, Capt. de C. M. Adam.*

MILAN, EPERVIER AND CASSARD CLASS.

1930 *Illustration.*

6 GUÉPARD and 12 AIGLE Classes:

1925 Programme.

	Builders.	Begun.	Launched.	Compl.	Trials.
Bison	Lorient	Feb. '27	29/10/28	1929	=41·2
Guépard			19/4/28	1929	69100=38·4
Lion	Ch. France	Apl.'27	5/8/29	1930	=40·2

1926 Programme.

Vauban	Ch. France	'27	5/29		
Valmy	Penhoët	'27	19/5/29		69,300=39·8
Verdun	Ch. Loire	'27	4/7/28		72,400=40·1

Displacement : 2,436 tons. About 29,000 tons full load.
Dimensions : 433·3×37·6×11·7 feet.
S.H.P. 64,000=36 kts.　Oil : 500-650 tons.　Radius : 3,000 miles at 18 kts.

1927 Programme.

Aigle	Ch. France	'29	2/31	1931	
Albatross	A. C. Loire	'29	6/30	1931	87,000=42·5
Epervier	Lorient	6/30	14/8/31		
Gerfaut	Ch. Bretagne	'29	14/6/30	1931	=42·78
Milan	Lorient	6/30	10/31		
Autour	F. C. Med. Havre	'29	9/31		80,000=40

1928—29 Programme.

Cassard	Ch. Bretagne	11/30	
Le Chevalier Paul	La Seyne	2/31	
Maille Breze	Penhoët	10/30	
Kersaint	Ch. Loire	9/30	
Tartu	Ch. Loire		
Vauquelin	Ch. France	3/30	

Displacement : 2,441 tons.　Dimensions : 4,235×38·6×12·7 feet.
S.H.P. 64,000=36 kts. (70,000 in *Milan* and *Epervier*).
Oil : 650 tons.　Radius : 2,500-3,000 miles at 18 kts.

ARMAMENT in all the above :
　Guns : 5—5·5 inch, 1—3 inch A.A. (last 12), 4—37 m/m, 4 D.C. Throwers.
　Tubes : 6—21·7 inch (7 in *Milan* and *Epervier*).
　Machinery : 2 sets geared turbines.
　Boilers : 4 small tube.

TIGRE.

1931 Photo, R. Perkins.

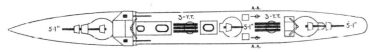

Note.—Classified on a tonnage basis these ships would rank as cruisers being above 2,000 tons standard displacement. They are employed in divisions and not as flotilla leaders.

1922 Programme

		Begun.	Launched.	Compl.	Trials.
Jaguar	Lorient		7/11/23	1026	52,000—36·1
Panthère	Dockyard		28/10/24	1926	=35·5
Léopard ..	Ch. de Loire		20/9/24	1927	
Lynx ..	St. Nazaire		24/2/25	1927	=35·5
Chacal ..	Penhoët		13/7/24	1926	52,000=36·1
Tigre ..	Ch. de Bretagne Nantes.		2/8/24	1926	58,000=36·7

Displacement : 2,126 tons ; 2,700 tons full load.

Dimensions : 392¾ (*p.p.*), 416 (*o.a.*)×36×11·1 feet. Complement : 204.

Guns :	5—5·1 inch.	Oil :	250/540 tons.
	2—2·9 inch A.A.	Radius :	3,500 miles at 15 kts.
	4—D.C. Throwers.		2,500 ,, ,, 18 ,,
Tubes :	6—21·7 inch.		900 ,, ,, full speed.

S.H.P. 50,000=35·5 kts. Breguet turbines (*Leopard* and *Lynx*.) Rateau in other four. 5 small tube boilers.

TIGRE.   *1926 Photo, M. Bar, Toulon.*

TIGRE.   *1926 Photo, M. Bar, Toulon.*

DESTROYER.

1 ex-German Boat. ("1916 Design.")

AMIRAL SÉNÈS

Photo added, 1931.

1 *Schichau, Danzig:* **Amiral Sénès** (ex-German *S 113*, launched 1917, completed May, 1918). 1525 tons*. Dimensions: 334½ × 36 × 13 feet draught aft. Guns: 4—5·9 inch (45 cal.). Torpedo tubes: 4—21·7 inch, in two twin deck mountings. Machinery: Turbine. Boilers: 4 Marine type (by Schichau). Designed S.H.P. 44,000=34 kts. (*trial* gave 36·9 kts.) 2 screws. Oil fuel: 210 tons *normal*, 720 tons *max.*=2500 miles at 20 kts.

> * *Standard* displacement 1525 tons; *normal* is 2100 tons.

Gunnery Notes.—5·9 inch have large degree of elevation and can be used as AA. guns. German directors, fire controls, R.F. and electric transmitters, etc., stripped before surrender.

Torpedo Notes.—Tubes, 32 feet long, electrically operated, and with special electric motors for loading. Axes diverge 15°.

General Notes.—Originally a unit of the German " 1916 Design " Class (*S 113—B 124*). A sister boat (*V 116*) now Italian *Premuda.* The class represents the largest and most powerful Destroyer type extant, but their sea performance as first completed was very bad indeed. Ran trials during spring of 1918, when engines and armament proved too powerful and heavy for the hull; they were sent back to the yards for alterations. The Germans are said to have lengthened these boats by about 11¼ feet at bows in an attempt to improve stability. They never joined German Flotillas during the war. French reports also say they never got beyond 30 kts. on trials. Hull strengthening and minor modifications are reported to have considerably improved the qualities of *Amiral Sénès*, and she is now good for 32 kts.

AMIRAL SÉNÈS

1922 Photo.

This vessel is rated in the Treaty cruiser category by virtue of her 5.9″ armament, but France does not accept this classification.

192

14 Adroit Class.

LE MARS.   1929 *Photo, M. Bar, Toulon.*

L'Adroit (April 6th, 1927).
Le Fortuné (Nov. 15, 1926), *Le Mars* (Aug. 28, 1926).
La Palme (June 30th, 1926), *La Railleuse* (Sept. 12th, 1926).
L'Alcyon (June 26th, 1926). (Launched at Harfleur and towed to Bordeaux for completion.)
Basque (May 25th, 1929), *Bordelais* (May 23rd, 1928), *Boulonnais* (June 1st, 1927), *Brestois* (May 19th, 1927).
Forbin (July 17th, 1928), *Foudroyant* (April 24th, 1929), *Fougueux* (Aug. 4th, 1928), *Frondeur* (June 20th, 1929).

Displacement : 1378 tons *standard*, 1495 tons *normal* (*about* 1750 *full load*). Dimensions : 330·9 × 32½ × 9½ feet. Complement, 145. Guns : 4—5.1 inch, 1—2.9 inch AA. (last eight to carry 2—37 m/m. AA. instead of latter gun). Torpedo tubes : 6—21.7 inch, in triple deck mountings. 2 sets geared turbines of Zoelly type in *Adroit* and *Alcyon*, Parsons in *Brestois* (types not yet advised in other cases). Designed H.P. 34,000 = 33 kts. Other particulars similar to those of *Simoun* class, but slightly increased boiler power is expected to give improved speed. On trials *Brestois* reached 34.5 kts, *Fougueux* 36.4. 16 Depth Charges carried.

Note.—Ordered under Programmes of 1924 (first six), 1925 (next four), and 1926 (last four). As compared with *Simoun* type, these vessels possess improved stability, higher rate of salvo firing, better aerial defence and lower fuel consumption. 5.1 inch guns said to possess a range of 19,000 yards, and can fire eight rounds a minute.

Name	Builders	Engines	Begun	Completed
L'Adroit	Ch. de France, Dunkerque	Fives, Lille		1928
L'Alcyon	Ch. de la Gironde	Ch. de la Gironde		1927
Le Fortuné	Ch. Navals Français, Blainville	A. & Ch. de la Loire	} 1925	Sept., 1927
Le Mars	Ch. Navals Français, Blainville	A. & Ch. de la Loire		April, 1927
La Palme	Ch. Dubigeon, Nantes	A. & Ch. de la Loire		1927
La Railleuse	Ch. Dubigeon, Nantes	A. & Ch. de la Loire		1927
Brestois	Ch. Navals Français, Blainville	A. & Ch. de la Loire		
Boulonnais	Ch. Navals Français, Blainville	A. & Ch. de la Loire	} Sept., 1926	1928
Basque	Ch. de la Seine Maritime	A. & Ch. de Bretagne		
Bordelais	Ch. de la Gironde, Bordeaux	Ch. de la Gironde		
Forbin	F. & Ch. de la Med., Havre			
Foudroyant	Dyle & Bacalan, Bordeaux		} 1927	1929
Fougueux	A. & Ch. de Bretagne, Nantes			
Frondeur	Ch. Navals Français, Blainville	A. & Ch. de la Loire		

12 Simoun Class.

SIMOUN.   1930 *Photo, M. H. le Masson.*

1 *Chantiers de France (Dunkerque):* **Bourrasque** (Aug. 5th, 1925).
2 *F. & Ch. de la Méditerranée (Havre):* **Cyclone** (Jan. 24th, 1925), **Mistral** (June 6th, 1925).
2 *Ch. Navals Français (Blainville).* **Orage** (Aug. 30th, 1924), **Ouragan** (Dec. 6th, 1924).
2 *A. & Ch. de St. Nazaire (Penhoët):* **Simoun** (June, 1924), **Sirocco** (October 6th, 1925).
1 *Ch. Dubigeon:* **Tempête** (Feb. 21st, 1925).
3 *Ch. de la Gironde:* **Tramontane** (Oct. 29th, 1924), **Typhon** (Nov. 1924), **Trombe** (May 22nd, 1925).
1 *Dyle & Bacalan:* **Tornade** (March 12th, 1925).

Displacement : 1319 tons *standard*, 1458 tons *normal*, 1727 tons *full load*. Dimensions : 326 × 31½ × 9½ ft. Complement, 146. Guns : 4—5·1 inch, 1—2.9 inch AA. Torpedo tubes : 6—21.7 inch, in triple deck mountings. Geared turbines of Rateau type in *Orage* and *Ouragan* ; Zoelly in *Typhon, Tramontane* and *Trombe* ; Parsons in other seven boats. H.P. 33,000 = 33 kts. (over 34 reached on trials). Boilers : 3 small tube. 2 screws. Oil : 165 tons *normal*, 350 tons *max*. Radius : 3000 miles at 15 kts.

Notes.—Authorised by Law of 18th August, 1922. 8 hours' trials : *Orage*, 34,000 = 33·8 kts. ; *Simoun*, 29,000 = 33·2 kts. (1 hour = 34.3) ; *Ouragan*, 35,000 = 34.4 ; *Bourrasque*, = 34.12 (36.4 for one hour) ; *Mistral* (12 hours), 34 kts. All completed 1926-27. It has been stated that these vessels lose their speed rapidly in a seaway. All have had funnels cut down by about 3 feet to improve stability.

Gunnery Notes.—*Sirocco* has been fitted experimentally with larger gun shields. All are being given bilge keels, increasing displacements as stated above by 20 tons without any reduction of speed.

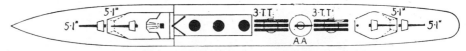

Distinguishing Numbers (Subject to Changes)

borne by vessels of *SIMOUN* and *ADROIT* classes.

1st Flotilla (Blue).		**3rd Flotilla (Red).**		**5th Flotilla (Black).**		**7th Flotilla (White).**	
Tempête	11	*Tornade*	31	*Cyclone*	51	*Le Mars*	71
Ouragan	12	*Trombe*	32	*Mistral*	52	*Le Fortuné*	72
Orage	13	*Typhon*	33	*Sirocco*	53	*La Railleuse*	73
Bourrasque	14	*Tramontane*	34	*Simoun*	54	*La Palme*	74

(First number represents flotilla and second the squadron numeral.)

2 Delage Class (ex-German "Mobilisation" type).

R. DE LA TOUCHE.   *1925 Photo, by courtesy of the Ministry of Marine.*

2 *Howaldt* boats: **Delage** (ex-German *H 147*) and **Rageot de la Touche** (ex-German *H 146*). Dimensions: 279.8 × 27.4 × 9.3 feet. Guns (German): 3—4.1 inch, 45 cal. AA. 1—2 pdr. Torpedo tubes (German): 6—19.7 inch, in two single tubes to port and starboard, under bridges, and two twin mountings amidships. Oil fuel: 166 tons *normal*, 330 tons *max.* = 1760 miles at 20 kts. Surrendered at Cherbourg and added to French Navy, September, 1920. (Other details as Table.) Were units of German *H 145—147* class. Can carry 40 mines.

To distinguish.—Boats carried "flying"; derrick-post close to *after* funnel with boom slung forward. Compass platform before amidships bandstand.

4 Deligny Class (ex-German "Mobilisation" type).

DELIGNY.   *1925 Photo, by courtesy of the Ministry of Marine.*

4 *Schichau* (Elbing) boats: **Chastang** (ex-German *S 133*), **Deligny** (ex-German *S 139*), **Mazare** (ex-German *S 135*) and **Vesco** (ex-German *S 134*). Dimensions: 272.3 × 27.3 × 8.4 feet. Guns and torpedo tubes: As *Delage* class above. Oil fuel: 162 tons *normal*, 305 tons *max.* = 1760 miles at 20 kts. Surrendered at Cherbourg and added to French Navy, September, 1920. Other details as Table. Were units of German *S 131—139* class.

To distinguish.—Derrick-post close to *fore* funnel with boom slung aft. No compass platform.

1 Vulkan Boat (ex-German "Mobilisation" type).

1925 Photo, by courtesy of the Ministry of Marine.

1 *Vulkan* (Stettin) boat: **Buino** (ex-German *V 130*). Dimensions: 269 × 27.2 × 9.2 feet. Guns and torpedo tubes: As *Delage* class. Oil: 167½ tons *normal*, 330½ tons *max.* = 2050 miles at 15 kts. Other details as Table. Surrendered at Cherbourg and added to French Navy, September, 1920. Was unit of German *V 125—130* class. Can carry 24 mines.

To distinguish.—Derrick-post *midway* between funnels with boom slung aft. Ventilator just aft of second funnel, *plus* long unbroken forecastle.

DELAGE and DELIGNY types and BUINO.

1 Vulkan Boat (ex-German "Mobilisation" type.)

1931 Photo, Official

1 *Vulkan* boat: **Pierre Durand** (ex-German *V 79*). Dimensions: As *Buino*, above. Guns and torpedo tubes: as *Delage* class, but single tubes are before bridges. Oil: 160½ tons *normal*, 317½ tons *max.* = Radius: 2060 miles at 15 kts, 656 miles at 22 kts. Surrendered at Cherbourg and added to French Navy, September, 1920. Was unit of German *V 67—84* class.

To distinguish.—Short forecastle.

1 Ganz-Danubius Boat.

MAT. LEBLANC.   1929 *Photo, M. Bar, Toulon.*

1 *Ganz-Danubius* (Fiume) boat: **Matelot Leblanc** (ex-Austrian *Dukla*). Dimensions: 275 × 25·7 × 8·3 feet. Guns (Austrian): 2—3·9 inch, 4—11 pdr., 2—11 pdr. AA. Torpedo tubes (Austrian): 4—20·8 inch. Other details as Table. 6 Yarrow boilers. Added to French Navy, September, 1920. Was unit of Austrian *Tatra* class. Four sister boats incorporated in Italian Navy. (For plan, vide Italian *Cortelazzo* class.)

12 Algérien Class.

(1917 War Programme.)

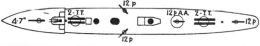

TONKINOIS.   1920 *Copyright Photo, M. Bar, Toulon.*

12 built by Japanese Yards: **Algérien, Annamite** (both by Yokosuka D.Y.), **Arabe, Bambara** (both by Kure D.Y.), **Hova, Kabyle** (both by Sasebo D.Y.), **Marocain, Sakalave, Sénégalais** (all three by Maidzuru D.Y.), **Somali** (Kawasaki Co., Kobe), **Tonkinois, Touareg** (both by Mitsu Bishi Z K). All begun March, 1917, launched May and July, 1917, and completed July and September, 1917. Average time of construction 5 months. *Standard* displacement, 601 tons, 830 *full load*. Dimensions : 260 (*p.p.*), 271¼ (*o.a.*) × 27¼ × 7¾ feet. *Normal* draught, 9⅝ feet; *load* draught, 8 feet. Armament : 1—4·7 inch, 4—12 pdr. (one 12 pdr. is AA.), 2 M.G. and 4—18 inch torpedo tubes in two twin deck mountings. Designed H.P. 10,000 = 29 kts. ; made about 30 on trials. Machinery : 3 sets 4-cyl. triple expansion. 4 Kansei (Modified Yarrow) boilers. Fuel : 100 tons coal + 120 tons oil = 3000 miles at 15 kts. and 950 miles at *full* speed. Complement, 87.

Note.—These boats are practically replicas of the Japanese *Kaba* class T.B.D. and are often referred to as the " Type Japonais." The 4·7 inch gun is being replaced by a 3·9 inch of superior range. (In *Marocain* this change has already been effected.) Radius : 1950 miles at 14 kts., 1200 miles at 22 kts. Made 27 kts. at sea after refit (1925), but now good for only 25-26 kts. at best.

4 Téméraire type:—Purchased Boats.

(Fitted for Minesweeping).

OPINIÂTRE. (*Téméraire* similar).   1920 *Photo, Bar, Toulon.*

Note.—Now have raised fore funnel, and retain the four funnels after refitting.

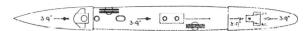

INTRÉPIDE. (*Aventurier* similar).   1928 *Photo, M. Dubois.*

4 *Chantiers de Bretagne* (*Nantes*) : **Aventurier** (ex-*Salta*), **Intrépide** (ex-*Rioja*), **Opiniâtre** (ex-*San Juan*), and **Téméraire** (ex-*Mendoza*) (all 1911). *Standard* displacement: 915 tons; *full load,* 1180 tons. Dimensions : 284½ × 28¼ × 8⅝ feet *normal* draught. *Full load* draught, 10¼ feet. Armament (Schneider-Canet) : 4—3·9 inch, (*Opiniâtre* and *Téméraire* 1—3 pdr). 4—18 inch tubes. Designed H.P. 18,000 = 32 kts. (light). First pair now develop 18,000 H.P. = 27 kts., at full load ; second pair H.P. 12,000 = 22 kts. Machinery Rateau-Bretagne turbines. *Intrépide* = 3 Schulz-Thornycroft boilers. *Aventurier* = 2 German, 1 Guyot du Temple. *Opiniâtre* and *Téméraire* = 1 Du Temple + 3 Guyot du Temple (coal), 1 Normand (oil). Fuel capacity : 240 tons coal + 75 oil in *Opiniâtre* and *Téméraire* ; 280 tons oil in *Aventurier* and *Intrépide.* Radii of action : 3,000 miles at 15 kts.

Note.—Built for Argentine Navy and purchased by France immediately before outbreak of war. Refitted 1924-27 and *Aventurier* and *Intrépide* reboilered with boilers out of German Destroyers broken up, and are good now for a maximum speed of 27 kts. All are now fitted for minesweeping, and constitute a special division. (13th flotilla.)

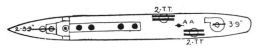

ENSEIGNE GABOLDE

1 Special Boat. (1913 Programme).

Note.—Torpedo tubes now mounted on centre line, *not* as in plan.

1 *Normand. Havre:* **Enseigne Gabolde** (22nd April, 1921). 802 tons. Dimensions: 269×26·9×10 feet. Armament: **3**—3·9 inch, **1**—14 pdr. **A A.**, **4**—21·7 inch torpedo tubes in two twin deck mountings. Designed H.P. 20,000=33 knots (reached on trials). Parsons geared turbines. Normand boilers. Fuel: 200 tons oil. Complement, 98.

Note.—Began in December, 1913. Work on this T.B.D. was suspended during the War and not resumed until September, 1918. Completed in summer of 1923 and joined Fleet early in 1924. 6 hours' trial=32·45 kts. (*max.* 33.45).

Forward superfiring 3.9 inch reported to have proved an unsatisfactory arrangement.

ENSEIGNE GABOLDE.　　　　1925 *Photo, by courtesy of the Ministry of Marine.*

(Fore funnels lowered).　　　　1931 *Photo.*

6 Bory Type.

M. P. LESTIN.　　　　1921 *Photo, H. Freund, Brest.*

General Notes.—All these boats are armed with **2**—3·9 inch, **4**—9 pdr., **1**—14 pdr. (A.A.), **4**—18 inch tubes in pairs. All adapted for mine sweeping and carry D.C. Endurance: about 1,500 miles at 15 kts. and 400—500 at full speed. Complement, 98. They differ according to builders in appearance, dimensions, H.P., turbines, &c.

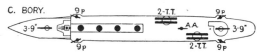

C. BORY.

War Losses: Boutefeu, Faulx, Fourche, Renaudin.

Removed from List: Magon, Francis-Garnier, Capitaine Mehl, Commandant Bory, Dehorter, Mangini.

(1913 Programme).

E. ROUX.　　　　1920 *Photo, M. Bar, Toulon.*

2 *Rochefort Dockyard:* **Enseigne Roux** (1915), **Mecanicien-Principal Lestin** (1915). 787 tons. Dimensions: 271×29·9×10 feet. Designed H.P. 17,000=30 kts. Fuel: 200 tons oil. Endurance for these two boats: about 2,000 miles at 15 kts. and 550 miles at full speed. Begun as M86 and M87. Still good for 30 kts. if pressed.

(*Continued on next page*)

6 Bory Type.—*continued*.

(1911 Programme Boats).

1924 *Photo, M. Bar.*

1 *Rochefort Dockyard* : **Protet** (1913). 679 tons. Dimensions : 272.4 × 26 × 10 feet. Laval turbines. 2 du Temple-Guyot boilers. Designed H.P. 15,000 = 31 kts. Fuel : 140 tons oil. Practically sister-boat to *C. Lucas* and *Bisson*. Begun as *M83*.

Note strutted foremast.   1921 *Photo, M. Bar, Toulon.*

1 *Toulon Dockyard* : **Commandant Lucas** (1914). 679 tons. Dimensions : 272·4 × 26 × 10 feet. Laval Turbines. du Temple-Guyot boilers. Designed S.H.P. 16,000 = 31 kts. Fuel : 140 tons oil. Practically sister-boat to *Protet* and *Bisson*. Begun as *M78*. Recently equipped for minesweeping.

6 Bory Type.—*continued*.

(1910 Programme Boats).

1919 *Photo, Comm. B. D. Holberton, R.N.*

1 *Toulon D. Y.* : **Bisson** (1912). 679 tons. Dimensions : 272·4 × 26 × 10 feet. Laval turbines. 2 du Temple-Guyot boilers. Designed S.H.P. 15,000 = 31 kts. Fuel : 140 tons oil. Practically sister-boat to *C. Lucas* and *Protet*. Can still touch 27 kts.

(1911 Programme Boat.)

COMMANDANT RIVIÈRE (Fore funnel raised).   1922 *Photo, H. Freund.*

1 *Soc de la Gironde (Bordeaux).* **Commandant Riviere** (1912). 679 tons. Dimensions : 256⅔ × 25⅔ × 10 feet. Breguet turbines. Du Temple-Guyot boilers. Designed S.H.P. 14,500 = 31 kts. Trials : 15,760 = 32·3 kts. Fuel : 140 tons oil. Has recently been fitted for minesweeping. Armed with 2—3·9 inch, 4—9 pdr, 1—14 pdr. AA. guns. 4—18 inch torpedo tubes, in pairs.

4 Patrol Boats.

1920 *Photo, Bar, Toulon.*

6 *Normand Type :* **Nos. 315, 321, 327, 336, 349, 369.** Built 1903—1907. Displ. 100 tons. H.P. 2000 = 25 kts. Compl. 23. Armament : 315,321 = 1—75 M/M. 1—15″ TT., 336 = no guns but 3—15″ TT., others 1—75 m/m., 1—37 M/M., 1—15″ TT.

14 Coastal Motor Boats.
(Vedettes rapides.)

B1—B7 Type.   1930 *Photo, " Flottes de Combat."*

4 *VT.A1—A4* type: 42 feet long, with single motor of Lorraine-Dietrich type, 500 H.P. = 34 kts. Armed with **1** M.G. and **1**—18 inch torpedo. Built by Chantiers Jeannin, Excelsior and Wisner, respectively. With 250 H.P. a speed of 30 kts. can be maintained.

7 *VT.B1—B7* type: Larger than above, with 2 motors. H.P. 1000 = 36 kts. 2 torpedoes carried. 3 built by Wisner, 3 by Ch. de la Loire.

3 Built under 1930 and 1931 Programmes.

Submarine Chasers.

C60.   1920 *Photo, H. Freund, Brest.*

37—*100 foot* type: Numbered between **C 25,** and **C 98.** Built by U.S. Navy Yards and smaller shipbuilding firms, 1917 -18, for U.S. Navy as *SC5—SC404,* but contracts transferred to French Government. *Designed* displacement, 54 tons ; *actual* displacement, 77 tons. Dimensions : 105 ft. (*p.p.*), 110 ft. (*o.a.*) × 14 ft. 8¾ in. × 5 ft. 5½ in. (*mean* hull draught). Machinery : 3 sets of 220 B.H.P. Standard petrol motors, totalling 660 B.H P. = 17 kts. Petrol : 2400 gallons = 900 miles at 10 kts. Armament : **1**—75 m/m (14 pdr.) field gun converted to naval mounting, but many have no guns now, and some have one of smaller calibre. Carry depth charges. Complement, 26.

SUBMARINE CHASERS.

Submarine Chasers (*Chasseurs de Sousmarins*).

Photo added 1927, by courtesy of M. Normand.

15 *Normand type* boats: **C 102—C 106** (Normand, Le Havre, 1918-21). **C 107—C 116** (respective builders unknown).* 133 tons. Dimensions : 136⅝ (*p.p.*), 142 (*o.a.*) × 17⅛ × 4¼ feet (draught amidships), 7¼ feet (draught below rudder support). Guns : 2—75 mm., 2 M.G. Designed I.H.P. 1300 = 16.5 kts. Triple expansion engines. 2 Normand boilers. Coal : 34 tons, except in *C 107, 110 111, 113-115* all 28 tons. Complement, 32. Contract for 2 other boats with Normand cancelled 1918. *C 101* swamped and sunk off Spanish Coast, December, 1920.
*Built by Chantiers de la Loire, Nantes, Chantiers Dubigeon, Nantes, and Chantiers Normand, Le Havre.
Note.— *C 111* and *C 112* have been given respective names of *Avalanche* and *Capitaine Bourdais* while serving in Indo-China.

C 105.

1930 *Photo.*

Note.—Funnels are slightly staggered, the foremost being to port and after one to starboard of the centre-line.

66 (+ 41 bldg. or authorised) = 107 Submarines (Sousmarins).

No. in Class.	Class, Type (Design).*	Date.	Displacement. Surface / Submerged	H.P.† Surface / Submerged	Speed† Surface / Submerged	Endurance. Surface / Submerged	Tubes or Gear.	Complement.
	First Class:		tons		kts.			
1	Surcouf	'27—?	2880 / 4304	7600 / 3400	18 / 10	10,000 at 10	?	150
5	Saphir class (NF)	'26—?	669 / 925	1300 / ?	12 / 9	?	4/32‡	?
31	Redoubtable class (FR)	'24—?	1374 / 2060	5000 / 2600	18 / 10	8000 miles at 10 kts. / 100 miles at 5 kts.	10	60
9	Requin class (FR)	'22—'27	974 / 1410	2900 / 1800	16 / 10	7000 miles at 9 kts. / 105 miles at 5 kts.	10	48
1	M. Callot (SL)	'17—'21	840 / 1298	2900 / 1640	16.5 / 10.5	2800 miles at 11 kts. / 118 miles at 5 kts.	6/27‡	44
1	P. Chailley (NF)	'17—'23	798 / 1181	1800 / 1200	14 / 9	2800 miles at 13.7 kts. / 80 miles at 9 kts.	4/48‡	44
2	Pierre Marrast class§	'17—'18	744 / 1011	2400 / 1160	16.2 / 8.5	6500 miles at 8 kts. / 95 miles at 3 kts.	6	30
1	Halbronn§	'16—'17	1841 / 3050	3300 / 1780	15.8 / 7.7	12600 miles at 8 kts. / 53 miles at 4 kts.	6	82
1	René Audry§	'17—'18	1041 / 1800	2400 / 1200	13.4 / 7.5	9000 miles at 7 kts. / 55 miles at 4 kts.	4/38‡	47
2	Léon Mignot class§	'16—'17	744 / 1053	2400 / 1160	16.5 / 8.5	9250 miles at 8 kts / 50 miles at 6 kts.	6	36
2	Joessel class (S)	'14—'20	838 / 1200—3	2900 / 1650	16.5 / 11	4200 miles at 10 kts. / 115 miles at 5 kts.	8	47
4	Lagrange class (H)	'14—'24	830 / 1317	2600 / 1650	16.5 / 11	4200 miles at 10 kts. / 115 miles at 5 kts.	8	47
2	Dupuy de Lôme class (H)	'15—'16	748 / 1291	2900 / 1600	16 / 11	1450 miles at 14 kts. / 115 miles at 5 kts.	8	43
2 {	Néréide (S)	'13—'16	771 / 1098	2400 / 1540	16.8 / 10.5	3500 miles at 12 kts. / 110 miles at 5 kts.	8	42
	Gustave Zédé (S)	'12—'14	771 / 1098	2400 / 1540	16 / 10.5	2300 miles at 10 kts. / 110 miles at 5 kts.		
	Second Class.							
20	Diane class (NF)	'27—?	571 / 809	1420 / 1000	14 / 9	3000 miles at 10 kts. / 78 miles at 5 kts.	7	39
11	Sirène class (various)	'21—'27	552 / 765	1300 / 1000	14 / 9.5	3500 miles at 10 kts. / 90 miles at 5 kts.	7	39
2	Fournier class (SL)	'17—'20	310 / 513	1000 / 460	14 / 8.5	1070 miles at 12 kts. / 63 miles at 5 kts.	4	24
3	Carissan class§	'17—'18	464 / 651—677	1100 / 760	14 / 8	7000 miles at 8 kts. / 45 miles at 4.5 kts	5	34
1	Victor Réveille§	'15—'16	681 / 980	1100 / 600	10.6 / 7.5	8000 miles at 7 kts. / 75 miles at 3 kts.	2/38‡	38
2	Armide class (S) *	'14—'16	418 / 665	2200 / 850	17.5 / 11	2600 miles at 11 kts. / 150 miles at 5 kts.	4	27
1	Daphné (S)*	'14—'16	647 / 950	1800 / 1400	15.3 / 11	2800 miles at 14 kts. / 100 miles at 5 kts.	10	35
3	Bellone class (H)	'14—'18	484 / 790	1500 / 800	15.8 / 9	1300 miles at 12 kts. / 115 miles at 5 kts	8	29

* (FR) = Fuzier-Roquebert.   (H) = Hutter   (L) = Laubeuf.   (NF) = Normand-Fenaux.   (S) = Simonot.
(SL) = Schneider-Laubeuf.
† As designed : not attained in some cases.   ‡ Figures in Italics = Mines.   § Ex-German boats, taken over 1920.
* To be scrapped very soon.

1 Cruiser Type.

Surcouf (Nov. 18th, 1929) laid down at Cherbourg Dec. 1927, under 1926 Programme. Dimensions : 393·7 × 29·5 × 23 feet = 2880/4300 tons. Machinery : Diesels 7,600 B.H.P. = 18 kts. *surface*. Motors 3,400 H.P. = 10 kts. *submerged*. Guns : 2—8″, tubes : 10—21″ adapted for salvo firing. Carries 22 torpedoes. Complement, 150. Radius of action : 10,000 miles at 10 kts.

(For photo see frontispiece).

25 Redoubtable Class.

VENGEUR.   1930 *Photo, favour of M. of Marine.*

31 *Fuzier-Roquebert type.*

1924 Programme.
Redoubtable (Feb. 24th, 1928) } Cherbourg.
Vengeur (Sept., 1928)

1925 Programme.
Pascal } (July 19th, 1928), Brest.
Pasteur
Henri Poincaré } (April 10th, 1929), Lorient.
Poncelet
Fresnel (June 8th, 1929), St. Nazaire (Penhoët).

1926 Programme.
Archimede (   ), Ch. Nav. Fr. Blainville.
Monge (June 25th, 1929), La Seyne.
Acteon (April 10th, 1929) } A. C. Loire.
Acheron (Aug. 6th, 1929)
Argo (April 11th, 1929), Ch. Dubigeon, Nantes.
Achille } (May 28th, 1930) Brest.
Ajax

1927 Programme.
Prométhée (   ), Cherbourg.
Persée (   ), C. N. F. Blainville.
Protée (Aug., 1930), F. C. Havre.

Pégase (   ), A. C. Loire.
Phénix (   ), Dubigeon.

1928 Programme.
Glorieux } Cherbourg.
Centaure
Heros } Brest.
Conquerant
Tonnant A. C. Loire.
Espoir La Seyne.

1930 Programme.
Agosta
Beveziers Cherbourg.
Ouessant
Sidi-Ferruch
Sfax
Casablanca

Displacement : 1,384 tons *surface* ; 2,080 tons *submerged* for first two ; remainder 1,379 tons *surface* ; 2,060 tons *submerged*. Dimensions : 302½ × 30½ × 15½ feet. Machinery : 2 sets Sulzer Diesels, combined H.P. 6,000 = 18 kts. (Trials, 19.5 kts.) Electric motors of H.P. 2,000 = 10 kts. *submerged.* 1 auxiliary Diesel, H.P. 750. 2 screws. Armament : 1—3·9″ AA., 1—37 m/m AA., 1—M.G., 11—21·7″ tubes, including 2 sets of revolving tubes, 1 bow, 1 stern. (Reported that in later boats 1—5·5″ will replace the 3·9″. Radius of action = 30 days cruising.

Notes.—Have proved very successful on trials. *Vengeur* and *Redoubtable* performed a cruise to the West Indies in 1930 without mishap, and were able to make 19 kts. easily without being pressed. *H. Poincaré* maintained an average of 17·60 kts. for 48 hours on trials

9 Requin class.

MARSOUIN.   1926 *Photo.*

9 *Fuzier-Roquebert* type : **Requin** (19th July, 1924), **Morse** (18th Nov., 1925), **Narval** (9th May, 1925), **Souffleur** (Sept., 1924), **Caïman** (3rd March, 1927), (all Cherbourg), **Dauphin** (1925), **Espadon** (26th May, 1926), both Toulon), **Marsouin** (Jan., 1925), **Phoque** (16th March, 1926), (both Brest). 974 tons (*on surface*), 1410 tons (*submerged*). Dimensions : 256½ (*p.p.*) × 21½ × 15 feet. Complement, 51. Machinery : 2 Diesel motors, of Sulzer or Schneider-Carels type, each 1450 H.P. Total 2900 H.P. = 16 kts. Electric drive : 248 "D" type batteries, 1800 H.P. = 10 kts. Radius : 7000 miles at 9 kts. (*on surface*), 105 miles at 5 kts. (*submerged*). Endurance : equal to 30 days' cruising. Guns : 1—3.9 inch, 2 M.G. AA. Torpedo tubes : 10—21.7 inch (4 bow and 2 stern submerged : 4 above water, revolving in pairs before and abaft C.T.). 32 torpedoes (24 of 1922 model, 8 of 1919 model) carried by *Caïman, Espadon, Phoque* ; 16 by others.

Notes.—Requin, Souffleur, Morse, Narval, Marsouin, Dauphin begun as Q 115—120 of 1922-1923 Programme. Other three came under Coast Defence Vote of June 30, 1923. All completed 1926-27. Freeboard about 7 feet. Top of C.T. is 13 feet above water. Can dive with safety to 100 metres (say, 55 fathoms). On commissioning, *Requin* carried out a 5,000 mile cruise, occupying 31 days in African waters, without mishap of any kind.

DAUPHIN.   1926 *Photo, M. Bar, Toulon.*

6 Saphir Class. (Minelayers.)

TURQUOISE.

1930 *Photo, A. Ganda.*

6 *Normand-Fenaux* type : **Saphir** (Dec. 20th, 1928) ; **Turquoise** (May 16th, 1929), Toulon, 1926 ; **Nautilus** (Mar. 21st, 1930), Toulon, 1927 ; **Rubis** (Sept. 30th, 1931), Toulon, 1928 ; **Diamant** (Toulon, 1929) ; **Perle** (Toulon, 1930). Displacement : 669 tons *on surface,* 925 tons *submerged.* Dimensions : 216¼ × 23¼ × 13½ feet. Machinery : 2 sets Vickers-Normand 4-cycle Diesels. B.H.P. 1300 = 12 kts. *Submerged* speed, 9 kts. Armament : 1—3 inch AA., 4—21.7 inch tubes, 32 minelaying chutes, arranged on Normand-Fenaux system. Carry **6** torpedoes and **32** mines of 460 lbs. weight. First two authorised under 1925 Programme, third under 1926, fourth 1927, fifth 1928-29.

1 Special Boat (Mine-laying—*Diesel.*)

PIERRE CHAILLEY.

1925 *Photo, by courtesy of Messrs. Normand.*

1 *Normand-Fenaux* type : **Pierre Chailley** (Ch. A. Normand Le Havre, 19th Dec., 1922). Displacements : 798 tons *on surface,* 1181 tons *submerged.* Dimensions : 229⅞ × 26¼ × 13 feet. Guns : 1—3·9 inch. Torpedo tubes : **2**—18 inch bow and **2**—18 inch immediately abaft C.T. in twin mounting on a revolving platform. (The latter pair are normally hidden by a cover which matches the deck.) Mines carried : 64 Sautter-Harle of 440 lbs. each (maximum stowage) in 32 chutes or cells—disposed 16 on each beam, 2 mines in each, about centre of boat, between inner and outer hulls. Laying rate has been *stated* to be 40 mines in 4 minutes, which at 6 kts. = 15 to 30 metres spacing between planted mines. Machinery : 2 sets of 900 H.P. 2-cycle 6-cylinder Sulzer-Diesel motors, totalling 1800 B.H.P. for a *max.* surface speed of 14 kts. When *submerged,* electric motors + batteries of 1200 H.P. = 9 kts. Oil fuel : 60 tons (sufficient for 20 days' cruising). Endurances : 2800 miles *on surface,* at 10 kts., 80 miles *submerged* at 9 kts. Built under 1917 Programme.

Note.—Actual number of mines normally carried in service is understood to be 40.

1 Special Boat (Mine-laying—*Diesel.*)

1921 *Photo, M. Bar, Toulon.*

1 *Schneider-Laubeuf* type : **Maurice Callot** (Ch. de la Gironde, Bordeaux ; launched March 26th, 1921). Displacements : 842 tons *on surface ;* 1298 tons *submerged.* Dimensions : 247¾ × 22 × 12¼ feet. Guns : 1—14 pdr. on AA. mount. Torpedo tubes : **4**—18 inch bow and **2**—18 inch midway between C.T. and stern. 8 torpedoes carried. Mines carried : 27—200 kg., in " wet " stowage on 3 horizontal belt conveyors (9 mines to each row) abaft C.T., above pressure hull and below superstructure deck. Laying rate believed to be one mine from each row at 12 seconds' intervals, which at 5 kts. = 30 metres spacing between planted mines.

Machinery : For *surface* running, 2 sets of 8 cyl. 2 cycle Schneider-Carels Diesel motors (16.1″ bore × 17.7″ stroke), each engine developing *about* 1450 B.H.P. at 330 r.p.m. Total B.H.P. 2900 = 16.5 kts. speed *on surface.* These are the same type of motors as those mounted in *Fulton* and *Joessel,* which have proved remarkably reliable after an extended series of trials. Electric motors + batteries of 1640 H.P. = 10.5 kts. *submerged.*

Endurance : 44.87 tons oil fuel carried, giving following endurances *on surface:* (*a*) 1960 miles at 13 kts. with both motors running ; (*b*) 2800 miles at 11 kts. with one engine running. When *submerged,* 118 miles at 5 kts.

Complement : 4 officers + 40 men. Double-hull design built on Laubeuf principle. Begun under 1917 Programme ; began acceptance trials, August, 1921. On a 50 day cruise is said to have maintained average speeds of $\frac{16}{10\cdot4}$ kts.

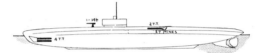

2 Léon Mignot Class (ex-German).

J. AUTRIC.   1924 *Photo, M. Bar, Toulon.*

2 *ex-German* "Mittel-U" type: **Jean Autric** (ex-German *U* 105), **Léon Mignot** (ex-German *U* 109). Both built by Krupp-Germania, Kiel, and completed 1917. Displacements: 744 tons *on surface*, 1053 tons *submerged.* Dimensions: *about* 235 × 20½ × 12½ feet. Periscope depth: 45 feet. Machinery: 2 sets 6 cylinder 4 cycle M.A.N. Type Diesel engines. B.H.P. 2400 = 16.5 kts. *on surface.* Speed *submerged*: 8.5 kts. Oil: 82 tons. Endurance: 9280 miles at 8 kts. *on surface;* 50 miles at 6 kts. *submerged.* Guns: 1—4.1 inch. Tubes: 6—19.7 inch (4 bow, 2 stern). Stowage for 13 torpedoes. Complement, 40.

Notes.—Units of the German *U 105—114* class. Are double-hull type.

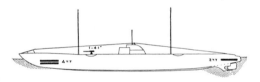

4 Lagrange Class.

ROMAZZOTTI.   1924 *Photo, M. Bar, Toulon.*

4 *Hutter* type: **Lagrange** (1917), **Regnault** (25th June, 1924), and **Romazzotti** (1917). All built at Toulon D.Y. **Laplace** (Rochefort D.Y., 1919). Displacements: 836 tons *on surface,* 1317 tons *submerged.* Dimensions: 246½ × 20.9 × 13.2 feet. Machinery: *on surface,* 2 sets 1300 B.H.P. Sulzer-Diesel engines, totalling 2600 B.H.P. for 16½ kts. *Submerged* speed: 11 kts. Endurance: *on surface,* 2500 miles at 14 kts., 4200 miles at 10 kts., 6000 miles at 8 kts. When *submerged,* 115 miles at 5 kts. Armament: 2—14 pdr. guns. 8—17.7 inch torpedo discharges, arranged as in *Dupuy de Lôme,* below. Stowage for 10 torpedoes and 440 rounds of ammunition for guns. Complement, 47.
Notes.—Begun as *Q 111—114* of 1914 Programme. General design as *D. de Lôme* class.

2 Dupuy de Lôme Class.

DUPUY DE LÔME.   1927 *Photo, H. Freund, Brest.*

2 *Hutter* type: **Dupuy de Lôme** (1915) and **Sané** (1916). Both built at Toulon D.Y. Displacements: 748 tons *on surface,* 1291 tons *submerged.* Dimensions: 246 × 20.9 × 13.7 feet. Machinery: *on surface,* Diesel engines (recently renewed) of 2900 H.P. = 16 kts. *Submerged* speed: 10 kts. Armament: 2—14 pdr. guns and discharge positions for 8—18 inch torpedoes as follows: 2 *submerged* tubes, W.T. parallel, built into bows; 2 *above water,* fixed, divergent, built into superstructure forward; 2 revolving, in twin mount, under superstructure abaft C.T.; 2 fixed, divergent, built into superstructure aft. Oil: 100 tons. Complement, 43.
Notes.—Begun as *Q* 105 and *Q* 106 of 1913 Programme. Both completed 1916. Are enlargements of M. Hutter's design for the *Bellone* class. *Dupuy de Lôme's* 2 Diesels are by Krupp. *Sané* has two Koerting motors.

SANÉ.   1930 *Photo, Lt. T. D. Manning, R.N.V.R.*

LAGRANGE AND DUPUY DE LÔME *Classes.*

2 Pierre Marrast Class

P. MARRAST.   *1924 Photo, M. Bar, Toulon.*

J. ROULIER   *1924 Photo, M. Bar, Toulon.*

2 *ex-German* "Mittel-U" type: **Pierre Marrast** (ex-German *U 162*), **Jean Roulier** (ex-German *U 166*), both built by Bremer-Vulkan, Vegesack, and completed 1918. Displacements: 744 tons *surface*; 1011 tons *submerged*. Dimensions: 235 × 21 ft. 1 in. × 12 ft. 9 in. Machinery: 2 sets 6-cylinder 2 cycle. M.A.N Diesel, B.H.P. 2400 = 16·2 kts. *on surface*. Submerged speed: 8·5 kts. Oil fuel: 47/109 tons. Endurance: 6500 miles at 8 kts. *on surface*; about 90-100 miles at 3 kts. *submerged*. Guns: 1—4·1 inch. Torpedo tubes: 6—19·7 inch (4 bow, 2 stern). Stowage for 12 torpedoes. Complement, 42.

Notes:— Units of German *U 160—172* class and among last submarines completed for the German Navy. Double-hull design. Appearance almost identical with *L. Mignot* type.

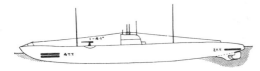

Photo added 1923.

1 *ex-German* "UK-*Helder*" type: **Halbronn** (ex-German *U 139* (*Schweiger*), built by Krupp-Germania, Kiel; completed 1917). Displacement: 1841 tons *on surface*, 3050 tons *submerged*. Dimensions: 302¾ × 29½ × 15½ feet. Machinery: 2 sets Krupp or M.A.N. 6 cylinder 4 cycle Diesel engines. B.H.P. 3300 = 15.8 kts.* *on surface*. Also 1—550 H.P. auxiliary engine, used for charging batteries which could be used for running at low cruising speeds through main motors. Speed *submerged*: 7.7 kts. Oil fuel: 104/295 tons. Endurance: 12,630 miles at 8 kts. *on surface*. Guns: 1—3.9 inch. Torpedo tubes: 6—19.7 inch (4 bow, 2 stern). Stowage for 19 torpedoes. Complement, 54.

Notes.—Unit of German *U 139--141* class. Double-hull type, fitted with anti-rolling tanks. Found deficient in stability by Germans; *U 141* of the same class had wood filling along upper deck to increase stability. This "Cruiser" design was a very qualified success.

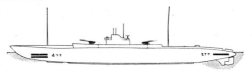

1920 Copyright photo, M. Bar, Toulon.

1 *ex-German* "UE II" type: **René Audry** (ex-German *U119*, built by Vulkan, Hamburg, completed 1918). Displacements: 1041 tons *on surface*, 1800 tons *submerged*. Dimensions: 267 ft. 5 in. × 24 × 13 ft. 10 in. Periscope depth: *about* 45 feet. Machinery: 2 sets of 6 cyl. 4 cycle M.A.N. Diesel engines *on surface*, B.H.P. 2400 = 13.4 kts.* *Submerged* speed: 7.5 kts.* Endurance: 9000 miles at 7 kts. *on surface*. Oil capacity: 93.5/194 tons. Guns: 1—5.9 inch (Krupp). Torpedo tubes: 4—19.7 inch (bow). 18 torpedoes or 42 mines., but only 38 can be carried with safety. Originally unit of German *U 117—126* class, designed for mine-laying off U.S. coast. Were double-hull boats. Complement, 40.

*A sister boat, *U 117*, delivered to U.S. Navy, had a *max. surface* speed of 14.7 kts.; *max.* speed *submerged*, 7.2 kts.

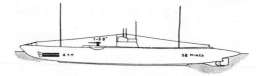

First Class—*continued.*

2 Gustave Zédé Class.

2 Joessel Class.

NÉRÉIDE   *Photo added* 1928.

1 *Simonot* type : **Néréïde** (Cherbourg D.Y., 1914).   *Surface* displacement 771 tons, draught 12.4 feet *submerged*; guns, 1—14 pdr ; displacement, other dimensions, tubes and complement, as *Gustave Zédé* (below).   Machinery : 2 sets 2 cycle 8 cyl. 1200 B.H.P. Schneider-Carels Diesel engines.   2400 H.P. = 16.8 kts. *on surface.*   Electric motors + batteries 1540 H.P. = 10.5 kts. *submerged.*   Radius of action : *about* 3500 miles at 12 kts. *on surface,* 110 miles at 5 kts. *submerged.*   Oil : 100 tons.

Notes.—Ordered January, 1911, as *Q 93* of 1911 Programme.   Completed, end of 1916.

1 *Simonot* type : **Gustave Zédé** (Cherbourg D.Y., 1913).   Displacements : 771 tons *on surface,* 1098 tons *submerged.* Dimensions : 242¾ × 19¾ × 13¾ feet.   Machinery : Diesels (2 sets M.A.N.) of 2400 total B.H.P. = 16 kts. Electric motors+ batteries, 1540 H.P.=10·5 kts. *submerged.*   Radii of action : 2300 miles at 10 kts. and 1800 miles at 14 kts. *on surface.*   Armament : 2—14 pdr.   Torpedo tubes : 2—18 inch tubes +6—18 inch torpedoes carried in external frames.   Complement, 42.

Notes.—Begun as *Q 92* of 1911 Programme.   Completed October, 1914.   Sank 1916, after accumulator explosion, but was salved and repaired.

FULTON.   1928 *Photo.*

2 *Simonot* type : **Fulton** (1919) and **Joessel** (1917).   Both built at Cherbourg D.Y.   Displacements : *Fulton,* 915/1203 tons.   *Joessel,* 838/1200 tons.   Dimensions : 242.8 × for *Fulton* 19.7 × 13.8 feet ; for *Joessel* × 23.4 × 14.5 feet.   Machinery : *on surface,* 2 sets of 8 cylinder 2 cycle Schneider-Carels Diesel engines (16.1″ bore × 17.7″ stroke) developing *about* 1450 B.H.P. at 330 r.p.m.   Total power : 2900 B.H.P. = 16½ kts.   *Submerged speed* : 11 kts.   Oil fuel : 125,000 litres.   Endurance : *on surface* and *submerged* about the same as *Lagrange* class in next column.   Armament : 2—14 pdr. guns on AA. mounts and 8—18 inch tubes (4 *submerged* in bow ; 2 fixed divergent on deck forward ; 2 revolving on deck aft).   Stowage for 10 torpedoes.   Complement, 47.

Notes.—*Joessel* reported to have made over 18 kts. *on trials.*   Reports on their recent performance during long cruises indicate that they are very reliable and successful boats.

Second Class.

12 Diane Class.

ARGONAUTE   1931 *Photo.*

All are of *Normand-Fenaux* type with minor differences, according to builders.

1926 PROGRAMME		1928 PROGRAMME	
		AS Q 163–168	
Argonaute (May 23rd, 1929)	} Schneider-Crensot	**Orphée** ....Normand	
Arethuse (Aug. 8th, 1929)		**Oreade** ....Worms	
Diane (May 5th, 1930)	} Normand	**Orion** (April 21st, 1931)..Loire	
Méduse (Aug. 25th, 1930)		**Ondine** (May 4th, 1931)..Dubigeon	
1927 PROGRAMME		1929 PROGRAMME	
AS Q 159–162		AS Q 174—177	
Amphitrite (1930)	} Normand	**Psyche** ....Normand	
Antiope (1930)	} Ch. Seine Maritime	**Sybille** ....Worms	
Amazone (1931)	} Worms	**Vestale** ....} Schneider	
Atalante (Aug. 6th, 1930)	Schneider	**Sultane** ....}	
		1930 PROGRAMME	
		AS Q 185—188	
		Minerva	
		Junon	
		Venus	
		Iris	

Displacement : 558 to 571/809 tons.   Dimensions : 219¾ ×18 ×14 feet.   Armament : 1—3″ AA., 1 M.G., 8—21·7″ tubes. Machinery : 2 sets of Diesels as under noted of B.H.P. 1,300–1,420 =14 kts. *surface.*   Electric motors, H.P. 1,000= 9 kts. *submerged.*   Radius : 3,000 miles at 10 kts ; 78 miles at 5 kts.

Note.—*Orion* and *Ondine* are of Loire-Simonet type, 558 tons.   *Diane, Méduse, Amphitrite, Amazone, Antiope, Orphée, Oreade, Psyche, Sybille* have each 2 sets of 4-cycle Vickers-Normand type Diesels.   Plans by Ch. Augustin Normand. *Arethuse, Argonaute, Atalante, Vestale, Sultane* each 2 sets of 2-cycle Schneider-Carel type ; and *Orion* and *Ondine* 2 sets of 2-cycle Sulzer type.

11 Sirène Class.

SIRÈNE.

1926 *Photo, H. Freund Brest.*

ARIANE.

1927 *Official Photo.*

3 *Normand-Fenaux* type, built by C. & A. Augustin Normand, Le Hâvre: **Ariane** (August 6, 1925), **Danäe** (Sept. 11, 1927), **Eurydice** (May 31, 1927). Displacement: 576 tons *surface*, 765 tons *submerged*. Dimensions: 216½ (*p.p.*)×16×11½ feet. Machinery: 2 sets 4-cycle Diesels, Vickers-Normand type. Electric motors by Schneider et Cie. 1,200 B.H.P. on *surface*, 1,000 *submerged*.

Note.—This type is reported to have given great satisfaction in service. A fourth boat, *Ondine*, lost by collision with a Greek Steamer, October 3rd, 1928.

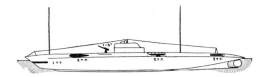

SIRÈNE.

1927_*Official Photo.*

4 *Simonot* type, built by A. & C. de la Loire, St. Nazaire: **Naïade** (Oct. 20, 1925), **Sirène** (August 6, 1925), **Nymphe** (April 1, 1926), **Galatée** (Dec. 18, 1925). Displacement: 552 tons surface, 745 tons submerged. Dimensions: 210 (*p.p.*) ×17×11½ feet. Machinery: 2 sets 2-cycle Sulzer Diesels, B.H.P. 1,300 on *surface*, 1,000 submerged.

Following particulars apply to all 12. Complement: 40. 140 to 144 "D" type electric batteries. Speed: 14 kts. on *surface*, 9·5 kts. *submerged*. Radius: *surface*, 2,000 miles at 10 kts; *submerged*, 90 miles at 5 kts. Endurance equal to 20 days' cruising. Can dive to 45 fathoms. Guns: **1**—3 inch AA., **2** M.G. AA. Torpedo tubes (19·7 inch): **7**. 13 torpedoes carried. Cost stated to be Frs. 8,500,000 each.

Notes.—*Ariane, Calypso, Circé, Naïade, Ondine, Sirène*, were laid down as *Q. 121—126* of 1922-23 Programme; others under Coast Defence Vote of Sept. 30, 1923.

DORIS.

1929 *Photo, M. Bar, Toulon.*

4 *Schneider-Laubeuf* type, building by Schneider et Cie, Chalon-sur-Saône: **Circé** (Oct. 29, 1925), **Calypso** (Jan., 1926), **Doris** (Nov. 25, 1927), **Thetis** (June 30, 1927). Displacement: 552 tons *surface*, 764 tons *submerged*. Dimensions: 204½ (*p.p.*)×17½×11 feet. Machinery: 2-cycle Schneider-Carels Diesels, 1,250 B.H.P. on *surface*, 1,000 *submerged*.

1 ex-German Boat (Mine-laying).

1924 *Photo, by courtesy of Ministry of Marine.*

1 *ex-German "UE 1" type:* **Victor Reveille** (ex-German *U 79*, built by Vulkan, Hamburg, completed 1916). Displacements : 681 tons *on surface*, 980 tons *submerged.* Dimensions : 186 ft. 4 in. × 19 ft. 10 in. × 15 ft. 1 in. Machinery : 2 sets of Diesel engines, B.H.P. 1100 = 10.6 kts. *on surface.* Submerged H.P. 600 = 7.5 kts. Endurance : 7880 miles at 7 kts. *on surface*, 75 miles at 3 kts. *submerged.* Oil capacity : 77/87 tons. Guns : 1—4.1 inch (Krupp). Torpedo tubes : 2—19.7 inch, bow tube to port, stern tube to starboard, and both *above water* when in surface trim. 2 horizontal mine-laying tubes under stern. Stowage for 38 mines and 2 torpedoes. Originally unit of German *U 71—80* class. Saddle-tank type of hull. Complement, 38.

2 Armide Class.

(To be discarded in near future; *Amazone* temporarily rechristened *Amazone II*.)

AMAZONE.

1921 *Photo, Dussau, Toulon.*

2 *Schneider-Laubeuf type " Dc ":* **Amazone** (1916) and **Armide** (ex-Japanese *No. 14*, 1915). Built by Schneider et Cie, Chalon-sur-Saône. Displacements : 418 tons on *surface*, 665 tons *submerged.* Dimensions : 184⅔ × 17 × 10½ feet. Machinery : 2 sets, Schneider-Carels Diesel engines, 2200 H.P. = 15 kts. on *surface.* Submerged speed : 10 kts. Endurance : 960 miles at 13 kts., 2600 miles at 11 kts. *on surface.* Armament : 1—1 pdr. (not always carried). Torpedo tubes (all 18 inch) : 2 in bow + 6 torpedoes carried in external frames. *Armide* has 2 additional tubes aft. Double-hull type.

Note.—*Amazone* begun for Greek Navy ; *Armide* for Japanese Navy ; but for all practical purposes they can be considered as a uniform class, taken over for French Navy during War. *Antigone* (sister to *Amazone*) condemned 1927.

1 Daphné Class.

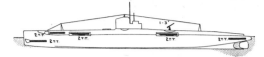

DAPHNE.   *Photo added* 1928.

1 *Simonot type:* **Daphné** (Toulon D.Y., 1915). Displacements : 647 tons *on surface*, 950 tons *submerged.* Dimensions : 223 × 18½ × 12½ feet. Machinery : 2 sets 900 B.H.P. Sulzer Diesel engines, 1800 H.P. = 15.3 kts. *on surface.* Submerged speed : 11 kts. Endurance : *on surface* (a) 2800 miles at 14 kts., (b) 4000 miles at 11-12 kts., 100 miles at 5 kts. when *submerged.* Armament : 1—14 pdr. gun. 10—18 inch torpedo tubes (2 *submerged*, parallel, at bow ; 2 *above water*, divergent, at bow ; 4, in revolving pairs, *above water*, under superstructure, before and abaft C.T. 2 at stern, *submerged*). Complement, 35. Is an enlarged *Archimede* design.

Notes.—Begun as *Q 108* of 1913 Programme. *Diane* of this type lost during the War. This type was derived from M. Simonot's designs for the larger *G. Zédé* class.

3 Bellone class.

1920 *Photo.*

3 *Hutter type:* **Bellone** (Rochefort D.Y., 1914) and **Hermione** (Toulon D.Y., 1913), **Gorgone** (Toulon D.Y., 1915). Displacements, 484 tons *on surface* ; 790 tons *submerged.* Dimensions : 196.8 × 17.7 × 12 feet. Machinery : 2 sets Sabathé-Diesel engines in first two, Sulzer Diesels in *Gorgone*, 1560 H.P. = 15.8 kts. *on surface.* Submerged speed, 9 kts. Endurance : *on surface*, 1300 miles at 12 kts., 115 miles at 5 kts. *submerged.* Armament : 1—14 pdr. gun. 2—18 inch bow torpedo tubes and 6—18 inch torpedoes carried in external frames under superstructure. Complement, 29.

Notes.—*Bellone* begun as *Q 102* of 1912 Programme and completed 1917. *Hermione* (completed 1918) and *Gorgone* (completed 1916), begun as *Q 103* and *Q 104* of 1913 Programme, as a " Modified *Archimede* " design.

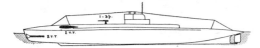

2 Fournier Class.

1924 Photo.

2 *Schneider-Laubeuf* type: **O'Byrne** (June, 1920), **Henri Fournier** (September, 1919), by Schneider, Chalon-sur-Saône. Displacements : 310 tons *on surface*, 513 tons *submerged*. Dimensions : *about* 173·9 × 15·4 × 8·2 feet. Machinery : 2 sets Schneider-Carels Diesel engines, 1000 B.H.P. = 14 kts. *on surface*. *Submerged* speed : 8½ kts. Armament : 1—3 pdr. Q.F. gun. Torpedo tubes : 2—18 inch bow and 2—18 inch torpedoes carried in frames under superstructure. Complement, 24.

Notes.—Originally ordered for Rumanian Navy but taken over under French 1917 Programme. Are double-hull boats. *Louis Dupetit-Thouars*, one of this type, condemned 1928.

3 Carissan Class (ex-German).

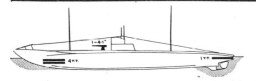

CARISSAN.   *1921 Photo, H. Freund, Brest.*

3 *ex-German* "*UB III*" type: **Jean Corre** (ex-German *UB 155*), **Carissan** (ex-German *UB 99*) and **Trinite-Schillemans** (ex-German *UB 94*), all completed 1918. Builders, Vulkan, Hamburg. Displacements : *on surface* 464 tons for *J. Corre*; *submerged* about 677 tons; other two boats are 464 tons *on surface*, 651 tons *submerged*. Dimensions : 181½ × 19½ × 12 feet. Periscope depth : 42 feet. Machinery : 2 sets 6 cyl. Diesel engines, B.H.P. 1100 = 14 kts.† *on surface*. *Submerged* speed : 8 kts.† Oil fuel : 35/71 tons. Lubricating oil : 8 tons. Endurance : 7000 miles at 8 kts. *on surface* ; 45 miles at 4½ kts. *submerged*. Gun : 1—4·1 inch (Krupp " Ubts. u. Tpbts " model). Torpedo tubes : 5—19·7 inch (4 bow, 1 stern). Stowage for 10 torpedoes. Double-hull type. *Max.* dive : 245 feet. "Crash-dive" to 29.5 feet in 40 secs. Complement, 34.

Notes.—Were units of German *UB 48—136* and *UB 137—249* classes.

†*On trial*, after surrender to the Allied and U.S. Navies, some boats of this type could not exceed 13.7 kts. *on surface* and 7.5 kts. *submerged*.

CONVOY SLOOPS
(Escorteurs.)

La Bayonnaise

La Cordelière

La Poursuivante

L'Incomprise

La Melpomène

La Flore

La Pomone

L'Iphigénie

Four of these were voted in the Estimates 1930–31 and four in the Budget 1931 to replace obsolete Submarines. The design is not yet decided upon.

(7 COLONIAL TYPE.)

BOUGAINVILLE (Apl. 21, '31).   **DUMONT D'URVILLE** (Mar. 21, '31).   **D'ENTRECASTEAUX** (June 22, '31). **SAVORGNAN de BRAZZA** (June 18, '31).

RIGAULT-de-GENOUILLY (   ).   *AMIRAL CHARNER* (   ).   *D'IBERVILLE* (   ).

1930 *Illustration.*

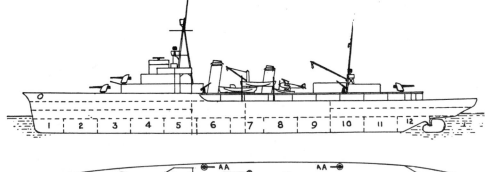

Note to plan : Forward guns are in centre-line and not staggered as shown.

Displacement, 1968 tons *standard* ; 2140 tons *normal*. Complement, 135. Dimensions : $334\frac{1}{2} \times 44\frac{1}{2} \times 12\frac{1}{2}$ feet. Guns : **3**—5.5 inch, **4**—37 m/m. AA., **6** M.G. Machinery : 2 sets Diesel engines (see *Notes*). Designed S.H.P. 3200 = 15.5 kts. Radius : 9000 miles at 10 kts. Provision to be made for carrying a seaplane. Heavy oil, 60 tons. Gas oil, 220 tons. They are fitted as mine-layers, carrying 50 mines. The 5·5″ gun is a new model firing an 80 lb. shell 26000 yds.

Notes.—Two of these vessels were authorised in 1927. Two in 1928 and Three in 1930. Builders of two are At. & Ch. du Sud-Ouest, Bordeaux. These two will have Sulzer Diesels, made by the At. & Ch. de la Loire and F. & Ch. de la Mediterranée, respectively. La Société d'Exploitation des Chantiers de la Gironde, Bordeaux, and Ch. & At. Provence, Port Bouc, are building one sloop each. Both will be engined with Burmeister & Wain Diesels manufactured by Schneider. Radius :—10,000 miles at 10 knots.

These vessels are designed for tropical service, with a special arrangement for circulation of cool air, and auxiliary plant is electrically driven through 3 Diesel groups 125 kws. each and 2 auxiliary petrol groups 22 kws. each. All will be fitted as flagships. Hulls, roofs and bridges are protected against bullets and splinters.

CALAIS (mast *before* funnel).   *Photographed 1920 for Builders by M. Bar, Toulon.*

VITRY-LE-FRANÇOIS.   *1931 photo, Capt. de C. M. Adam.*

COUCY.   *1920 Photo, H. Freund, Brest.*

DUNKERQUE (mast *abaft* funnel).   *1920 Photo, by courtesy of " Le Yacht."*

("ARRAS" CLASS.—29 SHIPS.)

7 built at Navy Yards :—

ARRAS (July, 1918), **DUNKERQUE** (July, 1918), **REIMS** (Nov., 1918), **LAFFAUX** (ex-*Verdun*) (Nov., 1918), all four built by Brest D.Y. **NANCY*** (Cherbourg D.Y., March, 1919). **BELFORT** (March, 1919), **BAPAUME** (Aug. 1918), both by Lorient D.Y.

22 built by Private Yards :—

LASSIGNY (July, 1919) and **LES ÉPARGES** (September, 1919), both by Ch. de Bretagne, Nantes. **REMIREMONT*** (July, 1920) and **REVIGNY** (September, 1920), both by Ch. de la Gironde, Bordeaux. **TAHURE** (——, 1919) and **TOUL*** (April, 1919), both by Ch. de la Loire, St. Nazaire. **BACCARAT*** (Jan., 1921) and **BÉTHUNE*** (July, 1921), both by Ch. de Provence, Port du Bouc. **COUCY** (June, 1919), **ÉPINAL*** (August, 1919), **VAUQUOIS** (August, 1919), **VIMY*** (December, 1919) and **VITRY-LE-FRANÇOIS** (March, 1920) all five by Ch. de St. Nazaire, Penhoët. **AMIENS** (May, 1919), **CALAIS** (November, 1919), **CRAONNE** (January, 1920), **LIÉVIN** (March, 1920), and **MONTMIRAIL*** (Sept., 1920), all five by F. et C. de la Med., La Seyne. **ÉPERNAY** (September, 1919), **LUNÉVILLE** (Jan, 1920), **MONDEMENT*** (June, 1920), and **PÉRONNE** (March, 1920), all four by F. et C. de la Med., Graville.

Despatch and Anti-Submarine Vessels of 644 tons. Dimensions : 246 ft. 0 in. × 28 ft. 6 in. × 9 ft. 2 in. Guns : 2—5.5 inch, 1—14 pdr. AA., 2 M.G. Carry depth charges. Fitted with from two to four searchlights ; also have hydrophones. Designed S.H.P. 5000 = 21 kts. in oil-burning boats ; = same speed in coal-burning boats. Machinery : 2 sets Parsons (geared) turbines. 2 screws. Boilers : 2 Normand or Guyot du-Temple oil-burning (small tube). Fuel : 200 tons oil = Endurance : 1000 miles at 17 kts. 3000 at 11 kts. *Craonne, Liévin, Montmirail, Mondement, Béthune, Baccarat* burn coal (185 tons carried). Complement, about 110.

Notes.—5·5 inch guns reported to be M.1910 (and perhaps M.1916), but some* have been armed with 145 m/m. guns (army pattern) 5·5 inch have large degree of elevation ; *max.* range 17,000 metres. They are very roomy and comfortable ships for their size, and their high bows make them very dry in head seas. But with sea on the beam they are said to roll " like old boots " (*comme des veritables-sabots*), owing to heavy topweight of guns, superstructure, etc. Oil burning boats can do 21-22 kts. on light draught in good weather, but in a seaway they drop down to 13 kts. Built under Programme VI and VII of 1917, and mostly completed 1919-21, though *Mondement* was not finished till 1922 and *Reims*, 1924. *Bar-le-Duc* wrecked and lost, December, 1920.

Vitry-le-François fitted as s/m. tender with armament of 2—2·9" AA. only. *Vauquois* and *Remiremont* act as training ships for naval cadets.

SCARPE.   1930 *Photo, M. Bar, Toulon*.

1924 *Photo, A. Dussau, Toulon*.

AILETTE (ESCAUT same).   The 3·9 inch guns are concealed within lidded ports at angles of superstructure.   A A. gun on forecastle.

1921 *Photo, Lieut. R. Steen Steensen, R.D.N.*

VILLE D' YS (ex-*Andromède*), Swan, Hunter & Wigham Richardson, Wallsend-on-Tyne, June, 1917.   Convoy sloop of **1191** tons.   Dimensions: 255 feet 3 inches (*p.p.*) 276 feet (*o a.*) × 35 feet × 12 feet 3 inches.   Guns: **1**—3·9 inch, **3**—3 inch AA., **2**—3 pdr.   **1** M.G.   Designed I.H P. 2500 = 17 kts.   Machinery: 1 set 4-cyl. triple-exp.   Boilers: 2-cyl.   1 Screw.   Coal: 270 tons = 2400 miles at 12 kts.   Complement, 103.

Note.—Generally same build as British convoy sloops.   Built under 1916 War Programme.   Begun for British Navy as *Andromeda* and turned over to French Navy.   Now employed on Newfoundland fisheries service.

SUIPPE (straight stem); ANCRE has same appearance.   1930 *Photo*.

AILETTE (Brest D.Y., March, 1918) }   ANCRE (Lorient D.Y., Jan., 1918) }
                                       } 570 tons.   SCARPE (Lorient D.Y., Oct., 1917) } 705 tons.
ESCAUT (Brest D.Y., March, 1918) }   SUIPPE (Lorient D.Y., April, 1918) }

Dimensions: first two, 229½ × 25½ × 8 feet; other three, 236¼ × 27½ × 8 feet.   Guns: **4**—3·9 inch, **2** to **6**—9 pdr. AA., **1** or **2** M.G.   Designed H.P. 5000 = 21 kts.   Machinery: 2 sets geared turbines.   Boilers: two du Temple.   2 screws.   Oil fuel: 140 to 145 tons = 4000 miles at 10 kts.   Complement, 65.

Note.—Modifications of *Aisne, Marne, Meuse,* &c., described on a later page.   Externally they are disguised by varying appearances as mercantile vessels, like convoy sloop *Ville D' Ys* opposite.   Built under 1917 War Programme.   *Ancre* is tender to Navigation School.

ALGOL.   1920 *Photo, M. Bar, Toulon.*

("ÉTOILE" or "STAR" Class—7 Ships.)

RÉGULUS.   1921 *Photo, H. Freund, Brest.*

ANTARÉS.   1920 *Photo, M. Bar, Toulon.*

ALDÉBARAN (May, 1916) ⎱ Barclay, Curle,   **BELLATRIX** (Henderson, Glasgow, 1916).
ALGOL (June, 1916)   ⎰   Whiteinch.   **CASSIOPÉE** (March, 1917) ⎱ Barclay, Curle,
ALTAIR (July, 1916)   ⎱ Wm. Hamilton, Port   **RÉGULUS** (April, 1917)   ⎰   Whiteinch.
ANTARÉS (1916)   ⎰   Glasgow.

Sloops. *Standard* displacement, 1121 tons. Dimensions : $255\frac{1}{4} \times 33\frac{1}{2} \times 11\text{-}12\frac{1}{4}$ feet. Guns :
   2—5.5 inch, 2—14 pdr. (AA.) or 2—3 pdr. and 1 AA., 2 M.G.   Are fitted as Fleet Sweeping
   Vessels.   Designed I.H.P. 2500 = 17 kts.   (All made 17.2-17.6 kts. on trials.)   Machinery :
   1 set, 4 cyl. triple expansion.   Boilers : Cylindrical.   1 screw.   Coal : 270 tons = 2400
   miles at 12 kts.   Complement, 103.

Notes.—These sloops are practically replicas of the British "Flower Class" Sloops, being built
   in pairs by British shipyards.   *Rigel,* the companion boat to *Bellatrix* by Messrs. Henderson,
   lost during the War.   All built under 1916 War Programme.   *On trials* they made from
   16.8 to 17.1 kts. with about 2675 H.P.   All employed on Colonial Service.

P

OISE (& SOMME).   *1919 Photo.*

YSER (& MEUSE).   *1920 Photo, M. Bar, Toulon.*

Note.

Though the design of these Despatch Vessels is uniform, the latitude allowed to the building yards has resulted in differing appearances. Vessels built by same yard have the same appearance.

AISNE (Lorient D.Y., July, 1917), 682 tons.   **SOMME** (Brest D.Y., March, 1917), 730 tons.

MARNE (Lorient D.Y., Nov., 1916), 717 tons.   **OISE** (Brest D.Y., Oct., 1916), 650 tons.

MEUSE (Rochefort D.Y. June, 1917), 670 tons.   **YSER** (Rochefort D.Y., Jan., 1917), 670 tons.

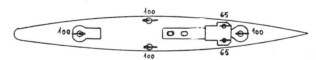

(Plan by courtesy of the Ministry of Marine.)*

MARNE (& AISNE).   *1919 Photo.*

Despatch Vessels, displacing 575-600 tons. Dimensions: $256 (o.a.) \times 26\frac{5}{12} \dagger \times 8\frac{5}{8}$ feet. Armament: *Aisne* and *Marne*, 4—3.9 inch, 3—47 m/m.; *Meuse*, 4—3.9 inch, 2—65 m/m., 1—47 m/m.; *Somme*, 4—3.9 inch, 1—3 inch, 2—47 m/m.; *Oise, Yser,* 4—3.9 inch, 2—65 m/m., 2—47 m/m. Designed I.H.P. 4000 = 20.5 kts. (5000 = 21 in *Aisne* and *Marne*). Machinery: 2 sets geared turbines. Boilers: 2 du Temple. 2 screws. Oil fuel: 135 tons, 145 tons in *Aisne* and *Marne* = 4000 miles at 10 kts. Complement, 107 All built under 1916 War Programme. Most of them employed as Training Ships for Cadets.

*On Plans, 100 mm. = 3.9 inch; 65 mm. = 9 pdr.

$\dagger$ $27\frac{1}{2}$ in *Aisne* and *Marne*.

(Continued on next page.)

"Avisos"—Despatch Vessels or Sloops—*continued.*

DUPERRÉ.

1921 *Photo, M. Bar, Toulon.*

"DUBOURDIEU' TYPE.—5 vessels.

DUBOURDIEU (April, 1918), **DUCHAFFAULT** (September, 1918), **DUPERRÉ** (December, 1918), **ENSEIGNE HENRY** (November, 1918), **DUCOUÉDIC** (April, 1919). *Standard* displacement, 452 tons. Dimensions: 210.8 (*o.a.*) × 26.2 × 8.75 feet (*max.* draught). Guns: 1—5.5 inch, 1—3.9 inch. S.H.P. 2000 = 17·4 kts. Machinery: 2 sets of Breguet de Wooch turbines. 2 screws. Boilers: 2 Du Temple-Guyot. Oil: 143 tons = 1985 miles at full speed. Complement, 72.

Notes.—Built under 1917-18 War Programme. Completed June, 1919—May, 1920. Sixth boat of this class, *Décrès*, cancelled. Originally rated as "Anti-Submarine Gunboats" (*Canonnières Contre Sous-marins*). In build they are very like *Arras* class. *Dubourdieu* is now tender to Boy Artificers Training Establishment at Lorient, and displaces 520 tons. *E. Henry* ex-*Dumont-D'Urville.*

Q. ROOSEVELT.   (*On North Sea Fishery Protection Service.*)   1927 *Photo.*

QUENTIN ROOSEVELT (ex-*Flamant*, Rochefort D.Y., December, 1916). Despatch Vessel of 585 tons. Dimensions: 154 × 28 × 13 feet. Guns: 1—14 pdr., 1—1 pdr. I.H.P. 1100 = 13 kts. Coal: 100 tons = 1500 miles at 10 kts. Complement, 53. Was begun 1913, stopped 1914-17, completed April, 1918.

Minesweepers (*Dragueurs de Mines*).

GRANIT.   1926 *Photo, M. Bar, Toulon.*

GRANIT CLASS—5 Steam-engined boats.

GRANIT, MICA, PORPHYRE, QUARTZ, MEULIERE (1918). 354 tons. Dimensions, 180 × 25 × 6½ feet. H.P. 550 = 12 kts. Guns: 1—65 m/m. Coal: 73—90 tons. Complement, 63.

CONQUÉRANTE.   Note that masts are stepped well to starboard of centre line.

VAILLANTE type :—2 Diesel-engined boats.

CONQUÉRANTE (1917), **VAILLANTE** (1917). Both by Brest D.Y. 374 tons. Dimensions: about 211 × 22⁷⁄₁₂ × 8¼ feet. Guns: 2—3·9 inch. Carry D.C. B.H.P. 1800 = 17 kts. Machinery: 2 sets of 900 B.H.P. Sulzer-Diesel engines. Oil fuel: 30 tons. Complement, 54.

Notes.—Are a modified *Friponne* design, for which see next page. Both built under 1917 War Programme. Are ex-Gunboats, fitted as Minesweepers.

(*Continued on next page.*)

1916-17.

ENGAGEANTE only has dummy funnel.

Distinguished from *Conquérante* and *Vaillante* by yacht stem.

1920 *Photo, H. Freund, Brest.*

DILIGENTE (straight stem,. No funnels.
Surveillante (yacht stem.)
Luronne „ „ and thin funnel.

FRIPONNE type :—4 Diesel-engined boats.

1921 *Photo, Dussau, Toulon.*

DILIGENTE (Brest D.Y., 1916), **ENGAGEANTE** (Brest D.Y., 1917), **LURONNE** (Brest D.Y., 1917), **SURVEILLANTE** (Brest D.Y., 1916). Displacement : 315 tons, except *Luronne*, 265 tons. Dimensions : $199\frac{2}{3} \times 22\frac{7}{12} \times 8\frac{1}{6}$ feet. Guns : **2**—3.9 inch. Carry D.C. and may also be equipped as Minesweepers. B.H.P. 900* = 15 kts. Machinery : 2 sets 750* B.H.P. Sulzer*-Diesel engines. Oil : 30 tons = 3000 miles at 10 kts., 1600 miles at 15 kts. Complement, 57.

Notes.—Generally the same design as the *Ardent* type (steam-driven) boats in next column, but above four boats have Diesel engines. All built under 1916 War Programme, except *Luronne*, of 1917 Programme. *Chiffonne, Friponne, Impatiente* and *Mignonne* sold to Rumania, January, 1920, *Bouffonne* condemned.

Luronne has two Fiat type Diesel engines of 650 B.H.P., total H.P. 1300, which are reported to have given a speed of 13.8 kts. She is employed as tender to the training establishment for boy artificers at Lorient, and *Surveillante* as small Seaplane auxiliary.

1916.

GRACIEUSE.

1921 *Copyright Photo, M. Bar, Toulon.*

BATAILLEUSE

1931 *Photo, M. H. le Masson.*

(ARDENT type—15 Steam-engined boats.)

AGILE (Brest D.Y., 1916).
ALERTE (Rochefort D.Y., 1916).
ARDENT (Brest D.Y., 1916).
AUDACIEUSE (Port de Bouc, 1917).
BATAILLEUSE (Port de Bouc, 1917).
CAPRICIEUSE (Nantes, 1916).
DÉDAIGNEUSE (Bordeaux, 1916).
ETOURDI (Lorient D.Y., 1916).

ÉVEILLÉ (La Seyne, 1917).
GRACIEUSE (Lorient D.Y., 1916).
IMPÉTUEUSE (Ch. de la Gironde, Bordeaux, 1917).
INCONSTANT (Brest D.Y., 1916).
MALICIEUSE (Chantiers de Provence, Port de Bouc, 1916).
SANS SOUCI (Lorient D.Y., 1916).
TAPAGEUSE (Port de Bouc, 1916).

Displacement : 265-310 tons. Dimensions : $197\frac{1}{2} \times 22\frac{7}{12} \times 8\frac{1}{6}$ feet. Guns : **2**—3.9 inch (and **1** small AA. in some). Carry D.C. Designed I.H.P. 1800-1200 = 17 to 15 kts. Machinery : Reciprocating. Boilers : Various water-tube types. Fuel : 85 tons coal = 3000 miles at 10 kts., 1600 miles at full speed. Complement. 65.

Notes.—Note that masts are stepped well to starboard of the centre-line. *Moqueuse* wrecked, 1923. *Curieuse* condemned, 1926, *Belliqueuse* and *Emporté*, 1927.

River Gunboats (*Canonnières Fluviales*).

FRANCIS-GARNIER. 1930 *Photo, by favour of M. Henri Le Masson.*

FRANCIS-GARNIER (Dec. 18, 1927). River Gunboat, for Lower Yangtse, ordered 1926 from Chantiers Navals Français, Blainville. Displacement, 630 tons. Complement, 103. Dimensions: $196\frac{3}{4} \times 32\frac{3}{4} \times 6$ feet. Guns: 2—4 inch, 1—3 inch AA, 2—2 pdr. 4 M.G. 2 sets triple expansion, H.P. 3200 = 15 kts. 2 Du Temple boilers. Oil fuel: 100 tons. Completed in 1929.

BALNY. *Photo added 1927, by favour of " Revue Maritime."*

BALNY (1920). Built by Chantiers de Bretagne, Nantes. 196 tons. Dimensions: $167\frac{1}{4} \times 23 \times 3\frac{1}{4}$ feet. H.P., 800 = 13·5 kts. Guns: 1—14 pdr., 2—1 pdr., 4 M.G. 2 Fouché w.t. boilers. Coal: 45 tons. Complement, 60.

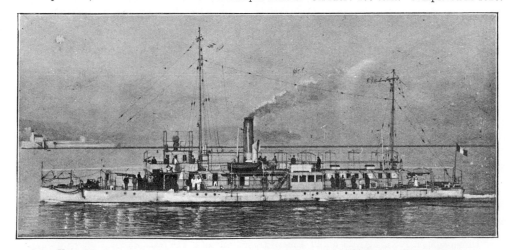

VIGILANTE. 1924 *Photo, A. Dussau, Toulon.*

ARGUS, VIGILANTE (1922, Toulon D.Y.) About 178 tons. Dimensions: *about* $163\frac{1}{2} \times 25 \times 2\frac{1}{3}$ feet. Guns: 2—75 mm. (14 pdr.), 4 M.G. I.H.P. 550 = 12 kts. 2 screws and 2 boilers Bullet-proof plating over conning position and W/T. cabinet. Ammunition carried: 300 rounds per 14 pdr. and 50,000 cartridges.

LA GRANDIÈRE. *Photo added 1927, by favour of " Revue Maritime."*

LAGRANDIÈRE (built at Brest D.Y.). Completed, 1923. 36 tons. Dimensions: 90·2 (*o.a.*) × 16·4 × 1·6 feet. Guns: 1-37 m/m, 2 M.G. Standard petrol motor 220 B.H.P. = 12 kts. Serves as tender to *Balny* and *D. de Lagrée* for Upper Yangtse. Is said to be very expensive to run, as she consumes petrol in large quantities. Fuel = 3 tons petrol.

River Gunboats—*continued.*

1920 *Photo, Ch. de Bretagne.*

DOUDART DE LAGRÉE (1909). 265 tons $167\frac{1}{4} \times 22 \times 3\frac{1}{4}$ feet. Guns: **1**—14 pdr. (field type), **4**—1 pdr., **4** M.G. H.P. 920 = 14 kts. Fouché w.t. boilers. Coal: 50 tons. Complement, 60. Built by Chantiers de Bretagne, Nantes.

Rhine Flotillas.

C.F. 1.   1926 *Photo, Freund, Brest.*

C.F. 1 (Brest, 1926). Steel flat-bottomed "Chaloupe Fluviale." Displacement: 40 tons. Dimensions: *About* $60 \times 12 \times 4$ feet draught. Guns: **1**—2 pdr. (short Army pattern), **2** M.G. 2 Bettus-Loire type semi-Diesel oil engines of 80 H.P. each = 10 kts.

C, G, H, I (1915). River Gunboats. 83 tons. $91.8 \times 16.4 \times 5$ feet. Armed with either **1**—5·5 inch or **2**—3·9 inch or **1**—14 pdr. guns, besides some smaller. H.P. 200 = 7 kts. Coal: 10 tons. Complement, 25.

Rhine Flotilla—*continued.*

1927 *Photo, R. Perkins, Esq.*

9 small "Chaloupes à moteur" *PI—PIX* completed 1920. for service on the Rhine. Each armed with **2** M.G. Have petrol motors. No other details known.

*Note.—*2 armed River Passenger Steamers, *Kléber* and *Marceau* are also attached to Rhine Flotilla.

Sailing Gunboat.

ZELÉE (purchased 1931). 122 tons. Length 98 feet.
    Machinery : **2**—40 H.P. oil engines = ? kts.
    Guns : **1**—3 pdr.
    For service in Oceania and Tahiti.

TWO SCHOONERS for cadet training have been ordered during 1931 from Ch. Nav. & Normande (Fecamp).
    Dimensions : 105 (*o.a.*) $\times 23.5 \times 11.4$ feet. Displacement : 215 tons.
    Accommodation for 3 officers, 30 cadets, 5 petty officers, 12 seamen.
    Machinery : 120 H.P. Sulzer engines = 6 kts.

Mine Layers (*Mouilleurs de Mines.*)

CASTOR.   1930 *Photo, M. Bar.*

CASTOR (ex-Russian Icebreaker *Kozma Minin*) (Swan Hunter, 1916.) Displacement : 3,700 (*normal*) tons. Dimensions : 248×57×19 feet. 3 sets triple expansion engines. 6 S.E. boilers. I.H.P. 6,400=14·5 kts. Coal : 686 tons. Carries 368 mines. Armament : 2—3·9″, 2—37 m/m. Complement : 167. Radius : 4,500 miles at 10 kts.

POLLUX.   1930 *Photo, courtesy of Ministry of Marine.*

POLLUX (ex-Russian Icebreaker *Ilya Murometz*) (Swan Hunter, 1915). Displacement : 2,900 (*normal*) tons. Dimensions : 200 (*p.p.*), 211 (*o.a.*)×50½×20 feet. Triple expansion engines. 6 cylindrical boilers. I.H.P. 4,950=14 kts. 2 screws. Coal : 367 tons. Carries 236 mines. Armament : 3—3·9″, 2—37 m/m. Complement : 5—157. Radius : 2,300 at 8 kts., 1,470 miles at 14 kts.

Note.—Both these vessels were converted into Mine Layers by Lorient Dockyard, 1928-29.

Note.—Following Submarines are fitted as Mine Layers :—

Name.	No. of Mines carried.	Name.	No. of Mines carried.
Saphir class (6)	32	*René Audry*	38
Pierre Chailley	40	*Victor Réveille*	38
Maurice Callot	27		

All described on preceding pages. Several Destroyers are also fitted for minelaying.

Net Layers.

GUEPE. Built, 1913. Dimensions : 210×46×9 feet. Displacement : 637 tons. H.P. 1,550 =9 kts. This is a paddle tug converted experimentally into a net layer. A net layer is provided for under the 1929–30 Programme of 2,293 tons displacement.

No details yet available.

LE GLADIATEUR.   (1930 Programme).

MISCELLANEOUS.

Transports (*Transports*), **Supply Ships** (*Soutiens d'Escadre*) and **Refrigerator Ships** (*Navires Frigorifiques*).

J. Cœur.   1920 *Photo, Freund.*

Cœtlogon.   1930 *Photo, M. Bar.*

Forfait.   1927 *Photo, H. Freund.*

CHAMPLAIN (April, 1919), **JACQUES COEUR** (April, 1919), **ALLIER** (ex-*Primauguet*, April, 1919), all three by Brest D.Y., **COËTLOGON** (June, 1919), **FORFAIT** (1920), **HAMELIN** (1920), **ALFRED DE COURCY*** (ex-*Adour,*) (ex-*Lamotte-Picquet*, 1920), by Ch. de Bretagne, Nantes. 700 tons. Dimensions: 157·5 (*p.p.*), 167.2 (*o.a.*) × 25.9 × 11 feet (*mean* draught), 14 feet (*max.* draught). Guns: 2—3.9 inch, 1 M.G. I.H P. 1250 = 12.5 kts. (light) and 1100 = 8 kts. (load draught). Triple expansion engines. 1 screw. 2 cylindrical boilers. Coal: 80 tons. 850 miles endurance.

* Usually employed as seaplane tender.

Surveying Ships. (*Navires Hydrographiques.*)
Commissioned for the six months April—November, and reduced to Reserve during other six months of the year.

Beautemps-Beaupré.   1921 *Photo, M. Bar.*

BEAUTEMPS-BEAUPRÉ (ex-*D'Estaing*) and **LA PÉROUSE** both launched 21st November, 1919. 768 tons. Dimensions: 196.8 (*p.p*) × 28.9 × 18 feet. Guns: 1—3 pdr. AA. in *La. P.*, 1—14 pdr. in *B.-B.* 2 Breguet turbines. H.P. 2000 = 17·5 kts. 2 w.t. boilers. Oil: 143 tons. Complement, 104. Ex-Navy Transports, completed as Surveying Ships, 1920. Both built at Brest D.Y.

Alidade.   1921 *Photo, M. Bar.*

Alidade (ex-*Martin-Pecheur*), **Astrolabe** (ex-*Mauviette*), **Boussol** (ex-*Pinson*), **Gaston Rivier** (ex-*Ortolan*), **Octant** (ex-*Pivert*). 460 tons. Length, 142¾ feet. Draught, 12¾ feet. I.H.P. 450 = 10 kts. Coal: 120 tons. Complement, 32.

                                       1928 *Photo.*

Utile (1894). Ex-Tug of 410 tons. Length, 164 feet. I.H.P. 700 = 13 kts. Guns: 1—3 pdr. Complement, 56.

Chimère (ex-*Zelée* ex-*Huron*) (1901). Ex-Tug of 337 tons *gross*. I.H.P. 880 = 14 kts.

Sonde (1911). 50 tons. 10 kts.   218

Fleet Repair Ship (*Navire-Atelier*).

                                       1924 *Photo, M. Bar, Toulon.*

VULCAIN (ex-Russian *Kronstadt*, 1894). 11,000 tons. Dimensions: 460 × 53 × 23 feet. I.H.P 6,000 = 12 kts. Coal: 1000 tons. Complement, 406. Took refuge at Bizerta with other ships of the Russian Black Sea Fleet under Gen. Baron Wrangel, 1920. Purchased by France, 1921, and refitted to replace *Foudre*, condemned 1921.

JULES VERNE. Authorised by 1926 Programme and laid down at Lorient in 1928. Displacement: 5,839 tons. Complement: 497 (including crews for submarines). Dimensions: 377½ × 59 × 19 feet. 2 sets high-speed 2-cycle Sulzer-Diesel engines, with total S.H.P. 7,000 = 16 kts.—4 auxiliary groups of 1,200 H.P. each of chaléassière model. 2 screws. Guns: 4—3·5″ AA., 4—37 m/m. AA. Complement: 24+473.

Note.—Diesels in this ship are of similar design to submarine engines.

VITRY LE FRANCOIS (*p.* 209) now commissioned as a submarine tender. [5]

Transports, Supply Ships, etc.—*continued.*

Notes.—*Champlain, J. Coeur* and *Allier* fitted as Refrigerator Ships. Completed from February, 1920 onwards. Ordered as a Class of 13 Patrol Vessels. Above 7 completed, 2 converted to Surveying Ships *B-Beaupré* and *La Pérouse*; other 4 (*Chateaurenault, La Clocheterie, Kerguelen, Seignelay*) stopped. *Hamelin* and *A. de Courcy* now refitted as Tenders to Naval Air Service.

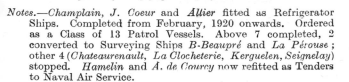

EINE.   1931. *Photo, Bar, Toulon.*

SEINE (1913). 3160 tons. Designed H.P. 1950 = 13 kts. Guns: 2 - 3·9 inch, 1—9 pdr. Coal: 295 tons.

LOIRET (ex-S.S. *Paris*, purchased 1900). 2200 tons. Guns: 1—9 pdr. H.P. 1060 = 11 kts. Coal: 193 tons.

JEANNE ET GENEVIÈVE (1917). Length, 147½ feet. Draught, 10¼ feet. 485 tons *gross*.

Note.—Transport *Rhin* has been deleted from this page, as she is now only a Harbour Ship.

Patrol Vessels.

TROUPIER.   1921 *Photo, M. Bar, Toulon.*

TROUPIER (1919). 432 tons. Dimensions: 187 × 26 × 6½ feet. Complement, 23. Sulzer-Diesel engines. B.H.P. 420 = 12 kts. Guns: 1—3 pdr. (On Fishery Protection duty.)

Patrol Vessels—*continued.*

Typical appearance.   1921 *Photo, M. Bar, Toulon.*

PASSEREAU, FAUVETTE (1916). 440 to 460 tons. Dimensions as *Troupier*, but *Fauvette* draws only 6 ft. I.H.P. 500 = 10 kts. Coal: 120 tons. Complement, 23.

ESTAFETTE.   1928 *Photo.*

ESTAFETTE (1918), **SENTINELLE** (1920). 460 tons. Dimensions: 142½ × 24 × 12½ feet. Guns: 1—3 pdr. I.H.P. 430 = 10 kts. Complement, 25. Both for Fisheries Protection.

PERCE-NEIGE (1918). 80 tons. Dimensions: 75 × 15 × 4½ feet. Guns: 1—14 pdr., 2—1 pdr. Oil engines. B.H.P. 325 = 13.5 kts.

CARIBOU, EOLE (1917). 420 tons. Dimensions: 131 × 24 × 13 feet. Diesel engines of 300 H.P. in *Caribou*, 250 in *Eole* = 13·5 and 9·5 kts. respectively. 2 screws. Petrol: 22-27 tons.

ASTER (1918). 118 tons. Dimensions: 88½ × 18 × 8½ feet. Oil engines. H.P. 250 = 8 kts. 1 screw. Oil: 4 tons.

PRIMEVÈRE (1912). 450 tons. Dimensions: 116 × 22 × 14 feet. H.P. 450 = 8·5 kts. 1 screw. Coal: 30 tons.

Oilers (*Pétroliers.*)

LE MÉKONG.   1929 *Photo by favour of M. Henri Le Masson.*

LE MÉKONG, by Ch. & At. de St. Nazaire (Penheöt) (Aug. 31, 1928), **LE NIGER,** by Ch. & At. Maritimes du Sud-Ouest, Bordeaux (March 14th, 1930) and 2 more laid down 1929. Displacement: 13,130 tons *full load.* Dimensions: 436¼ (*p.p.*), 455¼ (*o.a.*) × 62 × 26¼ feet *max.* draught. Guns: 2—4 inch, 2—2 pdr. 2 sets Burmeister & Wain Diesel engines. H.P. 6600 = 13.5 kts. (exceeded on trials). Capacity of tanks: 33,900 cubic feet. Deadweight: 9600 tons, of which oil fuel absorbs 9000; distilled water, 500; lubricating oil, 100, both in commission 1930.

           1928 *Photo, R. Perkins, Esq.*

LE LOING (At. & Ch. de la Seine Maritime, Le Trait, 4th April, 1927). 9900 tons. Guns: 2—4 inch, 2—2 pdr. AA. Dimensions: 403½ × 50½ × 25 feet. 2 sets 4-cycle single-acting Diesel engines by Burmeister & Wain. H.P. 4100 = 13.5 kts. (exceeded on trials). Carries 5900 tons oil. Constructed on Isherwood system.

AUBE.   1921 *Photo, H. Freund.*

AUBE (July, 1920), **DURANCE** (1920), **NIÈVRE** (March, 1921), **RANCE** (July, 1921), all by Lorient D.Y. 2500 tons. Dimensions: 242.8 (*o.a.*) × 38 × 15.7 feet. S.H.P. 1000 = 10 kts. Breguet turbines. Carry 1500 tons oil. Endurance: 1580 miles at 10 kts. Complement, 70.

Oilers (*Pétroliers*).—continued.

1927 Photo, H. Freund.

LOIRE (ex-*Bakou*), Nikolaieff, 1915. Displacement, 12,200 tons. 5400 tons *gross*. Dimensions : 400 × 53 × 26 feet. Oil engines. H.P. 3400 = 10 kts. Carries 8000 tons oil. (Taken over from Gen. Wrangel at Bizerta.)

1921 Photo, H. Freund.

DORDOGNE (ex-*San Isidoro*, Armstrong, 1914). Displacement, 24,000 tons. 15,160 tons D.W. Carries 13,000 tons oil. Dimensions : 530 × 66½ × 28 feet. H.P. 4150=11.7 kts.

1920 Photo, H. Freund.

GARONNE (1911). 10,800 tons. H.P. 2600=13 kts. Carries 7000 tons oil as cargo. Complement, 65.

Oilers (*Pétroliers*)—continued.

1931 Photo,

RHÔNE (1910). 7830 tons. H.P. 2100=11 kts. Carries 4500 tons oil as cargo. Complement, 57.

Two Tankers have been ordered in Germany from the Deutsche Werft (26/8/1929) under the Dawes plan.

VAR (1931) 9600 tons. 436 ft. long A.E.G. Diesels. H.P. 4400 = 13.5 kts. Twin screws.

ADOUR (1930). 15,150 tons.

Armed Yacht.

1921 Photo by courtesy of Lieut. de V. Théry.

DIANA (1896). 1400 tons. Dimensions : 256 × 27¾ × 15¾ feet. Guns : 2—14 pdr. I.H.P. 900 = 10 kts. Coal : 200 tons. Complement, 65. Serves as Yacht for the Senior French Naval Officer in the Levant.

Fleet Tugs. (*Remorqueurs de Mer.*)

"Fighting Ships" Classification limits List to Vessels of over 600 H.P.

		Tons.	H.P.	Speed.	
Mammouth	1918	970	1,800	12	
Centaure	1913	600	1,500	12	
Pingouin	1917				
Pintade	1917	780	750	10	Cherbourg
Ramier	1919				
Lutteur	1919	600	750	9	
Tumulte	1918	370	700	11·5	
Sioux	1918	340	650	10·5	
Mastodonte	1918	970	1,800	12·5	
Hippopotame	1918				
Indefatigable	1898	1,050	1,250	10·5	
Faisan	1917	780	750	11	
Athlète	1917	600	750	10	Brest
Gladiateur	1917				
Courageux	1915	370	750	9	
Haleur	1887	370	650	11·5	
Guepe	1913	637	1,582	9	
Loup-Cervier	1898	600	1,500	12	
Six-Fours	1917	600	1,500	10	
Goliath	1908	1,150	1,400	11·5	
Samson	1901	660	1,000	11	
Travailleur	1892	520	900	9·5	Toulon
Milon	1901	500	900	9·5	
Gélinotte	1917				
Paon	1917	780	750	10	
Colombe	1917				
Tapage	1918	370	700	11·5	
Rhinocéros	1918	970	1,800	11·5	
Mehari	1913	600	1,500	13	
Cyclope	1901	600	1,000	13	
Vigoreux	1915	500	1,000	8·5	
Taillebourg	1892	450	800	11·5	Bizerte
Héron II	1918	780	750	10·5	
Canard	1918	780	750	11	
Tintamarre	1918	370	700	11·5	
Fracas	1917	370	700	11	
Vacarme	1918	370	700	12	
Tourterelle	1918	780	750	11	Algiers
Pigeon	1918	780	750	11	
Seminole	1895	600	1,200	14	Senegal
Clameur	1918	370	700	12	

Minister of Defence: General W. Gröner.
Chief of Navy Department: Vice-Admiral Räder.

Uniforms.
INSIGNIA OF RANK ON SLEEVES.

| Admiral. | Vice-Admiral. (Vice-Ad.) | Kontre-Admiral. (Rear-Ad.) | Kapitän zur See. (Captain.) | Fregatten-kapitän & Korvetten-kapitän. (Commander.) | Kapitän leutnant. (Lieut.-Comm.) | Oberleut z. See. (Lieut.) | Leutnant z. See. (Sub-Lieut.) |

Flaggoffiziere.   Stabsoffiziere.   Subalternoffiziere.

NOTE.—In above sketch, a *star* should replace the devices which appear in the 5 junior ranks.

Uniforms and distinguishing marks of rank are the same for officers of all branches of the service ; but in place of the star on the sleeve, which distinguishes the military branch, there is worn by :

Engineer Officers, a pinion wheel
Medical Officers, the rod of Æsculapius } As in sketch above.
Accountant Officers, an eagle

Officers of the legal and administrative sections of the Naval Department, when attached to the staff of a command, or acting as advisers on questions concerning naval accounts in the Ministry for Defence of the State, wear *silver stripes* on their sleeves, with a silver eagle above, and silver facings to their uniforms.

The difference between a *Kapitän zur See* and a *Fregattenkapitän* is indicated by stars on the shoulder straps.

Kommodores wear the same sleeve stripes as a *Kapitän zur See*, but with the cords and shoulder bands of a Flag Officer.

Flags.

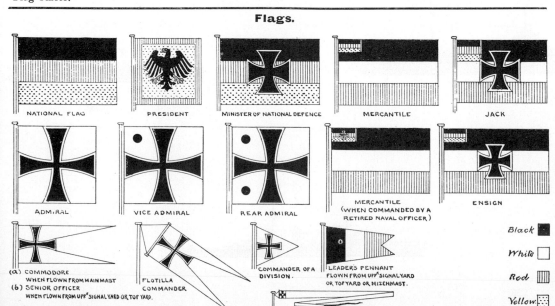

NATIONAL FLAG   PRESIDENT   MINISTER OF NATIONAL DEFENCE   MERCANTILE   JACK

ADMIRAL   VICE ADMIRAL   REAR ADMIRAL   MERCANTILE (WHEN COMMANDED BY A RETIRED NAVAL OFFICER)   ENSIGN

(a) COMMODORE WHEN FLOWN FROM MAINMAST
(b) SENIOR OFFICER WHEN FLOWN FROM UPPᴿ SIGNAL YARD OR TOP YARD.

FLOTILLA COMMANDER

COMMANDER OF A DIVISION.

LEADERS PENNANT FLOWN FROM UPPᴿ SIGNAL YARD OR TOP YARD OR MIZENMAST.

PENNANT

Black ■
White □
Red |||
Yellow ⋮

Naval Guns.

Calibre		Usual Naval Designation.	Length in cals.	Date of Model.	Weight of Gun.	Weight of A.P. shot.	Initial Velocity.	Maximum penetration, direct impact against K.C. at			Danger space against average ships at			Approximate Muzzle Energy.
								9000 yds.	6000 yds.	3000 yds.	10,000 yards.	5000 yards.	3000 yards.	
inch.	c/m.				tons.	lbs.	foot-secs.	in.	in.	in.	yards.	yards.	yards.	foot tons.
11	28		...	'28	...	670	...	...	...	...	...	...	...	31,600
11	28		40	'01	32·2	661·4	2756	6	10	14	150	450	740	
6·7	17		40	'01	7·5	154·5	2756	...	3	5	80	240	460	8,275
5·9	15		50	...	5·5	3084		...	...	...	...	...	...	6,690
5·9	15		45	'09	5	101·4 { 2920		...	...	5	...	200	420	5,990
5·9	15		40	'01	4·9	2756		...	...	3½	...	140	350	5,335
4·1	10·5		45	'16	...	38·2	...	...	...	...	...	...	...	...
4·1	10·5		40	...	1·7	35·2	2756	...	...	...	...	...	...	1,860

Brass cartridge cases to all guns.

Lesser guns : 3.4 inch (88 m/m) firing 22 lb. projectiles in modern and 15 lb. in old models ; also 2 inch (4 pdr.) of 55 and shorter calibres.

A.A. guns : 6 inch, 4·1 inch, 3·4 inch War Marks on H.A. mounts (" Flak ").

Projectiles : Guns of 11 inch and over fire A.P., Ersatz A.P., H.E., and common shell.

The 1899 and later models have the recoil utilized to return the gun to firing position for pieces over 6 inch. In 6 in. springs are employed. German guns have a lower muzzle pressure than normally obtains.

11 inch, 40 cal., M. '01 in *Deutschland* and *Braunschweig* classes.

Personnel.

(a) **TOTAL PERMITTED ESTABLISHMENT**, Active List, Officers and Men, inclusive of Administrative Staffs ashore, Shore Establishments, Schools, Coastal Defence Units and Signalling Companies, 1,500 Officers + 13,500 Men = 15,000. All officers and men to enter as volunteers : Officers to serve for 25 years, men for 12 years.

(b) Total personnel, 1929, 1,040 officers ; 13,955 men.

Colour of Ships.

Big Ships : Light grey all over.
Torpedo craft : Dark Grey.

Mercantile Marine.

(From " Lloyd's Register." 1931 figures.)
Total *gross* tonnage, 4,254,601 including 19 vessels of 16 knots and over.

Navy Estimates.

1930-31, 191,855,500 marks
1929-30, 180,000,000 ,,
1928-29, 213,000,000 ,,
1927-28, 220,000,009 ,,

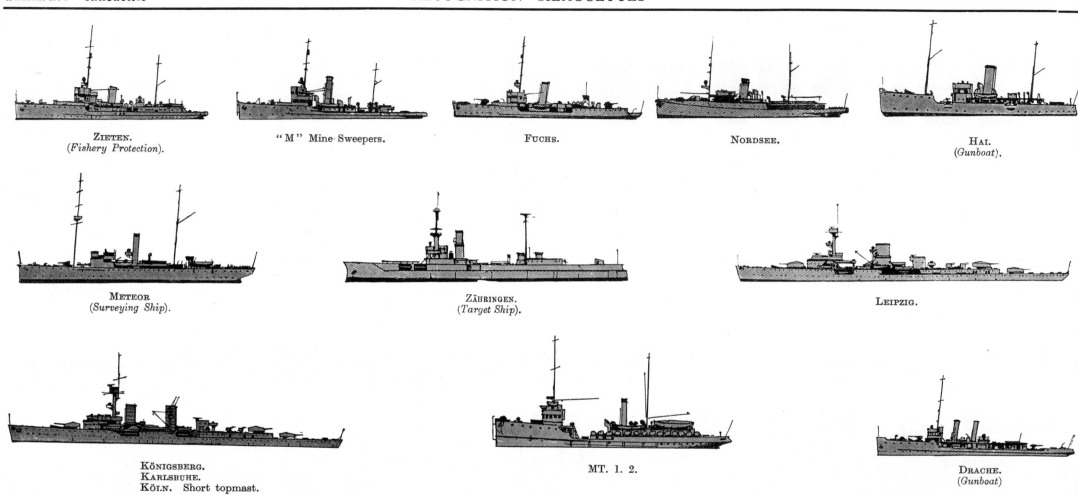

ZIETEN.
(Fishery Protection).

"M" Mine Sweepers.

FUCHS.

NORDSEE.

HAI.
(Gunboat).

METEOR
(Surveying Ship).

ZÄHRINGEN.
(Target Ship).

LEIPZIG.

KÖNIGSBERG.
KARLSRUHE.
KÖLN. Short topmast.

MT. 1. 2.

DRACHE.
(Gunboat)

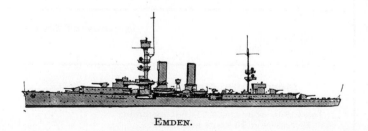

EMDEN.

BREMSE.

SCHLESIEN.
SCHLESWIG-HOLSTEIN.

T 185.

BERLIN.

HESSEN.

TISI, 153, 155—158.

G. 7—11.
S. 23 and T 190—196 very similar.

HANNOVER.

MÖWE *class*.
WOLF   „

Battleship—Special Note.—Establishment permitted by Treaty: 6 in Commission, 2 in Reserve. Age Limit: 20 years. Not to be replaced by ships of more than 10,000 standard tons displacement.

DEUTSCHLAND (Laid down at Deutsche Werke, Kiel, September, 1928). Launched May 31st, 1931. To be completed Autumn 1932.

Ersatz *LOTHRINGEN* (Laid down Wilhelmshaven, June 25th, 1931. To be completed 1934.

Ersatz *BRAUNSCHWEIG* (projected. To be commenced 1932).

Ersatz *ELSASS* (projected. To be commenced 1934.)

Standard displacement, 10,000 tons. Complement 634.

Length, 609¼ (*o.a*) feet. 593 feet (*w.1*). Beam, 67½ feet. Draught 21⅔ feet.

Guns :
  6—11 inch.
  8—6 inch.
  4—3.4 inch AA.
Torpedo tubes :
  6—19.7 inch (*above water*).

Armour :
  Amidships belt and 2 protective decks. Anti-submarine and mine protection is claimed to represent a big advance on anything previously devised.

  The belt armour is incorporated as part of the hull, a method of construction adopted for the first time in the German Navy.

1930, *Illustration*.

General Notes.—She is the first ship of her size to have an electrically welded hull and to be propelled by Diesel engines. By these means a saving in weight of 550 tons is said to be effected, the engines being of exceptionally light construction, developing one unit of horsepower for every 17½ lbs. of weight. Speed reported as 450 r.p.m. The 11 inch guns are a new Krupp model, firing a 670 lb. projectile, with a range of 30,000 yards and an elevation of 60°. Cost will be £4,000,000. Two more ships of this type are projected to replace *Braunschweig* and *Elsass*.

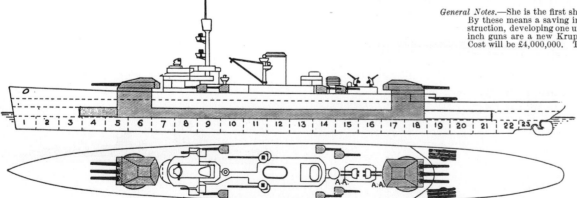

(Plan furnished by courtesy of the Naval Staff, Berlin, 1929.)

Note to Plan :—Launch photos show upper deck is continued aft to about section 20, and T. Tubes will probably be fired through a revolving shield as in *Hessen*.

Machinery : 8 sets M.A.N. Diesels, of 6,250 H.P. each. H.P. 50,000 = 26 kts.
Radius : 10,000 miles at 20 kts.

Note.—Old Battleships on this and succeeding pages have had some of their lighter guns landed and placed in store in order to provide better accommodation for crews.

(DEUTSCHLAND CLASS—1ST SHIP.)

HANNOVER (Sept., 1905).

Displacement, 13,200 tons.   Complement, 705.

Length (*waterline*), 413 feet.   Beam, 72⅖ feet.   *Mean* draught, 25¼ feet.   Length (*over all*), 419 feet.

Guns (M. '01):
  4—11 inch, 40 cal.
  14—6·7 inch, 40 cal.
  4—3.4 inch A.A.
  23 Machine.
Torpedo tubes:
  4 (19·7 inch) *above water*.

Armour (Krupp):
  9½″ Belt (amidships)......
  4″ Belt (ends) ....
  3″—1½″ Deck ....
  11″ Barbettes ....
  10″ Turrets to these, 8″
    Lower deck (side)......
  6¾″ Battery.................
  12″ Conning tower (fore).
  6″   „   „   (aft).

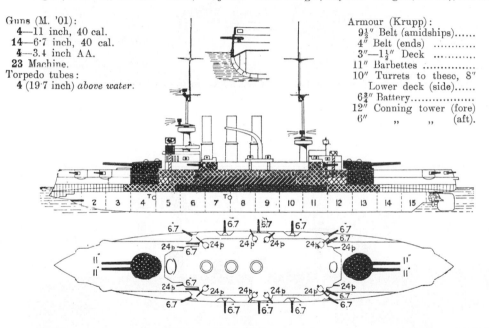

HANNOVER (after alterations).

1930 *Photo.*

Machinery: 3 sets 3 cylinder vertical triple expansion.   3 screws.   Boilers: 12 Schulz Thornycroft.   Designed H.P. 17,000/19,300 = 18 kts.   Coal: *normal* 800 tons; *maximum* 1750 tons. Also 200 tons oil fuel.   *Nominal* radius 5200 kts. at 10 kts.

Notes.—Built at Wilhelmshaven D.Y., '04/'07; Refitted 1929-30.

(DEUTSCHLAND CLASS—2ND AND 3RD SHIPS.)

SCHLESIEN (May, 1906), **SCHLESWIG-HOLSTEIN** (Dec. 1906).

Displacement, 13,200 tons   Complement, 708 (743 as Flagship).

Length $\begin{cases} (w.l.) & 413 \\ (o.a.) & 419 \end{cases}$ feet. Beam, $72\frac{1}{5}$ feet. *Mean* draught, $25\frac{1}{4}$ feet.

Guns :
 4—11 inch, 40 cal.
 12—6 inch, 45 cal.
 4—3.4 inch AA.
 23 Machine.
Torpedo tubes :
 4—19.7 inch (*above
  water*).

Armour :
 $9\frac{1}{2}''$ Belt (amidships) ......
 $4''$ Belt (ends) ....
 $3''$—$1\frac{1}{2}''$ Deck ....
 $11''$ Barbettes ....
 $10''$ Turrets to these, $8''$
  lower deck (side) ....
 $6\frac{3}{4}''$ Battery ....
 $12''$ Conning tower (fore) ....
 $6''$,,   ,,   (aft) ..

SCHLESIEN.

1931 *Photo.*

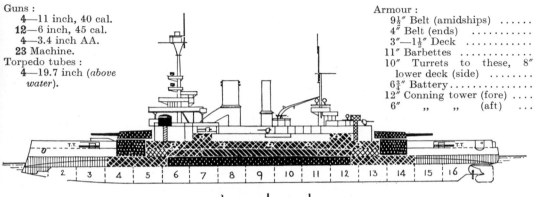

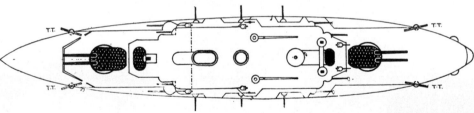

NOTE : After upper 6in. guns removed, 1931.

Machinery : 3 sets 3 cylinder triple expansion.   3 screws.
 Boilers : 12 Schulz-Thornycroft. Designed H.P. 17,000/19,300
 =18 kts. Coal : *normal*, 800 tons ; *maximum*, 1800 tons.
 Oil fuel : 230 tons.   *Nominal* radius : 5900 miles at 10
 kts.

Notes.—*Schlesien* and *Schleswig-Holstein* built by Schichau, Danzig, 1904-08,
 and 1905-08, respectively. Both were reconstructed and partially re-armed
 in 1926-28.

SCHLESIEN.

1927 *Photo, Renard, Kiel.*

HESSEN.

1931 *Photo.*

HESSEN (Sept., 1903), Germania Kiel.
Displacement, 13,200 tons. Complement, 708.
Length (*waterline*), 413⅓ feet. Beam, 72⅘ feet. *Mean* draught, 25¼ feet. Length (*over all*), 419 feet.

Guns (M. '01.):
4—11 inch, 40 cal. (A³).
12—6·7 inch, 40 cal.
4—3·4 inch (22 pdr.).
4—3·4 inch AA.
23 Machine.
Torpedo tubes :
4 (19·7 inch) *above water*.
(Arranged as in *Schlesien.*)

Armour (Krupp) :
8¾″ Belt (amidships)
4″ Belt (ends) ....
3″ Deck on slopes ...
11″ Barbettes to these
11″ Turrets (side) ......
5″ Lower deck.........
6″ Battery...............
6¾″ Small turrets......
12″ Conning tower .....
6″   ,,   ,, (aft).

Machinery : 3 sets 3 cylinder vertical inverted triple expansion. 3 screws. Boilers : 8 single-ended coal-burning and 2 single-ended oil-burning Schulz-Thornycroft. Designed H.P. 16,000 = 18 kts. Coal : 1,090 tons. Oil : 200 tons. Radius : 3,000 miles at 16 kts., 5,000 miles at 10 kts. Builder : Germania, Kiel ; begun 1902, completed 1906, refitted 1923–25. *Craunschweig, Elsass, Preussen, Lothringen* has been removed from effective list.

Cruisers—Special Note.

Establishment permitted by Treaty : 6 in commission, 2 in reserve.

Not to be replaced under 20 years old.

New ships not to exceed 6000 standard tons displacement, or to be armed with a gun heavier than 6 inch.

(LEIPZIG CLASS—1 SHIP)

LEIPZIG (October 18th, 1929).

Displacement, 6,000 tons Complement, 534.
Length, 543 feet 10½ inches (*p.p.*), 544½ feet (*w.l.*), 580 feet (*o.a.*).

Beam, 53 feet 5½ inches.

Mean draught, 15 feet 7¼ inches.

LEIPZIG.

1931 *Photo.*

Guns :
9—6″ 50 cal. (Dir).
4—3·4″ AA.
18—Machine.
Torpedo tubes :
12—19·7″, *above water*, tripled.

Armour :
3″—4″ Belt
......Gun houses.
......C.T.

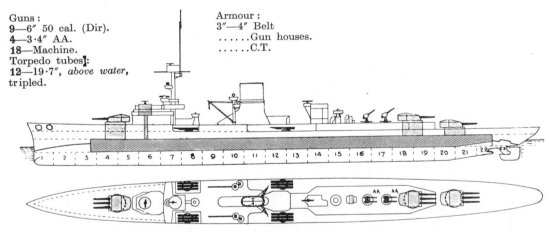

Machinery : Geared turbines, 60,000 S.H.P. with Diesel engines of 12,000 B.H.P. Speed : 32 kts. Triple screws (centre—system " Helix "). Boilers : 6 " Marine " type (modified Schulz-Thornycroft), double-ended oil burning. Centre shaft Diesel driven : can be used for cruising or combined with turbines to give full speed. Radius of action with Diesel engines at 14·5 kts : 3,800 miles ; with turbines at 14·5 kts. : 3,200 miles=7,000 miles. Radius could be greatly augmented if all bunkers were filled with Diesel fuel only.

General Notes.—Laid down at Wilhelmshaven April 18th, 1928. To be completed in 1931. Modified *Königsberg* design with after turrets in centre-line and uptakes trunked into one funnel : fitted with bulges below water-line which are to be filled with oil fuel and are designed to improve speed lines rather than to act as a means of protection.
Diesels reported to develop 1 H.P. per 12½ lbs. weight.

LEIPZIG.

1931 *Photo.*

KARLSMÜHE.

1930 *Photo, Schäfer.*

(Königsberg Class—3 Ships.)

KÖNIGSBERG (March 26th, 1927), **KARLSRÜHE**
(August 20th, 1927), **KÖLN** (May 23rd, 1928).

Displacement, 6000 tons.   Complement, 516.

Length, 554 feet 5½ inches (*w.l.*), 570 feet (*o.a.*),
Beam, 49 feet 10½ inches.

Designed draught, 17 feet 9 inches.

KÖNIGSBERG.

1929. *Photo, Renard.*

Guns :
  9—6 inch, 50 cal. (**Dir. Con.**)
  4—3.4 inch AA.
18 Machine.
Torpedo tubes :
  12—19.7 inch, *above
water,* tripled.

Armour :
  3″—4″ Belt ....
  ″ Gun Houses ....
  ″ C.T.

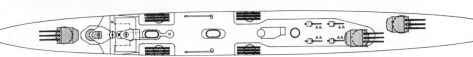

Name	Building Yard	Begun	Completed	Trials	Boilers	Best recent speed
Königsberg	Wilhelmshaven	12/4′26	Spring, 1929		Schulz-Thornycroft	32.2
Karlsrühe	Deutsche Werke, Kiel	27/7/26	Autumn, 1929			
Köln	Wilhelmshaven	7/8/26				

General Notes.—Every possible expedient for saving weight has been employed in these ships. A very high grade of
steel was selected, and electric welding has taken the place of riveting.

Gunnery Notes.—Triple 6 inch can fire simultaneously at rate of 6 to 8 salvoes a minute, and range to 20,000 yards.
Disposition of after turrets is governed by arrangement of ammunition handling rooms. The 3.4 inch guns are
now paired in *Karlsrühe* and *Köln.*

Machinery : Geared turbines with Diesel engines for cruising purposes. Boilers : Schulz-
Thornycroft. Designed H.P. 65,000 = 32 kts.   Fuel : 1200 tons oil.   Radius : at 14 kts.,
5500 miles ; at 10 kts., 10,000.

Staggered after Turrets, and Twin AA Guns.

KÖLN.

KÖLN and KARLSRÜHE now have short fixed Topmasts.

1931 *Photo.*

KÖNIGSBERG.

1929 *Photo, Renard.*

KÖNIGSBERG. (retains lowering Topmast).

1930 *Photo, Schäfer.*

EMDEN (Wilhelmshaven, 7th January, 1925).

Standard displacement, 5,600 tons.   Complement, 506.

Dimensions : 493¾ (*w.l.*), 508½ (*o.a.*) × 46¾ × 17½ feet (*mean* draught).

Guns :
8—6 inch 45 cal. (**Dir. Con.**).
2—22 pdr. AA.
18—Machine.
Torpedo tubes :
4—19.7 inch (*above water*).

Armour :
3″—4″ Belt ....
″ Gun Houses ....
″ C.T.

Notes to plans.—1st plan refers to present arrangement of armament ; 2nd, that which will ultimately be adopted. Control top lowered and funnels equalised, 1926.

EMDEN.   (With stump main mast.)

1931 *Photo.*

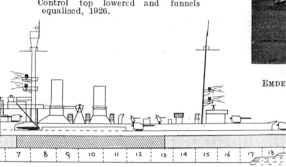

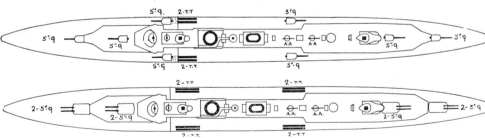

Machinery : Geared turbines.   Boilers : 10 Schulz-Thornycroft "Marine" type (4 coal-burning, 6 single-ended oil-burning).   Designed H.P. 46,500 = 29 kts.   Fuel : 1120 tons coal and oil.   Effective cruising radius : 6500 miles.   Laid down in summer of 1921 ; commissioned 15th October, 1925.

Armour Notes.—Belt ceases about 33 feet short of ends.

Engineering Notes.—Designed to maintain a speed of 27.5 kts. in fair weather.   Revs. per minute : 2435 H.P. turbines, 1568 L.P. turbines, geared down to 295 R.P.M. on propellers.   Mixed firing was adopted in this ship, with the object of being independent of overseas oil supplies if necessary.   On trials, designed speed was slightly exceeded with 46,500 H.P.

General Notes.—To save weight, electric welding was extensively used in construction of this cruiser.   The tubular foremast is about 5 feet in diameter.   Masting modified and second funnel heightened, 1926-27.   *Emden* was designed for foreign service, particular attention being paid to accommodation.

EMDEN.

Photo added 1930, *W. W. Stewart, Esq.*

CRUISER (1931).

1931 *Illustration.*

BREMSE (Wilhelmshaven, Jan. 24, 1931).

Displacement, 1225 Tons   Complement, 112.

Dimensions, 318·4 × 31¼ × 9½ feet.

Guns :
  4—4·1 inch.
  4—1 pdr. AA.

Permission withheld.

Machinery : 8 M.A.N. double acting, 2 stroke, geared Diesels. 2 screws. Designed H.P. 25,000 = 27 kts. Oil fuel : ?   Radius :

Note.—This ship is to be employed on gunnery school duties, but design suggests that she may be intended as a minelayer.

Old Cruiser.

BERLIN. (now has short mainmast).

1925 *Photo, Renard.*

BERLIN (September, 1903).

Normal displacement, 3650 tons *metric.* Complement, 349.

Dimensions : 362·9 × 43·3 × 16⅔ feet (designed draught).

Guns :
  8—4.1 inch, 45 cal.
  18 M.G.
Can carry 108 mines.
Torpedo tubes :
  2—19.7 inch *above water.*

Armour (Krupp) :
  2″ Deck ....
  ¾″ Deck (at ends) ..
  4″ C.T. ....

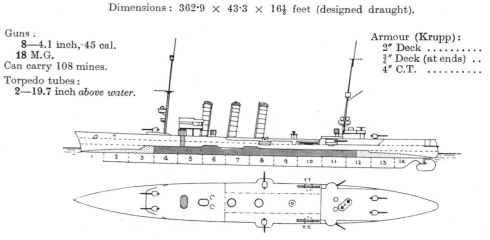

Machinery : 2 sets 3-cylinder triple expansion. 2 screws. Boilers : 10 Schulz-Thornycroft. Designed H.P. 10,000 = 22 kts. Coal : *normal,* 400 tons ; *maximum,* 860 tons. *Nominal* radius : 5900 at 10 kts. Begun 1902, completed 1904. At Kiel in reserve. *Hamburg* scrapped 1921.

26 Destroyers and Torpedo Boats.

*Permitted Establishment 22 boats + 11 in Reserve.

General Notes.

Age limit under Treaty, 15 years. Displacement of new destroyers must not exceed 800 tons, and of torpedo boats 200 tons.

Practically all German Torpedo Craft now in service have had fore funnel heightened and clinker screen added.

"G boats" built by Krupp's Germania Yard, S boats by Schichau. All are officially rated as "Grosse Torpedoboote," or "Big Torpedo Boats," and not as Destroyers ("Torpedoboots-Zerstörer"). Unless otherwise noted, all boats have Schulz-Thornycroft (or "Marine Type") boilers. The details tabulated are generally simplified to the average design of each group.

"T-boats" were built with the usual G, S and V builders' index letters, but were given letter T to avoid duplication of numbers with the later boats numbered from V 1 up to S 23, and the "War Types," V 25—S 223. In description of T boats, G refers to Krupp-Germania boats, and V to Vulcan boats.

1926.

WOLF.   1930 Photo, Schäfer.

6 Wilhelmshaven Yard: **Iltis, Wolf** (both Oct. 12th, 1927), **Jaguar, Leopard, Luchs, Tiger** (all March, 1928). Laid down 1927 as W 109–114, for completion in summer of 1928 to replace worn out destroyers and torpedo boats. Displacement: 800 tons (1000 tons deep load). Dimensions: 292 (p.p.), 304 (o.a.) × 28 × 9 feet. Guns: **3**—4.1 inch, 45 cal. Torpedo tubes: **6**—19.7 inch (tripled parallel). Designed S.H.P.: 23,000 = 34 kts. Geared turbines and Schulz-Thornycroft boilers. Oil fuel: 330 tons. Complement, 115. Other details not yet reported, but are of same general type as Möwe class, with minor improvements.

1924-25.

ALBATROSS.   (All now have above appearance.)   1928 Photo, Wilh. Schäfer, Kiel.

6 Wilhelmshaven Yard: **Möwe** (March 4th, 1926), **Albatross, Greif, Seeadler** (all three July 15th, 1926), **Falke, Kondor** (both Sept. 22nd, 1926). Displacement: 800 tons (960 tons deep load). Dimensions: 277¾ × 27½ × 9¼ feet draught. Guns: **3**—4.1 inch, 45 cal., **2 S.L.** Torpedo tubes: **6**—19.7 inch (tripled parallel). Geared turbines. 3 Schulz-Thornycroft boilers. Designed S.H.P. 23,000 = 33 kts. (exceeded on trials). Oil fuel: 320 tons. Complement, 111.

Notes.—Laid down under 1924 and 1925 Programmes, as W 102-107. Möwe commissioned October 1st, 1926, others passed into service during 1927, replacing old destroyer T 175 and the worn-out torpedo boats of T 149 type. Have longitudinal framing and double bottom to hull. Guns said to elevate to 80°. The cost of these vessels is extraordinarily high, working out at about £215 per ton.

WOLF and MÖWE types.

1912-13.

1911-1912 (and two **1913** Replace Boats).

S 23.

1928 *Photo, Renard, Kiel.*

G 7 (as modified and lengthened).

1930 *Photo.*

1 *Schichau :* **S 23.** Launched 1913. 640 tons. Dimensions : 234⅔ × 24⅓ × 9¾ feet Armament : **2—4·1** inch, 45 cal. **7** M.G. Torpedo tubes : **2—19·7** inch. Designed S.H.P. 15,700=31 kts. Schichau turbines. Fuel : 146 tons coal + 65 tons oil. Complement, 82.

Now carry two single tubes in centre-line.

4 *Krupp-Germania :* **G 7, G 8, G 10, G 11** (launched 1911-12).

Displacement : 760 tons. Dimensions : 249½ × 24½ × 9¾ feet. Armament : **2—4·1** inch, 45 cal. Torpedo tubes : **2**—19·7 inch. Machinery : turbines, Parsons in Germania boats. Designed H.P. : 16,000 = 31 kts. ; Fuel : 156 tons coal, 80 tons oil ; 3 Schulz-Thornycroft boilers (oil burning). Complement, 82.

G 7, G 8, G 10, G 11 have been lengthened 14¾ feet during alterations 1928-31.

DESTROYERS—*continued*.

1910-11.

T 196.

1930 *Photo, Schäfer.*

1 *Krupp Germania,* **T 196** (ex *G 196*). ⎫
1 *Vulkan,* **T 190** (ex *V 190*). ⎭ launched 1911.   Big refit 1927-28.

Displacements : *G* boat 648 tons, *V* boat 656 tons *normal* (800 tons *full load*).   Dimensions : 242¾ × 25¾ × 10¼ feet. Armament : **2** 4·1 inch, 45 cal.   Torpedo tubes : **2**—19·7 inch.   Machinery : Parsons turbines in *G* boat, A. E. G. Curtis in *V* boat.   Designed H.P. : *T 196,* 18,200 = 27·5 kts. ; *T 190,* 18,000 = 30·5 kts.   Fuel : *T 196,* 204 tons ; *T 190,* 198 tons oil.   4 Schulz-Thornycroft boilers (oil burning).   Complement, 82.

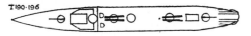

(Now carry two single tubes only.)

1909-10.

1 *Vulkan,* **T185** (ex *V185*) (1910)

Displacements : 637 tons (718 tons *full load*).   Dimensions : 242¾ × 25¾ × 10¼ feet.   Armament ; 2—4.1 inch, 45 cal.   Torpedo tubes : 2—19.7 inch.   Machinery : A. E. G. Curtis turbines.   Designed H.P. 18,000 = 30 kts. Fuel : 198 tons oil.   Complement, 82.

Note.—This class are unsatisfactory.   T 196 only reached 26·6 kts. on trials after re-construction.

TORPEDO BOATS.
1907-08.

T 158.

1928 *Photo, Renard.*

6 *Vulkan,* **T 151—153, T 155—158** (ex *V 151,* etc.), launched 1907-8.   Displacement : 554 tons, *normal* (675 tons *full load*).   Dimensions : 237½ × 25½ × 9¾ feet (*mean draught*).   Guns : **2**—3·4 inch (15 pdr.), 45 cal.   Torpedo tubes : **2**—19·7 inch (paired).   Machinery : Reciprocating engines.   Designed H.P. 10,900 = 30 kts.   Oil : 175 tons. Complement, 97.   **T 152** scrapped.

Ex-Torpedo Boats.

Blitz.

1929 *Photo, by favour of Lieut-Commdr. Steen Steensen, R.D.N.*

Blitz (ex *T 139*), *Pfeil* (ex *T 141*).   Old boats used for target control, manœuvring the ex-battleship *Zahringen* by radio.

Target Service Ship.

ZÄHRINGEN (1901). 1930 *Photo.*

ZÄHRINGEN, (ex-Battleship, completely reconstructed 1926–28 for use as a wireless controlled target ship on similar lines to British *Centurion.* Displacement : 11,800 tons. Dimensions: $393\frac{1}{2} \times 68\frac{1}{6} \times 25$ feet. H.P. 5,000=13 kts. 2 screws. Oil fuel and automatically fired boilers. Controlling vessel is ex-T.B. *Blitz.*

Fishery Protection Cruisers.

Completing

ELBE, WESER (both launched Jan. 24, 1931 at Wilhelmshaven). Displacement: 600 tons. Dimensions: $157\frac{1}{2} \times 27\frac{1}{4} \times 10\frac{1}{4}$ feet. Armament : none. Machinery : 2 sets Linke-Hofmann—Busch 6-cylinder 4-stroke Diesel engines. 2 screws. Designed H.P. 1600=15 kts. Radius: 7000 miles at 11 kts. Complement : 33.

Gunnery School Ships.

FUCHS. 1930 *Photo.*

FUCHS (ex-*M* 130, 1919). Displacement : 525 tons. Dimensions : $184 \times 24 \times 7\frac{1}{2}$ feet. Guns : 2—4·1″ AA. Machinery : 2 sets triple expansion. Boilers : 2 Schulz w.t. 2 screws. D.H.P. 1,800=16 kts.

Mine Layer.

MT1 *ex*-HEPPENS. 1930 *Photo.*

MT1 ex-*Heppens,* **MT**2 (ex-*Mariensiel*), both launched 1917 at Neptun Yard, Rostock. Displacement : 570 tons. Dimensions : $164 \times 30\frac{1}{2} \times 7\frac{1}{2}$ feet. Armament : none. Machinery : 2 screws triple expansion. Boilers : 2 single-ended coalburning Schulz-Thornycroft. 2 screws. Designed H.P. 375=10 kts. Radius : 1,200 miles at 7 kts. Complement : 47.

Harbour Tender.

NIXE. 1930 *Photo.*

NIXE. Displacement : about 100 tons. Dimensions : $98\frac{1}{2} \times 16\frac{1}{3} \times 5\frac{1}{2}$ feet. Machinery : 2 carbureting engines. 2 screws. H.P. 200=13 kts.

Tenders.

HELA.   1925 *Photo, Renard.*

HELA (ex Minesweeper *M 135*). (March 15th, 1919), **WACHT** (ex *M 133*, 1920), **DELPHIN** (ex *N 108*, 1919), **FRAUENLOB** (ex *M 134*, 1919), **JAGD** (ex *M 82*, 1918). Displacement, 525 tons, except *Jagd*, 500 tons. Dimensions : 184 × 24 × 7⅙ feet. Armament : None. Machinery : 2 sets triple expansion. Boilers : 2 Schulz water tube. 2 screws. Designed H.P., 1800 = 16 kts.

1925 *Photo, Renard.*

DRACHE (Germania, 1908). 790 tons. Dimensions : 177 × 30½ × 9¾ feet. Complement, 66. Guns : 4—4.1″. H.P. 1675 = 15. Coal : 150 tons. (Gunnery.)

Tenders—*continued.*

HAI (Geestemünde, 1907). 640 tons. Dimensions : 141 × 28¾ × 9¾ feet. Complement, 53. Armament : **6—3·4 inch.** H.P. 1100 = 12 kts. Coal : 84 tons. (Gunnery.)

1928 *Photo.*

GRILLE (ex-Trawler *Von der Goltz*, 1916). Purchased 1927 for use as Tender to Mining and Torpedo School. 470 tons. Dimensions : 118¾ × 24 × 10½ feet. 1 screw. H.P. 400 = 10 kts. Classed as Experimental Vessel (*Versuchsfahrzeug*).

Surveying Vessels (*Vermessungsfahrzeuge*).

1928 *Photo, Renard, Kiel.*

METEOR (Danzig, 18 Jan., 1915). 1200 tons. Complement, 111. Dimensions : 219⅖ × 33½ × 11⅛ feet. Guns : None. Machinery : 2 sets triple expansion. 2 screws. Boilers : 4 Schulz-Thornycroft. Designed H.P. 650 = 11.5 kts. Coal : tons. Completed June, 1925.

Fleet Tender & Repair Vessel.

1930 *Photo.*

NORDSEE (Atlas Werke, Bremen, 1914). 830 tons. Complement, 27. Dimensions: $175\frac{3}{4} \times 30\frac{3}{4} \times 12$ feet. Armament: Nil. H.P. 1680 = 12 kts. 2 screws. Well deck built up 1923.

Fishery Protection Vessel (*Fischereischatzboot*).

1927 *Photo, Topical.*

ZIETEN (ex-*M*138, Tecklenborg, Feb. 17th, 1919). Displacement: 550 tons. Dimensions: $183\frac{1}{3} \times 24 \times 7\frac{1}{6}$ feet. Guns: none. 2 sets Diesel engines each 420 B.H.P. = 12 kts. Complement, 43. Fuel: 90 tons.

Note.—Ex-Minesweeper converted for present service in 1924.

Training Ship (*Segelschulschiff*).

1928 *Photo, Wilh. Schäfer, Kiel.*

NIOBE (launched 1913). Displacement: 650 tons. Dimensions: $151\frac{1}{4} \times 30\frac{1}{6} \times 15\frac{3}{4}$ feet. Auxiliary motor, H.P. 240 = 7 kts. 1 screw. Oil fuel, 20 tons.

Mine Sweepers (*Minensuchboote*).

PELIKAN (ex-*M* 28). 1925 *Photo, Renard.*

Mine Sweepers—*continued.*

NAUTILUS (ex-*M 81*). 1925 *Photo, Renard.*

29 boats :—

M 157	M 126	M 110	M 98	M 72
*M 146	M 122	M 109	M 89	*M 66
M 145	M 117	M 107	M 85	M 61
*M 136	M 115	M 104	M 84	*M 60
M 132	M 113	M 102	M 75	M 50
M 129	M 111			

* NAUTILUS (ex *M 81*), *** PELIKAN** (ex *M 28*).

Built 1916-1920. Displacement: *M 157—98*, 525 tons; *M 89—28*, 480 to 500 tons. Dimensions: 182 (*w.l.*), 192 (*o.a.*) $\times 23\frac{1}{2} \times$ 7 feet. Guns: 2 M.G. in some. Engines: 2 sets triple expansion. Boilers: 2 water-tube "Schulz." I.H.P. 1800 = 16 kts. 2 screws. Coal: 130 tons.

Notes.—Only a few units are maintained in commission (marked * above.) *Nautilus* and *Pelikan* are rated as Experimental Boats (*Versuchsboote*).

Motor Patrol Vessels (*Bewachungsfahrzeuge*).

1930 *Photo.*

8 boats: **UZ 27, 28, 29, 30, 32, 33, 34, 35** (1919-20). 60 tons. Dimensions: $101\frac{1}{2} \times 14\frac{1}{2} \times 3\frac{3}{4}$ feet. H.P. 500 = 14 kts. 2 screws.

Motor Patrol Vessels.

Photo wanted.

UZ (S).   1931 *Photo.*

3 Boats : **UZ (S) 15, 17, 21** (1917–21). Displacement : 12 tons. Dimensions : $57\frac{2}{5} \times 8\frac{1}{5} \times 2\frac{2}{5}$ feet. Armament : none. Machinery : 3 screws carbureting engines. 3 screws. Designed H.P. 840＝29 kts. Fuel : 1·5 tons Benzol. Complement : 8.

W1 *ex*-UZ (S) 16.   1931 *Photo.*

2 Boats : **W1, 2** (1930–31). Displacement : about 20 tons. Dimensions : ? × ? × ? feet. Armament : 2 torpedo-tubes (special design). Machinery and other details unknown.

Motor Patrol Vessels.

R 1.   1931 *Photo.*

2 Boats : **R1, 2** (1930–31 Lürssen, Vegesouk). Displacement : 45 tons. Dimensions : unknown. Armament : none. Machinery : 2 MWM Diesel engines. Designed H.P. 600＝18 kts. Complement : 14.

Photo wanted.

UZ (S) 18.

1 Boat : **UZ (S) 18** (1927). Displacement : 26 tons. Dimensions : $70 \times 13\frac{3}{4} \times 3\frac{1}{4}$ feet. Armament : none. Machinery : 3 sets carbureting engines. 3 screws. Designed H.P. 720＝27 kts. Fuel : 13 tons Benzol. Complement : 8.

There are 16 boats, belonging to the Blocking Division : **C1—16** (1906–15), old steamers of 75–80 tons.

Officially revised by courtesy of the Chief of the Naval General Staff, Athens, 1931.

Special Note.

The services of a British Naval Mission of 5 officers, under Captain L. E. Holland, R.N., are at present lent to the Hellenic Navy.

Flags.

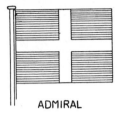

ADMIRAL

Vice-Admiral's flag similar, but has a white ball in upper left canton.

Rear-Admiral's has a white ball in each left canton.

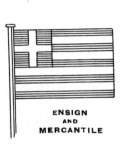

ENSIGN AND MERCANTILE

CAPTAIN COMMANDING A DIVISION

SENIOR OFFICER

Sky **Blue**

White

*Personnel :—*About 9,500 (conscript, 18 months or enlistment).
*Minister of Marine :—*Mons. P. Avgyropoulos.
*Chief of General Naval Staff :—*Capt. C. Louis.
*Naval Attaché, London :—*Capt. D. Fokas.
Mercantile Marine :—(1931 official figures), Total Gross Tonnage, 1,458,000

Uniforms.

| 1 | 2 | 3 | 4 | 5 | 6 | 7 | 8 | 9 |

(1) Navarkhos. *Admiral.*   (2) Andinavarkhos. *Vice-Admiral.*   (3) Yponavarkhos. *Rear-Admiral.*   (4) Ploiarkhos. *Captain.*   (5) Andiploiarkhos. *Commander.*

(6) Plotarkhis. *Lieutenant-Commander.*   (7) Ypoploiarkhos. *Lieutenant.*   (8) Anthipoploiarkhos. *Sub-Lieut.*   (9) Simæophoros. *Act. Sub-Lieut.*

Other branches without curl :—
Constructors: *black velvet.*
Engineers : *violet velvet.*
Paymasters : *scarlet velvet.*
Surgeons : *purple velvet.*
Apothecaries : *green velvet.*
Aviation : *light green velvet.*
Dockyard : *black.*

Tonnage.
At Standard Displacement.

NAUTILUS.

PLEIAS.

TENEDOS.
KORGIALENIOS.
PARALOS.

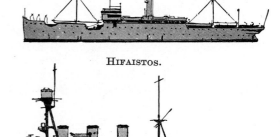

HIFAISTOS.

AVES.

HELLE.

AVEROFF.

HYDRA CLASS.

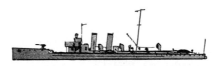

PERGAMOS AND KIOS CLASSES.

AIGLI CLASS.

AETOS CLASS.

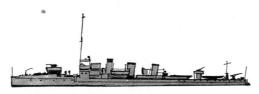

ASPIS. NIKI.

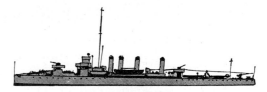

THYELLA.
SPHENDONI.

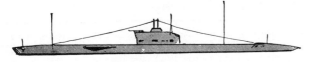

KATSONIS CLASS.

NEREUS CLASS.

(1907) Armoured Cruiser.

AVEROFF

1931 Photo, Official.

AVEROFF (March, 1910).

Displacement, 9,450 tons.   Complement, 670.

Length (over all), 462 feet.   Beam, 69 feet.   Maximum draught, 24⅔ feet.

Guns (Armstrong) :
4—9·2 inch, 45 cal. (**Dir. Con.**)
8—7·5 inch, 45 cal.
16—14 pdr.
2—3 inch A.A. (Vickers).
4—3 pdr.
2 M.G.
Torpedo tubes (18 inch) :
2 submerged (broadside).
1   „   (stern).
Searchlights :
2—36 inch.

Armour (Terni) :
8″ Belt (amidships) ......
3¼″ Belt (ends) ....
2″ Deck ....
7″—6″ Upper belt ..
4″ Upper belt (ends) ......
8″ Main barbettes (N.C.)....
6½″ Turrets (N.C.) ....
7″ Citadel ....
7″ Second'ry turrets (N.C.)
7″ Conning tower ....

Ahead :
2—9·2 in
4—7·5 in.

Astern :
2—9·2 in.
4—7·5 in.

Broadside : 4—9·2 in., 4—7·5 in.

Machinery : 2 sets 4 cylinder triple expansion. 2 screws. Boilers : 22 Belleville. Designed H.P. 19,000 = 22·5 kts. Trials : 21,500 = 23·9. Coal : normal 660 tons ; maximum 1500 tons = 7125 miles at 10 kts. ; 2489 miles at 17¾ kts. Built by Orlando.

Gunnery Notes.—All big guns hydraulically controlled. 2—12 pdr. AA. guns mounted on after superstructure.
General Notes.—Cost £950,750. Sister to Italian Pisa. Reboilered and completely refitted by Forges et Ch. de la Mediterranée, at La Seyne 1925-27, the alterations effected including the installation of new heavy type tripod foremast with director tower, additional rangefinders and searchlights, AA. guns, new boats, etc.

Cruiser Minelayer.

HELLE.

1931 Photo, Official.

HELLE (ex-Chinese Fei Hung, May, 1912).

Displacement, 2115 tons.   Complement, 232.

Length (over all), 322 feet.   Beam, 39 feet.   Draught, 14 feet.

Guns (Armstrong) :
3—6 inch.
2—3 inch. AA. (Vickers).
4—6 pdr.
Torpedo tubes (18 inch) :
2 above water.

110 Mines carried.

Armour (steel):
2″ Deck on slopes ...
2″ Deck on flat........

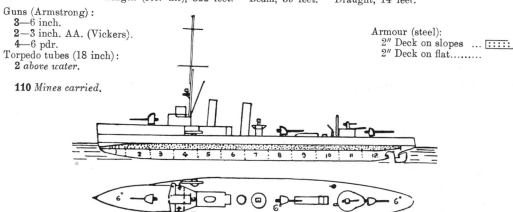

Machinery : 3 Parsons geared turbines. 3 screws. Boilers : 3 Yarrow. Designed H.P. 7500 = 20.5 kts. Oil : normal 600 tons = 7000 miles at 10 kts.

| Name | Builder | Machinery | Laid down | Completed | Trials : | | Boilers | Best recent speed |
					4 hours.	Full Power.		
Helle	N.Y. Shipblg.	N.Y. Shipblg.	1910	Nov.,'13	7500 = 20·3	8650 = 21	Yarrow	

General Notes.—Built as the Fei-Hung for China. Purchased 1914. Originally fitted with Thornycroft boilers, mixed coal and oil burning. Now converted to oil fuel only. Original turbines have also been replaced, and vessel equipped for mine-laying, 1926-28. This cruiser has been completely transformed by the reduction of her armament, 4 broadside guns being removed and main battery arranged on centre-line, as well as by the removal of the old poop and other heavy weights. The whole of this work was carried out by the F. & Ch. de la Mediterranée, La Seyne. On fresh trials original speed was exceeded.

4 Hydra class

HYDRA.

1931 *Illustration.*

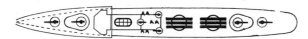

4 *Hydra* class: ***Hydra, Spetsai, Psara, Condouriotis*** ordered from Odero, October, 1929. Displacement: 1350 tons, 2050 tons *deep load.* Dimensions: 303 × 32 × 10¾ feet. Armament: **4**—4.7 inch, **3**—40 m/m AA., **6**—20.8 inch tubes. 2 sets Parsons geared turbines. 3 Express type boilers. S.H.P. 50,000 = 39.5 kts. Cost about £255,000 each. Two fitted to carry 40 mines. Radius 5,000 miles at 20 kts. Complement, 156.

4 Aetos Class.

AETOS type.

AETOS.

1931 *Official Photo.*

PANTHER. Equipped as a minelayer.

1927 *Official Photo.*

4 *Cammell-Laird* type: ***Aetos, Ierax, Leon, Panther*** (all launched 1911). 1013 tons *normal*, 1300 *full load.* Dimensions: 293 × 27¾ × 8½ feet, *normal* draught; *full load* draught, 10 feet. Armament: **4**—4 inch Bethlehem (DIR. CON.), **2**—Pom-poms. Tubes: **6**—21 inch, in triple deck mountings. 3 searchlights. S.H.P. 19,750 = 32 kts. Combined Parsons and Curtis turbines. 4 Yarrow boilers. Oil: 260 tons. These were 4 boats, *San Luis, Santa Fe, Tucuman* and *Santiago*, built for Argentina. Purchased by Greece, Oct., 1912. Reconstructed and re-boilered by Messrs. J. S. White & Co., Ltd., E. Cowes, 1924-25.

General Notes.—The refit of these destroyers has proved a great success, the original speed being exceeded by 2 kts. From obsolescent craft they have been transformed into efficient and up-to-date destroyers little inferior to the British "W" type. *Aetos* and *Panther* are fitted for mine-laying, and carry 40 mines each.

2 Thyella Class.

THYELLA.

1931, *Official Photo.*

2 *Yarrow* type : **Thyella, Sphendoni** (1906-07).   305 tons.   Dimensions : 220¼ × 20½ × 6 feet, *mean* draught ; *max.* draught, 9 feet.   Armament : **2**—3.4 inch Krupp, **1**—2.7 inch AA.   **2** tubes (18 inch)   Speed : 30 kts.   Coal : 80 tons.   Endurance : 1140 to 1250 miles at 15 kts.   Complement, 70.

Notes.—Both refitted 1926–28. *Navkratousa*, of this class, lost in 1921. **Lonkhi** sold 1931.

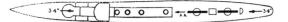

2 Niki Class.

NIKI

1931 *Official Photo.*

2 *Vulkan Stettin* type : **Aspis** (1906), **Niki** (1905).   275 tons.   Dimensions : 220¼ × 20½ × 6 feet, *mean* draught ; *max.* draught, 9 feet.   H.P. 6700 = 30 kts.   Armament : **2**—12 pdr., **4**—6 pdr.   **2** tubes (21 inch).   Coal : 90 tons.   Complement, 70.   Endurance : 1140 to 1250 miles at 15 kts.   *Doxa* of this class, lost during the War.

Note.—Both underwent a thorough refit, 1928–29. **Velos** sold 1931.

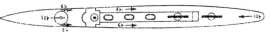

4 Torpedo Boats.

AIGLI.

1931 *Official Photo.*

4 *Vulkan* type : **Aigli, Alkyone, Arethousa, Doris,** (all launched 1913).   145 tons.   Dimensions : 147⅞ × 9⅓ × 4 feet.   Armament : **2**—6 pdr. Bethlehem. **3**—18 inch tubes.   I.H.P. 2600 = 25 kts. (about 24 kts. best speed now).   Trials : *Aigli* 26·2, *Doris* 25·7.   Coal : 60 tons.

Note.—These four boats were completely refitted, 1926–30. **Dafni** and **Thetis** sold 1931.

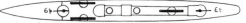

Submarines.

4 Glavkos Class.

GLAVKOS.   1929 *Photo, by favour of M. Henri Le Masson.*

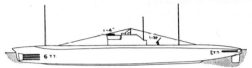

4 *Simonot* type. **Nereus** (Dec., 1927), **Proteus** (Oct. 24th, 1927), **Triton** (April 4th, 1928), all built by At. & Ch. de la Loire, at Nantes, **Glavkos** (1928), by Chantiers Navals Francais, at Blainville. Displacement : 700/930 tons (metric). Dimensions : 225 (*p.p.*) × 18.8 × 13.7 feet. Machinery (supplied by At. & Ch. de la Loire): On *surface*, 2 sets 2-cycle Sulzer-Diesels, totalling 1420 B.H.P. for 14 kts.: *submerged* 1200 B.H.P. for 9½ kts. Endurance on *surface* : *normal* 1500 miles, *maximum* 4000 miles; both at 10 kts. When *submerged*, 100 miles at 5 kts. Armament : 1—4 inch, 1—3 pdr. AA., 6 21 inch internal bow tubes, 2–21 inch internal stern tubes. Stowage for 8 torpedoes, 150 rounds of 4 inch ammunition. Complement, 41. *Maximum* depth of submergence : 40 fathoms. Approximate cost £119,000 each.

2 Katsonis Class.

KATSONIS.   1929 *Photo, M. Bar, Toulon.*

2 *Schneider-Laubeuf* type. **Katsonis** (20 March, 1926), by Ch. de la Gironde, at Bordeaux; **Papamicolis** (Nov. 1926), by At. & Ch. de la Loire, at Nantes. Displacement: 576/775 tons. Dimensions : 204½×(*p.p.*) 17½×11 feet. On *surface*, 2 sets of 2-cycle Machinery : Schneider-Carels Diesels, totalling 1300 B.H.P. for 14 kts. *Submerged*, 1000 B.H.P. for 9½ kts. Endurance, on *surface* : *normal* 1500 miles, *maximum* 3500 miles, both at 10 kts ; when *submerged*, 100 miles at 5 kts. Armament : 1—4 inch, 1—3 pdr. AA., 2—21 inch internal bow tubes, 2—21 inch external bow tubes, 2—21 inch external stern tubes. Stowage for 7 torpedoes, 100 rounds of 4 inch ammunition. Complement, 39. *Maximum* depth of submergence: 40 fathoms. First boat delivered at Piraeus, Dec. 29th, 1927.

Patrol Vessels (ex-Torpedo Boats).

PERGAMOS.   1922 *Official Photo.*

2 *Ex-Austrian* boats : **Pergamos** (ex-95 *F*), **Prousa** (ex-92 *F*). Built by Ganz-Danubius Yard, Fiume (1914-1915). 241 tons. Dimensions : 188½ × 19 × 4·9 feet *max.* draught. H.P. 5000= 28 kts. 2 turbines. 2 Yarrow boilers (1 coal and 1 oil). Fuel : 21 tons coal + 31 tons oil. Guns : 1—11 pdr. Skoda (*Pergamos* has 2). No torpedoes carried. Complement, 25.

Note.—These boats underwent a general refit at Piraeus, 1926. Original speed exceeded.

KYZIKOS.   1922 *Official Photo.*

3 *Ex-Austrian* boats : **Kyzikos** (ex-98 *M*), **Kios** (ex-99 *M*), **Kidonia** (ex-100 *M*). Built at Monfalcone (1914). 241 tons. Dimensions : 197 × 18 × 4·9 feet *max.* draught. Other details as *Pergamos* type, above.

Note.—All three boats underwent a general refit at Piraeus, 1926. Original speed exceeded.

Mine Layers.

Note.—In peace time these vessels are employed as follows *Pleias* as a Lighthouse Tender, the other three as "Communication Boats" Despatch Vessels).

PLEIAS. 1931 *Official Photo.*

PLEIAS (Soc. Italiana Ernesto Breda, Nostre Yard, Venice, 28th April, 1926). Displacement : 520 tons. Dimensions : 162 × 27 × 12½ feet. I.H.P. 1000 = 14 kts. Coal : 90 tons. Carries 50 mines.

1931 *Official photo.*

PARALOS (Rotterdam, 1925). Displacement : 395 tons. Dimensions : 150 × 22 × 10½ feet. I.H.P. 550 = 13 kts. Coal : 35 tons. Carries 52 mines.

Mine Layers—*continued.*

1931 *Official photo.*

KORGIALENIOS (Rotterdam, 1916). Displacement : 380 tons. Dimensions : 150 × 21½ × 10 feet (depth). I.H.P. 550 = 13½ kts. Coal : 35 tons. Carries 50 mines.

1931 *Official photo.*

TENEDOS (Glasgow, 1906). Displacement : 460 tons. Dimensions : 142 × 24 × 10 feet (*mean* draught). I.H.P. 560 = 13 kts. Coal : 40 tons. Carries 40 mines.

Old Gunboats

KISSA. 1931 *Official Photo.*

KISSA, KICHLE (Blackwall, 1884). 86 tons. Dimensions : 76 × 16 × 7 feet. I.H.P. 162 = 10 kts. Coal : 20 tons. Guns : Nil. (*Kissa* now used as a Lighthouse Tender).

Surveying Ship.

1931 *Official Photo.*

NAUTILUS (Dumbarton, 1884, Rebuilt 1895-7). 404 tons. Dimensions : 131¼ (*p.p.*) × 24⅓ × 11 feet. Guns : Nil. H.P. 400 = 11 kts. (8 kts. best speed now). Coal : 55 tons. Complement, 60.

246

Training Ship.

1928 *Photo, Marius Bar.*

ARES (Forges et Chantiers de la Méditerranée, La Seyne, Jan. 28th, 1927). Steel Barquentine. Displacement: 1870 tons. Dimensions: 208 (*p.p.*) × 39½ × 13¼ feet. Guns: **4**—3 inch. Auxiliary steam engine (reciprocating) I.H.P. 1000 = 10 kts. 2 oil-fired Babcock & Wilcox boilers. Fitted with lecture rooms, workshops and accommodation for 100 Naval Cadets and 150 Boys. Total complement: 419. Carries an exceptionally full equipment of boats for training purposes.

Note.—On trials, H.P. 1144 = 11·38 kts.

Oil Tanker.

1931 *Official Photo.*

PROMETHEUS (Newcastle, 1889.) 3193 tons, *gross* tonnage. Dimensions: 318½ × 42 × 29½ feet depth. I.H.P. 1150 = 10 kts. Carries 4175 tons of oil fuel.

Fleet Repair and Submarine Tender.

1931 *Official Photo.*

HIFAISTOS (ex-*Khios*) (ex-German Cargo Ship *Marie Reppel*, Rostock, 1920). *Gross* tonnage, 4549. Dimensions: 360⅓ × 50 × 23 feet. I.H.P. 2500 = 11½ kts. Guns: **4**—4 inch AA. Converted into a Repair Ship by Messrs. Palmers, Jarrow-on-Tyne, 1925. Fitted with up-to-date workshops and plant.

Water Carrier.

1931 *Official Photo.*

AVRA (Greenock, 1894, reconstructed, 1918). Displacement, 1221 tons. Dimensions: 210 × 29 × 14 feet. I.H.P. 695 = 12 kts. Coal: 110 tons. Water capacity: 750 tons.

Hospital Ship.

AMPHITRITI (Birkenhead, 1876.) 1172 tons displacement. Dimensions: 206 × 30⅓ × 16½ feet depth. I.H.P. 1630 = 13½ kts. Coal: 160 tons. Originally built as troopship. Rebuilt 1885 as Royal Yacht. Converted 1918 as Naval Hospital Ship.

Mine Sweeping Trawlers.

1931 *Official Photo.*

Y1, Y2 (Leith, 1910). Displacement, 140 tons. Dimensions: 85 × 18 × 6½ feet draught. I.H.P. 200 = 10 kts. Guns: **1**—12 pdr. Krupp, **1** M.G. Purchased from British Admiralty, 1918.

Two Thornycroft 55 ft. type (1929). Two motors each 375 H.P. = 37 kts. (40 kts. reached on trials.) 2 Lewis guns, **2**—18 inch torpedoes, **4** D.C.

One of Thornycroft 45 ft. type (1921). Y12 type motor of 350 B.H.P. = 38 kts. No armament. Complement, 3.

HUNGARY.

(Danube Flotilla).

Flag.—Ensign is rectangular, divided horizontally into three equal parts of red, white and green, with the national arms slightly to the left of the centre.

Principal Base.—Budapest.

Under Law XIV of 1922, the Royal Hungarian Riverguard (M. Kir. Folyamorseg) was established for police purposes on the Danube.

The maintenance of the following craft is permitted :—

    8 Patrol Vessels of 128 tons each *maximum*, armed with 2—70 m/m. and 2 M.G.

    2 Motor Launches, of 20 to 30 tons each, armed with 1—47 m/m. and 1 M.G.

    10 Motor Boats, of 12 to 20 tons each, armed with 1 M.G.

The total strength of personnel must not exceed 96 officers and 1524 petty officers and men. The Royal Hungarian River-guard is under the control of the Ministry of the Interior.

Colour of Ships: Khaki, and Green below waterline.

Mercantile Marine (1925).—7 ships, of 31,790 tons *gross.*

Insignia of Rank.

Vezérkapitany.   Fökapitany.   1 Törzs-   2 Törzs-   Kapitany.
(*Rear-Admiral.*)   (*Captain,*   kapitany.   kapitany.   (*Lieut.-*
     senior.)   (*Captain, junior.*)   (*Commander.*)   (*Commander.*)

Föhajónagy.   Hajónagy.   Gyakornok.
(*Lieut.*)   (*Sub-Lieut.*)   (*Midshipman.*)

Without curl, and with colour between stripes :—
    Surgeons : Black velvet.
    Engineers : Cherry-coloured cloth.
    Constructors : Cherry-coloured velvet.
    Paymasters : Green cloth.
    Judge Advocates : Red cloth.
    Musical Directors : Violet cloth.

Uniform Cap.—Same shape as the former Austro-Hungarian cap. Badge is a golden anchor surrounded by a laurel wreath and surmounted by the Holy Crown of Hungary.

4 River Patrol Boats.

(Ex Austro-Hungarian.)

DEBRECEN.   (Masts now of equal height).   1925 *Official Photo.*

DEBRECEN (ex-*Komaron*, ex-Austro-Hungarian *Lachs*) (Ganz-Danubius Yard, Budapest, 1918). Displacement : 140 tons. Dimensions : $149\frac{1}{4} \times 19\frac{1}{2} \times 3\frac{1}{4}$ feet *mean* draught. H.P. 1400 = 15 kts. A.E.G. turbines. 2 Yarrow boilers. Tunnel screws. Guns : 2—3 inch, 2 M.G. 1 S.L. Oil fuel : 18 tons. Complement, 44. Refitted 1924.

SZEGED.   (Masts now of equal height).   1925 *Official Photo.*

KECSKEMÉT.   (Masts now of equal height).   1925 *Official Photo*

SZEGED (ex-*Bregainica*, ex-Austro-Hungarian *Wels*, 1915), **KECSKEMÉT** (ex-Austro-Hungarian *Viza*, 1916). Both built at Ganz-Danubius Yard, Budapest. Displacement : 133 tons. Dimensions : $144\frac{1}{2} \times 16\frac{1}{2} \times 3\frac{1}{4}$ feet *mean* draught. H.P. 1100 = 15 kts. A.E.G. turbines. 2 Yarrow boilers. Tunnel screws. Guns : 4—3 inch, 2 M.G. 1 S.L. Oil fuel : 18 tons. Complement, 44. *Szeged* refitted 1921, *Kecskemet* 1923.

1926 *Photo, Baron Heribert Thierry.*

SIOFOK (ex-Austro-Hungarian *Csuka*) (D.D.S.G. Werft, Budapest, 1915). Displacement : 60 tons. Dimensions : 118 × 15 × $2\frac{3}{4}$ feet *mean* draught. H.P. 800 = 14.5 kts. Guns : 1—3 inch, 2 M.G. Complement, 28.

In addition to the above, there are a number of small Motor Launches and Guard Boats.

(ROYAL) ITALIAN NAVY.

Officially corrected by courtesy of the Ministry of Marine, 1931.

Uniforms.

(*Note.*—A five pointed silver star is worn on lapel of coat.)

INSIGNIA OF RANK ON SLEEVES.

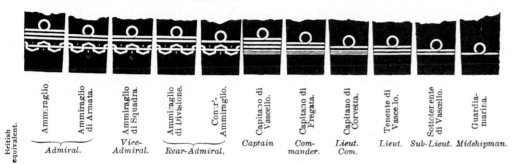

The ranks of Grande Ammiraglio (four stripes) and of Ammiraglio (three stripes) can only be conferred for special merit on flag officers who have commanded fleets in time of war. The rank of Ammiraglio has now been abolished, except "ad personam" to the Royal Princes.

Lesser ranks are: Aspirante; Allievo dell' Accademia Navale (*Naval Cadet*).

Other branches distinguished by following Colours: Armi Navali (*Ordnance Constructors*), yellow-brown; Genio Navale (*Naval Constructors* and *Engineers*), dark purple; Sanitario (*Doctors*), blue; Commissariato (*Paymasters*), red.

Note.—All officers under arms on duty wear a blue sash over right shoulder, ending in a blue knot at left hip; worn with belt. Officers on staff duty wear it on opposite shoulder, and without belt. Tropical white tunic has insignia of rank on shoulder straps, with stars as stripes. Senior lieutenants wear a piece of gold under the stars of shoulder strap.

Navy Estimates: 1931-32.

Total Personnel: Officers, 2,400. Men, 48,000.

Minister of Marine: Ammiraglio di Divisione Giuseppe Sirianni.

Secretary of Marine Ministry: Generale Ispettore del Genio Nav. (R.N.) Gioacchino Russo.

Chief of Naval Staff: Ammiraglio di Sqadra Gino Ducci.

Naval Attaché, London: Capitano di Vascello A. Iachino.

Flags.

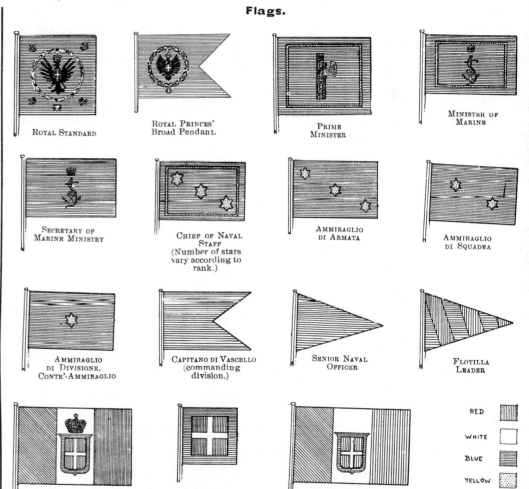

Mercantile Marine.

From "Lloyd's Register" 1931 figures.
Total Gross Tonnage, 3,335,672.
Including 31 vessels of 16 kts. and over.

Future Shipbuilding Programme.

Building Programme for 1931-32:

4 Destroyers (*Maestal class*) 4 1st and 6 2nd class Submarines.   12 coastal Submarines.

OFFICIAL TABLE OF NAVAL ORDNANCE. (Revised, 1931).

Official Designation.—Calibre mm length cal. Mark A=Armstrong, V=Vickers An=Ansaldo, S=Schneider. Date of introduction. Mark O.T.O.=Odero-Terni-Orlando.	305/46 A., V. 1909	254/45 A. 1907	254/45 V. 1906	203/53 An. 1929	203/50 S.-An. 1924	190/45 A., V. 1908-1906	152/53 An. O.T.O. 1927-29	152/50 A. 1918	152/45 S. 1911	120/50 An. 1926.	120/50 A., V. 1909	120/45 A. 1918	102/45 S.-A. 1917	102/35 S. 1914-15	100/47 O.T.O. 1929	76/50 A., V. 1909	76/45 S. 1911	76/40 A. 1916	76/17 S. 1912
Designation by Calibre, **c/m.** ..	30.479	25.4	25.4	20.3	20.3	19.05	15.24	15.24	15.24	12	12	12	10.2	10 2	10.0	7.62	7.62	7.62	7.62
Calibre, in **inches**	**12**	**10**	**10**	8	8	**7.5**	**6**	**6**	**6**	**4.75**	**4.75**	**4.75**	**4**	**4**	**3.9**	**3**	**3**	3	**3**
Lengths / Total, in feet	47.77	39.07	38.715	36.545	34·593	29.22	27.83	25.94	23.42	19.57	20.38	18.38	15.715	12.247	15.721	13.271	11.722	10.292	4.593
Lengths / Rifled Bore, in inches ..	477.9	358.4	370.5	358.66	——	281.7	——	256.6	219.2	——	204.64	174.64	150.74	114.29	12.365	126	107.2	101.57	44.88
Lengths / Powder Chamber, in inches ..	97.7	74.91	74.91	64.66	——	51.65	——	44.6	44.6	——	28.64	35.03	27.16	23.50	3.112	22	25.4	——	——
Lengths / Bore, in calibres	37.3	35.84	37.05	——	——	37.5	——	42.77	36.54	——	43.31	36.96	37.53	28.46	15.371	42	35.73	28.42	14.96
No. of Grooves	72	60	70	52	52	44	44	36	56	36	36	36	40	32	26	28	2⅜	16	24
Twist of Rifling, in calibres ..	30	30	00–30	——	30	00–30	30	33	36	30	30	30	——	——	30	30	35.9	33	22
Total Weight, in tons	62.99	34.49	35.339	19,170	20.800	14.478	7.700	8.100	7.025	3.00	3.662	4.035	2.327	1.200	2.020	1.122	0.698	0.660	0.104
Firing Charge / Armour-piercing projectile lb.	346	185	185	111.994	103.19	70.987	43	——	——	19	——	——	——	——	——	——	——	——	——
Firing Charge / Common Shell H.E., lb. ..	279.9	185	185	——	——	70.987	——	32.79	30.64	——	14.66	9.589	9.479	6.50	10.319	3.02	3.571	2.281	0.529
Weight / Armour-piercing projectile, lb.	997.2	494	494	275.573	260	200.39	103.5	——	——	50.5	——	——	——	——	——	——	——	——	——
Weight / Shell H.E., lb.	884.4	489.8	489.8	——	——	498.5	——	110.22	103.61	——	48.74	48.74	30.31	30.31	30.318	14.05	14.05	13.954	11.68
Weight / Shrapnel, lb.	——	——	——	——	——	——	——	——	——	——	——	——	——	——	——	——	——	——	11.68
Bursting Charge / Armour-piercing projectile, lb.	16.63	4.37	4.37	——	——	2.332	——	——	——	——	——	——	——	——	——	——	——	——	——
Bursting Charge / Shell H.E., lb.	53.13	29.86	29.86	——	——	11.706	——	5.996	7.528	——	2.711	2.711	2.866	2.866	——	1.102	1.102	—	0.782
Bursting Charge / Shrapnel, lbs.	——	——	——	——	——	——	——	——	——	——	——	——	——	——	——	——	——	——	0.165
Muzzle Velocity, in ft.secs. ..	2755.9	2788 77	2788.77	3031.180	2743.20	2788.77	2785	2854	2723	2786	2788	2460	2788	2460	2438.40	2460	2460	2214	1230
Muzzle Energy —Total tons per sq. inch ..	18.63	17.71	17.71	——	——	17.98	——	18.37	16.86	——	18.37	15.75	18.37	18.37	——	18.37	15.75	——	12.47

Note.—German 5·9 in. and 4·1 in.; Austrian 3·9 in., retained in ex-enemy L.C., and T.B.D's. An old Armstrong 10 in., 40 cal., is still mounted in training cruiser *F. Ferruccio.*

12″	46 cal.	*Duilio* class (2 ships), *Cesare* class (2 ships).
10″	45 ,,	*S. Marco* class (2 ships) and *Pisa.*
8″	53 ,,	*Zara* class.
8″	50 ,,	*Trento* classes.
7.5″	45 ,,	*San Marco* class (2), and *Pisa.*
6″	53 ,,	*Condottieri* class.
6″	45 ,,	*Duilio* class (2 ships).
4.7″	50 ,,	*Cesare* class (2 ships), *Quarto*, and *Libia.*
3.9″	47 ,,	*Trento* class, *Zara*, and *Condottieri* class.

Displacement.

Now given in English Tons, "Standard" calculation.

Directors, Rangefinders, &c.

Supplied by the Galileo and S. Giorgio Companies, of Florence and Genoa, respectively.

Hydrophones.

Special schools for Training ratings in use of above apparatus have been instituted.

Torpedoes, Mines, D.C., Air Bombs, &c.

No reliable details available. Torpedoes manufactured by State Arsenals, Societa Italiana, Whitehead & Co., Fiume, and Silurificio Italiano, Naples.   Latter have recently perfected a new type, with warhead carrying 550 lbs. of explosives, which is officially stated to be of remarkably high speed. Tubes are no longer relied upon for accurate aim, which is obtained instead by gyro setting of Torpedoes.

Colour of Ships.

Battleships, Cruisers, Light Cruisers, Destroyers, are all dark grey. Destroyers have identity letters, taken from their names, painted on bows, *e.g.*, AC = *G. Acerbi*, AU=*Audace*, NV = *I. Nievo*, IV = *Impavido*, PL=*R. Pilo*, OR=*V. Orsini*, MT=*A. Mosto*. etc.

BRONDOLO.
MARGHERA.
(Minelayers.)

S. CABOTO.

RD 31 type.

TESEO.

A. BAFILE class (5).

GEN. ARIMONDI.

FASANA class.

G. MIRAGLIA.

CIRENE.

PANIGAGLIA class (3).
(Munition Carriers.)

QUARNARO.

E. CARLOTTO.

PALMAIOLA.

CAMPANIA.

C. COLOMBO   A. VESPUCCI.

SAVOIA.
(Royal Yacht.)

COTRONE.
VIESTI.

OSTIA class.

CHERSO.
LUSSIN.

A. PACINOTTI.
A. VOLTA.

DORIA, DUILIO.

CAVOUR, CESARE.

TRENTO, TRIESTE.

ZARA, FIUME.

CONDOTTIERI *class.*

ANCONA.

BARI.

TARANTO.

S. GIORGIO, S. MARCO.

PISA.

QUARTO.

BRINDISI, VENEZIA.

LIBIA.

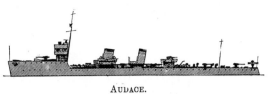

AUDACE.

C. MIRABELLO *class*.

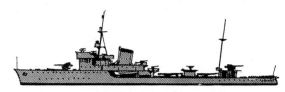

DARDO *class*

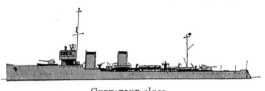

CURTATONE *class*.

LEONE *class*.

FOLGORE *class*.

A. POERIO *class*.

PREMUDA.

COASTAL BOATS O.L.T. Type.

NAVIGATORI *class*.

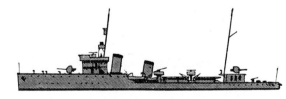

F. NULLO *class*.

T.B. O.L A.S. O.S. P.N. Types.

Q. SELLA *class*.

ARDIMENTOSO.

(*Continued next page*)

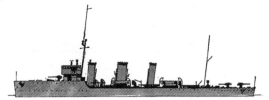

ABBA, INDOMITO & ARDENTE *classes.*

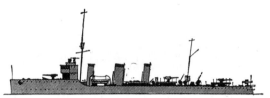

SIRTORI, COSENZ, & GENERALI *classes.*

AQUILA, FALCO.

C. ROSSAROL.

CORTELLAZZO *class.*

H *class.*

X 2, X 3.

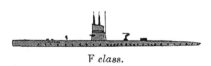

F *class.*

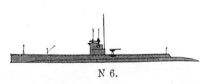

N 6.

N 3, N 4.

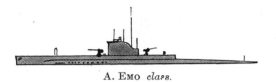

A. EMO *class.*

G. NANI.

G. MAMELI *class.*

BALILLA *class.*

(DUILIO CLASS— 2 SHIPS).

DUILIO (ex-*Caio Duilo*, April, 1913) and **DORIA** (ex-*Andrea Doria*, March, 1913).

Standard displacement, 21,555 tons; *normal* displacement, 22,930 tons. Complement, 1198.

Length (*p.p.*) 554·3 feet. Beam, 91·8 feet. *Mean* draught, 30·7 feet. Length *over all*, 575 feet, 9ins.

Guns (Armstrong or Vickers):
- **13**—12 in., 46 cal. (A^5).
- **16**—6 inch (45 cal.)
- **13**—14 pdr.*
- **16**—14 pdr. (A.A.)
- **8** M.G.
- **2** landing.
- Torpedo tubes (18 inch):
- **2** broadside (*submerged*).

*3—14 pdr. temporarily removed during war.

Armour (Terni):
- $9\frac{3}{4}''$-8" Belt (amidships)
- 5" Belt (ends)
- $1\frac{3}{4}''$ and $1\frac{3}{8}''$ Decks
- $6\frac{3}{4}''$ Lower deck side
- $9\frac{1}{4}''$ Barbettes
- 11" Turrets to these
- $6\frac{3}{4}''$ Battery
- 11" Conning tower (fore)
- $6\frac{3}{4}''$ Conning tower (aft)

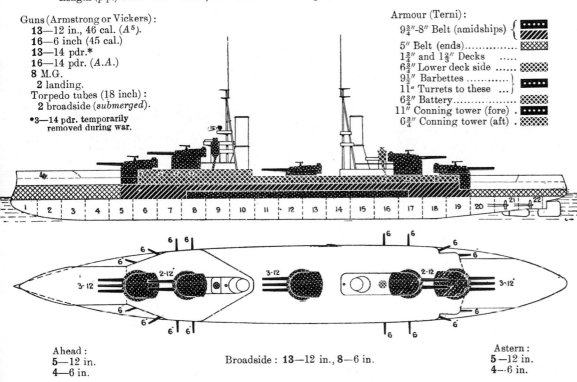

Ahead:
5—12 in.
4—6 in.

Broadside: **13**—12 in., **8**—6 in.

Astern:
5—12 in.
4—6 in.

Machinery: Parsons turbine. 4 screws. Boilers: 20 Yarrow (small tube). Designed S.H.P. 24,000 = 22 kts., but actually need 33,000–35,000 S.H.P. for this speed. Coal: *normal* 580 tons; *maximum* 1450 tons + oil fuel: *normal* 340 tons, *maximum* 850 tons = about 4000 miles at 10 kts. and 2600 miles at 19 kts.

†*Gunnery Notes:* As *Cavour* class on next page. Range-finders mounted to the rear of roof of each barbette shield in armoured hoods and over each C.T. 3 inch (14 pdrs.) are 50 cal. Armstrong or 60 cal.
†*Torpedo Notes:* Vickers. 8 searchlights. †All details unofficial.

Name	Builder	Machinery	Laid down	Com-pleted	Trials H.P.=kts.	Boilers	Best recent speed
Duilio	Castellamare D.Y.	Ansaldo	Apr.'12	1915	31.000 = 21·3 at 22,135 tons	Yarrow	23 ?
Doria	Spezia	Ansaldo	Mar.'12	May '15	34,000 = 21. at 23.620 tons.	Yarrow	

General Notes.—Are improved *Cavour* design, 16—6 inch being substituted for 18—4.7 inch. Otherwise—and excepting altered appearance—there is very little difference between the classes. Machinery, main guns, hull form and internal sub-division, exactly as *Cavours*, and also with same form of triple bottom. Designed by Engineer-Gen. Masdea. These ships exceed their designed displacement of 22,500 tons in the same manner as *Cavour* and *Cesare*, and require to develop 10,000 S.H.P. in excess of designed S.H.P., to reach their designed speed.

DORIA.

1924 *Official Photo.*

DUILIO.

1924 *Official Photo.*

DUILIO.

1931 Photo. Capitan Mateo Mille.

DORIA.

Photo added 1927.

CESARE.

1926 *Photo, Cassar, Malta.*

CAVOUR.

1926 *Photo, Cassar, Malta.*

257

(CESARE CLASS—2 SHIPS).

CAVOUR (ex-*Conte di Cavour*, Aug., 1911), **CESARE** (ex-*Giulio Cesare*, Oct., 1911).

Standard displacement, 21,818* tons.   *Normal* displacement : *Cavour*, 23,089 tons, *Cesare*, 22,380 tons.
Complement, 1197.

Length (*p.p.*) 554·3 feet.   Beam, 91·8 feet.   *Mean* draught, 30·7 feet.   Length *over all*, 557 feet 9 inches.

Guns (Armstrong) :
13—12 in., 46 cal.
18—4·7 inch, 50 cal.
13—14 pdr., 50 cal.⁂
6—14 pdr. AA.
8 machine.
2 landing.
Torpedo tubes (18 inch) :
2 broadside (*submerged*).

3—14 pdr. temporarily removed
during war.

* Cavour 21,604 tons.

Armour (see *Notes*) :
9¾″–8″ Belt (amidships)
5″ Belt (ends)...............
1¾″ & 1⅔″ Decks...........
6¾″ Lower deck redoubt
9½″ Barbettes.............
11″ Turrets to these.....
5″ Battery.................
11″ Conning tower (fore)...
6¾″ Conning tower (aft)...

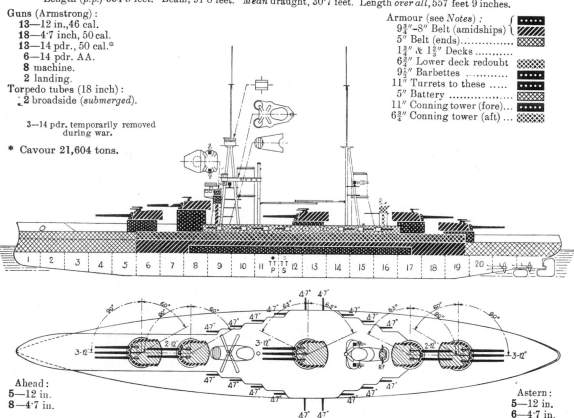

Ahead :
5—12 in.
8—4·7 in.

Astern :
5—12 in.
6—4·7 in.

Broadside : 13—12 in., 9—4·7 in.

CAVOUR.

1922 Photo, by the courtesy of the Ministry of Marine.

Machinery : Parsons turbine.   4 screws.   Boilers : various, see *Notes*.   Designed S.H.P. 24,000 =
22 knots, but actually require 32,000 to 32,500 S.H.P. for this speed.   Coal : *normal* 580 tons;
maximum 1450 tons.   Oil : *normal* 340 tons, *maximum* 850 tons.   Endurance : about 4540 miles at 10
kts., and 2900 miles at 19 kts.

Gunnery Notes.—Arcs of fire : End triples 300°, super-firing twin barbettes 310°, amidships triple 130° each beam.   14 pdr.
can be transferred to different mountings in various positions in these ships.   These notes are unofficial.⅜   CV.

Armour Notes.—*Cavour*, Terni ; *Cesare*, Bethlehem.   Hull has triple bottom around keel.   Usual Torp. Pro. Bulk'hd's
over machinery and magazine spaces, but it is officially admitted such protection is inadequate to-day.   Triple
turret, armour, guns, mountings, weighs about 700 tons, twin turret, about 500 tons.

Name	Builder	Machinery	Laid down	Completed	Trials Full Power		Boilers	Best recent speed
					H.P.	kts.		
Cavour	Spezia D.Y.	Orlando	Aug.,'10	Jan. '15	31.278	= 22	20 Blechynd'n	
Cesare	Ansaldo	Ansaldo	Jun. '10	Mar. '14	30,700	= 21·16	24 Babcock	

General Notes.— Designed by Engineer Gen. Masdea, 1908.   Were designed to displace 22,500 tons at 27½ feet *mean* draught.
Alterations during construction added 2000 tons to displacement and 3 feet to *mean* draught.   They can only reach their
designed speed with difficulty.   Third ship of class, *Leonardo da Vinci*, blew up at Taranto, August, 1916, salved
and docked upside down 1920.   Re-capsized Jan., 1921, and since sold for scrap.

Aircraft Notes.—Catapult on forecastle.   Plane is now stowed there instead of amidships, as formerly.

CAVOUR (showing flight from catapult on forecastle).

1927 Photo.

(San Giorgio Class—2 Ships.)

SAN GIORGIO (July, 1908), SAN MARCO (December, 1908).

Standard displacement $\begin{cases} \text{San Giorgio, 9232 tons.} \\ \text{San Marco, 9353 tons.} \end{cases}$ *Normal* displacement $\begin{cases} \text{San Giorgio, 10,200 tons.} \\ \text{San Marco, 11,000 tons.} \end{cases}$

Complement, 726.

Length (*p.p.*), 429 feet 11 in. Beam, 69 feet. $\begin{cases} \text{S.G. mean draught: 24 feet, max. } 26\frac{1}{4} \text{ feet.} \\ \text{S.M. mean } \quad \text{,, } 25\frac{1}{2} \text{ feet, max. 27 feet.} \end{cases}$

Length *over all*, $462\frac{1}{4}$ feet.

SAN MARCO.   1925 *Photo, Bassan.*

Guns :
4—10 inch, 45 cal.
8—7·5 inch, 45 cal.
10—14 pdr.
6—14 pdr. A.A.
6 machine.
2 landing.
Torpedo tubes (18 inch) :
2 *submerged* (broadside)

Plans revised, 1926.

Armour (*S.M.*, Midvale ;
S.G., Terni) :
8″ Belt (amidships) ...
$2\frac{1}{4}$″ Belt (ends)
$1\frac{3}{4}$″ & $1\frac{1}{2}$″ Decks.........
7″ Lower deck redoubt $\begin{cases} \end{cases}$
8″ Main barbettes ...
$5\frac{1}{4}$″ Turrets to these.
7″ Citadel ....
$6\frac{1}{4}$″ Secondary turrets
$9\frac{3}{4}$″ Conning towers (4)

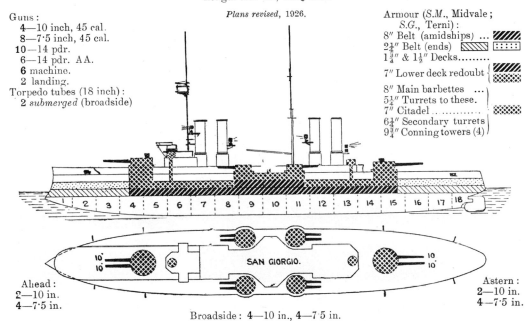

SAN GIORGIO.

Ahead :
2—10 in.
4—7·5 in.

Astern :
2—10 in.
4—7·5 in.

Broadside : 4—10 in., 4—7·5 in.

Machinery : *S. Marco,* Parsons turbine ; 4 screws. *S. Giorgio,* 2 sets 4 cylinder inverted triple expansion ; 2 screws. Boilers : various. See *Notes.* Designed H.P., *S. Giorgio,* 18,000 I.H.P.=22·5 kts. ; *S. Marco,* 20,000 S.H.P.=23 kts. Coal : *normal* 700 tons ; *maximum* 1570 tons for *S. Giorgio,* 1400 for *S. Marco.* Endurance : at 10 kts., 6270 miles for *San Giorgio,* 4800 miles for *San Marco* ; 2640 miles at 20 kts. for *San Giorgio,* about 2500 miles at $21\frac{1}{4}$ kts. for *San Marco.*

Gunnery Notes.—All guns electrically controlled. Central pivot mountings. Fore 10 inch, 31 feet above waterline ; after 10 inch. 22 feet ; 7·5 inch guns 22 feet above water.

Name	Builder	Machinery	Laid down	Completed	Trials : full power		Boilers	Best recent speed
					H.P.	Kts.		
S. Giorgio	Castellamare D.Y.	Ansaldo	May,'05	June'10	19,595 = 23·2 at 9670 tons		14 Blechynden	
S. Marco	Castellamare D.Y.	Ansaldo	Jan.,'07	July'10	23,030 = 23·75 at 10,175 tons		14 Babcock	

General Notes.—Designed by Engineer Lieut-Gen. Masdea. In 1913, *S. Giorgio* grounded badly off C. Posillipo (Bay of Naples), but was salved and repaired. She was again badly damaged by stranding in Straits of Messina early in 1914. Both have been recently employed as Cadets' Training Ships.

SAN GIORGIO.   1925 *Photo, Pucci.*

To distinguish between these two ships note positions of S.L.

Officially rated as 2nd Class Battleship, but at present employed as Sea-going Training Ship for Cadets.

PISA (Sept., 1907).

Standard displacement, 8760 tons. *Normal* displacement, 10,600 tons. Complement, 729.

Length (*p.p.*), 426½ feet. Beam, 68 feet 11 ins. *Mean* draught, 24⅓ feet. *Maximum* draught, 25⅙ feet.
Length *over all*, 460 feet 11 ins.

Plans revised, 1926.

Guns (Vickers) :
    4—10 inch, 45 cal.
    8—7·5 inch, 45 cal.
    12—3 inch, 40 cal.
    6—3 inch, (AA.)
    4 M.G.
    6 landing.
Torpedo tubes (18 inch) :
    2 *submerged* (broadside)

Armour (Vickers) :
    8″ Belt (amidships) ......
    3¼″ Belt (ends) ...
    1¾″ & 1½″ Decks ....
    7″ Lower deck redoubt

    6½″ Main barbettes ...
    8″ Turrets to these......
    7″ Citadel ....
    7″ Secondary turrets ..
    7″ Conning tower ......

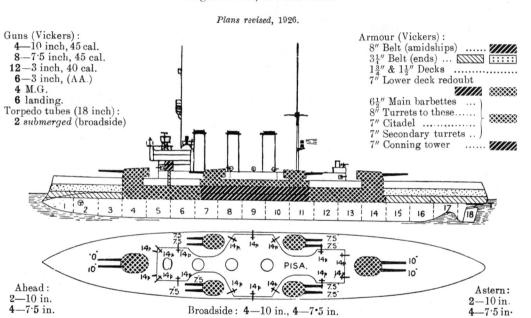

Ahead :
2—10 in.
4—7·5 in.

Broadside : 4—10 in., 4—7·5 in.

Astern :
2—10 in.
4—7·5 in·

1925 *Photo, Bassan.*

Machinery : 2 sets 4 cylinder inverted triple expansion. 2 screws. Boilers : 22 Belleville.
Designed H.P. 20,000 = 23 kts. Coal : *normal* 680 tons ; *maximum* 1510 tons + 140 oil. Endurance :
6,270 miles at 10 kts., 2,300 miles at 21¼ kts.

Gunnery Notes.—All guns electrically controlled. Central pivot mountings. Guns 22 feet above water. Secondary
armament is being reduced to allow of increased accommodation for cadets.

Name	Builder	Machinery	Laid down	Completed	Trials	Boilers	Best recent speed
Pisa	Orlando, Leghorn	Orlando	July,'05	Dec.,'09	24 hrs. = 21·4 kts. 6 hrs. 20.808 = 23·5 ,, (at 10,130 tons)	Belleville	

General Notes.—Designed by Ing. Giuseppe Orlando. The *San Giorgio* class (v. preceding page) is a slightly enlarged
Pisa. A sister-ship, *Amalfi*, lost in the war.

(MODIFIED " TRENTO " TYPE).

BOLZANO.

Standard displacement, 10,000 tons.   Complement, 723.
Length (o a.) 627 feet.   Beam 68 feet.   Draught 18¾ feet

BOLZANO.

1930 Illustration.

Guns :
  8—8″ 53 cal. (new model)
  16—3·9″ 47 cal. AA.
  2—3″
  16—smaller.
Torpedo tubes :
  8—21 inch.

Armour (unofficial) :
  2¾″ side amidships.
    ″ Turrets.
  3″ C.T.
  2″ Deck.

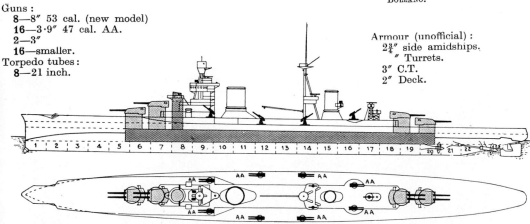

    Machinery : Parsons geared turbines, S.H.P. 150,000=35·5 kts.   4 screws.   12 Yarrow boilers
(300 lbs. pressure).   Oil fuel :   tons.

General Notes.—Laid down under 1929 Programme as a third unit of the *Trento* class, but differs from these in dimensions
    and in having a forecastle deck, besides various alterations in rig, bridgework, etc.   She resembles *Trento* in sacrificing
    a certain amount of protection for an additional 3·5 kts. compared with *Zara*—a modern rendering of the " battle
    cruiser " rôle applied to cruisers.

(Zara Class.—4 Ships.)

ZARA, FIUME (Both Apl. 27th 1930), **GORIZIA** (Dec. 28, 1930),
POLA (Dec. 1931).

Standard displacement, 10,000 tons. Complement,

Length (*p.p.*), 599½ feet. Beam, 67⅔ feet. Draught, 19½ feet.

Guns :
  8—8 inch, 53 cal.
  16—3.9 inch, 47 cal. AA.
  16—Smaller.
Torpedo tubes :
  Nil.

Armour :
  Belt* ....
  Turrets* ....
  Transverse Bulkheads* ..
  ″ C.T. ....
  ″ Deck ....

*These ships have better protection than the " Trento " Class, for which about 3 knots nominal speed is sacrificed. Details omitted pending confirmation.

ZARA. (Running trials without guns or turrets aboard).

1931 *Official Photo*.

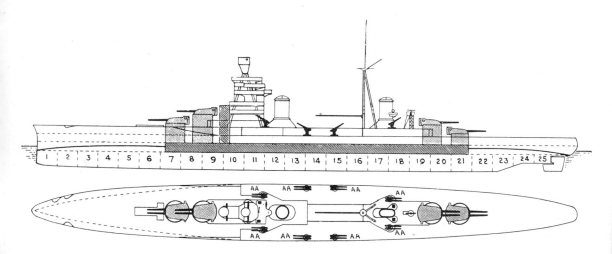

Machinery : Parsons geared turbines. S.H.P. 95,000 = 32 kts. 2 screws. Oil fuel : 1450 tons *normal*, 2200 tons *maximum*. Radius : 3200 miles at 25 kts.

General Notes.—Zara, Fiume laid down under 1928 Programme, *Gorizia* under that for 1929, *Pola*, 1930.

Name	Builder	Machinery	Laid down	Completed	Trials
Zara	Odero-Terni	Odero-Terni	1928	1931	33·80
Fiume	Stab. Tecnico	Stab. Tecnico	1928	1931	
Pola	} Orlando	Orlando	1931	1933	
Gorizia			1929	1932	

" ZARA." (note reduction of bridge-work)

1931 *Photo, Official.*

TRENTO CLASS.—2 SHIPS.

TRENTO (Orlando, Leghorn, Oct. 4th, 1927),

TRIESTE (Stab. Tecnico, Trieste, Oct. 24th, 1926).

Standard displacement, 10,000 tons. Complement, **723**.

Length (*p.p.*), 624, (*o.a.*), 642 feet. Beam, 67½ feet.

Mean draught, 19 feet.

TRENTO.

1930 *Official Photo.*

Guns :
  8—8 inch, 50 cal. (new model)
  16—3·9 inch, 47 cal. AA.
  2—3 inch.
  4—40 m/m. pom-pom. AA.
Torpedo tubes (21 inch) :
  8, in pairs, *above water*, on
    main deck.

Armour :
  2¾″ Side amidships
  ″ Turrets
  3″ C.T.
  2″ Deck

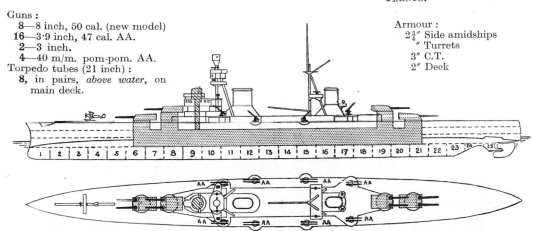

Plan revised 1928.

TRENTO.

1928 *Photo, by favour of Capitan Mateo Mille.*

Machinery : Parsons geared turbines. S.H.P. 150,000 = 35.5 kts. 12 Yarrow boilers (300 lbs. pressure). Oil fuel : 3000 tons.

General Notes.—Laid down under 1923-24 Programme. *Trento*, 8/2/25 ; *Trieste*, in March, 1925. Carry three scouting seaplanes, equipped for bombing. Design modified during construction. They were originally to have had hangar amidships, but this idea has been abandoned and a catapult installed on forecastle. In the revised design, after C.T. is dispensed with, AA. armament redistributed, and additional mast control tops added. These ships are believed to be much more lightly constructed than British *Kent* class, in order to attain a high speed. Completion dates: *Trento*, Sept., 1928 ; *Trieste*, Dec., 1928.

Gunnery Notes.—8 inch reported to be remarkably powerful weapons with exceptional range. *Maximum* elevation is 45°.

Engineering Notes.—Trials in August, 1928, are said to have given an *average* speed of 35 kts. with 149,000 H.P. and consumption of 68 tons of oil per hour. *Maximum* figure reached reported to have been 38 kts.

TRENTO.

1928 *Photo, by courtesy of "L'Italia Marinara."*

TRIESTE.

1929 *Photo, by favour of Capitan M. Mille.*

TRIESTE.

1929 *Official Photo.*

TRIESTE.

1930 *Official Photo.*

("CONDOTTIERI" CLASS—8 SHIPS.)

A {
GIOVANNI DELLE BANDE NERE (April 27, '30)
BARTOLOMEO COLLEONI (December 21, '30)
ALBERTO DI GIUSSANO (April 27, '30)
ALBERICO DI BARBIANO (August 23, '30)
}

B {
LUIGI CADORNA (Sept. 30, '31)
ARMANDO DIAZ ( )
MONTECUCCOLI ( )
MUZIO ATTENDOLO ( )
}

Displacement : 5250 tons.

Dimensions : 555 × 51 × 14 feet.

H.P.: 90,000.

5550 tons.

555 × 51 × 15 feet.

105,000.

A. DI GIUSSANO.

1930 *Photo, Official.*

Guns :
8—6 inch.
6—37 m/m. AA.
3—M.G.

Torpedo tubes (21 inch) :
4 *above water* (paired).

Armour :
Belt.
Deck.   thin plating
Turrets.   only. }

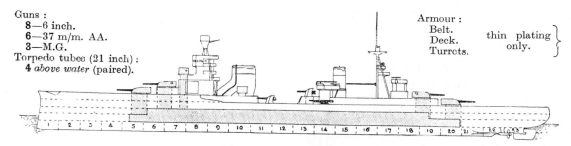

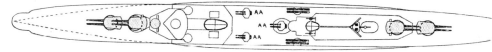

Machinery : 2 Geared Belluzzo turbines.   Designed H.P. $\left.{90,000 \atop 105,000}\right\}$ = 37 kts.   6 Boilers.   Oil: 500/1000 tons.   Radius = 2,500 miles at 25 kts.

Gunnery Notes.—6 inch guns are of a new and very powerful model.

Name	Builder	Machinery	Laid down	Completed	Trials
Bande Nere	Castellamare D.Y.	Trieste	1928	1931	
Colleoni	Ansaldo	Ansaldo	1928	1931	
Barbiano	Ansaldo	Ansaldo	1928	1931	42.048
Giussano	Ansaldo	Ansaldo	1928	1931	40.7 kts.
Cadorna	S. T. Trieste	Trieste	1930	1932	
Diaz	Odero		1930	1932	
Montecuccoli	Ansaldo	Ansaldo	1931		
Attendolo	C.R.A. Trieste	C.A.R.	1931		

General Notes.—This class have been built as a reply to the French destroyers of the *Lion* type, over which they have every advantage. They represent an extraordinary efficient and novel type of cruiser which is capable of overtaking the fastest destroyer. On trials the *A. di Barbiano* reached 42·04 knots at 5,607 tons, and maintained 39·74 knots for 8 hours with her full armament aboard. (Dec., 1930). Their appearance is particularly striking, as they present the profile of a battleship, with their lofty bridgework squat funnels, and general sense of aggressiveness. The original design has been somewhat modified as regards the AA. gun arrangement, superstructures and rig. The present fire control top is 95 feet over water. A catapult of the Magaldi type is fitted along the forecastle. The policy of placing an order for three ships at once with one firm has resulted in all sorts of constructural economies, and the Ansaldo ships were all launched with their masts and funnels up and proceeded on trials very soon after taking the water.

A. DI GIUSSANO.   Running preliminary trials.   *Photo 1930, Messrs. Ansaldo.*

1928-30 CRUISERS.

Condottieri Class

Alberto di Giussano on trials, making 40·7 kts. Sept. 1930.

A. DI GIUSSANO.   Showing alterations to Upper Bridge, Main Mast and Superstructures, 1931.   1931 *Photo, Official.*

1 ex-German Cruiser.

1925 *Photo, by courtesy of the Ministry of Marine.*

BARI (ex-German *Pillau*, ex-Russian *Muraviev Amurski*, April, 1914).

Standard displacement; **3248** tons. *Normal* displacement, 4600 tons. Complement, 398.

Length (*p.p.*), 403 feet. Beam, 46 feet. $\begin{cases} Mean \text{ draught, 16 feet.} \\ Max. \quad ,, \quad \text{19 feet.} \end{cases}$ Length (*o.a.*), 441 feet.

BARI.   1930 *Photo, Capt. Mateo Mille.*

Guns (German):
8—5·9 inch, 42 cal., S.A.
3—76 m/m. AA.
3 M.G.
Torpedo tubes (19·7 inch,
German): **2** *above water.*
Can carry 120 mines.

Armour :
1½″ Deck (on slopes)... ..
¾″ Deck (bow) ....
3″ Deck (over rudder) ...
4″ Conning tower ....

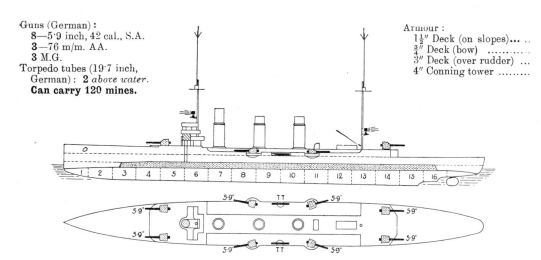

Machinery : Schichau (Melms & Pfenninger) turbines. 3 screws. Designed H.P. 27,400 = 27½ kts.
Boilers : Schichau. Coal : *normal* 500 tons and 750 tons oil fuel = 4500 miles at 10 kts.

General Notes.—Built by Schichau, Danzig, April, 1913—December, 1915. A sister ship, *Elbing*, sunk in the Battle of Jutland. Both vessels were seized by Germany on outbreak of war with Russia, for whom they were originally laid down. *Bari* taken over by Italy, 1920.

ANCONA.   1930 *Photo, Capt.*

ANCONA. (Forecastle extended to accommodate catapult.) 1931 *Photo.*

ANCONA (ex-German *Graudenz*, October, 1913).

Standard displacement, 3838 tons. *Normal* displacement, 5300 tons. Complement, 427.
Length (*waterline*), 456 feet. Beam, 45 feet. *Mean* draught, 16 feet. (*Max.* 17 feet).

Guns (German) :
  7—5·9 inch, 43 cal.
  3—76 m/m AA. (Italian).
  5 M.G.
Torpedo tubes (19·7 inch)
  German : **2** *above water*.

Can carry 120 mines.

Armour :
  4″ Belt (amidships)
  2½″ Belt (ends)
  2″ Deck (amidships)
  4″ Conning tower

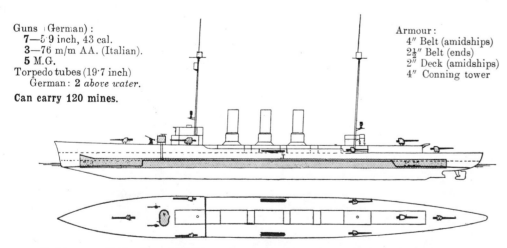

Machinery : " Marine Type " Turbine. 2 screws. Boilers : 12 Schulz-Thornycroft. Designed H.P.
26,000 = 27·25 kts. Coal : *normal* 470 tons ; *maximum* 1300 tons. Oil : 220 tons.

Armour Notes.—Belt is rather deeper than in *Taranto.*

General Notes.—Belongs to German 1912 Programme. Built by Kiel D.Y. Laid down 1912 and completed 1914.
    Radius of action : *about* 5,500 to 6,000 miles at cruising speed. Taken over by Italy, 1920, and gun positions modified.

1930 *Photo, Capt. Mateo Mille.*

TARANTO (ex-German *Strassburg*, Aug., 1911).

Standard displacement, 3184 tons. *Normal* displacement, 4550 tons ; 5100 tons *full load*. Complement, 445.
Length (*p.p.*) 440·3 feet (*w.l.*), 446⅕ feet. Beam, 43·6 feet. *Mean* draught, 16¾ feet.

Guns (German) :
  7—5·9 inch, 43 cal.
  2—76 mm. anti-aircraft.
  3 M.G.
Torpedo tubes (19·7 inch, German) :
  2 *above water*.

Can carry 120 mines.

Armour :
  2⅓″ Belt (amidships)......
  2¼″ Belt (ends) ....
  2″ Deck (amidships)......
  4″ Conning tower ....

Note to plan.—Now rigged as photo

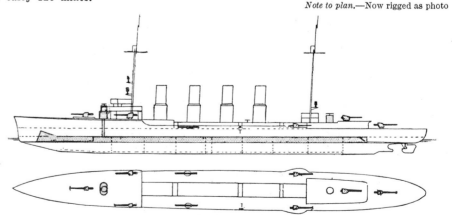

Machinery : Parsons turbine. 2 screws. Boilers : 16 Schulz-Thornycroft. Designed H.P. 26,000 =
27 kts. (on trials, 25,650 = 26·9). Coal : *normal*, 880 tons ; *maximum*, 1330 tons. Oil : 130 tons.

Notes.—Laid down for German Navy at Wilhelmshaven, April, 1910 ; completed December, 1912. Taken over by
  Italy, 1920. Sister ship, *Mulhouse* (ex-*Stralsund*), now in French Navy, to which refer for any further notes.
  4 boilers are oil burning. Maximum speed now 24 kts.

1911-12 EX-ENEMY CRUISERS.

VENEZIA.

1927 *Official Photo.*

MODIFIED "ADMIRAL SPAUN" TYPE—2 SHIPS.

BRINDISI (ex-Austrian *Helgoland*, Nov., 1912). **VENEZIA** (ex-Austrian *Saida*, Oct., 1912).

Standard displacement, 2756 tons. *Normal* displacement, 3500 metric tons. Complement, 350.
Length (*w.l.*), 410¾ feet. Beam, 42 feet. *Mean* draught, 15 feet. Length *over all*, 428½ feet.

Guns (Austrian) :
  9—3·9 inch, 47 cal.
  2—3 inch (anti-aircraft).
Torpedo tubes (18 inch) :
  4 *above water* (paired).
Can carry 170 mines.

Armour (steel) :
  2⅓″ Belt (amidships)
  2″ Bulkheads ………
  ¾″ Deck………………

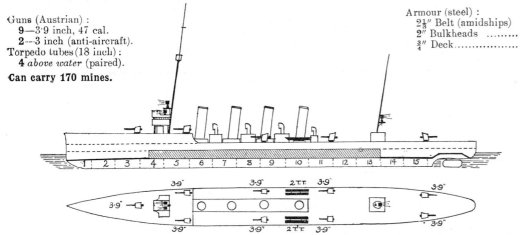

Machinery : Turbine (*See Notes*). 2 screws. Boilers : 16 Yarrow. Designed H.P. 25,600 = 27 kts.
Coal : *normal*, 450 tons ; *maximum*, 750 tons. Radius of action : 860 miles at 27 kts., 1,600 miles at 24 kts.

Name	Builder	Machinery	Laid down	Completed	Trials	Turbines	Boilers	Best recent speed
Venezia	Monfalcone	Prager Masch.	Sep.'11	May,'14	24,500=27	Melms & Pfenninger	Yarrow	
Brindisi	Fiume	Ganz-Danubius	Oct.'11	Oct., '14	25,600=27	A.E.G.	Yarrow	

General Notes.—Ex-Austrian ships, assigned to Italy, 1920. Sister ship, *Thionville* (ex-*Novara*), now in French Navy.

1909 SCOUT CRUISER (Mine Layer).

QUARTO.

1930 *Photo, Capt. Mateo Mille.*

QUARTO (Aug., 1911).

Standard displacement, 2903 tons. *Normal* displacement, 3442 tons. Complement, 322.
Length (*p.p.*), 413·4 feet. Beam, 42·1 feet. *Mean* draught, 13 feet. Length *over all*, 431¾ feet.

Guns :
  6—4·7 inch (50 cal.)
  7—3 inch AA.
  3 M.G.
Torpedo tubes (18 inch) :
  2 *above water.*
  (200 mines.)

Armour :
  1⅝″ Deck (amidships)
  ¾″ Deck (ends) ……
  2″ C.T.

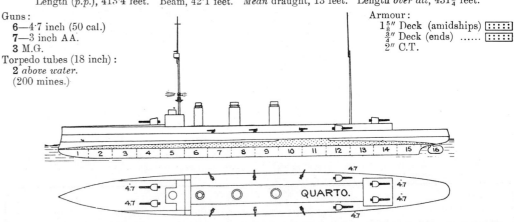

Machinery : Parsons turbine. 4 screws. Boilers : 10 Blechynden (8 oil-burning, 2 mixed firing).
Designed S.H.P. 25,000 = 28 kts. Fuel capacity : *maximum*, 50 tons coal + 490 tons oil = 2600 miles at 15 kts., or 1220 miles at 25·7 kts. Laid down Venice D.Y Oct., 1909. Completed Sept., 1912.

General Notes.—Carries 200 blockade mines. Designed by Engineer-Col. Truccone. Boilers renewed at Fiume, 1924.

1913 COLONIAL CRUISER (*Cannoniera*).

1931 *Photo.*

CAMPANIA (July, 1914).

Displacement, 2530 tons (sheathed and coppered).   Complement, 240.

Length (*p.p.*) 249·4 feet.   Beam, 41⅔ feet.   *Max.* draught, 16⅔ feet.   Length *over all*, 272·3 feet.

Guns :
4—6 inch, 40 cal.
2—14 pdr.
2—76 mm. AA.
2 M.G.

Armour :
1″ Deck   ..
2″ Conning
tower......

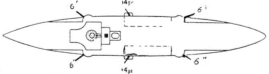

Ahead :
2—6 in.

Astern :
2—6 in.

Broadside : **2—6 in.**

Machinery : 2 sets vertical triple expansion.   2 screws.   4 cylindrical boilers.   Designed H.P. 5000
=16·5 kts. (*not attained on trials*)   Coal : *normal* 300 tons, *full load* 470 tons=4300 kts. at 10 kts. and
about 2000 miles at 15 kts.

Name	Builder	Machinery	Laid down	Com-pleted	Trials :	Boilers	Best recent speed
Campania	Castellamare D.Y.	Off. Mec., Naples	Sept. '13	Aug. '16	About 5000 H.P.=15·7 kts.	Cyl.	

General Notes.—Built for Colonial Service.   Sister ship *Basilicata* sunk by boiler explosion, Port Tewfik, Suez Canal, 1919.
Re-floated 1920, but not considered worth repair.   Fore and aft centre-line 6 in. guns removed, reducing armament
by two guns.

1907 COLONIAL CRUISER (*Cannoniera*).

1929 *Official Photo.*

LIBIA (ex-Turkish *Drama*, Nov., 1912).   **3701 tons.   Complement, 331.   Dimensions : 340 (*o.a.*)
× 47½ × 16 feet.   Armament : **8**—4·7 inch, 50 cal., **3**—76 m.m. AA., **2** M.G., **2**—18 inch tubes
(*above water*).   Deck, 4″.   Designed H.P. 12,500 = 22 kts.   16 Niclausse boilers.   Coal : *normal*
275 tons, *maximum* 675 tons.   Endurance : 4500 miles at 10 kts.   Built and engined by Ansaldo.
Was begun by Ansaldo for Turkish Navy in 1911 and appropriated by Italy on outbreak of
Turko-Italian War.   Not completed until 1913.   Rearmed for foreign service in 1924.   Trials :
H.P. 11,500 = 22·9 kts.

270

Esploratori : High speed vessels of 3,000—1,300 tons.
Cacciatorpediniere : Destroyers of less than 1,300 and more than 700 tons.
Torpediniere : Torpedo Boats less than 700 and more than 200 tons.
Torpediniere Costiere : Under 200 tons.

118* + 12 † Torpedo Craft.

Summary.		†Building.	*Completed.	Projected.
SCOUTS (Esploratori)	...	---	20	
DESTROYERS (Cacciatorpediniere)	...	8	28	4
TORPEDO BOATS (Torpediniere)	...	—	36	
COASTAL Boats	...	—	32	

The following list of distinctive letters, painted on bows of destroyers, and torpedo boats, has been furnished officially to "Fighting Ships" by the courtesy of the Ministry of Marine 1931.

A B .. .. ABBA	C T .. .. CURTATONE	M B .. .. MONZAMBANO	R C .. .. RICASOLI
A C .. .. ACERBI	C Z .. .. CORTELLAZZO	M D .. .. MEDICI	R S .. .. ROSSAROL
A D .. .. AUDACE	C P .. .. CRISPI	M F .. .. MONFALCONE	
A L .. .. AQUILONE		M N .. .. MONTANARI	
A M .. .. ARDIMENTOSO	D Z .. .. DEZZA	M S .. .. MISSORI	S F .. .. SCHIAFFINO
A R .. .. ARDENTE	D R .. .. DARDO	M T .. .. MOSTO	S L .. .. SOLFERINO
A T .. .. ARDITO		M A .. .. MANIN	S M .. .. SAN MARTINO
	E R .. .. EURO		S R .. .. SIRTORI
	E S .. .. ESPERO		S O .. .. STOCCO
			S E .. .. SELLA
	F E .. .. FRECCIA		S U .. .. SAURO
B S .. .. BASSINI	F B .. .. FABRIZI	N V .. .. NIEVO	S A .. .. STRALE
B T .. .. BATTISTI	F C .. .. FUCILIERE	N C .. .. NICOTERA	S T .. .. SAETTA
B R .. .. BOREA	F R .. .. FARINATI	N B .. .. NEMBO	
B O .. .. BALENO	F G .. .. FOLGORE	N L .. .. NULLO	
	F N .. .. FULMINE		T B .. .. TURBINE
	G D .. .. GRADO	O R .. .. ORSINI	
C A .. .. CARINI	G V .. .. GIOVANNINI	O T .. .. OSTRO	
C D .. .. CASTELFIDARDO			Z F .. .. ZEFFIRO
C E .. .. CANTORE	I P .. .. IMPAVIDO		
C F .. .. CONFIENZA	I D .. .. INDOMITO		
C I .. .. CASCINO	I R .. .. IRREQUIETO	P E .. .. PEPE	
C L .. .. CAIROLI	I S .. .. INSIDIOSO	P L .. .. PILO	
C M .. .. CALATAFIMI		P O .. .. POERIO	
C H .. .. CHINOTTO	L F .. .. LA FARINA	P A .. .. PAPA	
C S .. .. COSENZ	L M .. .. LA MASA	P R .. .. PRESTINARI	
	L P .. .. LAMPO	P T .. .. PALESTRO	

SCOUTS. (*Esploratori.*)
12 "Navigatori" class (ordered 1926.)

DA MOSTA.

1931 *Official Photo.*

2 *Ansaldo* boats : **Luca Tarigo** (Dec. 9th, 1928), **Lanzerotto Malocello** (March 14th, 1929).
2 *Odero* boats : **Ugolino Vivaldi** (Jan. 9th, 1929), **Antoniotto Usodimare** (May 12th, 1929).
2 *Tirreno* (Riva Trigoso) boats : **Leone Pancalao** (Feb. 6th, 1929), **Antonio da Noli** (May 21st, 1929).
2 *Riuniti* (Ancona) boats : **Emanuele Pessagno** (August 12th, 1930), **Nicoloso Da Recco.**
4 *Quarnaro* boats : **Nicolo Zeno** (Aug. 11, 1928), **Giovanni Da Verazzano** (Dec. 15th 1928), **Alvise Da Mosta.** (July 1st, 1929), **Antonio Pigafetta.**

Displacement : 1654 tons, *standard* ; 2010 tons *deep load.* Dimensions : 352 (*o.a.*) 351 (*p.p.*) × 33½ × 16¾ feet. I.H.P. 53,500 = 38 kts. Guns : **6**—4.7 inch, 2—40 m/m. AA., 6—37 m/m. AA. **8** M.G. Tubes : 6—21 inch, in triple deck mountings. Mines to be carried in some.

Note.—The *Da Mosta* has attained the speed of 44 kts. with 71,000 H.P.—the highest yet recorded for destroyers.

L. MALOCELLO. (Showing alterations to bridge.)

1931 *Photo, Capt. Mateo Mille.*

EMANUELE PESSAGNO.

1931 *Photo.*

3 Leone Class.

LEONE. (*Pantera* has S.L. on platform, low on foremast.)

1925 Photo, by favour of Messrs. Ansaldo.

TIGRE.

1925 Photo, by favour of Messrs. Ansaldo.

3* *Ansaldo* type: **Leone, Pantera, Tigre** (1923). 1550 tons (*standard*), 2283 tons (*full load*). Dimensions: 372 (*o.a.*), 359½ (*p.p.*) × 34 × 11·5 feet (*mean*). Guns: 8—4.7 inch (45 cal.), 2—14 pdr. (40 cal.) AA., 2—2 pdr. AA. Tubes: 6—18 inch, in two triple deck mountings. Designed S.H.P. 42,000 = 34 kts. (Trials, 50,000 = 35 kts.). Best recent speeds, 33 kts. or less. 4 Parsons turbines (geared). 4 Yarrow oil-burning boilers. 2 screws. Oil fuel: 200 tons *normal*, 400 tons *max.* Carry 60 mines (*normal* stowage), or 100 (*maximum*).

Leopardo and *Lince* cancelled

Notes.—Internally these ships are most elaborately fitted. Each is equipped with a different system of fire-control—British, Italian and German respectively. 4.7 inch guns are paired very closely—only 1 foot apart. Max. elevation: 30°. Special apparatus for smoke screen production is fitted on starboard quarter of each. The distinctive appearance conferred by the upright funnels, of unequal height, and straight stem is a noteworthy feature of these vessels.

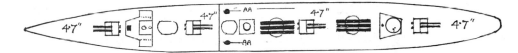

Funnel bands: *Pantera*, none; *Leone*, 1 white on fore funnel; *Tigre*, 1 white on after funnel.

TIGRE.

Photo added 1931, W. A. Fuller, Esq.

Esploratori.

1 Ex-German Boat ("1916 Design.")

1924 *Official Photo.*

1 *Vulkan* boat : **Premuda** (ex-German *V* 116, built 1916-18). Displ :2,200 tons. *Standard* Dimensions : 334.6 (*p.p.*) 360 (*o.a.*) × 36¾ × 12.8 feet (*mean*). Guns : **4**—5.9 inch (42 cal.) **3**—40 m/m. AA., Tubes : **4**—19.7 inch, in 2 twin deck mountings. Machinery : A. E. G.-Vulkan turbines. Boilers : 4 " Marinetype " (Schulz-Thornycroft). Trials : H.P. 53,975=33.7 kts. 2 screws. Oil fuel : 280 tons *normal,* 720 tons *max.* Complement, 154. Carries 40 mines.

Notes.—German " 1916 Design " boat, taken over by Italy, 1920. For other remarks, refer to *Amiral Sénès* (sister boat), in French Navy Section.

PREMUDA.

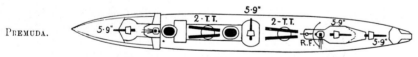

Four more Esploratori are included among the destroyers, i.e. *Falco, Aquila, C. Mirabello* and *A. Riboty*, p.

Cacciatorpediniere.

4 Maestrale class (ordered 1931).

2 *Ancona* MAESTRALE ( ), GRECALE ( ).
2 *Riva Trigosa* LIBECCIO ( ), SCIROCCO ( ).

Displacement : 1,472 tons. Dimensions : 341×33× ? feet. I.H.P. 50,000=38 kts.

Armament : **4**—4·7 in. 50 cal.   ?—21 inch T. tubes.
           2—1·4 in. A.A.
           2—M.G

Cacciatorpediniere.
4 Fulgore Class (ordered 1929).

1931 *Illustration.*

2 *Cant. Partenopei Napoli* boats : **FOLGORE** (Apl. 26th, 1931), **LAMPO** (July 26th, 1931).
2 *Cant. Nav. Quarnaro* boats : **BALENO** (Mar. 22nd, 1931), **FULMINE** (Aug. 2nd 1931).

Displacement : 1,240 (*standard*). Dimensions : 309½ × 30½ × 11 feet. I.H.P. 46,000 = 38 kts. 2 sets Parsons geared
turbines. 3 Thornycroft boilers. Guns : 4—4·7″, 4—37 m/m. AA., 4 M.G. Tubes : 6—21″ in triple mountings.
Oil : 225 tons.

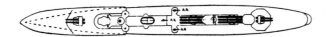

Cacciatorpediniere.
8 Dardo class (ordered 1928).

FRECCIA.

1930 *Photo, "Italia Marinara."*

2 *Odero* boats : **DARDO** (Sept. 6th, 1930), **STRALE** (Mar. 26th, 1931).

2 *Tirreno* boats : **FRECCIA** (Aug. 3rd, 1930), **SAETTA** (

Displacement 1225 tons *standard*, 1450 tons *normal*. Dimensions : 302½ × 30½ × 11 feet. 2 sets Parsons geared turbines
and Thornycroft oil fired boilers, 4 M.G. I.H.P. 44,000 = 38 kts. Guns : 4—4.7 inch, 4—37 m/m AA. Tubes :
6—21 inch in triple deck mountings. Oil : 225 tons. Complement, 150.

For plan see addenda.

Notes.—As first designed these boats had two funnels and a straight bow, resembling " Turbine " in profile. During
construction the design was changed, the uptakes being trunked into one stack, and the bridge and upperworks
modified, while the bows were given an overhang. As a result they present an entirely new profile and will probably
influence future destroyer designs.

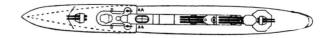

T

TURBINE.   1931 *Photo.*

4 *Ansaldo* boats: **Borea** (Jan, 1927), **Espero** (Aug. 31st, 1927), **Ostro** (Jan. 2nd, 1928), **Zeffiro** (27th May, 1927). 2 *Odero* boats: **Aquilone** (Aug. 3rd, 1927), **Turbine** (21st April, 1927). 2 boats by Cant. del Tirreno, Riva Trigoso: **Euro** (July 7th, 1927), **Nembo** (27th Jan., 1927).

All ordered or laid down 1924-25. Displacement: 1090/1100 tons *standard*, 1355 tons *full load*. Dimensions: $299\frac{1}{2}(p.p.)$, $307\frac{1}{2}(o.a) \times 30\frac{1}{2} \times 10\frac{3}{4}$ feet. Geared turbines. 3 Thornycroft boilers, with superheaters. S.H.P. 35,000 = 36 kts. *Turbine*, 4 hours = 38.9. Best mile run = 39.6. Guns: **4**—4.7 inch, **3**—40 m/m. AA., **2** M.G. Tubes: **6**—21 inch, in triple deck mountings. Oil: 240 tons.

TURBINE.   1931 *Photo, Capitan M. Mille.*

BOREA. (Note control tower on bridge.)   1931 *Official Photo.*

4 Sauro class. (Minelayers.)

SAURO.

1927 *Official Photo.*

2 *Odero* boats: **Cesare Battisti** (11th Dec., 1926), **Nazario Sauro** (12th May, 1926).
2 *Quarnaro* boats: **Daniele Manin** (24th June 1925), **Francesco Nullo** (Oct., 1925). All designed by Odero
and laid down 1924. Displacement: 1075 tons *standard.* Dimensions: 295½ × 30½ × 10½ feet. Parsons geared turbines.
3 Thornycroft oil-fired boilers, with superheaters. S.H.P. 32,000 = 35 kts. (On trials, *N. Sauro* 37,000 =
36.5, *D. Manin* 36.8). Guns: **4**—4.7 inch, **3**—40 m/m. AA., 2 M.G. Tubes: **6**—21 inch, in triple deck mountings.
30 mines carried. Oil: 230 tons.

Deck plan, *Sauro* and *Turbine* classes.

4 Sella class ("Improved Palestro design").
(All fitted as Minelayers).

G. NICOTERA

1928 *Photo, Pucci.*

Q. SELLA.

1926 *Photo, by courtesy of Ministry of Marine.*

4 *Pattison* type: **Francesco Crispi** (Oct., 1925), **Giovanni Nicotera** (24th June, 1926), **Bettino Ricasoli**
(29th Jan., 1926), **Quintino Sella** (25th April, 1925). All laid down 1922-23. 950 tons *standard.* Dimensions: 270¾
× 27 × 9¾ feet. Guns: **3**—4.7 inch (45 cal.), **2**—40 m/m. AA., 4 M.G. Torpedo tubes: **4**—21 inch in two pairs.
Machinery: Turbines (Belluzzo in *Crispi*, Parsons in others). 28,000 S.H.P. = 35 kts. (Trial speeds have been
from 35.9 to 38 kts.). 3 Thornycroft boilers. Oil fuel: 200 tons *normal*, 255 tons *max.* Radius: 2750 miles at
15 kts. Complement, 120.

Note.—On *trials* B. Ricasoli is reported to have exceeded 38 kts. with H.P. 40,000; *F. Crispi* 38.7; *Q. Sella* 37.6.
Average figures: *B. Ricasoli*, 35 kts. (8½ tons consumption); *F. Crispi*, 34 kts. (9½ tons); *Q. Sella*, 35 kts. (8
tons); *G. Nicotera*, 34.5 kts. (9 tons).

8 Palestro/Curtatone class.

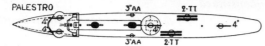

PALESTRO

(All fitted for Minelaying.)

SAN MARTINO.

Photo added 1925.

8 ORLANDO TYPE, viz.:—

4 *Palestro* class: **Confienza** (1920), **Palestro** (1919), **San Martino** (1920), **Solferino** (1920). 875 tons *standard* (1076 *full load*). Dimensions: 256½ (*p.p.*) × 24⅜ × 8½ feet (*mean*). Guns: 4—4 inch, 45 cal., 2—3 inch, 40 cal. AA., 4 M.G. Tubes: 4—18 inch in twin deck mountings. 10 mines carried. 2 Zoelly turbines. Designed S.H.P. 18,000 = 32 kts. Trials: 22,000 = 31.1 to 32.4 kts. (Best recent speed, *about* 29 kts.). 4 Thornycroft boilers. 2 screws. Oil: 170 tons. Complement, 105.

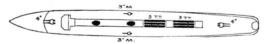

MONZAMBANO.

1924 *Photo, by courtesy of Flli Orlando.*

4 *Curtatone* class: **Calatafimi** (17th March, 1923), **Castelfidardo** (1923), **Curtatone** (1922), **Monzambano** (6th August, 1923). 982 tons (1190 *full load*). Length (*p.p.*) 262½ feet. Designed S.H.P. 18,000 = 32 kts. Trials: H.P. 27,500 = 34 kts. Other details as *Palestro* class, but **4 inch guns are in pairs,** and there are **6—18 inch tubes in triple deck mountings,** as plan above.

6 "Generali" class.

GENERALE ANTONIO CANTORE. (Fore funnel now raised.)

1922 *Photo.*

6 *Odero* type: **Generale Achille Papa** (1921), **Generale Antonio Cantore** (April, 1921), **Generale Antonino Cascino** (1922), **Generale Antonio Chinotto** (1921), **Generale Carlo Montanari** (1922), **Generale Marcello Prestinari** (1922). Displacement: 645 *Std.* tons. Dimensions: 237.9 × 23.9 × 9 feet. Guns: 3—4 inch, 45 cal., 2—3 inch AA., 2 M.G. Tubes: 4—18 inch in two twin deck mountings. Tosi Turbines. S.H.P. 17,000 = 33 kts. (*about* 30 kts. best speed now). 4 Thornycroft boilers. Oil: 150 tons. Complement, 105. Radius: 2200 miles at 14 kts.; 600 miles at 33 kts.

7 Cosenz class. *(Minelayers.)*

Deck Plan of COSENZ class (*Generale* class similar, but only **1—4 inch** on forecastle).

E. COSENZ.

1925 *Photo, Pucci.*

7 *Odero* type: **Enrico Cosenz** (ex-*Agostino Bertani*), **Giacomo Medici, Giuseppe la Farina,** and **Nicola Fabrizi** (all 1917); **Angelo Bassini, Giacinto Carini, Giuseppe la Masa,** (all 1916). 645 tons (810 *full load*). Dimensions: 238 (*p.p.*) × 24 × 9·2 feet (*mean*). Guns: 4—4 inch, 2—3 inch, AA. 4 M.G. Tubes (in all): 4—18 inch, in two twin-deck mountings. 10 mines carried. S.H.P. 17,000 = 33 kts. (On trials made 34.1 kts. Now good for *about* 30 kts.) Fuel: 150 tons. Complement, 100. 2 Tosi turbines. 4 Thornycroft oil-burning boilers. 2 screws. Endurance: 1700 miles (15 kts.), 470 miles (full speed). *Benedetto Cairoli,* of this class, lost during War.

Esploratori
2 Aquila class. Mine Layers, carrying 50 mines each.

AQUILA.

1925 *Photo, Pucci.*

2 *Pattison* type : **Falco** (1919), 1306 tons **Aquila** (1916). 1430 tons 1733 tons *normal.* Dimensions : 308.5 (*p.p.*) ×30·8×10·7 feet (*mean*). Guns : 4—4.7 inch, 45 cal.; 2—3 inch, 40 cal. AA.; 4 M.G. Tubes : 4—18 inch, in two twin deck mountings. Designed S.H.P. 39,800 = 36·5 kts. 2 Tosi turbines. 5 Thornycroft oil-burning boilers. 2 screws. Endurance : 1700 miles (15 kts.), 380 miles (full speed). Oil : 120 *normal,* 260 tons *max.* Complement, 150.
Note.—These two destroyers were to have been built for the Rumanian Navy. Appropriated for Italian Navy on outbreak of war with Austria-Hungary. Two boats, *Nibbio, Sparviero,* sold back to Rumania, 1920.
* Are Mine Layers, carrying 50 mines each.

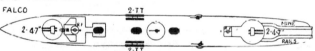

Torpediniere
4 Sirtori class. (Minelayers).

V. ORSINI.

1919 *Photo, Commr. Holberton, R.N.*

4 *Odero* type : **Giuseppe Sirtori, Francesco Stocco, Giovanni Acerbi, Vicenzo Orsini** (all 1916). Displacement : 580 tons. *Standard* Dimensions : 238 (*p.p.*) × 24 × 9·2 feet (*mean*). Guns : 6—4 inch, 35 cal., 2—40 m/m. AA. 4 M.G. Tubes : 4—18 inch, in twin mountings. 2 Tosi turbines. S.H.P 17,000 = 32 kts. 4 Thornycroft oil-burning boilers. 2 screws. Radius : 1700 miles at 15 kts., 470 miles at 33 kts. Fuel 150 tons. Complement, 100. Carry 10 mines.

Esploratori
2 Mirabello class.
Mine Layers, each carrying 100 mines.

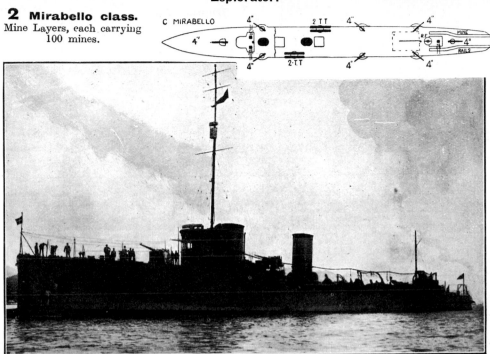

1926 *Photo, Capitan M. Mille.*

2 *Ansaldo* type : **Carlo Mirabello** (1914), **Augusto Riboty** (1915). 1405 tons *standard,* 1785 tons *deep load.* Dimensions : 331.4 (*p.p.*) × 32 × 10.6 feet (*mean*). Guns : 8—4 inch, 6—40 m/m AA. 4 M.G. Tubes : 4—18 inch in twin deck mountings. Designed S.H.P. 35,000 = 35 kts. Made 33.75 and 35.03 kts. on *trials* respectively. 4 Yarrow oil-burning boilers. 2 Parsons geared turbines. 2 screws. Oil fuel: *normal* 200 tons, *maximum* 350 tons. Endurance : 2840 miles (15 kts.), 500 miles (full speed). *C. A. Racchia* mined off Odessa, 21st July, 1920.

1 Special Boat.

AUDACE.

1925 *Photo, Bassan.*

1 *Yarrow* type : **Audace** (ex-Japanese *Kawakaze*, Scotstoun, Glasgow, 1915). 633 tons (over 1000 tons *full load*). Dimensions : 275 (*p.p.*), 283 (*o.a.*) × 27½ × 9½ feet (*max.*). Guns : 7—4 inch, 2—40 m/m. AA. 4 M.G. Tubes : 4—18 inch, in two twin mountings. Fuel : 252 tons. 2-shaft Brown-Curtis turbines and 3 Yarrow large-tube, oil-burning boilers. Endurance : 2180 miles (15 kts.), 560 miles (full speed). S.H.P. 22,000 = 30 kts. Complement, 113.

Note.—This boat must not be confused with *Audace* built in 1912-13 by Orlando, as a sister boat to *Animoso* (v. next page). The Orlando *Audace* was sunk during the War, and the Japanese *Kawakaze* (closely resembling the lost *Audace*) was purchased by Italy and re-named *Audace*.

2 Ex-German boats (Minelayers).

C. ROSSAROL.

1925 *Photo, Bassan.*

1 *Blohm & Voss* boat : **Cesare Rossarol** (ex-German *B 97*, 1914). 1316 tons (*deep load*). Dimensions : 321.5 × 30⅔ × 9.4 feet. Guns and tubes : 3—4.7 inch, 2—3 inch AA., 4 M.G., AA., 4—19.7 inch tubes, in 2 twin deck mounts. Turbines and Schulz-Thornycroft boilers. Designed S.H.P. 40,000 = 34 kts. (Made 36 kts. on *trials* and is reported to have reached this speed under normal conditions in 1926). Oil : 150 tons *normal*, 520 tons *maximum* = 2620 miles at 20 kts. Taken over by Italy, 1920. Complement, 114. Carries 24 mines.

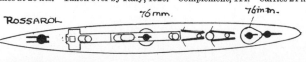

ROSSAROL　　　76 mm.　　　　76 mm.

2—4.7″.　　　　　　　4·7″.

1930 *Photo, Official.*

1 *Schichau* boat : **Ardimentoso** (ex-German *S63*, 1915). 816 tons (1050 *deep load*). Dimensions : 273.4 × 27½ × 9.2 feet. Guns and tubes : 3—4 inch, 2—40 m/m. AA. 4 M.G. ; 4—19.7 inch tubes, in two twin mountings. Schichau turbines and Yarrow boilers. S.H.P. 24,000 = 33 kts. Oil : 162 tons normal, 280 tons *max.* = 1960 miles at 20 kts. Taken over by Italy, 1920. Complement, 85. Was fitted to carry 24 mines when first completed. Forecastle well deck built in Circa, 1928.

2 Poerio class (Minelayers).

A. POERIO.

1925 *Photo, Pucci.*

2 *Ansaldo* type : **Alessandro Poerio** (1914), **Guglielmo Pepe** (1914). 858 tons (1028 *deep load*). Dimensions : 272·6 (*p.p.*) × 26·3 × 9·3 feet. Armament : 5—4 inch, 2—40 m/m. AA., 4 M.G. 4—18 inch tubes in two twin-deck mountings. H.P. 22,500 = 32 kts. 3 Yarrow oil-burning 2-shaft boilers. Parsons turbines. Oil : 200 tons. Endurance : 2930 miles (15 kts.). 745 miles (full speed). *Trials :* 33.4 kts. Fitted as Minelayers. Complement, 137.

A. POERIO.

8 Abba class.

ANTONIO MOSTO.   1025 *Photo, Bassan.*

2 *Pattison* boats : **Fratelli Cairoli,** (*Ex-Francesco Nullo*), **Antonio Mosto,** (both 1914).
6 *Odero* boats : **Rosolino Pilo, Giuseppe Abba, Ippolito Nievo, Simone Schiaffino,
Giuseppe Dezza** (*Ex-Pilade Bronzetti*), (all 1914), **Giuseppe Missori** (1915). 625 tons. Dimensions : 236.2
(*p.p.*) × 24 × 8.8 feet (*mean*). Guns : 5—4 inch, 2—40 m/m. AA. 4 M.G. Tubes : 4 single 18 inch. Made about 31.8 kts.
on trials. 2 Tosi turbines and 4 Thornycroft oil-burning boilers. 2 screws. Endurance : 1700 miles (15 kts.). 440
miles (full speed). S.H.P. 17,000 = 32 to 33.8 kts. except 2 Pattison boats, S.H.P. 14,500 = 30.8 kts. Fuel :
150 tons. Complement, 94.

4 Cortellazzo class (ex–Austrian).

1922 *Photo, G. F. Jewitt, Esq.*

4 *Ganz-Danubius* type : **Cortellazzo** (ex-*Lika*), **Grado** (ex-*Triglav*), **Monfalcone** (ex-*Uszok*), all built
1914-17 : **Zenson** (ex *Pola*), (ex-*Orjen*, 1913). 577 tons. Dim. : 274 × 25⅜ × 8¼ feet. Guns and torpedo tubes
(Austrian) : 2—3.9 inch, 4—66 m/m., 2—66 m/m., AA. 4 M.G. and 4—20.8 inch tubes. A. E. G. turbines and 6 Yarrow boilers. S.H.P. 22,000 to 23,700 = 32 to 32.5 kts. Fuel : 110 tons coal, 140 tons oil. Complement, 114. Added
to Italian Navy, Sept., 1920. A fifth of this type, *Muggia,* was wrecked in Chinese waters, March 15th, 1929.
Sister boat, *Matelot Leblanc* (ex-*Dukla*), now in French Navy.

4 Indomito class.

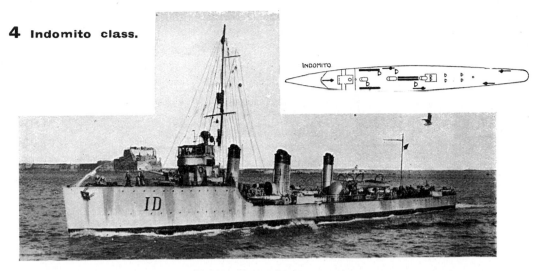

INDOMITO.   1919 *Photo, Commr. Holberton, R.N.*

4 *Pattison* type (Thornycroft design) : **Indomito** (1912), **Impavido, Insidioso, Irrequieto** (1913). 550 tons.
Dimensions : 238 (*p.p.*) × 24 × 8.4 feet. Guns : 5—4 inch, 1—40 m/m., 4 M.G. (except *Impavido,* which carries
1—4 inch, 4—3 inch). All believed fitted for minelaying. Tubes : 4—18 inch. *Trials :* S.H.P. 17,000 to 18,000 =
33 to 35.7 kts. 2 Tosi turbines and 4 oil-burning Thornycroft boilers. Fuel : 128 tons. Complement, 94.
Endurance : 1520 miles (15 kts.). 360 miles (full speed). *Impetuoso* and *Intrepido* of this class lost in the War.

2 Ardente class.

ARDITO.   1919 *Photo, Commr. Holberton, R.N.*

2 *Orlando* type : **Ardito** (1912), **Ardente** (1912). 570 tons. Dimensions : 238 (*p.p.*) × 24 × 8.4 feet (*mean*). Guns :
5—4 inch, 1—40 m/m. AA. 4 M.G. Tubes : 4 single 18 inch. On *trials,* 15,700 S.H.P. = 33.4 kts. 2-shaft
Parsons turbines and 4 oil-burning Thornycroft boilers. 2 screws. Endurance : 1450 miles at 13.5 kts. 360 miles
(full speed). Fuel : 130 tons. Complement, 94.

Torpedo Boats (*Torpediniere*).

ASCARO.   1919 *Photo*.

1 *Ansaldo* type :—**Fuciliere** (1909) 320/424 tons. Dimensions : 211¼ (*p.p.*) × 20 × 6⅔ to 7 feet (*mean*). Guns : **4**—3 inch. **1** M.G. Tubes : **3** single 18 inch. On trials, 6500 I.H.P. = 29·1 kts. 3 Thornycroft boilers and 2 screws. Complement, 50. 90 tons oil fuel. Endurance : 1250 miles at 15 kts. *Garibaldino* lost during War. *Ascaro* scrapped 1929.

Coastal Boats.

(2 funnels.)   1919 *Photo, by courtesy of Flli. Orlando*.

2 *Orlando* boats : **74 O.L.T., 75 O.L.T.,** Built at Leghorn. Begun 1917. Launched Oct., 1917–Jan., 1918, finished June–Sept., 1918. 172 tons. Guns : **2**—3 inch AA. **1** M.G. Torpedo tubes : **2**—18 inch. S.H.P. 4500 = 29 kts. 2-shaft turbines and 2 water-tube boilers. Coal : 20 tons.

Coastal Boats (*continued*).

63 O.L.   1931 *Photo*.

5 *Orlando* boats : **58 O.L–63 O.L.** Built at Leghorn. Begun 1915–16, launched April–Sept., 1916. Completed May–Oct., 1916. 135 tons *standard*. Guns : **2**—3″ AA. **1** M.G. Details generally as 11 Pattison boats described on next page. But I.H.P. 3700 = 28.1 kts. 59 O.L. scrapped 1931.

6 *Ansaldo* boats : **52 A.S.–57 A.S.** Built 1915–16 at Sestri-Ponente. Details as 11 Pattison boats described on next page, but **1**—3″ AA. **1** M.G. 55, 56, 57, carry 2—3″ AA.

Note to Illustration.—14 pdrs. not combined " Y " type. Guns are in echelon and happened to coincide at the moment the photo was taken.

48 O.S. (2 funnels).   1922 *Photo, G. F. Jewett, Esq.*

4 *Odero* boats : **47, 49-51 O.S.**   Built, 1915-16, at Sestri-Ponente. Details as 11 Pattison boats described in next column, but 1—3″ AA. 1 M.G.

7 *Pattison* boats : **41 P.N., 45 P.N.** (begun 1915, launched and completed 1916), **64 P.N., 65 P.N., 69 P.N., 70 P.N.** (ex-*66 P.N*) **71 P.N.** (ex-*68 P.N*), (begun 1916 and completed 1917-18).   All built at Naples. Displacement 135 tons *standard*. Dimensions : 139½ × 15 × 5 feet. Guns : 2—14 pdr. AA. 1 M.G. 1 D.C. thrower. Tubes : 2—18 inch in one twin mounting. I.H.P. 3500 = 28 to 29 kts. Machinery : 2 sets recipro. triple expansion. Boilers : Thornycroft. Oil fuel : 26 tons. 43 P.N. scrapped 1930.

Appearance of all boats as above.   *Official Photo.*

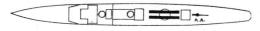

7 *Pattison* boats : $\left\{\begin{array}{l}\textbf{33 P.N.—35 P.N. 38 P.N.}\\ \textbf{12 P.N.}\\ \textbf{9 P.N.}\\ \textbf{7 P.N.}\end{array}\right.$ 9 boats in all. Launched 1911-13. Completed 1911-14. Average 125 tons. Dimensions : 139½ × 15 × 5 feet. Guns : 1—14 pdr. 1 M.G. Tubes : 2—18 inch. I/S.H.P 2700-3200 = 27·5-31·5 kts. Oil : 15 tons. Complement, 23.

1 *Ansaldo* boat : **29 A.S.**

Boilers : 2 Thornycroft oil-burning. Machinery : 2 sets triple expansion. 5 P.N., 17 O.S., 36 P.N., lost in War. Other missing numbers removed from effective list.

75 Submarines:

CLASSIFICATION OF TYPES, 1930.

(1) SOMMERGIBILI DI GRANDE CROCIERA.

(Ocean going). Displacing more than 1,000 tons. **5 + 4** *projected.*

(2) SOMMERGIBILI DI MEDIA CROCIERA.

(Sea going). Displacing more than 650 tons. **24 + 6** „

(3) SOMMERGIBILI DI PICCOLA CROCIERA.

(Coastals.) Displacement under 650 tons. **32 + 4** „

(Mine-layers may belong to any of these classes.)

SUBMARINE RECOGNITION LETTERS. (Official List, 1930).
Painted on Conning Tower.

A G	ARGONAUTA		**G M**	MAMELI
B N	BAUSAN		**M O**	MOCENIGO
B A	BANDIERA		**M R**	MANARA
B G	BRAGADINO		**M U**	MEDUSA
B L	BALILLA		**N A**	NANI
C R	CORRIDONI		**N R**	NARVALO
C N	COLONNA		**P N**	PISANI
P C	CAPPONI		**T S**	SPERI
D L	DELFINO		**S B**	SETTEMBRINI
G A	GALVANI		**S C**	SCIESA
G P	DA PROCIDA		**R S**	SETTIMO
D N	DES GENEYS		**S Q**	SQUALO
F S	FISALIA		**S P**	SALPA
F M	FIERAMOSCA		**S N**	SANTAROSA
J N	JANTINA		**T O**	TORRICELLI
J A	JALEA		**T R**	TRICHECO
M E	MENOTTI		**T T**	TOTI
M L	MILLELIRE			

OCEAN GOING **5 Built** +4 *projected.*

SEA GOING **24 Built** +6 „

COASTAL. **17 Built** +15 *building.* 4 *projected.*

Ocean-going
1 "Fieramosca" Class.

E. FIERAMOSCA.

1931 *Official Photo.*

1 *Bernardis-Tizzoni* type : **Ettore Fieramosca** (April 15th, 1929). Laid down August, 1926, by Cantiere Navale Franco Tosi, Taranto. 1,453 tons *surface* displacement, 1,788 tons *submerged*. *Surface* speed with Diesels of 5,500 S.H.P.=19 kts. *Submerged* speed with electric motors of 2,000 H.P.=10 kts. Guns : **1**—3·9″, **10**—21 inch tubes. Originally reported to be fitted for mine-laying and to carry a seaplane stowed in a deck hangar. These items of equipment have been officially deleted, and number of tubes increased from 6 to 10.

Ocean-going—*continued*.
4 + 4 projected "Balilla" Class.

E. Toti.

1931 *Photo, Capitan Mateo Mille.*

D. Millelire. (stern view).

1930 *Photo, Capitan Mateo Mille.*

4 *Odero* type : **Balilla** (20th Feb., 1927), **Antonio Sciesa,** (Aug. 12th, 1928), **Enrico Toti, Domenico Millelire** (Sept. 19th, 1927). Building at Spezia by Odero-Terni Co. *Surface* displacement, 1390 tons ; *submerged,* 1904 tons. Dimensions: 282 (*o.a.*) × 24½ × 14 feet *mean* draught. Machinery: 2 sets Fiat Diesels, of H.P. 4900 = 18·5 kts. *on surface,* Electric motors of 2200 H.P. = 9·5 kts. *submerged.* Guns: **1—3·9** inch AA. **2 M.G.** Tubes: **6—21** inch (4 bow, 2 stern), also special long tube aft for minelaying (16 mines carried).

Note.—Above submarines are designed for deep diving, and are of exceptionally strong construction. The design of these boats embodies a number of innovations, such as the placing of the Diesel engines and electric motors much further forward than usual ; the elimination of bow hydroplanes ; novel distribution of ballast tanks ; and an improved form of hull. In consequence, an unprecedented degree of safety, both in diving and manœuvring, is claimed for this type. They were laid down early in 1925. *Balilla* reached a depth of 55 fathoms in diving trials, May 1928. 4 more boats of this type are to be built :—

3 of displacement 1354/1997 tons.
1 minelayer displacement 1393/1913 tons.

Sea-going
2 "Corridoni" Class.

F. Corridoni.

1930 *Official Photo.*

Launch of M. Bragadino.

1930 *Official Photo.*

2 *Bernardis* type : **Marcantonio Bragadino** (July 3rd, 1929), **Filippo Corridoni.** Building by Cant. Nav. F. Tosi, Taranto. Displacement: 815 tons *surface,* 1,085 tons *submerged.* Diesels of H.P. 1,500 = 14 kts. *surface* speed. Electric motors of 1,000 H.P. = 8 kts. *submerged.* Guns : 1—4″, 2 M.G. Tubes : 4—21″. 2 mine-launching chutes. 24 mines.

4 "Santarosa" Class.

C. MENOTTI.

1930 *Photo, Cap. Mateo Mille.*

4 *Bernardis* type, ordered 1927: **Santorre Santarosa, Ciro Menotti** (both Odero-Terni Co., Spezia); **Fratelli Bandiera, Luciano Manara** (both Cant. Nav. Triestino, Monfalcone, Oct., 1929); Displacement: 890 tons on *surface*, 1,095 tons *submerged*. 2 sets Diesels, (Fiat type in Odero and Monfalcone boats, Tosi in remaining two.) H.P. 3,000=17·5 kts. *surface;* electric motors, B.H.P. 1,200=9 kts. *submerged.* Guns: 1—4″, 2 M.G. Tubes: 8—21″. Are an improvement of *Pisani* design. Launched 1929–30.

2 + *4 projected* "Settembrini" Class.

LUIGI SETTEMBRINI.

1930 *Photo, Cap. Mateo Mille.*

Luigi Settembrini, Ruggiero Settimo (Cant. Nav. F. Tosi, Taranto, both launched 1930). 810 tons standard *surface* and 1,150 tons *submerged.* 2 Tosi-Diesel motors 1,500 H.P.each=17 knots. Electric motors 650 H.P. each (Ansaldo)=9 knots *submerged.* Guns: 1—4″, 2 M.G. Tubes: 8—21″. 16 torpedoes carried. Radius: 9,000 miles at 8 kts. *surface,* 80 miles *submerged.*

4 boats projected.

4 + *2 projected* "Squalo" Class.

SQUALO.

1931 *Photo.*

LAUNCH OF DELFINO.

1930 *Photo ,Capitan M. Mille.*

4 *Bernardis* type, ordered 1928 from Cant. Nav. Triestino, Monfalcone: **Delfino, Narvalo, Squalo, Tricheco.** Names translated are respectively *Dolphin, Swordfish, Shark, Walrus.*

Dimensions: 228¾ × 19 × 14½ feet.	Guns: 1—3·9″ 43 cal., 2 M.G.
Displacement: 885/1094 tons.	Tubes: 8—21″.
Machinery: 2 sets Fiat Diesels, H.P. 3,000 = 16·5 kts.	Launched 1929–30.
2 electric motors. H.P. = 9 kts.	

4 "Mameli" class.

G. MAMELI.   1928 *Official Photo.*

4 *Cavallini* type : **Goffredo Mameli** (ex-*Masaniello*, 9th Dec., 1926), **Pier Capponi** (19th June, 1927), **Tito Speri** (May 25th, 1928), **Giovanni da Procida.** Ordered from Cantiere Navale F. Tosi, Taranto, 1924-25. Displacement : 780 tons *on surface*, 1010 tons *submerged*. Dimensions : 213¼ × 21¼ × 13 feet. 2 Tosi Diesel 8-cyl. 4-cycle engines. H.P. 3000 = 17 kts. *on surface.* Electric motors of 1000 H.P. = 9 kts. *submerged.* Guns : **1**—4 inch. **2** M.G. Torpedo tubes : **6**—21 inch.

Note.—In March, 1929, *G. Mameli* dived to a depth of 64 fathoms during trials, remaining submerged for 20 minutes and in March, 1930, to 350 ft. for 1 hour.

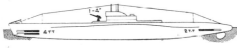

4 "Pisani" class.

VITTOR PISANI.   1930 *Official Photo.*

M. COLONNA.   1930 *Official Photo.*

4 *Bernardis* type : **Vittor Pisani, Giovanni Bausan, Marcantonio Colonna, Ammiraglio dei Geneys** (Nov. 14th, 1928). Ordered from Cantiere Navale Triestino, Monfalcone, 1924-25. Displacement : 804 tons *on surface*, 1057 tons *submerged*. Dimensions : 223 × 19 × 14 feet. Machinery : 2 sets Diesels = H.P. 3000 = 17.5 kts. *on surface.* Electric motors of 1000 H.P. = 9 kts. *submerged.* Guns : **1**—4 inch. **2** M.G. Tubes : **6**—21 inch.

3 "P. Micca" class.

L. MOCENIGO.   1930 *Photo, Capitan Mateo Mille.*

3 *Cavallini* type : **Angelo Emo,*** **Lazzaro Mocenigo,** **Luigi Galvani,** (Spezia Navy Yard). Displacement : 792 tons *on surface*, 1006 tons *submerged*. Dimensions : 206⅔ × 19⅔ × 14 feet. Guns : **2**—3 inch (40 cal.) A.A. **1** M.G. **6**—17·7 inch torpedo tubes. Machinery : In first two, 2 Fiat Diesel motors *on surface* and 2 Savigliano electric motors *when submerged* ; next pair have 2 Fiat Diesel and 2 Ansaldo electric motors ; and *Torricelli* has 2 Tosi Diesel 4-stroke motors *on surface* and 2 Ansaldo electric motors. Carry 35 tons oil fuel. B.H.P. 2600 = 13.7 kts. *on surface*, 1800 = 10.9 kts. *submerged.* Radius 1900 miles at 10 kts. *on surface*, 250 miles at 3·4 kts. *when submerged.* Complement, 37.

*Begun at Venice D.Y., Aug., 1914. Dismantled and taken to Spezia in the summer of 1915 and laid down for a second time. Completed 1918. *E. Torricelli, P. Micca* and *L. Marcello,* have been scrapped.

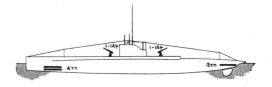

Sea-going Type.

1925 Photo, Pucci.

1 *Fiat-Laurenti* type : **Giacomo Nani** (Fiat-San Giorgio Co., Spezia, 1915). Displacement : 720 tons *on surface*, 925 tons *when submerged*. Dimensions : 213¼ × 19¾ × 13½ feet. Guns : **2**—3″ AA., 1 M.G. **6**—17.7 inch torpedo tubes. Machinery : 2 Fiat Diesel engines *on surface*, 2 Savigliano electric motors *when submerged*. 2600 H.P.= 16 kts. *on surface*, 1400 H.P. = 9.8 kts. *when submerged*. Radius : 1500 miles at 11.4 kts. *on surface*, 100 miles at 6 kts. *when submerged*. Oil fuel : 36 tons *normal*, 60 tons *maximum*. Complement, 30. Completed 1919. *Sebastiano Veniero* lost, 26th Aug., 1925 ; 2 others scrapped, 1927-28.

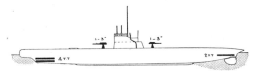

36 Coastal Boats—(*Sommergibili Costieri*).
(Under 650 tons).

New Construction.

19 Argonauta Class

3 *C.N.T. Monfalcone* boats : **Argonauta** (Jan. 1931), **Fisalia** (May 1931), **Medusa**.
2 *Odero-Terni-Orlando-Spezia* : **Jalea, Jantina.**
2 *C. Tosi-Taranto* : **Serpente, Salpa.** All ordered 1929.
6 *Monfalcone* : **Sirene, Naiade, Nereide, Anfitrite, Galatea, Ondina.**
2 *C. N. Quarnaro* : **Diamante, Smeraldo.**
2 *Odero-Terni-Orlando* : **Ametista, Zaffero.**
2 ——————— : **Rubino, Topazio.**

Displacement : 636 *on surface*, 791 *submerged*. Dimensions : 200 × 16½ × 13 feet. Guns : 1—4″, 35 cal., 2 M.G. Tubes : **6**—21″ plus 2 deck (revolving). Machinery : 2 Diesel Fiat motors 1,500 H.P. at 460 revs. = 14 kts. Submerged : 2 electric motors each 300 H.P. *normal* and 400 H.P. *full charge* = 8.5 kts.

X 3.   *1928 Photo, Pucci.*

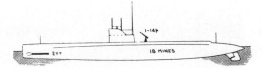

2 *Bernardis* type : **X2, X3** (Ansaldo, Sestri Ponente, 1916). Displacement : 394 tons *on surface* ; 460 tons *when submerged*. Dimensions 140 × 18 × 13 feet. Guns : 1—3″ AA. 1 M.G. Torpedo tubes : **2**—18 inch. Carry 18 mines in 9 discharge chutes. Machinery : 2 Ansaldo Diesel *on surface* ; 2 Ansaldo electric *submerged*. 660 H.P. = 10 kts. *on surface* ; 320 H.P. = 7·9 kts. *when submerged*. Carry 18 tons of fuel. Radius : 1360 miles at 6·5 kts. *on surface* ; 96 miles at 4 kts. *when submerged*.

Coastal Boats—*continued.*

Coastal Boats—*continued.*

5 *Fiat Laurenti* type : **F10, F13,** built by Fiat-San Giorgio Co., Spezia ; **F18,** by Odero, Sestri-Ponente ; **F6, F20,** built by Orlando, Leghorn, 1916-17. Displacement : 245 tons *on surface,* 318 tons *when submerged.* Dimensions : 149½ × 13¾ × 10¼ feet. Guns : 1—3 inch (30 cal.) A.A. 1 M.G. 2—17.7 inch bow tubes. Machinery : 2 Fiat Diesel *on surface* ; 2 Savigliano electric motors *when submerged.* 670 H.P. = 13·5 kts. *on surface,* 250 H.P. = 7·9 kts. *when submerged.* Radius : 1100 miles at 9 kts. *on surface,* 110 miles at 1·5 kts. *when submerged.* Oil : 12 tons. Complement, 22.

Note.—Missing numbers have been disposed of for scrapping.

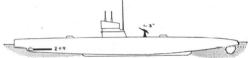

Photo wanted.

N.6.

1927 *Photo, Pucci.*

2 *Bernardis* type : **N3, N4,** (Ansaldo Co., Sestri Ponente, 1916). Displacement, 265 tons *on surface,* 350 tons *when submerged.* Dimensions : 150½ × 14¾ × 10 feet. Guns : 1—14 pdr. (30 cal.) A.A. 2 bow 18 inch tubes. Machinery : 2 Sulzer-Ansaldo Diesel engines *on surface* ; 2 Tecnomasio Italiano electric motors *when submerged.* H.P. 650 = 12·5 kts. *on surface,* 270 H.P. = 7·6 kts. *when submerged.* Oil : 8-10 tons. Radius : 1300 miles at 10 kts. *on surface,* 200 miles at 2·5 kts. *when submerged.* Complement, 21. Completed, 1917-18.

1 *Bernardis* type : **N 6** (1918). Built by Cantiere Navale Franco Tosi, Taranto. Displacement, 276 tons *on surface,* 35 tons *submerged.* Dimensions : 152½ × 14½ × 10 feet. Machinery : 2 Tosi Diesel engines, H.P. 700 = 13·5 kts. *on surface.* Electric motors H.P. 320 = 7·9 kts. *submerged.* Guns : tubes as *N 3—4* below. Completed Dec., 1917.

N.6 Similar to *N 3-4* but with flush deck.

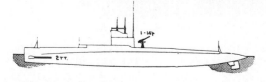

H. 2.

1931 *Photo.*

7 *Holland* type : **H1, H2** (1916), **H3, H4, H6, H8** (1917), by Canadian Vickers Co., Montreal. Displacement : 341 tons *on surface,* 440 tons *when submerged.* Dimensions : 150½ × 15¾ × 12½ feet. Guns : 1—3″ (30 cal.) A.A. 1 M.G. 4—18 inch bow tubes. Machinery : 2 Nelseco Diesel engines *on surface* ; 2 Electric Dynamic Co. motors *when submerged.* 960 H.P. = 12·8 kts. *on surface,* 680 H.P. = 10·8 kts. *when submerged.* Radius : 2000 miles at 7·5 kts. *on surface.* 130 miles at 2 kts. *when submerged.* Complement, 22. Oil : 18 tons. *H5* War loss, *H4* badly damaged by fire in Dec., 1928 and removed from effective list.

Aircraft Tender. (*Nave appoggio Idrovolanti*).

G. MIRAGLIA.   *1927 Photo, Capitan Mateo Mille.*

G. MIRAGLIA.   *1927 Photo, Capitan Mateo Mille.*

GIUSEPPE MIRAGLIA (ex-*Citta di Messina*, 20th December, 1923). Displacement: 4960/5400 tons. Dimensions: 377 × 49 × 17 feet. Guns: 4—4 inch, AA., 1—M.G. Parsons geared turbines. I.H.P. 12000 = 21·5 kts. Oil Fuel: 440 tons. Complement, 180. Reconstructed at Spezia D.Y., 1923-25. Carries 4 large and 16 smaller planes, with usual facilities for repairs and renewals and catapults at either end of flight deck for launching planes.

Minelayers. (*Navi Posamine.*)

Note.—Cruisers *Bari, Ancona, Taranto, Brindisi, Venezia, Quarto;* all Flotilla Leaders and many Destroyers and Submarines are fitted for minelaying.

MILAZZO.   *1928 Photo, by courtesy of Builders.*

6 *Ostia* type: **AZIO** (May 4th, 1927), **LEGNANO** (May, 1926), **LEPANTO** (May 22nd, 1927), **DARDANELLI** (1925), **MILAZZO** (1925), **OSTIA** (1925). All ordered 1924, the first three from Cant. Nav. Riuniti, Ancona, the second three from Cant. Nav. Triestino, Monfalcone. Displacement, 700 tons (*full load,* 850 tons). Dimensions: 204 × 28½ × 8½ feet. H.P. 1,500 = 15 kts. Oil fuel. Guns: 2—4 inch, 35 cal., 1—3 inch AA. First three are to be employed on colonial service, and have an effective radius of 3500 miles. All fitted for sweeping if required. 80 mines carried.

ALBONA, LAURANA, ROVIGNO (ex-Austrian Minesweepers *M.T.* 130—132). 130 tons. Guns: 1—3 inch. H.P. 280 = 11 kts.

BRONDOLO.   *1920 Official Photo.*

BRONDOLO (1909), **MARGHERA** (1909). 120 tons. Dimensions: 125 × 11 × 2¼ feet. Guns: 1—14 pdr. During War, each fitted to carry and lay 60 mines. Designed H.P., 540 = 13 kts. Coal: 14 tons. Complement, 27.

290

BUCCARI.

1928 *Photo, Pucci.*

4 *Fasana* type : **BUCCARI** (1926), **DURAZZO** (1st April, 1926), **FASANA** (1924), **PELAGOSA** (1926). All built at Castellamare. 610 tons. Dimensions : 192 (*p.p.*) × 32 × 5.7 feet. Engines : 2 sets Diesel engines, together 700 B.H.P. = 10 kts. Guns : 1—3 inch AA. Carry 54 mines.

Mine Sweepers (*Navi Dragamine*).

RD 31.

1928 *Photo, Pucci.*

39 small tugs, of 150/170 tons, bearing various numbers, RD 4 to 57, are also fitted for mine sweeping. Majority are H.P. 800 = 13 kts. All armed with 1—3 inch AA.

Convoy Gunboats (*Cannoniere di Scorta*).
5 Bafile class.

VIESTI.

1926 *Photo, by courtesy of Ministry of Marine.*

COTRONE (ex-*Abastro*, ex-German *M* 120), **VIESTI** (ex-*Meteo*, ex-German *M* 119.) Built at Neptun Yard, Rostock, 1918, and taken over by Italy in 1919. Displacement : 515 tons. Dimensions : 182 (*w.l.*), 192 (*o.a.*) × 23½ × 7 feet. I.H.P. 1600 = 16 kts. Guns : 2—4 inch. 2 Smaller.

T. FARINATI.

1925 *Photo, by courtesy of the Ministry of Marine.*

5 *Pattison* type : **Alessandro Vitturi, Ernesto Giovannini, Andrea Bafile, Tolosetto Farinati, Carlo del Greco.** (1919-22). 230 tons. Dimensions : 170·6 × 19 × 5·6 feet. Guns : 2—4 inch. 45 cal., 2 M.G. Torpedo Tubes : 2—18 inch in one twin mounting. S.H.P. 2800 = 23 kts. Trials : H.P. 3270 = 23.7 kts. Oil : 40 tons. Radius : 900 miles at 20 kts.

Note.—These vessels are classed officially as " Cannoniere di Scorta " (Convoy Gunboats), but resemble T.B., corresponding in some respects to the British *P*-boats. They were originally designed as small Minelayers, hence shape of hull. A sixth vessel of this class, *E. Rosso*, was burned on stocks and hull scrapped.

U

Convoy Gunboats - *continued.*

CIRENE.   1925 *Photo, by courtesy of the Ministry of Marine.*

CIRENE (ex-*G 13*, ex-*Hoyo Maru*, 1912).   500 tons.   Guns: 2—14 pdr., AA., **1** M.G.   H.P. 300 = 12·3 kts.

VALOROSO (Purchased 1917).   420 tons.   Guns: **1**—14 pdr., AA., **1** M.G.   H.P. 477 = 10 kts.

Colonial Gunboats (*Cannoniere per Servizio Coloniale*).

Note.—Cruisers *Campania* and *Libia* are also so classed.

1920 *Photo, A. Boo, Cheefu.*

SEBASTIANO CABOTO (Palermo, 1913).   Displacement: 877 tons.   Complement, 104.   Dimensions: 196.8 × 31.8 × 9.2 feet.   Guns: 6—14 pdr., 4 machine.   Designed H.P., 1200 = 13 kts.   2 screws,   2 cyl. (direct flame) boilers.   Coal: *normal* 87 tons, *maximum* 187 tons.

PALMAIOLA.   1925 *Photo, by courtesy of the Ministry of Marine.*

Colonial Gunboats—*continued.*

PALMAIOLA (ex-*Mary*. 1916).   562 tons.   Dimensions: 133 × 19½ × 12 feet.   H.P. 380 = 8.5 kts.   Guns: **1**—6 pdr. AA.

GEN. ARIMONDI.   1925 *Photo, by courtesy of the Ministry of Marine.*

GENERALE ARIMONDI (Glasgow, 1910, purchased 1917, ex-*Gorgo*, ex-*Pelican*).   580 tons.   H.P. 540 = 9 kts.   Guns: 2—14 pdr., AA., 2 M.G.

The following were all acquired from Japan, 1917, and are employed in colonial service.   All launched 1911-12, and mostly armed with **1** or 2—14 pdr. AA.   Some may carry minesweeping gear.

ALULA (ex-*G 23*, 1912).   (Depôt ship, Red Sea).   430 tons.   Speed: 13 kts.

PORTO CORSINI (ex-*G 15*, ex-*Fumi Maru*).   380 tons.   Speed: 12 kts.

RIMINI (ex-*G 16*, ex-*Fuku Maru*).   420 tons.   Speed: 9.5 kts.

GALLIPOLI.   1929 *Photo, by courtesy of Ministry of Marine.*

GALLIPOLI (ex-*G 31*, ex-*Hakata Maru No. 8*).   400 tons.   Speed: 10·5 kts.

OTRANTO (ex- *G 36*, ex-*Sumiye Maru*).   385 tons.   Speed: 10 kts.

AUGUSTA (ex-*G 37*, ex-*Oshima Maru*).   390 tons.   Speed: 12 kts.

MAGGIORE TOSELLI (ex-*G 3*, ex-*Toyo Maru*).   370 tons.   Speed: 8 kts.

China Gunboat (*Cannoniera fluviale per la China*).

(*For service on Yangtsze.*)

ERMANNO CARLOTTO (Shanghai Dock & Engineering Co. 1921).   Shallow-draught river gunboat.   220 tons.   Dimensions: 140 × 24½ × 3 feet.   Guns: 2—14 pdr., 4 machine.   Designed H.P., 1100 = 14 kts.   2 Yarrow boilers.   Complement, 73.

Royal Yacht.

SAVOIA.   1926 *Photo, by courtesy of the Ministry of Marine.*

SAVOIA (ex-*Citta di Palermo*, 1st September, 1923).   5800 tons.   Dimensions: 390 (*w.l.*) × 49 × 17 feet.   Guns: 4—14 pdr. AA.   2 sets Parsons geared turbines.   8 Yarrow boilers, oil-fired.   I.H.P. 15,750 = 22·4 kts.

Note.—Built at Spezia and reconstructed by Cant. Nav. Riuniti, Palermo, as a yacht.

Armed Yacht (*Yacht Armati*).

(*Classed as Gunboat.*)

1928 *Photo, by courtesy of Ministry of Marine.*

AURORA (ex-*Marechiaro*, ex-Austrian *Taurus*, ex-*Nirvana*).
(D. & W. Henderson, Glasgow, 1904). Reconstructed 1928.
Displacement: 950 tons (Std). Dimensions: 261 (*o.a.*) × 30
× 14 feet (*mean*). Triple expansion engines. 2 Pattison
boilers. H.P. 3255 = 14·7 kts. Oil: 117 tons. Guns:
2—57 m.m.

M. A. S. 92—434 (*Motobarche Anti-Sommergibili*).

Note.—Correspond to British C.M.B. and M.L. types. Many
sold out, scrapped, etc. Present total 43

New Construction

3 S.V.A.N. boats.

Nos. 435, 436,   13·7 tons.
No. 437.   15 tons.
H.P. 1,500 =   ? Kts.

"TIPO VELOCI" (17 boats) : 5 S.V.A.N. boats : **M.A.S. 423
—426, 430, 432—434.** 1 Baglietto boat : **M.A.S. 431.**
13 tons.   Length : 52½ feet.   1500 B.H.P.=40 kts.   2 M.G.
Torpedo tubes : 2.   5 D.C. carried.

1926 *Official Photo.*

2 S.V.A.N. boats : **M.A.S. 418, 422** (1922).   21 tons.   Length :
59 feet.   1200 B.H.P. = 26 kts.   2 M.G.   Torpedo tubes :
2—17.7 inch.   3 D.C. carried.

4 Baglietto boats : **M.A.S. 397—400** (1920).   30 tons.   Length :
69 feet.   Motors (Isotta Fraschini) : 1600 B.H.P. = 33 kts.
Guns : 2 M.G.   Torpedo tubes : 4—18 inch in some.

2 S.V.A.N. boats : **M.A.S. 428, 429** (1925).   31 tons.
Length : 72.2 feet.   Motors (Isotta Fraschini) : 1200 B.H.P. =
28 kts.   Guns : 1—14 pdr., 2 M.G.   Torpedo tubes : 2—18 inch.

1919 *Photo.*

With two torpedoes.   1919 *Photo.*

"TIPO A" : 23 boats (S.V.A.N., Ansaldo, Orlando, Baglietto,
etc., 1916-19).   11½—12 tons.   Length : 52½ feet.   Motors
(Isotta Fraschini or Sterling, or F.I.A.T.) : 400 to 500 B.H.P.
=22—26·5 kts.   Guns : 2 M.G.   Several have 2 torpedo
tubes or dropping gears : others carry 4 mines.

M.A.S. Nos. 92, 94, 100, 141, 145, 179, 188, 200, 204, 206,
208, 210, 212, 213, 216, 217, 219, 222, 223, 228—230, 320.

Training Ships (*Navi Scuol*).

Note.—Old cruisers *S. Giorgio*, *S. Marco* and *Pisa* described on earlier pages, are, or have been employed in Training Service.

C. COLOMBO. 1928 *Photo, Capitan M. Mille.*

CRISTOFORO COLOMBO (April 4th, 1928). Built at Castellamare. Designed by Lieut.-Colonel F. Rotundi and laid down April, 1926. Displacement : 2832 (S) 2985 (N) 3500 (f.l.). Dimensions : 218 (*p.p.*) × 48½ × 20⅓ feet. Guns : **6**—3 inch A.A., **5** M.G. Machinery : 2 Tosi Diesel-driven generating units and 2 Marelli electric motors. H.P. 1600/1100 = 10·5 kts. 1 screw. Fuel : 103 tons. Radius : 6000 miles at 8 kts.

Notes.—*C. Colombo* usually depends on sail power, machinery being treated as auxiliary. Hull, masts and yards, are all of steel. Loud speakers and echo sounding gear form part of her equipment. About 140 midshipmen and cadets (or an equal number of boys) are usually carried.

Submarine Depôt Ships. (*Navi per appoggio sommergibili*).

A. PACINOTTI. 1926 *Photo, by courtesy of the Ministry of Marine.*

ALESSANDRO VOLTA (ex-*Caprera*, 1921), **ANTONIO PACINOTTI** (ex-*Citta di Sassari*, 1922). Both reconstructed at Castellamare D.Y., 1924-25. 2400 tons. Dimensions : 288¾ × 36 × 15 feet. Parsons geared turbines. H.P. 4500 = 19 kts. Guns : **1**—4·7 inch, **2**—3 inch AA. **1**—M.G.

Training Ships (*Navi Scuola*).

1931 *Official Photo.*

AMERIGO VESPUCCI (March 22, 1930). Built at Castellamare, laid down May 12, 1930. Completed : June, 1931. Displacement : 2832 (S), 3700 (f.l.) tons. Dimensions : 229·6 × 51 × 22 feet. Guns : **4**—3 inch AA., **9** M.G. Machinery : Two Fiat motors of 1250 H.P. driving 2 Marelli dynamos : single propelling Diesel. 2000 B.H.P. Speed 10 kts. Sail area : 2100 sq. metres. Complement : 400 + 150 midshipmen.

Transports (*Trasporti*)

CHERSO. 1928 *Photo, Pucci.*

CHERSO (ex-*Amalfi*), **LUSSIN** (ex-*Marsala*). Built by Neptun Yard, Rostock. Displacement: 4,500 tons. Dimensions: 300 × 41 × 17½ feet. H.P. 1,100 = 10·5 kts. Guns: 4—4.7 inch., 1—3″, 2—3″ AA. Classed as "*Navi Trasporto Materiale.*" Cargo: 3,000 tons.

GIANNUTRI (ex-*Elba*, 1915). 770 tons. Guns: 4—3 inch AA. H.P. 1150 = 13.3 kts.

TRIPOLI (1928). 2,500 (s) tons. H.P. 600 = 8·5. Guns: Nil.

Munition Carriers. (*Navi Trasporto Munizioni.*)

BUFFOLUTO. 1928 *Photo, Pucci.*

PANIGAGLIA (10th July, 1923), **BUFFOLUTO** (1924), **VALLELUNGA** (1924). All built by Ansaldo San Giorgio Co. 1035 tons. Dimensions: 184½ (o.a.), 172¼ (p.p.) × 29½ × 11 feet. Guns: 2—4 inch, 1—40m/m. AA. H.P. 1500 = 12 kts. Radius at this speed, 960 miles

Research Ship.

CITTA DI MILANO. 1929 *Official Photo.*

CITTA DI MILANO (ex *Grossherzog von Oldenburg*, 1905). 5900 tons. Dimensions: 305 × ? × ? feet. Guns: 2—4 inch, 1—3″ AA., 1 M.G. Speed: 11.5 kts. (Originally intended for cable laying.)

Surveying Ships (*Navi per Servizio Idrografico*).

AM. MAGNAGHI. 1929 *Photo, Capitan M. Mille, R.Sp.N.*

AMMIRAGLIO MAGNAGHI (Ansaldo, –/8/14). 2050 tons. Complement, 137. Dimensions: 229½ × 37½ × 12¼ feet. Guns: 4—3″ AA. I.H.P., 2000 = 14 kts. Machinery: 2 sets vertical triple expansion. Boilers: 4 cylindrical. Was originally laid down as a Fassenger Steamer.

Surveying Ships—*continued.*

SCILLA. 1929 *Official Photo.*

SCILLA (ex-*Panaria*, ex-*Fantasma*, 1916). 470 tons. Guns: 2—6 pdr. H.P. 450 = 11 kts.

CARIDDI (ex-*G.21*, 1917). 440 tons. Guns: 2—6 pdr. Speed: 10 kts.

TRITONE. 1929 *Official Photo.*

TRITONE (ex-*G19*, ex-*Tamashima Maru*, 1913). 450 tons. H.P. 450 = 10 kts. Guns: 2—3″ AA. 2 M.G.

Fuel Ships (*Navi rifornimento carbone e naftetine*), and Oil Tankers (*Navi Cisterne per nafta*).

Note.—A 2000 ton Oiler is reported to have been ordered in 1928.

1928 *Photo, by courtesy of Ministry of Marine.*

TARVISIO. Oil Tanker (Castellamare, April 11th, 1927). 11,700 tons. Dimensions : 468·8 × 52 × 24¼ feet. H.P. 2,800 = 11 kts. Guns : **4—4·7 inch, 2—3 inch AA.** Cargo : 8,000 tons. Protective arrangements as *Brennero*.

BRENNERO. 1925 *Photo, by courtesy of Ministry of Marine.*

BRENNERO (Societa Esercizi Bacini, Riva Trigoso, 1921). Displacement : 10,600 tons (7400 tons *d.w.c.*). Length (*p.p.*) : 428 feet. Beam : 52.5 feet on *w.l.* and 59 ft. *outside bulges*. Draught : 24·3 feet. Guns : **4—4·7 inch** (50 cal.), **2—3 inch AA.** Magazines are well protected. I.H.P. 9,500 = 10·5 kts. (for *trials*), 9·5 kts. (in service). Triple expansion engines. 1 screw. Oil fuel only. Special Protection : "Pugliese" type bulges, with central "shock-absorbing" cylinders.

Fuel Ships & Oil Tankers—*continued.*

URANO. *Photo added 1927.*

URANO (Deutsche Werke, Kiel, 1922). Oil tanker, built under War Reparations account. Diesel engines. B.H.P. 1,900 = 10 kts. 11,500 tons. Dimensions : 398 × 54 × 23½ feet. Guns : **2—4·7 inch, 2—3 inch AA., 1 M.G.** Cargo 8,000 tons.

NETTUNO. 1928 *Photo, by courtesy of Ministry of Marine.*

GIOVE, NETTUNO (1916). Oil tankers. 10,310 tons. Dimensions : 416½ × 50¾ × 24 feet. Armament : **3—4·7", 1—3" AA.** H.P. 3,000 = 10·5 kts. Cargo : 6,000 tons oil fuel.

BRONTE (1904). Fleet Collier, Oil Tanker and Transport. 9,460 tons. Complement, 79. Guns : **2—4·7", 2—3" AA., 2—3", 1 M.G.** With full cargo, 3,700 I.H.P. = 11·5 kts.; with reduced cargo, 4,300 I.H.P. = 14·5 kts. 2 screws. 4 cyl. boiler. Carries 6,000 tons coal or 4,000 tons oil + 2,000 tons coal. Own coal : 550 tons. *Sterope* (sister ship) lost during War.

Fuel Ships and Oil Tankers—*continued.*

STIGE (1922). Petrol Carrier. **COCITO, LETE,** (1914-15). Oil tankers. 1,204 tons. Fiat Diesel engines. H.P., 400 = 8·5 kts. , Cargo : 760 tons.

Guns: *Stige* **1—4·7. 1—3" AA.**
Cocito
Lete } **3—2" AA.**

PROMETEO. 1928 *Photo, Pucci.*

PROMETEO (ex-*Ostia*). (1923). 1,080 tons. Speed : 10 kts. Guns : **2—14 pdr. AA.**

Fuel Ships & Oil Tankers—*continued.*

NIOBE. 1929 *Photo, by courtesy of Ministry of Marine.*

NIOBE (ex-German *Sylt*, Reiherstieg Yard, Hamburg, 1916). Collier. 3400 tons. Speed : 11 kts. Guns : 2—4.7 inch, 1—14 pdr. AA. Cargo capacity : 2000 tons coal.

CERERE. 1929 *Photo, by courtesy of Ministry of Marine.*

CERERE (ex-*Baltrum*, 1915). 2,730 tons. Speed : 10 kts. Guns : 1—4.7 inch, 2—3 inch AA. Capacity : 1,500 tons.

MARTE (ex-Austrian *Vesta*) (Armstrong, 1892). 2,500 tons. I.H.P. 1200 = 10 kts.

Submarine Salvage Ship.
(*Pontone per ricupero Sommergibili.*)

ANTEO (Smulders, Schiedam, 1914). Special Salvage Ship for Submarines. 2100 tons. Dimensions : 164 × 73¾ × ? feet. I.H.P., 750 = 8 kts. 2 screws. 2 cyl. boilers. 2 cranes, each lifting 200 tons.

High Sea Tugs (*Rimorchiatori d'Alto Mare*).

GIASONE (*built* at Cantiere Breda, Venice). Displacement, 1520 tons. Dimensions : 210 × 33¾ × 13 feet. H.P. 2500. Guns : 2—3 pdr. AA.

TESEO. 1931 *Photo.*

TESEO (ex-Austrian *Herkules*, 1910 ; taken over 1920). Salvage Vessel and Tug. 1500 tons. Dimensions : 210 × 33¾ × 13 feet. Guns : 1—3 inch AA. Designed H.P. 2500 = 10 kts. 2 screws. Yarrow boilers. Complement, 81.

POLIFEMO (ex-*Einigkeit*, 1925). Salvage Vessel and Tug. 1180 tons. H.P. 1250 = 12 kts. Thornycroft boilers. Guns : 2—3″ AA.

High Sea Tugs—*continued.*

TITANO. *Photo added* 1927.

TITANO (1913). High Sea Tug. 970 tons. Guns : 2—6 pdr. H.P., 1970 = 15 kts. 2 screws. 2 Gennardini boilers. Coal : 160 tons. (s/m Salvage ship.)

CICLOPE. 1930 *Photo, Capitan M. Mille.*

CICLOPE (1903). 840 tons. Guns : 2—6 pdr. H.P. 1900 = 13.6 kts. 2 screws. Pattison boilers.

Note.—There are 70 Tugs of 350—500 tons and 104 smaller Tugs.

Repair Ship (*Nave Officina.*)

1928 *Official Photo.*

QUARNARO (Scoglio Ulivi Yard, Pola, July 30, 1924). 8140 tons. Dimensions : 360 × 48½ × 22 feet. Triple expansion engines. H.P. 2,300 = 11·5 kts. Guns : 3—4 inch AA., 1 M.G.

Tugs—*continued.*

L. F. MARSIGLI.   *1929 Official Photo.*

LUIGI FERDINANDO MARSIGLI (ex-*Tremiti*, 1916). 450 tons. Speed : 9 kts. Guns : **1**—M.G.

LUNI (1914).
MARITTIMO (1915) } 450 tons. H.P. 970 = 12 kts.
EGADI (1915) } Guns : **1**—14 pdr.

MONTECRISTO (1921). 475 tons. H.P. 500 = 10 kts. Guns : **1**—14 pdr.

ATLANTE (1928). 460 tons. H.P. 964 = 11·3 kts. Guns : **1**—14 pdr.

ERCOLE (1928) } 470 tons. H.P. 908 = 11 kts.
AUSONIA (1920) } Guns : **1**—15 pdr.

LIPARI (1921). 318 tons. H.P. 500 = 10 kts. Guns : **1**—14 pdr.

Water Carriers *(Navi Cisterne per Acqua.)*

DALMAZIA.   *1929 Official Photo.*

DALMAZIA (Fiume, 1922), **ISTRIA** (Fiume, 1923). Displacement : 3000 tons. Speed : 12 kts. Guns : **1**—4.7 inch, **1**—3 inch, AA. Cargo : 1800 tons. Both built at Quarnaro Yard.

PAGANO, VERDE (1921). 1490 tons. Fiat Diesel engines. B.H.P. 400 = 8.5 kts. Guns : **1**—4.7 inch,. **1**—3 inch, AA. Capacity : 950 tons.

FLEGETONTE (1915). Similar to Oil Tankers of *Cocito* type. 1200 tons. **3**—3 inch AA. Capacity : 750 tons.

BORMIDA
MINCIO } 1930. 655 tons. H.P. 670 = 9 kts.

ARNO
BRENTA } 1929. 644 tons. H.P. 645 = 9 kts.

Photo 1930.

ERIDANO (1911). 1260 tons. Guns : **1**—3 inch AA. Designed H.P., 1200 = 12.7 kts. 2 screws. 2 Yarrow boilers. Coal : 120 tons. Carries 400 tons water.

Water Carriers—*continued.*

TEVERE (1897). 960 tons. Guns : **2**—6 pdr. H.P., 620 = 11 kts. 1 screw. 2 Thornycroft boilers. Coal : 150 tons Carries 320 tons water.
(There are 28 smaller Tanks, besides 7 *building.*)

FRIGIDO (1916). 304 tons. H.P. 221 = 9 kts.

1930 Photo, Capitan M. Mille.

ADIGE (1929). 793 tons. H.P. 280 = 8 kts.

IMPERIAL JAPANESE NAVY.

Revised, at the Navy Department, Tokyo, by courtesy of H. E. The Minister of Marine, 1931.

Flags.

1 *Standard of H.I.M. the Empress.*—A forked flag with a gold chrysanthemum on a red ground (as sketch for Imperial Standard).

2 *Standard of H.I.H. the Crown Prince.*—As Imperial Standard, but the chrysanthemum is enclosed in a square white border set a little distance within edges of flag.

3 *Imperial Princes and Princesses.*—A square white flag, with red border run round edges of flag and gold chrysanthemum in centre.

4 *Duty Flag.*—As sketch for transport, but *white* stripes over *red* ground.

5 *Repair Ship Flag.*—As transport flag, but with red stripes along upper and lower edges of flag.

6 *Pendant for Men of War.*—Usual narrow triangulated shape, with Rising Sun next to hoist, as in sketch for Commodore.

Minister of Marine: Admiral Baron Kiyokazu Abo.
Chief of Naval Staff: Admiral Naomi Taniguchi.
Naval Attaché, London: Capt. Shiro Takasu.
Assistant Naval Attaché, London: Lieut.-Commander S. Kaneko.

Mercantile Marine.

(From "Lloyd's Register," 1930 figures).
Total gross tonnage, 4,276,341 (including 24 vessels of 16 kts. and over).

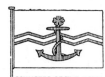

MINISTER OF THE NAVY

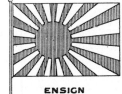

ENSIGN

JACK & MERCANTILE ENSIGN

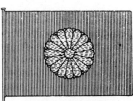

IMPERIAL STANDARD

TRANSPORT

Red
White
Gold
Blue

SENIOR OFFICER

OFFICER COMMANDING TORPEDO DIVISION

ADMIRAL

VICE ADMIRAL

REAR ADMIRAL

COMMODORE

Personnel and Uniforms.

INSIGNIA OF RANK—EXECUTIVE OFFICERS—SLEEVES. (Changed to this; 1908).

Navy Estimates.

1930-31, Yen 37,800,000.

Personnel: About 85,000, all ranks.

Sho-i Ko-hoshei.
Midshipman.

Executive Branch:	Tai-sho.	Chu-sho.	Sho-sho.	Tai-sa.	Chu-sa.	Sho-sa.	Tai-i.	Chu-i.	Sho-i.	Has a stripe
Corresponding British:	*Admiral*	*Vice-Ad.*	*Rear-Ad.*	*Captain.*	*Commander.*	*Lieut. Com.*	*Lieutenant.*	*Sub-Lieut.*	*Acting Sub-Lieut.*	half the width of a Sho-i.

BAND
between stripes. (BRANCHES, with but after Executive).

Violet Kikwan (*Engineer*) (with executive rank and curl. Titles as above with the prefix Kikwan).
Red Gun-i (*Doctor*).
White Shukei (*Paymaster*).
Brown Zosen (*Constructor*).
„ Zoki (*Engineer-Constructor*). ⎫ with curl, as Executive.
Purple–Brown Zohei (*Gun Constructor*). ⎬
Blue Suiro (*Hydrographer*). ⎭

CAP.

The cap is the same as the British (but without gold embroidery in the senior ranks).

CAP BADGE.

Small anchor, surrounded by cherry leaves.

The senior officer of any branch on board the ship always carries the affix "*cho.*" Thus: Ho jitsu-cho (*Gunnery*), Sui-rai-cho (*Torpedo*), Ko-kai-cho (*Navigator*), Gun-i-cho (*Senior Doctor*), Shukei-cho (*Senior Paymaster*).

Undress is a military tunic (dark blue) with the sleeve insignia of rank in black braid only, with curl, and with collar insignia of rank and branch.

NAVAL ORDNANCE.

Principal Naval Guns.

Notation.	Calibre.	Length in calibres.	Model.	Weight of Gun.	Weight of A.P. shot.	Maximum Initial Velocity.	Maximum penetration firing A.P. capped at K.O.		Danger space against average ship, at			Service rate of Fire. Rounds per minute.
							5000 yards.	3000 yards.	10,000 yards.	5000 yards.	3000 yards.	
	inches.			tons.	lbs.	F.S.	inches.	inches.				
HEAVY.	16	45	K.M.	105	...	2600	...	...	...	...	...	...
	14	45	V	82	1400	...	...	...	...	...	...	...
MEDIUM.	8	45	O	15½	188	2800	7½	10½	105	430	625	1
	8	45	A	17½	250	2740	7	10	110	425	600	1·2
	8	40	A	15½	250	2580	5½	7½	100	400	580	1·2
	6	45	('04)	8½	100	3000	4½	6½	75	250	475	...
	6	50	V	8	100	3000	4½	6½	75	250	475	6
	6	40	A	6½	100	2500	3	4½	65	210	435	7
	6	40	A	6	100	2220	2½	4	35	150	360	8
	5·5	50	...	6¼	82	2725	...	...	...	...	...	12
	4·7	45	...	...	...	...	...	...	...	...	...	
	4·7	40	A	2	45	2150	...	2½	...	...	...	8
	4·7	32	A	1⅔	36	1938	...	...	...	...	...	8-6
LIGHT	3	...	...	...	14	...	...	...	...	...	...	...
	3	40	...	2	12	2200	...	...	...	...	...	...
AA	3	40	...	...	13	...	...	...	...	...	...	...

In the Model column A = Armstrong; O = Obukhoff (Russian); V = Vickers.

K.M. = Kure Arsenal and Muroran Steel Works.

16 inch, 45 cal. in *Nagato* and *Mutsu*.
14 inch, 45 cal. *Fuso* class (2), *Kongo* class (4); in *Ise* class (2).
8 inch, of a new model in cruisers of *Nachi*, *Kinugasa*, and *Kako* classes.
6 inch, 50 cal. in *Fuso* class (2), *Kongo* class (4).
6 inch, 40-45 cal. in 1st and 2nd Class Cruisers, &c.
5·5 inch in *Nagato* class (2), *Ise* class (2), *Tatsuta* class (2), *Kuma* class (13).
(All details tabulated above are unofficial.)

Gunnery Notes.

Heavy and Light Marks of Directors have been perfected, both of which are being mounted in Capital Ships in service. Type of Directors in Light Cruisers unknown. Nothing known of the system used; there is only a vague report of doubtful accuracy that the Japanese Director is "intermediate between the German Navy and 'Petravic' systems." They are mounted in towers, like British Navy, i.e., in Capital Ships Main Director Tower at masthead, Light Directors on bridges, or legs of tripod masts.

Range-finders.—Barr & Stroud is used. In Capital Ships, large-base R.F. are mounted on turret roofs, as in British Navy.

General efficiency and accuracy of Fire Control system in latest ships believed up to standard of British and U.S. Navies.

Torpedoes.

21 inch, said to be a Japanese modified Whitehead heater type; effective range, 10,000 yards Is said to be powerful and very accurate in running and depth-keeping. A specially heavy mark may be used for tubes of Battleships and Battle Cruisers.

A special 18 or 21 inch mark of short range and heavy charge is said to be built for Submarines; also a short-range (2000 yards) mark for torpedo-dropping 'planes.

Output.—Kure Arsenal, Muroran Iron Works and Osaka Iron Works produced 320 torpedoes per annum during the War. Kobé Steel Works said to have produced 250 torpedoes during 1920. Present capacity (excluding torpedoes ordered from Messrs. Whiteheads, Weymouth), probably over 600 torpedoes per year. Mitsu Bishi Zo K. and Kawasaki Co. probably manufacture torpedoes. Five private establishments are known to be engaged in this work.

Ships to be built under Fleet Replenishment Law 1931–38

Builders.

4 *Cruisers.*	8600 tons.	6 inch guns.	1 each Mitsubishi (Nagasaki), and Kawasaki D.Y., 2 at Naval Yards.
12 *Destroyers.*	1400 tons.		2 Yokohama D. Co. Rest at Naval Yards.
1 *Submarine.*	1970 tons.		Kawasaki D.Y. (Kobe).
6 *Submarines.*	1300 tons.		2 Mitsubishi (Kobe), 4 Navy Yards.
2 *Submarines.*	900 tons.		Navy Yards.
1 *Minelayer.*	5000 tons.		Asano D.Y. Co.
3 *Minelayers.*	600 tons.		1 Fujinagata Co., 2 Uraga D. Co.
4 *Submarine Chasers.*			Navy Yards.
5 *Minesweepers.*	600 tons.		2 each Mitsui Z. and Harina Z., 1 Osaka I.W.
1 *Gunboat.*			
1 *Repair Ship.*			Navy Yards.
1 *Fast Tanker.*			

Naval Air Force is to be triple present day strength.

NOMENCLATURE AND "KANA" OF JAPANESE WARSHIPS.

The system of nomenclature now being used is thus :—
Battleships, Battle-Cruisers and Aircraft Carriers : Named after Provinces and Mountains.
Cruisers : Named after Rivers and Towns.
Destroyers (First Class): Named after Winds.
Destroyers (Second Class): Named after Trees, Flowers and Fruits.

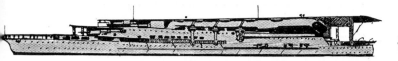

KAGA.

HOSHO.
(Aircraft Carrier.)

AKAGI.
(Aircraft Carrier.)

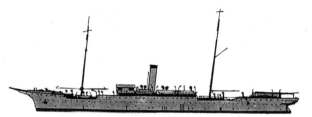

KARASAKI.
(Torpedo Depot Ship.)

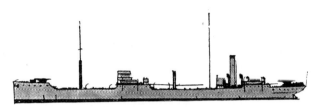

ERIMO class (9).
(Oilers.)

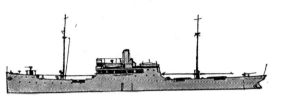

SEITO.
(Store Ship.)

TAKASAKI.
(Store Ship.)

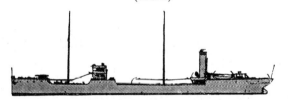

SUNOSAKI.
(Oiler.)

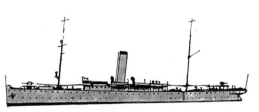

MANSHU.

KOSHU.
(Surveying Ship.)

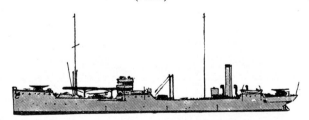

NOTORO.
(Aircraft Tender.)

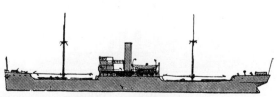

NOSHIMA.   MUROTO.
(Colliers.)

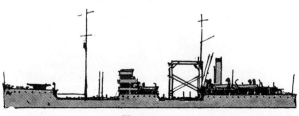

KAMOI.
(Tanker-Collier.)

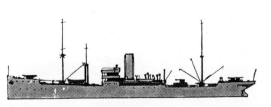

MAMIYA.
(Supply Ship.)

RECOGNITION SILHOUETTES.

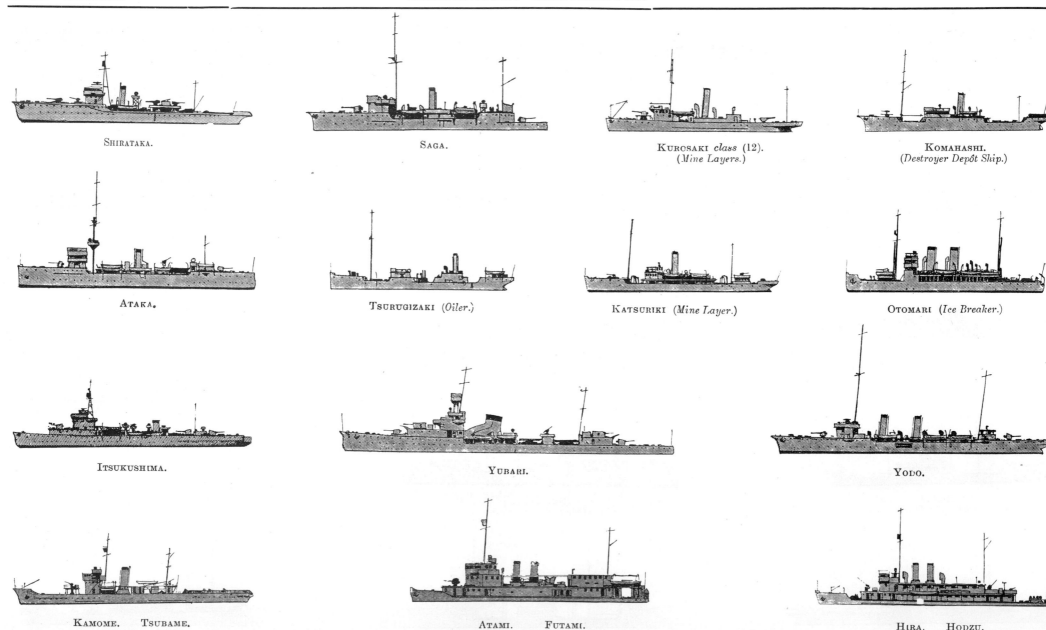

SHIRATAKA.

SAGA.

KUROSAKI *class* (12).
(*Mine Layers.*)

KOMAHASHI.
(*Destroyer Depôt Ship.*)

ATAKA.

TSURUGIZAKI (*Oiler.*)

KATSURIKI (*Mine Layer.*)

OTOMARI (*Ice Breaker.*)

ITSUKUSHIMA.

YUBARI.

YODO.

KAMOME. TSUBAME.

ATAMI. FUTAMI.

HIRA. HODZU.
SETA. KATATA.

302

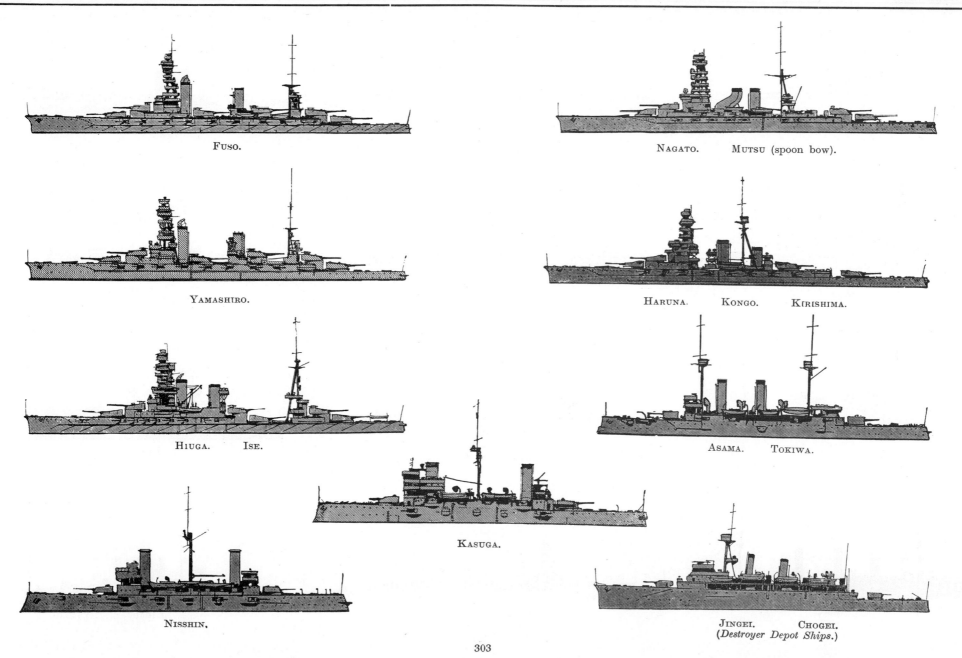

FUSO.

NAGATO.   MUTSU (spoon bow).

YAMASHIRO.

HARUNA.   KONGO.   KIRISHIMA.

HIUGA.   ISE.

ASAMA.   TOKIWA.

KASUGA.

NISSHIN.

JINGEI.   CHOGEI.
(Destroyer Depot Ships.)

NACHI *class* (8).

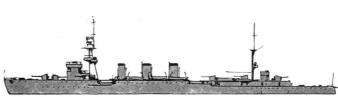

KUMA.   TAMA.   OII.
KISO.   KITAKAMI.

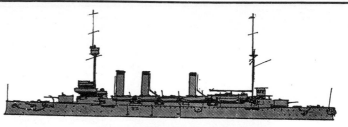

ADZUMA.

KINUGASA.
AOBA.

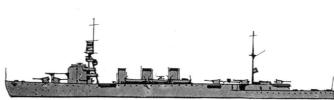

ISUDZU.   NATORI.   KINU.
NAGARA.   YURA.   ABUKUMA.

IDZUMO.
IWATE.

FURUTAKA.
KAKO.

TATSUTA.
TENRYU.   (Now fitted with Tripod foremast.)

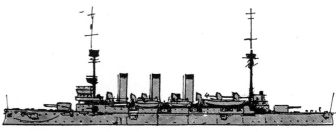

YAKUMO.

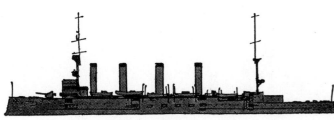

ASO.

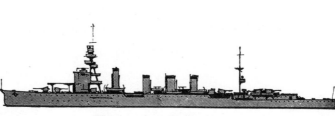

NAKA.   JINTSU.
SENDAI (Spoon bow).

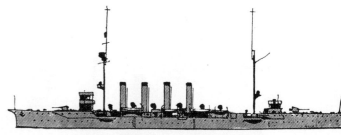

HIRADO.   YAHAGI.

Minesweepers Nos. 1—6.

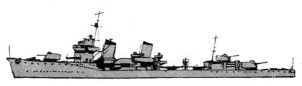

FUBUKI *class* (24).

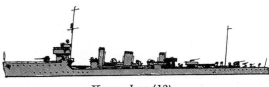

KABA *class* (12).

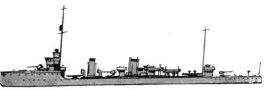

MOMO *class* (10).

MINEKAZE *class* (12).

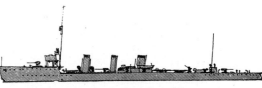

AMATSUKAZE *class* (4).

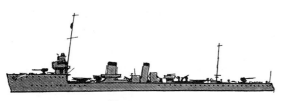

URAKAZE.

KAMIKAZE *class* (12).
(Note main mast and after guns).

TANIKAZE.   KAWAKAZE.

MOMI *class* (20).

MUTSUKI *class* (12).
(Note bow and amidships t.t.).

UMIKAZE.   YAMAKAZE.

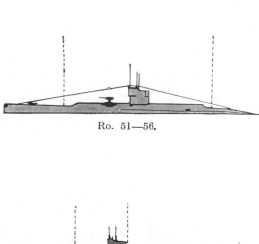

Ro. 51—56.

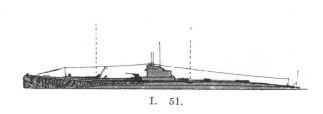

I. 51.

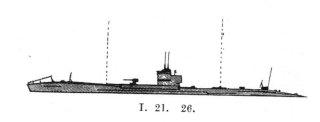

I. 21. 26.

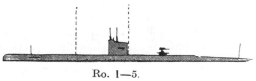

Ro. 1—5.

Ro. 29. 32.

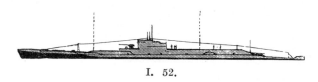

I. 52.

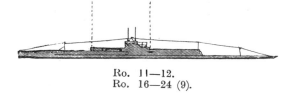

Ro. 11—12.
Ro. 16—24 (9).

Ro. 26. 27. 28.

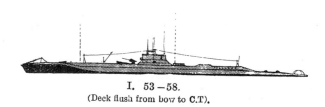

I. 53—58.
(Deck flush from bow to C.T).

Ro. 57. 58 59

Ro. 60—68.

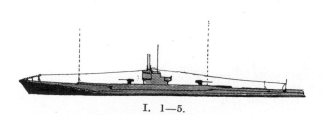

I. 1—5.

(Nagato Class—2 Ships).

とがな **NAGATO** (Nov. 9th, 1919).

つむ **MUTSU** (May 31st, 1920).

Standard displacement, 32,720 tons.

Complement, $\left\{ \begin{array}{l} 74 \text{ officers} \\ 1258 \text{ men} \end{array} \right\} = 1332.$

Length, $\left\{ \begin{array}{l} 660' \; 7'' \; p.p. \\ 700' \; 0'' \; o.a.* \end{array} \right\}$ Beam, 95 feet. Draught, 30 feet *max.*

* Approximate.

NAGATO

1928 *Photo.*

Guns (Japanese):
8—16 inch, 45 cal. $\left. \right\}$ **Dir. Con.**
20—5·5 inch, 50 cal. $\left. \right\}$
4—3 inch (13 pdr.) 40 cal. AA.
4 M.G.
4 Landing.
Torpedo tubes (21 inch):
4 *above water.*
4 *submerged.*
Searchlights: 10.

Armour: (*unofficial*)*
13″ or 12″ Belt ....
8″—4″ Ends ....
3½″ Deck ....
7″ deck above magazines, boilers and engine rooms.
14″ Turrets ....
″ Battery ....
12″ Conning tower ......
(Special anti-torpedo protection.)
* See notes on opposite page.

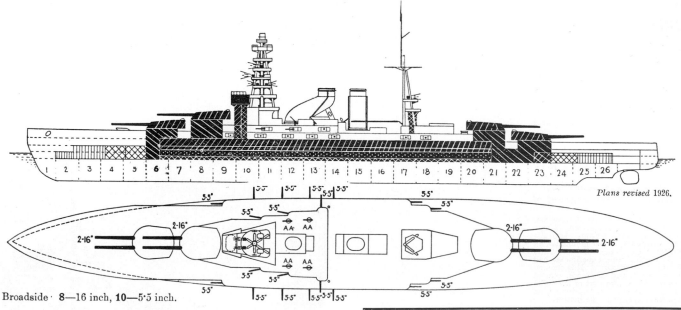

Plans revised 1926.

Ahead:
4—16 inch.
6 to 8—5·5 inch.

Astern:
4—16 inch.
4—5·5 inch.

Broadside· 8—16 inch, 10—5·5 inch.

'Machinery: Geared turbines. Screws. Boilers: 12 Kampon. Designed H.P. 46,000 = 23 kts.
Fuel: (coal and oil) *normal* tons, *maximum* over 5000 tons.

Name	Builder	Machinery	Laid down	Completed	Trials	Boilers	1st Period ends
Nagato	Kure D.Y.	Kure D.Y.	28 Aug.,1917	25 Nov., 1920	,48,000=23·5	} Kampon	1928
Mutsu	Yokosuka D.Y.	Yokcsuka D.Y.	1 June, 1918	24 Oct., 1921	=23·4		1929

Illustrations for "Mutsu" class.

NAGATO.   1928 *Photo.*

MUTSU.   1929 *Photo.*

NAGATO.   1929 *Photo.*

These Notes are not from any official data.

Gunnery Notes.—16 inch guns can range up to 35,000 yards with 35° elevation. Arcs of fire : *about* 270-300° for Turrets Nos. 1, 2, 4. No. 3 *about* 320-330°. 5.5 inch guns *about* 120-130°.

Armour and Protection Notes.—General scheme of armouring is believed to be akin to that for H.M.S. *Queen Elizabeth*. Protective decks are thickened in vicinity of magazines. Special protection below waterline is reported to be a "modified form of bulge" which does not interfere with speed.

Searchlights.—Ten 30 inch, distributed as eight to foremast, two to mainmast.

Aircraft Notes.—Three planes have been or are being added to the equipment of these ships.

Appearance Notes.—The outstanding feature is the colossal heptapodal foremast, with its numerous tops and bridges, for Heavy and Light Directors, Range-Finders and Searchlights. Two of its supporting legs rake forward, two aft, and one out to each beam. The central trunk is so thick, it accommodates an electric lift, running between Upper Deck and the Main Director Tower at the masthead. This mast is said to have been evolved after many experiments had been made to determine the most rigid and vibrationless structure. It is claimed to be almost indestructible by shell-fire, but its weight, and the target offered must be enormous. The shape of the stem, which differs from that of the usual Japanese "yacht" bow, should also be noticed. The trunked fore-funnel, as fitted 1924-25, renders the appearance of these ships still more distinctive.

General Notes.—*Nagato* provided for by 1916 Programme, and laid down in dry dock at Kure D.Y. during the summer of 1917, floated out Nov. 9th, 1919. *Mutsu* provided for by 1917 Programme ; estimated cost is about eight million pounds for *Mutsu*. Plans for this type were completed during the spring of 1916, and the Japanese claim that the design ante-dates the U.S.S. *Maryland* class (with same main armament) by four months. As the first battleship in the world to be completed with 16 inch guns, she is said to be a most successful ship in all respects. Her design and construction certainly reflect the highest credit on her authors and builders.

See previous page for plans and general details.

1915 BATTLESHIPS.

せい ISE (Nov., 1916),

か ろ ひ HIUGA (Jan., 1917).

Standard Displacement, 29,900 tons. Complement, 1,360.

Length (*p.p*). 640 feet. Beam, 94 feet. *Max.* draught, 28⅔ feet. Length (*o.a.*), 683 feet.

Guns (Japanese) :
- **12**—14 inch, 45 cal. } **Dir.**
- **20**—5·5 inch, 50 cal. } **Con.**
- **4**—3 inch (13 pdr.) 40 cal. AA.

Torpedo tubes (21 inch) :
- **6** *submerged.*

(Plan redrawn, 1928).

Armour (Japanese) :
- 12″—8″ Belts.....
- 5″–3″ Belt (Ends)
- 2½—1¼″ Decks ...
- 12″—8″ Turrets...
- 6″ Battery.........
- 12″—6″ C.T. .....

ISE. after refit, 1930.

1930 *Photo.*

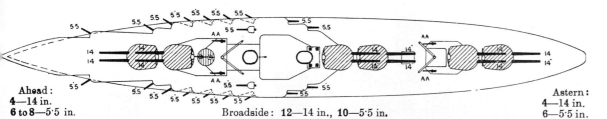

Ahead :
4—14 in.
6 to 8—5·5 in.

Astern :
4—14 in.
6—5·5 in.

Broadside : **12**—14 in., **10**—5·5 in.

Machinery : Brown-Curtis turbines in *Ise* ; Parsons turbines in *Hiuga.* 4 screws. Boilers : 24 Kansei.* Designed H.P. 45,000 = 23 kts. Fuel : *normal* 1000 tons ; *maximum* 4000 tons coal +1000 tons oil.
*General Note concerning boilers of these and certain other ships : " Kansei-Hombu " is a Japanese Admiralty type of W.T. boiler, resembling Yarrow type, with Japanese modifications.

Name	Built by	Machinery	Laid down	Completed	Trials. H.P. = kts.	1st Period ended
Ise	Kawasaki Co.	Kawasaki Co.	May '15	Dec. '17	= 23·3.	1925
Hiuga	Mitsu Bishi Co.	Mitsu Bishi Co.	May '15	Apr. '18		1926

HIUGA. (Detail view).

Photo added 1927.

General Notes.—Built under the 1914 Naval Programme. These ships are an improved and slightly faster *Fuso* type. It is unofficially reported that they are strongly protected against aerial attack by three specially thick protective decks over vital parts of the hull. Special attention is reported to have been paid to the rapid replenishment of fuel, stores, ammunition, &c. Usual internal protection against mine and torpedo explosions by minute sub-division w'ing bulkheads over machinery and magazine spaces. 10—30 inch searchlights, two on foremast, four on funnel, four on mainmast. Reconstructed 1926-27, additional tops being fitted. *Ise* fitted with searchlight positions similar to *Hiuga* in 1930.
Gunnery Note.—Maximum elevation of 14 inch guns reported to be 25°.—(Unofficial).
Aircraft Note.—Three planes added to equipment, 1927.

HIUGA.   1928 *Photo.*

HIUGA.   1929 *Photo.*

HIUGA   1928 *Photo*.   ISE. (after refit 1930.)   1930 *Photo.*

引さふ **FUSO** (March, 1914),

ろしまや **YAMASHIRO** (Nov. 1915).

Standard Displacement, 29,330 tons.
Complement, 1243 and 1272.

Length { (p.p.) 630 feet. } Beam, 94 feet. *Max.* draught, 28½ feet.
       { (o.a.) 673 feet. }

Guns (Japanese):
12—14 inch, 45 cal. } **Dir. Con.**
16—6 inch, 50 cal. }
4—3 inch (13 pdr.), 40 cal., AA.
4 machine.
4 landing.
Torpedo tubes (21 inch):
 6 *submerged.*

Armour—*continued.*
 12″ & 6″ C.T. ....
 (Bulkheads 12″ to 4″)
 2″ & 1¼″ Decks ....
 —″ Roofs { Gunhouses }
          { C.T. .... }
Searchlights : 10—30 inch.

Armour:
12″–8″ Belt (amidships)
5″, 4½″, 4″ Belt
        (bow)
 4″ Belt (stern) ....
 8″ Upper belt ....
 6″ Battery ....
12″—8″ Barbettes .... }
12″—8″ Gunhouses .... }

FUSO.

Photo added 1926.

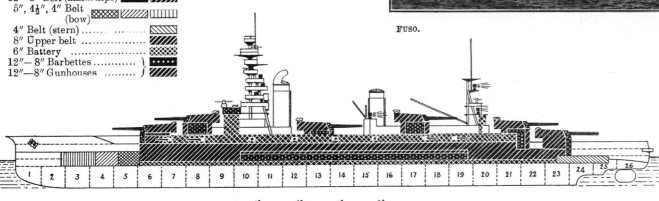

Ahead :
4—14 in.
4—6 in.

Broadside: **12**—14 in., **8**—6 in.

Astern :
4—14 in.
4—6 in.

Machinery: Brown-Curtis turbines. 4 screws. Boilers: 24 Miyabara ; *Yamashiro* may have Kansei. Designed H.P. 40,000 = 22·5 kts. Fuel: *normal* 1000 tons, *maximum* 4000 tons coal + 1000 tons oil fuel.

General Notes.—*Fuso* 1911 Naval Programme, *Yamashiro* 1913 Programme. *Fuso* built in dry dock and floated out March, 1914. First periods expired (*F*) 1923 (*Y*) 1925. 3 planes added to equipment, 1927. *Yamashiro* is at present attached to Torpedo Training Establishment.

Name.	Builder.	Machinery.	Laid down	Com- pleted.	Trials. H.P. = kts.		Turbine	Boilers	Best recent speed
Fuso	Kure	Kawasaki	Mar.'12	Nov. '15	46,500 =	23.	Curtis	Miyabara	
Yamashiro	Yokosuka	Kawasaki	Dec.'13	Apl.,'17	...	...	Curtis	Miyabara	

311

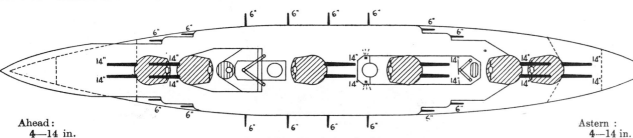

FUSO.

Photo added 1926.

Gunnery Notes.—Maximum elevation of 14 inch guns reported to be 25°.—(Unofficial.)

1915 BATTLESHIPS. 1912-13

HIUGA.   1928 *Photo.*

FUSO.   1928 *Photo.*

YAMASHIRO.   1929 *Photo.*

(Kongo Class— 3 Ships.)

うかんこ   **KONGO** (May, 1912),

なるは   **HARUNA** (Dec., 1913), まりりき **KIRISHIMA** (Dec., 1913).

(**HIYEI** of this class being de-militarised for Training purposes).
Standard displacement, 29,330 tons.   Complement, 980.

Length (*o.a*) 704 feet. { *Kirishima* :   Beam, 92½ feet.   *Max.* draught, 27 feet.
               Kongo   „   92   „   „   „   27½ „
               Haruna   „   95   „   „   „   27½ „

Guns (*see Notes*) :
   8—14 inch, 45 cal.
   16—6 inch, 50 cal.
   4—3 inch (13 pdr.) 40 cal. AA.
   4 machine.
   4 landing.
Torpedo tubes (21 inch) :
   4 submerged.

Ahead :
   4—14 in.
   2 to 4—6 in.

Astern :
   4—14 in.
   2 to 4—6 in.

Broadside :   8—14 in., 8—6 in., 4—21 in. T.T.

Machinery : Parsons 4-shaft (in *Haruna* only Curtis 4-shaft) turbines.   Designed H.P. 64,000 = 26 kts.
Boilers : See *Notes*. Fuel : About 4,500 tons oil.

HARUNA. (To show anti-flare caps to funnels as fitted in 1930.)   *Photo* 1930.

Armour (Krupp) :
   8″ Belt (amidships) ......
   3″ Belt (ends) ....
   6″ Upper belt .... }
   6″ Battery ....
   9″, 6″, 5″ Bulkheads (*f*)
   8″, 6″ Bulkheads (*aft*.)
   10″— ″ Barbettes ......
   9″— ″Gunhouses ......
   ..″ C.T. base ......
   10″ C.T. (″ hood) ......
   ″ Fore comm. tube ..
   6″ Torpedo con. tower
   ″ Tube (C.T. tower) ...

Armour (H.T. ?) :
Decks : { ″ Forecastle ....
       2¾″ Main ....
       ″ Middle ....
       ″ Lower ....
Special Protection H.T.
Torpedo Protection Bulkheads.
   During reconstruction 4″ was added to deck protection, raising displacement by 3,000 tons.

These Notes are not from any official data.

Gunnery Notes.—In *Kongo* guns are Vickers models ; but in other three ships all calibres are of Japanese manufacture. *Kongo* has combined Vickers (hydraulic) and Janney-Williams (electric) manœuvring systems for her barbettes ; there is also a small auxiliary hydraulic installation, generally used for cleaning purposes, which can be used in emergency for working the 14-inch guns. Maximum elevation of 14 inch guns, 18°.

Armour Notes.—Main belt is 12′ 5″ deep, 8″ thick, and extends between Barbettes Nos. 1 and 4.* Upper belt between Barbettes Nos. 1 and 3, 6″ thick, and carried up to forecastle deck. Bulkheads : Main belt is closed by diagonal bulkheads of 8″—6″ aft and by a 6″—5″ bulkhead forward. Upper belt closed by 6″ bulkhead aft and 9″—6″ bulkhead forward. There is also a narrow 3 inch strip of armour, 2 feet 6 inch deep under whole length of main belt ; this is not shown on plans.

Anti-Torpedo Protection Notes.—Internal sub-division by longitudinal and cross bulkheads. Extra protection given by armour to all magazine spaces. Port and starboard engine rooms are divided by an unpierced longitudinal bulkhead along keel-line. It is said contract for *Kongo* stipulated she should float with 50 feet of her side blown away, should not heel more than 11°, and *automatically* regain the vertical in a specified length of time, though at an increased draught.

Torpedo Notes.—Tubes are twin submerged type, at varying levels, some being only 6 feet below waterline. Except in the case of the tubes in wake of No. 3 Barbette, starboard Tube is before Port Tube. *Kongo* has combined hydraulic and electrically-operated tubes. In *Haruna*, tubes are Armstrong 21-inch side-loading, hydraulically operated.

Engineering Notes.—In *Kongo*, and *Kirishima* Parsons turbines have H.P. rotors on outboard shafts and L.P. on inner shafts, with astern turbines aft and in same casing. Reconstruction included new Kampon boilers.

Name	Builder	Machinery	Laid down	Completed	Trials F.P.	Turbine	Boilers	Re-fit	1st Period ended
Kongo	Vickers	Vickers	Jan.'11	Aug.'13		Parsons	Kampon	1925	1921
Haruna	Kawasaki	Kawasaki	Mar.'12	Mar.'15		Curtis	Kampon	1926	1923
Kirishima	Mitsu Bishi	Mitsu Bishi	Mar.'12	Apr.'15		Parsons		1925	1923

General Notes.—*Kongo* 1910-11 Programme, others 1911-12 Programme. Designed by Sir George Thurston. For *Haruna* 30% of material was imported and erected in Japan. 3 planes added to equipment, 1927. *Haruna* refitted 1926-28, and bulges added, reducing speed by over a knot. Funnels altered on conversion to oil fuel only, appearance having previously been like *Hiyei*. *Kirishima* and *Kongo* now altered similarly

313

KIRISHIMA.   (note height of S.L. before funnel.)   1931 *Official Photo.*

HARUNA.   (*note "bulges"*)   1928 *Photo.*

HARUNA.   1929 *Photo.*   HARUNA.   1928 *Photo.*

RYUJO (Yokohama D.Y., April 2, 1931).

Displacement, 7,600 tons.

Length 548 feet. Beam 60½ feet. Draught 15⅓ feet.

Complement 600.

Guns : **12**—5·1 inch (12·7 cm.) AA.

Machinery : Geared turbines. Kampon boilers. D.H.P. 40,000 = 25 kts. Laid down in Jan:, 1930. To be completed in 1932.

RYUJO.

Photo, April, 1931.

KAGA

KAGA.

1929 *Photo.*

KAGA.

1931 *Photo*

がか   **KAGA** (Kawasaki Co., Kobe, 17th Nov., 1921).

Displacement, 28,100 tons.

Length (*p.p.*) 715 feet.   Beam $102\frac{3}{4}$ feet.   Draught $21\frac{1}{3}$ feet.

KAGA.

1930 *Photo.*

Guns: Armour :
- **10**—8 inch.   ″ Belt.
- **4**—4.7 inch.   ″ Gunhouses.
- **12**—4.7 inch AA.

Note to plan.—8″ turrets now placed a deck higher.

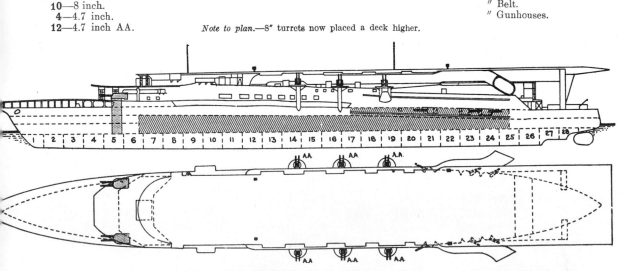

Machinery: Geared turbines.   Designed S.H.P. 91,000 = 25 kts.   (23 kts. was to have been speed originally).   Fuel :

Notes .—Originally laid down July 20th, 1920, as a battleship of 39,900 tons, but has been converted into an aircraft carrier as the result of the Washington Treaty: Smoke is discharged through huge trunks on both sides, extending for nearly half the length of the ship and turning outboard towards the stern: There is accommodation for 60 planes.

316

KAGA.

1930 *Photo.*

ぎかあ AKAGI (Kure Dockyard, April 22nd, 1925).

Displacement : 28,100 tons.   Length (*p.p.*), 763 feet.   Beam, 92 feet.   Draught, 21¼ feet.

| 3—8″ Guns | AA. Guns. | AA. Guns. | AA. Guns. | Funnels. | 8″ Turret. | 1930 *Photo.* |

Guns :
10—8 inch
4—4.7 inch
12—4.7 inch AA.

Armour :
″ Belt.
″ Gunhouses.

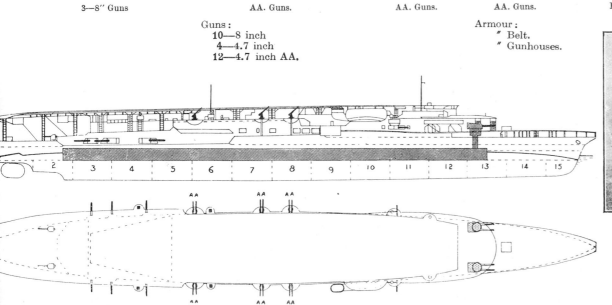

Turrets forward now raised a deck higher.

AKAGI   1929 *Photo, Enseigne de Vaisseau Lafargue.*

Machinery : Geared turbines. Original designed S.H.P. 131,200=28.5 kts. (likely to be exceeded).   Fuel: Coal + oil in original design.

Notes.—Originally laid down on 6th Dec., 1920, as battle cruiser of 42,000 tons, but converted into aircraft carrier as result of Washington Treaty. Funnels are arranged on starboard side so that the foremost (which is internally divided into four) is trunked outward and downward amidships, while the second projects slightly above flight deck abaft of the first. Though she has accommodation for 50 planes, only about 30 are carried normally. There are 2 aircraft lifts on starboard side, one abaft funnels and a smaller one right astern.

Sister ship, *Amagi,* laid down at Yokosuka Dockyard, and launched late in 1922, was so badly damaged by earthquake and fire, September, 1923, that her construction was abandoned, and *Kaga's* hull was appropriated to replace her.

AIRCRAFT CARRIER.

1930 *Photo.*

AKAGI

1929 *Photo.*

1929 *Photo.*

(Note absence of funnels on port side.)

1931 *Photo.*

HOSHO with funnels lowered to horizontal position.

Photo added 1927.

HOSHO.

Photo 1931.

HOSHO.
(Plan reversed to illustrate funnel arrangement.)

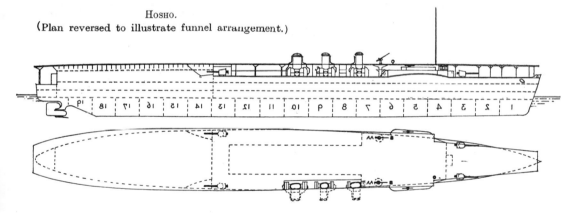

HOSHO. Starboard side amidships.

1925 *Photo, by courtesy of the Navy Dept., Tokyo.*

HOSHO (as modified).

Note removal of former island superstructure and biped mast.

1925 *Photo, by courtesy of the Navy Dept., Tokyo.*

HOSHO (Asano Co., Tsurumi, 14th November, 1921). Displacement, 9,458 tons. (About 10,000 *full load*). Dimensions: 510 (*p.p.*) × 62 × 20¼ feet. Guns: **4**—5·5 inch, **2**—3 inch AA. 2 geared turbines. S.H.P. 30,000 = 25 kts. 8 Kampon boilers. Fuel: Oil only, 550 tons. Can carry 26 seaplanes with all accessories, etc. Sperry gyro-stabiliser fitted. 2 searchlights.

Note.—Laid down 16th December, 1920; completed December, 1922. First Period ends Dec. 1930. The building of a second ship of this type (to have been named *Shokaku*) was cancelled owing to Washington Treaty.

(NACHI CLASS—8 SHIPS.)

NACHI (June 15th, 1927), **MYOKO** (April 16th, 1927), **ASHIGARA** (May 22nd, 1928),
HAGURO (March 24th, 1928), **ATAGO** (June 16th, 1930), **TAKAO** (May 12th, 1930),
     CHOKAI (April 5, 1931), **MAYA** (Nov. 8, 1930).

Standard displacement, 10,000 tons.

Complement, 692.

Length (*p.p.*), 630 feet. Beam, 57 feet. Draught, 16½ feet.

NACHI. (p. 306.)

1929 *P*

ns :
0—8 inch, 50 cal.
6—4.7 inch AA.
st 4 ships have only 4—4.7 in.)
rpedo tubes (21 inch) :
2 *above water.*
(Last 4 ships have 6 only).

Armour (unofficial) :
     3-4″ Belt ....
     Deck ....
     Turrets ....

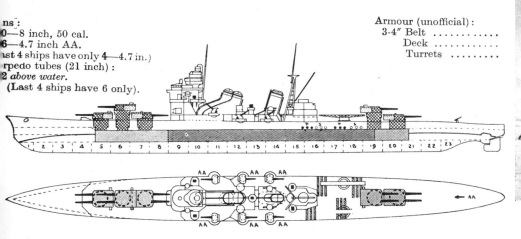

Machinery : Geared turbines. Boilers : Kampon. S.H.P. 130,000 = 33 kts. *max.* (32 kts.
at deep load). Oil : 2,000 tons. Radius at 14-15 kts. : 14,000 miles.

otes.—Provided for under 1923 and later Programmes. Triple hull, designed to give greatest possible protection against
submarines. Vertical and deck protection over boiler and machinery spaces is 410 feet long. Guns are a new model
with very high muzzle velocity. 4 planes carried. To cost £2,200,000 each.

Name	Builder	Machinery	Laid down	Completed	Trials
Nachi	Kure	Kure	26/11/24	Nov. 1928	
Myoko	Yokosuka	Yokosuka	25/10/24	31st July, 1929	
Ashigara	Kawasaki, Kobe	Kure	—/4/25	March, 1929	
Haguro	Mitsu Bishi	Yokosuka	—/3/25	April, 1929	
Atago	Kure	Kure	1926	} To be 1931	
Takao	Yokosuka	Yokosuka	1926		
Chokai	Mitsu Bishi	Mitsu Bishi	(?) 5/28		
Maya	Kawasaki, Kobe	Kawasaki	26/3/28	To be 1932	

FORE FUNNEL MARKINGS, 1931 :

     MYOKO   1 white band.

     NACHI   2 white bands.

     ASHIGARA   3 white bands.

     HAGURO   1 thick and 1 thin white band.

ASHIGARA.

1931 *P*

HAGURO.

1930 *Photo.*

MYOKO.

1930 *Photo.*

NACHI.

1929 *Photo.*

(KINUGASA CLASS—2 SHIPS.)

KINUGASA (Oct. 24th, 1926), **AOBA** (Sept. 24th, 1926).

Standard Displacement, 7,100 tons. Complement, 604.

Length (*w.l.*), 580 feet. Beam, $50\frac{3}{4}$ feet. Draught, $14\frac{3}{4}$ feet.

AOBA.   1927 *Photo* (added 1928).

Guns :
6—8 inch.
4—4.7 inch AA.
2—M.G.
Torpedo tubes (21 inch):
12 *above water*.

Armour :
? Side amidships ....
2″ Deck ....
?″ Turrets ....

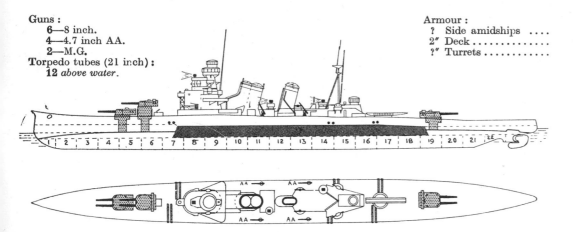

Machinery : Geared turbines. Boilers : Kampon. S.H.P. 95,000 = 33 kts. Coal and oil : 1,600 tons. 2 planes carried.

Name	Builder	Machinery	Laid down	Completed	Trials
Kinugasa	Kawasaki, Kobe	Kawasaki	Jan., 1924	Sept., 1927	
Aoba	Mitsu Bishi, Nagasaki	Mitsu Bishi	Feb., 1924	Dec., 1927	

Notes.—Provided for under 1923 Programme. 2 planes carried. Although of same general design as *Kako* class, they differ in arrangement of armament.

KINUGASA.   1928 *Photo Navy Dept.*

FIRST CLASS CRUISERS.

AOBA.   Photo, Oct., 1927.

AOBA.   1928 Photo.

With catapult fitted.   1928 Photo.

1922 FIRST CLASS CRUISERS. (*Junyokan.*)

(KAKO CLASS—2 SHIPS.)

KAKO (10th April, 1925), **FURUTAKA** (26th Feb., 1925).

Standard displacement, 7100 tons. Complement, 604.

Length (*w.l.*), 580 feet. Beam, $50\frac{3}{4}$ feet. Draught, $14\frac{3}{4}$ feet.

Guns :
6—8 inch.
4—3 inch AA.
2 M.G.
Torpedo tubes (21 inch) :
12 *above water.*
Catapult :
2 'planes.

Armour :
?" Side amidships.........
2" Deck ....
?" Turrets ....

KAKO. Detail view before alteration to funnels.

Photo added 1926.

Machinery : Geared turbines. Boilers : Kampon. S.H.P. 95,000 = 33 kts. Fuel : 400 tons coal, 1200 tons oil.

FURUTAKA, after refit. (Funnels raised and S.L. rearranged).

Name	Builder	Machinery	Laid down	Completed	Trials
Kako	Kawasaki, Kobe	Kawasaki	Jan., 1923	} 1926.	
Furutaka	Mitsu Bishi, Nagasaki	Mitsu Bishi	Dec., 1922		

General Notes.—Provided for under 1922 Programme. A most original design, the undulating deck line, gun disposition in six single turrets, curious bridge work and mast, trunked funnels, and angled hull side all being noteworthy. Suffer from limited axial gun fire and it is reported that they are deficient in sea-going qualities. *Aoba* and *Nachi* designs have been developed from *Kako*, and the outstanding feature of the type is the sacrifice of accommodation and freeboard in order to utilise tonnage for military qualities.

Appearance Notes.—These ships and *Kinugasa* class are now differentiated thus :—

KAKO......1 white band on after funnel.
FURUTAKA..2 ,,   ,,   ,,
AOBA ......1 red   ,,   ,,   ,,
KINUGASA..2 ,,   ,,   ,,

FURUTAKA.   *Photo added 1927.*

KAKO.   1930 *Photo.*

FURUTAKA.   *June, 1928 Photo.*

KASUGA.

Photo 1931.

6 inch guns removed from main deck and bridge altered.

KASUGA (October, 1902).　　　かすか

Displacement, 7,080 tons.　Complement, 595.

Dimensions as *Nisshin.*

Guns :　　　　　　　　　　　　　Armour :
　　1—10 inch.　　　　　　　　　　as *Nisshin.*
　　2—8 inch 45 cal.
　　4—6 inch 45 cal.
　　4—3 inch AA.
　　2 M.G.

Torpedo Tubes.

Machinery, Boilers, H.P., Speed and Fuel as *Nisshin.*

NISSHIN.

1919 *Photo, Seward, Weymouth.*

(*Now rated as First Class Coast Defence Vessels.*)

んしつに　　　**NISSHIN** (Feb., 1903)

Displacement, 7080 tons.　Complement, 610.

Length (*waterline*), 357 feet.　Beam, 61 feet 11 ins.　*Maximum* draught, 25¼ feet.

Guns (Armstrong) :　　　　　Armour (Terni) :
　　　　　　　　　　　　　　　　6″ Belt (amidships)　......
　　4—8 inch, 45 cal.　　　　4½″ Belt (ends)　...........
　14—6 inch, 45 cal.　　　　1½″ Deck (on slopes)......
　　4—3 inch AA.　　　　　　5½″ Turrets　..............
　　2 Maxims.　　　　　　　　5½″ Turret bases (N.C.)...
Torpedo tubes (18 inch) :　　6″ Lower deck side　......
　4 *above water* (incasemates).　4½″Lower deck bulkheads
　　　　　　　　　　　　　　　　6″ Battery (N.C.)　.........
　　　　　　　　　　　　　　　　4½″ Battery (bulkheads)...
　　　　　　　　　　　　　　　　4¾″ Conning tower　......

Machinery : 2 sets 3 cylinder vertical triple expansion.　2 screws.　Boilers : 12 Kampon.
Designed H.P. 13,500 = 20 kts.　Coal : *normal,* 650 tons ; *maximum,* 1,200 tons.　4 searchlights.

Nisshin and *Kasuga*—Laid down for Argentina by Ansaldo, Genoa, in 1902, as the *Moreno* and *Rivadavia.*
Purchased end of 1903 by Japan for £760,000, just before outbreak of Russo-Japanese War.

YAKUMO.   1929 *Photo.*

もくや **YAKUMO** (Vulcan Co., 1899). Displacement, 9010 tons. Complement, 698. Length (*p.p.*), 390 feet. Beam, 64¼ feet. *Mean draught*, 23¾ feet. Length *over all*, 434 feet. Guns: 4—8 inch, 40 cal., 8—6 inch, 40 cal., 6—3 inch, 4. S.L. Torpedo tubes (18 inch): 4 *submerged*. Armour (Krupp): 7″ Belt (amidships), 3½″ Belt (ends), 2½″ Deck (slopes), 6″ Turrets (N.C.), 6″ Turret bases (N.C.), 5″ Lower deck side, 6″ Casemates (8), 10″ Conning tower. (Total weight, 2040 tons.) Machinery: 2 sets vertical triple expansion. 2 screws. Boilers: 24 Belleville. Designed H.P. 15,500 = 20½ kts. Coal: *normal* 550 tons; *max.* 1200 tons. Third Period expired 1924. Employed as Midshipmen's Training Ship.

IWATE.   1929 *Photo.*

もつい **IDZUMO** (Armstrong, 1899) & てばい **IWATE** (Armstrong, 1900). Displacement, 9180 tons. Complement, 658. Length (*p.p.*), 400 feet. Beam, 68½ feet. *Max.* draught, 24¼ feet. Length *over all*, 434 feet. Guns (Armstrong): 4—8 inch, 40 cal., 8—6 inch, 40 cal., 1—3 inch AA., 5—3 inch, 3 M.G., 4 S.L. Torpedo tubes: 4 *submerged*. Armour (Krupp): 7″ Belt (amidship), 3½″ Belt (ends), 2½″ Deck (slopes), 5″ Lower deck (redoubt), 6″ Turrets and bases, 6″ Casemates, 14″ Conning tower. (Total 2100 tons.) Machinery by Humphry and Tennant: 2 sets 4 cylinder triple expansion. 2 screws. Boilers: Belleville. Designed H.P. 16,000 = 20·75 kts. Coal: *normal* 550 tons; *maximum* 1400 tons. Begun at Elswick 1898-99, and completed 1900-01. Third Periods expired 1924-25. *Iwate* employed as Cadets Training Ship, *Idzumo* as Midshipmen's Training Ship.

     1931 *Photo, Official*

まつあ **ADZUMA** (St. Nazaire, 1899). Displacement, 9227 tons. Complement, 644. Length (*waterline*), 430 feet. Beam, 59½ feet. *Maximum* draught, 25 feet. Length *over all*, 452½ feet. Guns (Armstrong): 4—8 inch, 40 cal., 8—6 inch, 40 cal., 6—3 inch, 4 S.L. Torpedo tubes: 4 *submerged*. Armour (Krupp mostly): 7″ Belt (amidships), 3½″ Belt (ends), 2½″ Deck (on slopes), 6″ Turrets and bases (H.N.), 6″ Casemates (H.N.), 5″ Side above belt. (Total weight, 2000 tons). Machinery: 2 sets vertical triple expansion. 2 screws. Boilers: 24 Belleville. Designed H.P. 17,000 = 21 kts. Coal: *normal* 600 tons; *maximum* 1200 tons. Third Period expired 1924.

     1924 *Photo, I. Perman, Esq.*

まさあ **ASAMA** (March, 1898). Displacement, 9240 tons. Complement, 648. Length (*o.a.*), 442 feet. Beam, 67¼ feet. *Maximum* draught, 24¼ feet. Guns (Armstrong): 4—8 inch, 40 cal., 8—6 inch, 40 cal., 5—3 inch AA., 4—2½ pdr. Torpedo tubes (18 inch): 4 (*submerged*). Armour (Harvey-nickel): 7″ Belt (amidships), 3½″ Belt (ends), 2″ Deck (slopes), 5″ Upper belt (amidships), 3½″ Bulkheads to it, 6″ Turrets and bases, 6″ Casemates (10), 14″ Conning tower (Total, 2100 tons). Machinery: 2 sets 4-cylinder triple expansion. 2 screws. Boilers: 16 Miyabara. Designed H.P. *forced* 18,000 = 21½ kts. Coal: *normal* 550 tons, *maximum* 1400 tons. 3 S.L. Built by Armstrong. Very "handy" ship. *Asama* was badly damaged by grounding on Pacific Coast of Central America, in December of 1914. Was salved, repaired and refitted. Third Period expired 1923. Employed as Cadets Training Ship.

(Jintsu Class—3 Ships.)

うづんじ　かな

JINTSU (8th Dec., 1923), **NAKA** (24th March, 1925),

いだんせ

SENDAI (30th Oct., 1923).

Standard displacement, 5195 tons. Complement, 450.

Length (*p.p.*), 500 feet ; (*o.a.*) 535 feet. Beam, 46¾ feet.
Draught, 15 feet 10½ ins.

Guns :
7—5.5 inch, 50 cal.
3—3 inch, 13 pdr., 40 cal.
AA.
2 M.G.

Torpedo tubes :
8—21 inch, *above water.*

Armour :
2″ Side (amidships) ....
2″ C.T. ....
Planes carried :
One.

SENDAI (*Jintsu* was similar, but after collision bow has been rebuilt as *Naka*).

Photo added 1926.

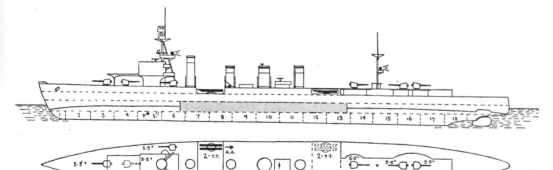

NAKA (Note bow).

Photo added 1927.

Machinery : 4 geared turbines. 4 screws. Boilers : 16 Kampon. Designed S.H.P. 90,000
= 33 kts. Fuel : 350 tons *normal*, 1500 tons *max.*

Name	Builder	Machinery	Begun	Completed	Trials	1st Period
Jintsu	Kawasaki, Kobe	Kawasaki	4 Aug., '22	31 July, '25		1925-33
Sendai	Mitsu Bishi, Nagasaki	Mitsu Bishi	16 Feb., '22	29 Apr., '24		1924-32
Naka	Yokohama Dock Co.	Mitsu Bishi	24 May, '24	30 Nov., '25		1926-34

General Notes.—Slightly enlarged and improved editions of *Natori* class on following page. Laying down of *Naka*
was delayed by earthquake of Sept., 1923. Catapult fitted to flight platform forward, 1929. Foremost boiler
is fitted for mixed firing.

SENDAI.

1925 *Photo, by courtesy of the Navy Dept., Tokyo.*

"NATORI" CLASS (6 SHIPS).

づすい　　らがな

ISUDZU (29th Oct., 1921).　　NAGARA (25th April, 1921).

りとな　　らゆ

NATORI (16th Feb., 1922).　　YURA (15th Feb., 1922).

ぬき　　まくぶあ

KINU (29th May, 1922).　　ABUKUMA (16th March, 1923).

Standard displacement, 5170 tons.　Comp., 438.

Length (*p.p.*), 500 feet, (*o.a.*) 535 feet.　Beam, 46¾ feet.
Draught, 15 feet 10½ ins.

Guns :—　　　　　　　　　　　Armour :
7—5.5 inch, 50 cal.　　　　　　2″ Side (amidships).
3—3 inch, 13 pdr. 40 cal.　　　　2″ C.T.
　AA.　　　　　　　　　　Planes carried :
2 M.G.　　　　　　　　　　One.
Torpedo tubes : (21 inch)
8 (*above water*).

KINU.

Photo added 1927.

Plan : Details generally as *Kuma*, but with aircraft hangar added forward.

Catapult is now being installed on flight platform forward.

Machinery : 4 geared turbines.　4 screws.　Boilers : 12 Kampon,
8 oil and 4 coal burning.　Designed S.H.P. 90,000 = 33 kts.
Fuel : 350 tons *normal*, 1500 tons *max.*

YURA.　(Showing catapult on flight platform).

1930 Photo.

General Notes.—Commencement authorised by 1919 Naval Programme.　Cost of each ship is said to be £1,750,000.

Name	Builder	Machinery	Begun	Completed	Trials (unofficial)	First Period
Isudzu	Uraga Dock Co.	Mitsu Bishi	10 Aug., '20	Aug., '23		1923-31
Nagara	Sasebo D.Y.	Kawasaki	9 Sept., '20	April, '22	65,000 = 33.4	1922-30
Natori	Mitsu Bishi, Nagasaki	Mitsu Bishi	14 Dec., '20	Sept., '22		1922-30
Kinu	Kawasaki Co., Kobe	Kawasaki	17 Jan., '21	Nov., '22		1922-30
Yura	Sasebo D.Y.	Kawasaki	21 May, '21	March, '23		1923-31
Abukuma	Uraga Dock Co.	Mitsu Bishi	8 Dec., '21	Sept., '23		1923-31

329

KUMA CLASS—5 SHIPS.

まく **KUMA** (July 14th, 1919), また **TAMA** (Feb. 10th, 1920),

るほね **OHI** (July 15th, 1920),

みかたき **KITAKAMI** (July 3rd, 1920), そき **KISO** (Dec. 14th, 1920).

Standard displacement, 5100 tons. Complement, 439.
Length (*p.p.*), 500 feet (*o.a.*), 535 feet. Beam, 46¾ feet. *Mean* draught, 15¾ feet.

KISO (fitted with anti-flare tops to funnels).

1931 *Photo.*

Guns :
 7—5.5 inch, 50 cal.
 3—3 inch (13 pdr.), 40 cal.
 — M.G.
Torpedo tubes (21 inch) :
 8 *above water.*
Searchlights :
 3—30 inch.
Mines :
 May be carried.

Armour (*unofficial*) :
 2″ (H.T.) Side (amidships).......
 2″ C T. ....

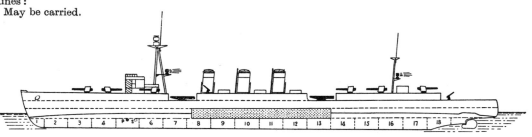

Ahead : **3**—5.5 inch. Broadside : **6**—5·5 inch, **4**—21 inch T.T. Astern : **1**—5.5 inch.

Machinery : Geared Parsons or Curtis Turbines. 4 screws. Boilers : 12 Kampon, 10 oil fuel, 2 mixed firing. Designed H.P. 90,000 = 33 kts. Fuel : *normal,* 350 tons ; *maximum,* about 1500 tons = 8500 miles at 10 kts.

Name	Builder	Machinery	Laid down	Completed	Second Period	First Trials.	Boilers.
Ohi	Kawasaki	Kawasaki	24/11/19	Sep., '21			
Kitakami	Sasebo D.Y.	Kawasaki	Sep., '19	Apl., '21	1929-37	—34	All 12 Kampon.
Kiso	{ Mitsubishi { Nagasaki	Mitsubishi	10/6/19	May, '21			
Kuma	Sasebo D.Y.	Kawasaki.	Aug. '18	Aug. '20	1928-36		
Tama	{ Mitsubishi { Nagasaki	Mitsubishi	Aug. '18	Jan., '21	1929-37		

General Notes.—No official data published concerning trials, but are reported to have averaged about 64,500 and about 33 kts. Cost about £1,000,000 each. An aeroplane was added to the equipment of these ships in 1927.

OHI.   1930 *Photo.*

General Notes.—*Kuma* and *Tama* begun under the 1917 Naval Programme ; *Ohi, Kitakami, Kiso* under 1918 Programme. Completion of *Ohi* delayed by failure of one of her engines when she was running trials at end of Dec., 1920. Said to be very efficiently sub-divided and the general scheme of protection has been developed since the war. Fuel supply is somewhat above the average = 6,000 miles at 15 kts., and between 1000 and 1100 miles at full speed.

1928 Photo.

Photo added 1926.

YUBARI (5th March, 1923).

Standard displacement, 2890 tons.   Complement, 328.
Length (*p.p.*), 435 feet.   Beam, 39½ feet.   Draught, 11 feet 9 ins.
Guns :

6—5·5 inch, 50 cal.	Armour (unofficial) :
1—3 inch AA.	2″ side (H.T.)
2—M.G.	

Torpedo tubes (21 inch) :
4 (*above water*).

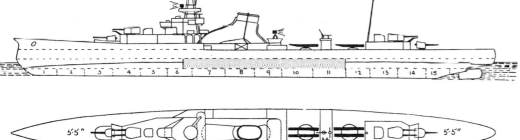

Machinery : Turbine. 3 screws. Boilers : 8 Kampon (coal and oil-burning).   Designed S.H.P. 50,000 = 33 kts. Fuel :   tons.
2 searchlights.

Note.—Laid down 5th of June, 1922, at Sasebo Dockyard. Completed 1924. First Period, 1924-32.

Torpedo Notes.—Tubes are arranged so that they can be moved to either broadside.

Engineering Notes.—Machinery was built by Sasebo Dockyard.

YUBARI.

Photo added 1928

Special Note.

This remarkable vessel represents an attempt on the part of Japanese naval constructors to combine, on a displacement of 2,890 tons, speed and offensive power little inferior to those of "Kuma" and "Natori" types. She is employed on Flotilla Leader duties at present. In appearance, she is quite unlike any other Cruiser in existence.

(Tenryu Class—2 Ships.)

たつた TATSUTA (29th May, 1918) & うりんて TENRYU (11th Mar., 1918).

Standard displacement, 3230 tons. Complement, 332.

Length (*o.a.*): 468 feet (*p.p.*), 440 feet. Beam: $40\frac{3}{4}$ feet. *Mean* draught: 13 feet.

Guns:
4—5·5 inch, 50 cal.
1—3 inch (13 pdr.) 40 cal. A.A.
2 M.G.
Torpedo tubes:
6 *above water* in two triple
U.D. mountings.
Searchlights:
2—30 inch.
Mines:
May be carried.

Armour (unofficial):
2" or $1\frac{1}{2}$" (H.T.) Side
amidships ....
—" Deck (H.T.) at
ends ....
—" C.T. ....

TATSUTA.

1921 *Photo, Navy Department, Tokyo.*

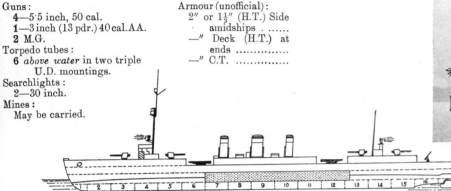

Ahead:
1—5·5 in.

Broadside: 4—5·5 in., 6—21 in. T.T.

Astern:
1—5·5 in.

Machinery: Parsons or Curtis turbines. 3 screws. Boilers: 10 Kampon. Designed H.P. 51,000 = 31 kts. Fuel: Coal and oil, *normal*, ? tons; *maximum*, 900 tons = 6000 miles at 10 kts. (unofficial).

Name	Builder	Machinery	Laid down	Completed	2nd Period	Trials	Boilers
Tatsuta	Sasebo D.Y.	Kawasaki	July, '17	31 Aug.,'19	1927—35		Kampon
Tenryu	Yokosuka D.Y.	Mitsu Bishi	May, '17	20 Nov., '19	1927—35	51,000 = 33 kts.	

General Notes.—Begun under the 1916 Naval Programme. Are said to be exceptionally fast and handy ships, able to turn in a little less than their own lengths. In design are simply enlarged destroyers, and very lightly framed. Both are employed as Flotilla Leaders.

TENRYU. (Now has tripod foremast.)

1923 *Photo, Navy Department, Tokyo.*

TATSUTA. (Blast screen added forward of third gun.)

Photo added 1926.

332

HIRADO.

1921 *Photo, Navy Dept., Tokyo.*

とらひ **HIRADO** (June, 1911), きはや **YAHAGI** (Oct., 1911).

Standard displacement 4400 tons. Complement, 452.

Length (*p.p.*), 440 feet; (*o.a.*), 475 feet. Beam, 46½ feet. *Max.* draught, 17⅔ feet.

YAHAGI.

1931 *Photo.*

Guns :
  8—6 inch, 50 cal.
  2—3 inch AA.
  2 M.G.
Torpedo tubes (18 inch) :
  3 *above water.*
    (363 tons.)

Armour :
  3″ Deck (amidships)
  2″ Deck (ends) ......
  4″ Conning tower...
    (439 tons.)
Weight of hull, etc., 2278 tons.

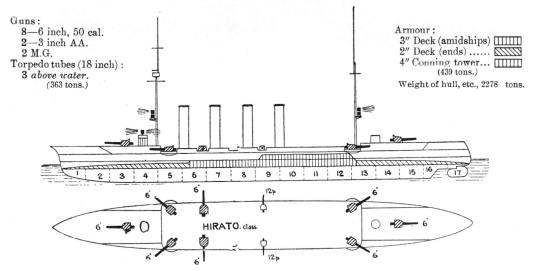

HIRATO. class.

Machinery : Curtis turbines ; (2 screws), except *Yahagi*, Parsons turbines. (4 screws). Boilers :
16 Kampon. Designed H.P. 22,500 = 26 kts. Coal : *normal* 500 tons ; *maximum* 900 tons + 300 oil =
10,000 miles at 10 kts.

Name	Builder	Machinery	Laid down	Completed	Third Period	Trials H.P. = kts.	Boilers
Hirado	Kawasaki Co.	Kawasaki Co.	Aug.,'10	June'12	1928-36	....	Kampon
Yahagi	Mitsu Bishi	Mitsu Bishi	June,'10	July,'12	1928-36	27,408 = 26.8	in all.

DESTROYERS.
67 1st Class Destroyers (over 1000 tons).
24 Fubuki Class.

ASAGIRI.

Fubuki to *Isonami* have cowls athwart funnels like *Hatsuyuki*: remainder have the collar ventilators around funnels.

1931 *Photo.*

24 boats

Fubuki ..	1927	*Uranami* ..	1928	*Ayanami*		*Yugiri* .. 1930	*Akatsuki*
Shirayuki		*Shinonome*		*Asagiri*		*Ushio*	*Hibiki*
Hatsuyuki	}1928	*Usugumo*	}1927	*Amagiri*	}1929	*Oboro*	*Ikadsuchi*
Miyuki		*Shirakumo*		*Sagiri*		*Akebono*	*Inadzuma*
Murakuma		*Isonami*		*Shikinami*		*Sazanami*	

Authorised under 1926 and subsequent sections of the Fleet. Replenishment Law. 1700 tons (1850 tons full load).
Dimensions: 367½ × 34 × 10¾ feet. Armament: **6**—5.1 (12.7 C.M.), 50 cal., **2** AA. M.G. and **9**—21 inch tubes.
Machinery: Parsons geared turbines. Boilers: Kampon. H.P. 50,000 = 35 kts. Oil: 400 tons ? Complement, 197.

Notes.—Builders not fully advised, but *Fubuki*, *Hatsuyuki* and *Shikinami* are by Maidzuru D.Y.; *Shirayuki* by Yokohama D.Y. Co.; *Miyuki*, *Ushio*, *Isonami* by Uraga D. Co.; *Shinonome* and *Asagiri* by Sasebo D.Y.; *Usugumo* and *Amagiri* by Ishikawajima Co.; *Shirakumo*, *Murakuma*, *Yugiri*, *Akebono* by Fujinagata Co.

Meanings of some of above names are as follows :—

Fubuki	Snowstorm	*Shinonome*	Day dawn	*Amagiri*	Heaven mist
Shirayuki	White snow	*Usugumo*	Fleecy clouds	*Sagiri*	Valley mist
Hatsuyuki	First snow of winter	*Shirakumo*	White cloud	*Yugiri*	Evening mist
Murakuma	Cloud clusters	*Asagiri*	Morning mis	*Shikinami*	Waves chasing each other.
				Ushio.	The tide.

AYANAMI (*Shikinami* similar).

1930 *Photo.*

(Note new type of gunhouse and ventilators around funnels).

ASAGIRI.

1931 *Photo.*

HATSUYUKI.

1930 *Photo.*

Fubuki class—*continued.*

1929 *Photo.*

SHINONOME.

1930 *Photo.*

SHIRAKUMO (note shields to torpedo tubes).

1931 *Photo.*

12 Mutsuki Class.

KISARAGI.

Photo added 1927.

UTSUKI.

Photo added 1927.

12 boats : **Mutsuki** (ex-No. 19), (by Sasebo Dockyard), **Kisaragi** (ex-No. 21), (by Maidzuru Dockyard), **Yayoi** (ex-No. 23), (by Uraga Dock Co.), **Utsuki** (ex-No. 25), (by Ishikawajima Co.), **Satsuki** (ex-No. 27), (by Fujinagata Co.,) **Minatsuki** (Uraga Dock Co.), **Fumitsuki** (Fujinagata Co.), **Nagatsuki** (Ishikawajima Co.), **Kikutsuki** (Maidzuru Dkyd.), **Mikadzuki** (Sasebo Dkyd.), **Mochidzuki** (Uraga Dock Co.), **Yudzuki** (Fujinagata Co.), (ex-Nos. 28–34). Enlarged editions of *Kamikaze.* Built under 1923, 1924 and 1925 sections of Navy Law. 1315 tons. Dimensions : 320 (*p.p.*) × 30 × 9⅝ feet (*max.* draught). Armament : 4—4.7 inch, 50 cal., 2 AA. M.G and 6—21 inch tubes (in triple deck mountings). 3 S.L. Machinery : Parsons 4-shaft turbines. 4 Kampon boilers. Designed H.P. 40,000 = 34 kts. Oil : 350 tons. Endurance : 4000 miles at 15 kts. Complement, 150.

Name.	Begun.	Launch.	Comp.	Name.		Begun.	Launch.	Comp.
Minatsuki	24/3/25	25/5/26	22/3/27	Mutsuki	..	21/5/24	23/7/25	25/3/26
Fumitsuki	20/10/24	16/2/26	3/7/26	Kisaragi	..	3/6/24	5/6/25	21/12/25
Nagatsuki	16/4/25	6/10/26	30/4/27	Yayoi	..	11/1/24	11/7/25	28/8/26
Kikutsuki..	15/6/25	15/5/26	20/11/26	Utsuki	..	11/1/24	15/10/25	14/9/26
Mikadzuki	21/8/25	12/7/26	7/5/27	Satsuki	..	1/12/23	25/3/25	15/11/25
Mochidzuki	23/3/26	28/4/27	31/10/27					
Yudzuki ..	27/11/26	4/6/27	25/7/27					

Note.—These 12 destroyers bear poetical names of the 12 months of the year. U.S. Navy Dept. official data, June 1930, credits *Mochidzuki, Yudzuki, Minatsuki, Mikadzuki, Nagatsuki* with six 5·1″ guns.

12 Kamikaze Class.

ASAKAZE.

1925 *Photo, by courtesy of the Navy Dept., Tokyo.*

HARUKAZE.

Photo added 1927.

12 boats : *Kamikaze* (ex-No. 1) and ***Asakaze*** (ex-No. 3) (both by Mitsu Bishi, Z.K.), ***Harukaze*** (ex-No. 5), ***Matsukaze*** (ex-No. 7), ***Hatakaze*** (ex-No. 9), (all three by Maidzuru D.Y.), ***Oite*** (ex-No. 11), (by Uraga Dock Co.), ***Hayate*** (ex-No. 13), (by Ishikawajima Co.), ***Asanagi*** (ex-No. 15), (by Fujinagata Co.), ***Yunagi*** (ex-No. 17), (by Sasebo Dockyard.) ***Namikaze, Numakaze, Nokaze.*** (all by Maidzurd Dockyard).
Of same general design as *Shiokaze* class. Built under 1921 and 1922 Sections of Navy Law. 1270 tons. Dimensions : 320 (*p.p.*) × 30 × $9\frac{7}{12}$ feet (*max. draught*). Armament : 4—4.7 inch, 50 cal., 2 AA. M.G. and 6—21 inch torpedo tubes. 2 S.L. Machinery : Parsons 4-shaft turbines. 4 Kampon boilers. Designed H.P. 38,500 = 34 kts. Oil : 350 tons. Endurance : 4000 miles at 15 kts. Complement, 148.

Name.	Begun.	Launch.	Comp.	Name	Begun.	Launch.	Comp.
Kamikaze	15/12/21	25/9/22	28/12/22	Hayate	11/11/22	23/3/25	21/12/25
Asakaze	16/2/22	8/12/22	16/6/23	Asanagi	5/3/23	21/4/24	29/12/24
Harukaze	16/5/22	18/12/22	31/5/23	Yunagi	17/9/23	23/4/24	24/4/25
Matsukaze	2/12/22	30/10/23	5/4/24	Namikaze			
Hatakaze	3/7/23	15/3/24	30/8/24	Numakaze			
Oite	16/3/23	27/11/24	30/10/25	Nokaze			

Meanings of some of the above names :—

Asakaze	Morning breeze	Matsukaze	Wind in the pine trees	Asanagi	Morning calm
Harukaze	Spring breeze	Oite	Fair wind	Yunagi	Evening calm

12 Minekaze class. (7 Minekaze + 5 Shiokaze.)

MINEKAZE

AKIKAZE.

1921 *Photo, Navy Department, Tokyo.*

5 *Shiokaze* class : ***Akikaze*** and ***Yukaze*** (both by Mitsu Bishi Z.K., Nagasaki); ***Hokaze, Shiokaze, Tachikaze,*** Believed authorised under the 1919 and 1920 Sections of the 1918-24 Navy Law. These boats have 4 Kampon boilers only.
7 *Minekaze* class : ***Minekaze, Okikaze, Nadakaze, Shimakaze.*** All by Maidzuru D.Y. ; ***Sawakaze, Hakaze*** and ***Yakaze*** all built by Mitsubishi Co., at Nagasaki or Kobé. Displacement : 1215 tons. Dimensions : 320 (*p.p.*), $336\frac{1}{2}$ (*o.a.*) × $29\frac{1}{4}$ × $9\frac{1}{2}$ feet (*mean* draught). Armament : 4—4.7 inch, 45 cal., 2 M.G. (AA.), and 6—21 inch torpedo tubes. 2—30 inch searchlights. Designed S.H.P. 38,500 = 34 kts. Machinery : Parsons 4 shaft turbines and 4 Kampon or Kansei boilers. Oil : 315 tons. Complement : *Minekaze, Sawakaze,* 145, others 148. *Minekaze* and *Sawakaze* belong to the 1917 Programme ; *Okikaze, Nadakaze, Shimakaze. Hakaze* and *Yakaze* to the 1918 Programme.

2 Tanikaze class.

TANIKAZE

TANIKAZE.

1921 *Photo, Navy Dept., Tokyo.*

2 *Tanikaze* class : ***Tanikaze*** (Maidzuru D.Y., July, 1918) and ***Kawakaze*** (Yokosuka D.Y., 1917). 1180 tons. Dimensions : 320 × $29\frac{1}{4}$ × $9\frac{1}{2}$ feet. Armament : 3—4.7 inch, 45 cal., 2 M.G., 6—21 inch tubes in three twin deck mountings. 2—30 inch searchlights. Designed H.P. 28,000 = 34 kts. Machinery : Parsons turbines. Boilers : 4 Kansei. Oil fuel only, 315 tons. Complement, 128. Begun under 1916 Programme.

1st Class Destroyers—*continued*.

1 Special Boat.

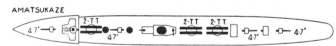

URAKAZE

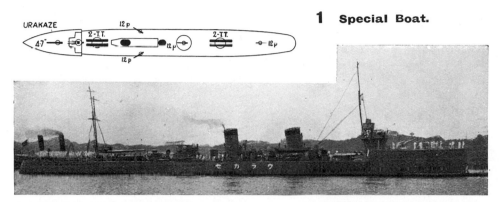

1921 *Photo, Navy Department, Tokyo.*

1 *Yarrow* type: **Urakaze** (Yarrow, Scotstoun, 1915). 810 tons. Dimensions : 275 (*p.p.*), 283 (*o.a.*) × 27·5 × 9·5 feet. Armament : 1—4·7 in., 4—12 pdr., 4—21 inch tubes in two twin deck mountings. Machinery : 22,000 H.P. turbines = 28 kts. Yarrow large tube boilers. Fuel : 248 tons oil only. Endurance about 1800 miles at 15 kts. Complement, 117. Trials : 30·26 kts. at 1082 tons load displacement.

Note.—It was intended that this boat should have a Diesel engine for cruising speed, combined by Föttinger hydraulic transmission to the turbines. Owing to the War, the Föttinger gear and Diesel engine were never delivered. They were replaced by a big oil tank. *Kawakaze* (sister-boat) ceded to Italy, and now Italian *Audace*.

4 Amatsukaze class.

AMATSUKAZE

AMATSUKAZE.   1921 *Photo, Navy Dept., Tokyo.*

4 *Amatsukaze* class : **Amatsukaze** and **Isokaze** (both launched at Kure, Oct., 1916). **Hamakaze** (Nagasaki, Oct., 1916), and **Tokitsukaze** (Kobé, Dec., 1916).* 1105 tons. Dimensions : 310 (*p.p.*), 326½ (*o.a.*) × 28 × 9¼ feet. Armament : 4—4.7 inch (40 cal.), 2 M.G., and 6—18 inch tubes in 3 twin deck mountings. 1 searchlight. Machinery : 3 sets Parsons turbines and Kansei boilers. Designed H.P. 27,000 = 34 kts. Fuel : 145 tons coal + 195 tons oil. Endurance : 4000 miles at 15 kts. Complement, 145. Built under the 1915 Naval Programme.

Note.—*Tokitsukaze* wrecked ; salved in three sections, March, 1918, and practically rebuilt at Maidzuru D.Y.

50 2nd class Destroyers. (1000 to 600 tons).

8 Wakatake Class.

ASAGAO.   1931 *Photo.*

8 *Wakatake class :* **Wakatake** (ex-No. 2) and **Kuretake** (ex-No. 4), (both by Kawasaki Co., Kobe); **Sanaye** (ex-No. 6) and **Sawarabi** (ex-No. 8), (both by Uraga Dock Co.); **Asagao** (ex-No. 10), and **Yugao** (ex-No. 12), (both by Ishikawajima Co.); **Fuyo** (ex-No. 16) and **Karukaya** (ex-No. 18), (both by Fujinagata Co.).

Built under 1921 Naval Programme. Particulars and general design are the same as *Ashi, Kiku* and *Momi* classes on next page, with the exception of displacement, which is increased to 820 tons, and dimensions, 275 × 26½ × 8¼ feet. All begun in 1921—22 and completed 1922—24.

All this class originally bore numbers only. Names were conferred on August 1st, 1928.

NIRE.   1930 *Photo.*

20 Momi class (13 Momi + 7 Ashi).

HASU   *Photo added* 1927.

YOMOGI.   *Photo added* 1927.

13 *Momi* class : **Momi** and **Kaya** (Yokosuka D.Y.), **Kuri** and **Nire** (Kure D.Y.), **Nashi, Take, Aoi** and **Kiku** (Kawasaki Co., Kobé), **Hagi** and **Kaki** (Uraga Co.), **Susuki** and **Tsuga** (Ishikawajima Co.), **Fuji** (Fujinagata Co., Osaka). 770 tons. Dimensions : 275 (*p.p.*) × 26 × 8 feet. Armament : 3—4.7 inch, 45 cal., 2 M.G. (AA.). 4—21 inch torpedo tubes in two twin-deck mountings. 1—30 inch searchlight. Designed S.H.P. 21,000= 31.5 kts. Machinery : Parsons direct drive turbines. + 3 Kampon boilers. 2 screws. Oil : 275 tons. Endurance : 3,000 miles at 15 kts. Complement, 110. Built under 1918-19 Programme.

7 *Ashi* class : **Ashi** and **Tsuta** (Kawasaki Co.), **Hasu** and **Hishi** (Uraga Dock Co.), **Sumire** and **Yomogi** (Ishikawajima Co.), **Tade** (Fujinagata Co., Osaka). All details as *Momi* class, but 2 searchlights carried. Begun under 1920 Naval Programme.

Note.—*Warabi*, of this class, lost by collision, 24th Aug., 1927. *Fuji*, in the above case, means *Wistaria*.

8 Momo class.

YANAGI.   1920 *Photo, Seward, Weymouth.*

8 *Momo* class : **Maki** and **Keyaki** (Sasebo D.Y., 1918), **Kuwa** and **Tsubaki** (Kure D.Y., 1918), **Yanagi** (1917) and **Momo** (1916), both built at Sasebo ; **Kashi** (1916) and **Hinoki** (1916), both built at Maidzuru. 755 tons. Dimensions : 275 (*o.a.*) × 25 × 7¾ feet. Armament : 3—4.7 inch, 2 M.G., 1 small AA. gun, and 6—18 inch tubes in two triple mountings. One searchlight. Machinery : 3 sets Curtis turbines and 4 Kansei boilers. Designed H.P. 16,000=31.5 kts. Fuel : 92 tons coal + 212 tons oil. Complement, 109. The first six provided for by Special 1917 Programme. The last four built under the 1915 Naval Programme. **Enoki** and **Nara** of this class converted into Mine Sweepers, 1930.

10 Kaba class.

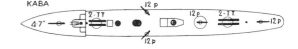

KUSUNOKI.   1929 *Photo.*

10 *Kaba* class :—**Kaba** (Yokosuka), **Kaede** (Maidzuru), **Kashiwa** and **Matsu** (Nagasaki), **Katsura** (Kure), **Kiri** (Uraga), **Kusunoki** and **Ume** (Kobe), **Sakaki** (Sasebo), and **Sugi** (Osaka). All launched February-March, 1915. 595 tons. Dimensions : 260 (*p.p.*) 274 (*o.a.*) × 24 × 7·9 feet. Armament : 1—4.7 inch, 4—12 pdr. (2 anti-aircraft model) and 4—18 inch tubes. Machinery : 3 sets, 4-cylinder triple expansion and 4 Kampon boilers. Designed H.P. 9,500=30 kts. Fuel : 90 tons coal + 135 tons oil. Endurance : 2,400 miles at 15 kts. Complement, 92. These boats are said to have been built in seven months. Built under 1914 Naval Programme, and majority served in Mediterranean during war. 12 Replicas built in Japanese Yards for French Navy—see French *Algerien* class.

2nd Class Destroyers—*continued*.

2 Sakura Class.

(Plan as for *Kaba* class, but beam 12 pdr. just abaft 1st funnel.)

SAKURA.

1921 *Photo, Navy Department, Tokyo.*

2 *Sakura* class:—**Sakura** (1911). **Tachibana** (1912). Both built at Maidzuru. 530 tons. Fuel: 125 tons coal + 30 tons oil ; otherwise as 10 *Kaba* class, on previous page.

Minesweepers.

2 ex-Umikaze Class.

No. 7.

1921 *Photo, Navy Department, Tokyo.*

No. 7 (**ex-Umikaze**) (Maidzuru, 1910) and **No. 8** (**ex-Yamakaze**) (Nagasaki, 1911). 1030 tons. Dimensions: 310 (*p.p.*) 323¼ (*o.a.*) × 27¾ × 9 feet (*mean* draught). Armament: 2—4.7 inch (40 cal.), 5—12 pdr. Torpedo tubes : removed. 1 searchlight. Machinery : 3 sets Parsons turbine and Kansei boilers. Designed H.P. 19,500 = 31.5 kts. Fuel : 250 tons coal + 180 tons oil = 2700 miles at 15 kts. Complement, 139. Trials : *Umikaze* 33.46 kts. Converted into minesweepers, April, 1930.

2 ex-*Momo* class (p. 343). **Nara** = **No. 9.**
Enoki = **No. 10.**

Minesweepers—*continued*.

MINESWEEPER No. 6. (note tripod foremast).

1930 *Photo.*

MINESWEEPER No. 1. (Now has tripod foremast.)

Photo added 1927.

Nos. 1 (Kobe Steel Works, March, 1923), **2** (Tama Works, 1923), **3** (Osaka Iron Works, 1923), **4** (Sasebo, 1923), **5,** and **6** (both Sasebo, Oct., 1928). All provided by 1920-28 Fleet Replenishing Law. 615 tons. 235 × 26⅓ × 7½ feet. Guns : 2—4·7 inch, 2—3 inch AA. 2 D.C. throwers. Complement, 87. Triple expansion engines. 3 Kampon boilers. H.P. 2000=20 kts.

72 Submarines. (*Sensuikan*).

Period.	No.	Type.	Date.	Displacement.	H.P.	Max. speed.	Fuel.	Complement.	T. Tubes.	Max. draug't.
		1st Class :—		tons		kts.	tons.			
	5	I 65—69 (K)	'27— ?	1638/2220	6000	19	?	61	6/8	16
	3	I 61—64 (M)	'26—'29	} 1635/2100	6000/1800	19/10	?	61	6/8	16¼
	9	I 53— 60, I 63	'24—'29							
	2	I 51—52 (K)	'21—'25	1400/2000	5200/6000 / 1800	19—17 / 10—9	Over 100 ?	57/60		17
	4	I 21—24 (KK) (Minelayers)	'24—'28	1150/1750	4000	19	?		4	14¼
FIRST	5	I 1—5 (KK)	'23—'29	1955/2500	6000	17.5	?	?	6	16
		2nd Class :—								
	9	Ro. 60—68 (M)	'21—'26	998/1300	2400/1600	16/10	75	48	6	13
	9	Ro. 51—59 (M)	'18— 23	900/1082	2400/1200	17/10	65	48	6	12¼
	4	Ro. 29—32 (KK)	'21—'25	665/1000	2400/1200	13/10	60	43	6	12
	3	Ro. 26—28 (K)	'21—'24	750/1000	2600/1200	16/10	65	40	4	12
	9	Ro. 16—24* (K)	'19—'22	740/986	2600/1200	17/10			6	12
	3	Ro. 13—15 (K)	'18—'21	740/986	2600/1200	17/10	} 65/75	40/45	6	12
Second	2	Ro. 11, 12 (K)	'17—'19	720/1035	1800/1200	18/9.7				
First	3	Ro. 3—5 (KK)	'19—'22	689/950	2600/1200	18/9.5	59/65	40	5	13½
Second	2	Ro. 1, 2 (KK)	'17—'20	689/1043						

* Ro. 25 non-effective, and being utilised for experimental purposes.
(K)=Kaigun (Navy Department) design. (KK) = Kawasaki-Kobe design. (SL)= Schneider-Laubeuf design.
(V)=Vickers type. (VK)=Vickers-Kaigun type. (M)=Mitsu Bishi or Mitsu Bishi-Vickers design. (SLK)=
Schneider-Laubeuf design modified by Navy Dept.
Details, all types, officially revised by Navy Dept., Tokyo, 1929, and can be considered as fairly reliable. All 5 and
6-tube boats are believed to carry 10 torpedoes ; others carry from 4 to 6, except Ro. 51—68, which have 8 or 10,
and non-minelaying 1st class boats, which may carry more still. Recently the patents of two German patterns of
periscope (Goerz and Humbrecht) were acquired.

The 1st class submarines are subdivided into following categories:—
Fleet (I 1—5), Cruising (I 51—67), Minelaying (I 21—24).

First Class Submarines (over 1000 tons).

5 Kaigun Type.

Completing.

5 boats : **I** 65–**I** 69.   1638/2100 tons.   Understood to be improvements upon I 53 class.   Armament : **1—3·9", 6—21"**
tubes.

3 Mitsu Bishi Type.

I 61.

1930 *Photo, Navy Dept., Tokyo.*

3 boats : **I** 61 (Nov. 12th, 1927), **I** 62 (Nov. 26th, 1928), **I** 64 (Oct. 5th, 1929).   Dimensions. 320¼ × 25¾ × 16 feet.
Displ : 1635/2100 tons.   Armament : **1—4·7", 6—21"** tubes.   Machinery : 2 sets Diesels combined H.P.=6,000.
Motors=1800 H.P.   Speed : 19/10 kts.   **I** 61, 62 by M.B.Z.K., Kobe.   **I** 64 by Kure D.Y.   **I** 61 completed
1929.   **I** 62 completed April 24th, 1930.

9 Kaigun Type.

I 55.   1928 *Photo.*

I 60.   1931 *Photo, Official.*

9 boats : *I 53* (ex-*No. 64*, Kure, Aug. 5th, 1925), *I 54* (ex-*No. 77*, Sasebo, March 15th, 1926), *I 55* (ex-*No. 78*, Kure, Sept., 1925), *I 56* (Kure, March, 1928), *I 57* (Kure, Nov., 1928), *I 58* (Yokosuka, Oct. 3rd, 1925), *I 59* (Yokosuka, March 25th, 1929). *I 60* (Sasebo, April 24th, 1929), *I 63* (Sasebo, Sept. 28th, 1927). Displacement : $\frac{1635}{2100}$ tons. Dimensions : *I 53–55*, 330 × 26 × 16¼ feet. *I 56–60* and *I 63*, 331¼ × 26 × 16¼ feet. Armament : **1**—4.7 inch, **1**—3 inch AA., **8**—21 inch tubes. Machinery : 2 sets Diesels, combined B.H.P. 6000. Designed speed : 19/9 kts. Believed begun under 1923-25 Programmes. Cruising radius is undoubtedly very large, 16,000 miles being spoken of. They are supposed to be capable of crossing the Pacific and returning without refuelling. This design is the fruit of experience gained with *I 51* and *I 52*.

2 Kaigun Type.

I 52.   1026 *Photo.*

I 52 (ex-*No. 51*) Kure, June, 1922. Laid down under 1920 Programme as an experimental boat. Displacement : $\frac{1390}{2000}$ tons. Dimensions : 330 × 25 × 17 feet. Armament : **1**—4.7″, **1**—3″ AA., **8**—21″ tubes. Machinery : 2 sets of Diesels = H.P. 6,000. Speed : 19/10 kts. Completed in May, 1925.

I 51 (*ex-44*).   *Photo added* **1927.**

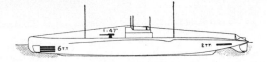

I 51 (ex-*No. 44*) Kure, Nov. 29th, 1921. Laid down under 1920 Programme as an experimental boat. Displacement : 1390/2000 tons. Dimensions : 300 × 28 × 15¼ feet. Armament : **1**—4.7″, **8**—21″ tubes. Machinery : Originally had 4 sets of Sulzer Diesels with 4 screws. H.P. = 5,200. Probably now engined as *I 52*. Speed : 17/12 kts. Completed June, 1924.

4 Kawasaki Boats (Minelayers).

I 22.

1930 *Photo.*

I 21.

1927 *Photo, by courtesy of Navy Dept.*

4 boats : **I 21** (March 30th, 1926), **I 22** (Nov. 8th, 1926), **I 23** (March, 1927), **I 24** (Nov. 12th, 1927), all by Kawasaki Co., Kobe, the first probably laid down under 1919 Programme. Displ.: 1142/1750 tons. Dimensions : 280×24¾×14¼ feet. Armament : 1—4.7 inch, 1—3 inch AA., 4—21 inch tubes. I 22 and I 23 completed at Kure, owing to temporary suspension of business by Kawasaki Yard. Construction of I 24 completed at Kawasaki by Naval Construction Dept. Design believed to be based on German *U B* types. Machinery : Diesels, H.P. 4,000 = 14/10 kts.

1 Experimental Boat.

Completing.

I 5. ( ). Displacement : 1955 tons. Dims. :—320 × 30·1 × 15·7 feet. Guns : 2—5·5 inch. Tubes : 6—21 inch. Machinery : Diesels, 6,000 H.P. = 17 kts. surface.

4 Kawasaki Boats.

I 1.

1926 *Photo, by courtesy of Navy Department.*

4 boats : **I 1—3** (ex-*Nos.* 74—76) (Kawasaki Co., Kobe, 1924-25), **I 4** (May 22nd, 1923), I 5 (*building*). Displacement : 1955/2500 tons. Dimensions : 320×29½×16 feet. Guns : 2—4.7 inch. Tubes : 6—21 inch. Design is based in its main features on the ex-German Submarine *O* 1 (ex-*U* 125). First three authorised by 1922 Programme. I 1 launched Oct., 1924, I 2, 23/2/1925, I 3, 8/6/1925; all completed 1926. I 1 carried out a test cruise of 2500 miles with complete success. A small seaplane with collapsible wings has been carried as an experiment in this class. I 4, laid down at Kawasaki, in April, 1926, built under direct superintendence of Naval Construction Department. Machinery : Diesels, H.P. 6,000 = 17 kts surface.

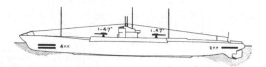

9 Mitsu Bishi Type.

Ro. 60.   *Photo added 1926.*

Ro. 62   *Photo added 1926.*

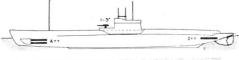

Ro. 64.   *1926 Photo, by courtesy of Navy Department.*

9 boats : **Ro. 60** (ex-*No.* 59), **Ro. 61** (ex-*No.* 72), **Ro. 62** (ex-*No.* 73), **Ro. 63** (ex-*No.* 84), **Ro. 64—68** (former numbers, if any, not known). All built by M.B.Z.K., Kobe, 1923-25. Dimensions : 250 (p.p.) × 24 × 13 feet. Guns : 1—3 inch AA., 1 M.G. Torpedo tubes : 6—21 inch. Understood to have 2 sets of 1200 B.H.P. 12-cylinder solid injection Vickers type Diesel engines. Other details as Table.
Notes.—Built under 1920-22 Programmes. Apparently an enlargement of the *Ro. 51—59* type. Completed—*Ro.* 60, 1923 ; *Ro.* 61–63, 1924 ; *Ro.* 64 and 68, 1925 ; *Ro.* 65—67, 1927.

9 Mitsubishi—Vickers type.

Ro. 58. (*Ro.* 57 and 59 same.) (Note absence of step forward.)   *Photo added 1926.*

Ro. 54.   *Photo added 1927.*

9 boats : **Ro. 51—56** (ex-*Nos.* 25—30), **Ro. 57** (ex-*No.* 46), **Ro. 58** (ex-*No.* 47), **Ro. 59** (ex-*No.* 57). (M.B.Z.K. Co., Kobé, 1919—22). Dimensions : 231½ × 23½ × 13 feet. Guns : 1—3 inch HA. Torpedo tubes : 6—18 inch in *Ro.* 51—56 ; 4—21 inch in *Ro.* 57—59. Endurance : *About* 7500 miles *on surface.* Other details as Table.

Notes.—Gun mounted on extended C.T. in *Ro.* 57—59. Begun under 1917-18 and 1919 Programmes. Completed 1920-23.

4 Kawasaki Boats (Minelayers).

Ro. 29.

1926 Photo, by courtesy of Navy Department.

4 boats : **Ro. 29—32** (ex-*Nos.* 68—71). (Kawasaki Co., Kobe, 1922-23). Dimensions : 243½ (*p.p.*) × 20 × 12 feet. Guns : **1—4·7** inch AA., **1—3** pdr. Torpedo tubes : Originally carried **5—21** inch, now **4—21** inch, and are fitted as minelayers. Probably have 2 sets of 1300 B.H.P. Fiat Diesel engines. Other details as Table.
Notes.—Built under 1919 Programme, and completed 1923-24. Understood to be a Kawasaki modification of *Ro.* 16—24 design, with certain improvements. *Ro.* 29 was completed Oct., 1923 ; *Ro.* 31 (ex-*No.* 70) sank during trials at Kobe, August, 1923, but was salved and rebuilt. *Ro.* 30 and *Ro.* 32 both completed during 1924-25. *Ro.* 31 completed at Kure, 1927, owing to financial crisis at Kawasaki Yard. She carries a special armament of **1—3** inch and **6—21** inch tubes.

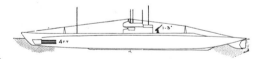

3 Kaigun Type.

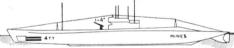

Ro. 26.

Photo added 1926.

Ro. 26.

1926 Photo, by courtesy of Navy Department, Tokyo.

3 boats : **Ro. 26** (ex-*No.* 45, Sasebo, 1921), **Ro. 27** (ex-*No.* 58, Yokosuka, 1922), **Ro. 28** (ex-*No.* 62, Sasebo, 1922). Dimensions : 230 × 20 × 12 feet. Guns : **1—3″**. Torpedo tubes : **4—21″** *Ro.* 26 reported to have 2 sets of 1300 B.H.P. Sulzer Diesel engines. Other details as Table.
Notes.—Built under 1919 Programme and completed 1922-24. An improvement of the *Ro.* 16—24 design.

9 Kaigun type.

Ro. 24.

1923 Photo, Navy Dept., Tokyo.

9 boats : **Ro. 16** (ex-*No.* 37) (Kure), **Ro. 17—19** (ex-*Nos.* 34—36) (Kure), **Ro. 20—23** (ex-*Nos.* 38—41) (Yokosuka), **Ro. 24** (ex-*No.* 42) (Sasebo). Dimensions : 230 × 20 × 12 feet. Guns : **1—3** inch. Torpedo tubes (18 inch) : **4** bow and **2** beam. Oil : 75 tons = 11,000 miles endurance at cruising speed *on surface.* For any other figured details, *v.* Table. Complement, 44.
Notes.—Built under 1918-19 Naval Programme. Completed 1921-22. *Ro.* 25 (ex-*No.* 43), built at Sasebo, foundered in March, 1924, and though salved, was so badly strained that she is being utilised for experimental purposes.

3 Kaigun type. (Modified Laubeuf).

Ro. 13.

Photo, Navy Dept., Tokyo.

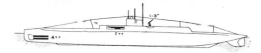

3 *Kaigun* type : **Ro. 13** (ex-*No.* 23, 29th April, 1919), **Ro. 14** (ex-*No.* 22, 31st March, 1919), **Ro. 15** (ex-*No.* 24, Oct., 1920). Dimensions : 220 × 20 × 12¼ feet. Guns : 1—12 pdr., 1—3 pdr. Torpedo tubes : 6—18 inch.

Notes.—Slightly larger than *Ro.* 11, 12, but of same general design. Kure D.Y. built *Ro.* 13, builders of other two boats not known. *Ro.* 14 was to have been ready early in 1921, but completion was delayed at last moment for some reason unknown. *Ro.* 13 completed 1920 ; *Ro.* 15 completed but damaged by fire, July, 1921. These boats were begun under 1917-18 Programmes.

2 Kaigun type. (Modified Laubeuf).

Ro. 11.

1921 Photo. Navy Dept., Tokyo.

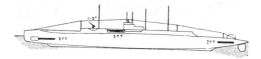

2 *Kaigun* type : **Ro. 11** (ex-*No.* 19). **Ro. 12** (ex-*No.* 20) (both launched at Kure, 1917). Dimensions : *About* 220 (*p.p.*) × 21 × 11¼ feet. Guns : 1—12 pdr. Torpedo tubes : 6—18 inch, distributed as two bow, two stern, two revolving on deck, in superstructure before C.T. Oil fuel : 75 tons = 6500 miles at economical speed *on surface.* Other details as Table A.

Notes.—Both begun April, 1917, completed Sept.-Oct., 1919. Designed for 16 kts. *surface* speed, but Ro. 11 has not exceeded 15.45 kts. *Surface* speed for Ro. 12 is fractionally higher. From photograph, this type appears to be a Navy Dept. enlargement of the Schneider-Laubeuf double hull design for Ha. 10. Built under 1916-17 Programme.

5 Kawasaki-Laurenti type.

Ro. 3.

1923 Photo Navy Dept., Tokyo.

Ro. 2.

1923 Photo. Navy Dept., Tokyo.

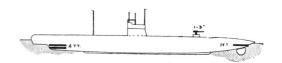

5 *Kawasaki-Laurenti* type : **Ro. 1** (ex-*No.* 18), **Ro. 2** (ex-*No.* 21), **Ro. 3** (ex-*No.* 31), **Ro. 4** (ex-*No.* 32), **Ro. 5** (ex-*No.* 33), all launched 1919-21 by Kawasaki Co., Kobe. Displacements : *Ro.* 1, 2, 689 tons *surface*, 1043 tons *submerged.* *Ro.* 3—5, 682 tons *surface*, 950 tons *submerged.* Dimensions : 215¼ (*Ro.* 1, 2) 218¼ (*Ro.* 3—5) × 20 × 13½ feet. Guns : 1—12 pdr. Torpedo tubes : 5—18 inch (4 bow, 1 stern). Machinery : Believed to have F.I.A.T.-San Giorgio Diesel engines. Endurance : *About* 3000 miles *on surface.*

Notes—Ro. 1 belongs to the 1915-16 Programme, Ro. 2 to the 1916-17 Programme, and Ro. 3—5 to the 1918-19 Programme. Completed 1919-1922. **Ro. 1** and **Ro. 2** have no gun now.

ITSUKUSHIMA (May 22nd, 1929.)

Laid down at Uraga Yard early in 1928. Completed Dec., 1929.

YAEYAMA (laid down 1930).

Standard displacement, 1,970 tons ; *normal*, 2,020 tons.

Dimensions, 328 × 42 × 10 feet. Complement, 235.

Guns :
  3—5·5″, 50 cal.
  2—3″ AA.
Mines :
  250 large or 500 small.
Depth charges throwers :
  1—each side amidships.

Armour : Nil.

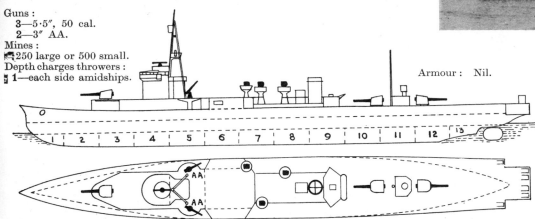

Machinery : Diesel engines. 3 sets of 1,000 B.H.P. each = 3,000 B.H.P. ; Speed, 17 kts.
Radius of action is 5,000 miles at 17 kts. 3 screws.

1930 *Photo.*

General Notes.—Is the first experimental Diesel-driven ship in the Japanese Navy. Design suggested by H.M.S. *Adventure* of which she is a small edition. In plan the second S.L. is replaced by an aircraft range finder (2 metre). Officers' cabins in superstructure deck under fore gun and bridge. Upper deck is for mine stowage 4 lines of mine laying rails extending from section 2 on plan to stern. Two outer lines start in section 6 and extend to the wing-ports at stern. There is a single line on the forecastle from starboard bow to gun for transport back to store of picked-up practice mines. Two sizes of mines can be carried and number stowed varies as the type—roughly twice as many of the smaller size.

1930 *Photo.*

1930 *Photo.*

1930 *Photo.*

TOKIWA (Armstrong, July, 1898). 9240 tons. Dimensions: $442 \times 67\frac{1}{4} \times 24\frac{1}{4}$ feet. Guns: 2—8″, 40 cal., 8—6″, 40 cal., 13—3″, (some not aboard). All other particulars as Cruiser *Asama* (of which she was originally a sister) on an earlier page.

Note :- *Tokiwa* means Evergreen. After turret removed 1929.

ITSUKUSHIMA   1930 *Photo.*

Mine Layers, 2nd Class (*Fusetsu tei*).

KUROKAMI.   1919 *Photo, Navy Dept., Tokyo.*

(KUROKAMI CLASS—12 SHIPS.)

KUROSAKI. Built at Yokosuka D.Y. under —— Programme.

NINOSHIMA. Built at Kure D.Y. 1918-19 Programme.

YENOSHIMA.* Built under 1917 Special Programme, at Maidzuru D.Y.

YENTO* (Mar., 1917), **KATASHIMA** (Feb., 1917), both built at Maidzuru D.Y., and **KUROKAMI** (Kure D.Y., Feb., 1917). Built under 1916-17 Programme.

ASHIZAKI and **KATOKU.** Both launched at Maidzuru D.Y., Oct., 1915. Built under 1915-16 Programme.

KUROSHIMA (Oct., 1914) and **TOSHIMA** (Oct., 1914). Both built at Sasebo D.Y.

SOKUTEN (March, 1913). Built by Maidzuru D.Y.

NATSUSHIMA (Yokosuka D.Y., March, 1911).

Details of all above ships : 430 tons. Dimensions : $150 \times 25 \times 7.5$ feet. Guns : Not known. H.P. 600 = 12 kts. Unofficially reported to carry 40-50 mines each.

*May also be referred to as *Enoshima* and *Ento*.

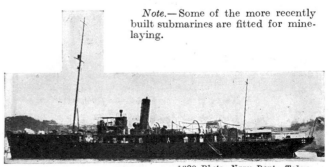

Note.—Some of the more recently built submarines are fitted for minelaying.

1920 *Photo, Navy Dept., Tokyo.*

KATSURIKI. (Kure D.Y., Oct., 1916). 1540 tons. Dimensions : $260 \times 39 \times 14$ feet. Guns : 3—4·7 inch. H.P. = 13 kts. Built under 1915-16 Programme. Fitted with 4 gallows for sweeps. Reported to carry 150 mines. **First Period expired 1925.**

OLD CRUISER & FIRST CLASS GUNBOATS.

Re-rated as Second Class Coast Defence Vessel, 1921.

ましつ TSUSHIMA.

TSUSHIMA (Dec., 1902). *Normal* displacement, 3420 tons. Complement, 311. Length, 334½ feet. Beam, 44 feet. *Maximum* draught, 16 feet. Guns (Armstrong): **6**—6 inch, 40 cal., **8**—3 inch, **1**—3 inch AA. Torpedo tubes: *None*. Armour (steel): 2½″ Deck (Cellulose belt), 4″ Conning tower (K.N.C.). Machinery: 2 sets triple expansion. 2 screws. Boilers: 16 Niclausse. Designed H.P. 9,400 = 20 kts. Coal: *normal*   tons; *maximum* 600 tons. Laid down 1900 at Yokosuka and Kure. Completed 1904. Third Period expired 1928. An excellent steamer. Sister ships, *Otowa*, wrecked 1917, and *Niitaka*, lost Aug., 1922.

1921 *Photo, Navy Dept., Tokyo.*

と よ **YODO** (Kobe, 1907). 1320 tons. Comp., 182   280 (*p.p.*) 305½ (*o.a.*) × 32 × 11 feet. Guns: **2**—4.7 inch, 50 cal., **4**—12 pdr. Armour: 2½″ deck. Torpedo tubes: **2**—18 inch. Machinery: 2 sets 4-cyl. triple expansion. Designed H.P. 6500 = 22 kts. Boilers: 4 Miyabara. Coal: *normal*,   tons; *maximum*, 340 tons + 80 tons oil. In Third Period. Completed April, 1908. Employed recently in Surveying Service. Standard displacement is 1320 tons.

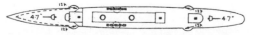

1st Class Gunboats (*Itto Hokan*). (Over 800 tons).

ATAKA.   1924 *Photo, by courtesy of the Ministry of Marine.*

ATAKA (Yokohama Dock Co., August, 1921). 725 tons. Complement, 118. Dimensions: 222 × 32 × 7½ feet. Guns: **2**—4.7 inch, **2**—3 inch AA. Machinery: Triple expansion. Designed H.P. = 16 kts. Boilers: 2 Kampon. Authorized under 1920-28 Fleet Law, laid down 1921, and completed 1922. In First Period. It is reported that this vessel has been specially equipped for submarine salvage work.

UJI (1903). 540 tons   Complement, 86. 180½ × 27¼ × 7 feet. Armament: **4**—12 pdr., **6** M.G. H.P. 1000 = 13 kts. Belleville boilers. Coal: 150 tons. Built at Kure D.Y. Third Period expired 1927.

2nd Class Gunboats (*Nito Hokan*). (Under 800 tons).

1918 *Photo, by courtesy of the Navy Department.*

SAGA (Sasebo, 1912). 710 tons. Complement, 99. 210×29½×7½ feet. Guns: **1**—4·7 inch, **3**—3 inch AA., **6** M.G. Machinery: Triple expansion, 3 screws. Boilers: 2 Kampon. Designed H.P. 1600=15 kts. Coal: *maximum* 400 tons. In Third Period. Completed Nov., 1912.

River Gunboats.

FUTAMI. 1930 *Photo, Lt. Malcolm Burnett, R.N.*

ATAMI (March 30th, 1929), **FUTAMI.** Both laid down 1928, by Tama Works and Fujinagata Co., respectively. Displacement: 400 tons *standard.* Dimensions: 148⅔ × 22¼ × 3 feet. Guns: **1**—3 inch, **1**—3 inch AA., **6** M.G. Speed: 16 kts. Machinery: 2 sets triple expansion. Boilers: 2 Kampon. Completed 1930.

River Gunboats—*continued.*

KATATA. *Photo added 1925.*

Name.	Builder.
HIRA (1922)	Mitsu Bishi, Kobe.
HODZU (1922)	
KATATA (1923)	Kobe Steel Works.
SETA (1923)	

Displacement, 305 tons. Dimensions: 180 × 27 × 3½ feet. Guns: **2**—12 pdr., **6** M.G. Machinery: 2 sets triple expansion. Boilers: 2 Kampon. Designed H.P. 2100=16 kts. In First Period. Authorised under 1920-28 Fleet Law. Laid down 1922 and completed 1923.

TOBA (1911). 215 tons. Complement, 59. 180 × 27·× 2½ feet. Guns: **2**—12 pdr., **6** M.G. 1400 H.P. = 15 kts. Coal: 80 tons. Built at Sasebo D.Y. In Third Period.

River Gunboats—*continued.*

FUSHIMI (1906). 150 tons. Complement, 45. 160×24½×2¼ feet. Guns: **2**—6 pdr., **6** M.G. 800 H.P. = 14 kts. Yarrow boilers. Coal: 25 tons. Built by Yarrow, at Poplar. In Third Period.

SUMIDA (1903). 105 tons. Complement, 40. 145×24×2 feet. Guns: **2**—6 pdr., **6** M.G. 600 H.P. = 13 kts. Thornycroft boilers. Coal: 40 tons. Built by Thornycrofts, at Chiswick. Third Period expired 1927.

KOTAKA (1929) 55 tons. 100 × 16 × 4·5. Guns: **5** M.G. H.P. = 15 kts. Laid down September, 1929, at Tama works, and completed January, 1930.

Anti-Submarine Net Layers.

1930 *Photo*.

TSUBAME.

Kamome similar. (2 white bands on funnel).

1931 *Photo*.

SHIRATAKA (Ishikawajima Co., Tokyo, 25th January, 1929). Displacement : 1345 tons *standard ;*
1405 tons *normal*. Dimensions : 260 × 38 × 9 feet. Guns : **3**—4.7 inch A.A., **1** M.G. Machinery :
2 sets triple expansion. Boilers : 2 Kampon. Speed, 16 kts.

TSUBAME (now has 1 white band on funnel).

1930 *Photo, Navy Dept., Tokyo.*

KAMOME (Osaka Ironworks, 27th April, 1929), **TSUBAME** (Yokohama Dock Co., 24th April,
1929), Displacement : 450 tons *standard*, 570 tons *normal*. Dimensions : 206⅔ × 23½ × 6⅓ feet.
Guns : **1**—3 inch. Speed : 19 kts.

Notes.—*Shirataka* laid down 24th November, 1927 ; other two in 1928. Meanings of these three names are as follows:
Shirataka—White Hawk. *Kamome*—Seagull. *Tsubame*—Swallow.

SHIRATAKA.

1930 *Photo*.

Destroyer Depot Ships

(Sui rai Bokan).

1917 *Photo, by courtesy of the Navy Department, Tokyo.*

KOMAHASHI. (Sasebo, 1913). 1230 tons. $227 \times 35 \times 17\frac{3}{4}$ feet. Guns : **2**—12 pdr., **1**—3 inch AA. H.P. 1824 = 13.9 kts. Was originally built as a Naval Transport.

KARASAKI (ex-*Ekaterinoslav*, 1896, captured 1904). 6,170 tons. Dimensions : $440 \times 49\frac{1}{2} \times 15\frac{3}{4}$ feet (*max.* draught). Armament : **1**—12 pdr., **1**—3 inch AA., **1**—3 pdr. H.P. 3200 = 13 kts.

Submarine Depot Ships *(Sensui Kan Botei).*

JINGEI.   1931 *Photo.*

CHOGEI.   *Photo added* 1926.

JINGEI (May, 1923), **CHOGEI** (24th March, 1924). Both by Mitsu Bishi Co., Nagasaki. 8500 tons. Dimensions : $380 \times 53\frac{1}{4} \times 19\frac{1}{2}$ feet. Turbine engines. 2 screws. *Jingei*, 6 Kampon boilers ; *Chogei*, 5. H.P. ? = 16 kts. Guns : **4**—5.5 inch, **2** M.G. 2 searchlights. Equipped to carry 1 seaplane.

JINGEI.   1924 *Photo, by courtesy of the Navy Department.*

Note.

All Vessels listed on this page are officially rated as Naval Storeships and Transports (*Unsokan*), and are grouped with various other auxiliaries under the general classification of "Special Service Ships." (*Tokumukan*).

Oilers & Tank Vessels.*

*This is not an official Rating. These ships are included in the general classification of "Naval Transports and Storeships (*Unsokan*)."

NOTORO CLASS—10 SHIPS.

SHIRIYA.   *Photo added* 1927.

NOTORO as Aircraft Tender.   1931 *Photo*.

IRO, SHIRIYA, TSURUMI, NARUTO, HAYATOMO, ONDO, SATA, ERIMO, NOTORO and **SHIRETOKO.** Displacement: 15,243—15,450 tons. (8000 tons *gross*.) Dimensions: 470⅔ (*o.a.*), 455 (*p.p.*) × 58 × 26⅔ feet. Guns: 2—5.5 inch, 2—3 inch AA. Reciprocating engines. 4 cylindrical boilers, (except *Naruto*, 6 Miyabara). I.H.P. 3,750 = 12 kts. Fuel: 8000 tons oil as cargo and 1000 tons oil for own bunkers. Complement, 155—157.

Name.		Builder.	Begun.	Launch.	Comp.
Erimo	..	} Kawasaki Co., Kobe.	3/5/20	28/10/20	16/12/20
Notoro	..		24/11/19	3/5/20	10/8/20
Shiretoko	..		16/2/20	17/7/20	8/9/20
Ondo	..	} Osaka I.W.	1922	1922	1923
Iro	..		1922	5/8/22	1923
Tsurumi	..		1921	29/9/21	1922
Sata	..	} Yokohama Dock Co.	1920	28/10/20	1921
Shiriya	..		7/3/21	12/11/21	1922
Hayatomo	..	Kure D.Y.	1922	1923	1923
Naruto	..	Yokosuka D.Y.	3/22	1/23	10/24

Oilers and Tank Vessels—*continued.*

1920 *Photo, Navy Dept., Tokyo.*

SUNOSAKI (Yokosuka D.Y., June, 1918). 9800 tons. Dimensions: 400 × 50 × 25.2 feet. Guns: 2—4.7 inch, 2—12 pdr. H.P. 6000 = 14 kts. Carries 5000 tons oil. Built under 1916–17 Programme.

1920 *Photo, Navy Dept., Tokyo.*

TSURUGIZAKI (Kure D.Y., June, 1917). 1970 tons. 220½ × 31 × 14 feet. H.P. 900 = 9 kts. Guns: 2—12 pdr. Cargo: 1,100 tons oil. Built under 1916-17 Programme.

Fleet Supply Ship.

MAMIYA.   *Photo added* 1926.

MAMIYA (Kawasaki Co., Kobe, 1923). Displacement: 17,500 tons. Dimensions: 475 × 61 × 28 feet. Guns: 2—4.7 inch, 2—3 inch AA. Triple expansion engines. 8 Kampon boilers. H.P. 7000 = 14 kts. Complement, 195.

Fleet Colliers.*

MUROTO.   1920 *Photo, Navy Dept., Tokyo.*

NOSHIMA (Feb., 1919), **MUROTO** (Oct., 1918). Both built by Mitsubishi Co., Kobé. 8750 tons. Dimensions: 345 × 50 × 23.9 feet. Guns: 2—4·7 inch, 2—3 inch AA. H.P. 2640 = 12.5 kts. Coal: 877 tons. Built under Special 1918-19 Programme.

*Officially rated as "Naval Storeships or Transports (*Unsokan*)."

Oil Tanker & Fleet Collier.

KAMOI.   *Photo added* 1927.

KAMOI (New York S.B. Co., completed 12th Sept., 1922) Authorised under 1920-21 Naval Programme, and laid down 23rd Sept., 1921. Displacement: 19,550 tons (10,222 tons *gross*.) Dimensions: 495 (*w.l.*), 478½ (*p.p.*) × 67¼ × 28 feet. Guns: 2—4·7 inch, 2—3 inch AA. S.H.P. 8000 = 15 kts. Machinery: G.E. (Curtis) turbines and electric drive. Boilers: 4 Yarrow. Fuel: Own Bunkers 2500 tons coal: Cargo 2000 tons coal and 7500 tons oil fuel, or about 10,000 tons oil if no coal carried.

Naval Storeships or Transports (*Unsokan*).

1920 Photo, Navy Dept., Tokyo.

SEITŌ (ex-*Tsingtao Maru*, ex-German S.S. *Durendart*, built at Flensburg, 1906, and captured 1914). 3844 tons *gross*. Dimensions: 240 × 49.2 × 21¾ feet. Guns: 2—12 pdr. H.P. 1525 = 9 kts.

1920 Photo, Navy Dept., Tokyo.

TAKASAKI (1902). 4746 tons. Dimensions: 375 × 47.9 × 15¾ feet. Guns: 2—12 pdrs. Speed: 10 kts. No other details known.

Salvage Vessel.

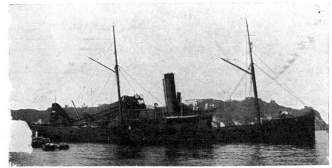

KURIHASHI (ex-*Herakles*, purchased from Swedish owners about 1909). 1040 tons. 182 × 30¼ × 11¾ feet. I.H.P. 1200 = 12.5 kts. Fitted with powerful steam pumps and derricks.

This name means " Chestnut Bridge."

Training Ships.

For Engineer Branch : **YURAGAWA.** 919 Tons: H.P: 625 = 11 kts.

For Cadets : **IWATE,** Cruiser. *For Midshipmen :* Cruisers **IDZUMO, YAKUMO.**

For Seamen, Stokers and Boys (but not respectively) : Disarmed battleships **FUJI** and **SHIKISHIMA.**

Ice Breaker.

OTOMARI. *Photo added 1925 by courtesy of the Ministry of Marine.*

OTOMARI (Kawasaki Co., October, 1921). 2700 tons. 200 × 50 × 18½ feet. Guns : 1—4·7 inch. Reciprocating engines. 5 cylindrical boilers. Speed : 13 kts.

Submarine Salvage Vessel and Repair Ship.

1929 Photo.

ASAHI (March, 1899). Ex-battleship of 14,765 tons original displacement, rendered non-effective and converted for present use. Dimensions : 425¼ (*o.a.*) × 75¼ × 27¼ feet.

Machinery : 2 sets vertical triple expansion. 2 screws. 4 cylindrical boilers (replacing original Bellevilles). Present speed 12 kts. The name of this ship means " Rising Sun."

Surveying Vessels.

1920 Photo, Navy Dept., Tokyo.

KOSHŪ (ex-German S.S. *Michael Jebsen*, built by Howaldt, Kiel, 1904, and captured 1914). 1521 tons *gross*. Dimensions : 251.1 × 36.1 × 18.9 feet (*depth of hold*). Guns : 2 —12 pdr. H.P. 800 = 9.5 kts. Ice-breaking stem.

Now has fore topmast.

MANSHU (ex-*Manchuria*, 1901). 3916 tons. Complement, 193. Guns : 2—12 pdr. I.H.P. 5000 = 17.6 kts. Coal : 400 tons.

Note.—The above ship is officially rated as a Second Class Coast Defence Vessel. To be scrapped at an early date.

LATVIAN NAVY.

Flags.

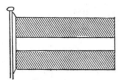

MERCANTILE.　　ENSIGN.　　JACK.　　ADMIRAL.

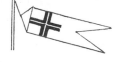

COMMANDER-IN-CHIEF OF FORCES.　　CAPTAIN IN CHARGE OF A DIVISION.

Colour of Ships : Light grey.
Personnel : About 450 permanent + 200 yearly conscripts.
Minister of War : Colonel R. Baugerski.
Commanding Officer, Naval Forces : Rear-Admiral Count A. Keyserling.

Naval Uniforms.

Admiral　　Captain　　Commander (Lett.=Captain)　　Lt. Commander (Lett.=Lt. Captain)　　Lieutenant　　Sub-Lieutenant

Note.—Admiral's top stripe should be thinner than shown above.

Mercantile Marine.

(From "Lloyd's Register," 1931 figures.)

Total *gross* tonnage : 206,686.

2 Submarines.

RONIS.　　1927 *Photo, A. & Ch. de la Loire (Builders).*

2 *Loire-Simonot* type : **Ronis** (At. & Ch. de la Loire, Nantes, July 1st, 1926), **Spidola** (Ch. & At. Augustin Normand, Havre, Oct. 6th, 1926). Displacement: $\frac{390}{514}$ tons. Dimensions : $180\frac{1}{2} \times 15 \times 10$ feet. Armament, **1**—3 inch AA., **3** M.G., **6**—17.7 inch tubes (2 fixed bow, other 4 in revolving twin mounts). Machinery: 2 sets Sulzer Diesels. H.P. $\frac{1300}{700}$. Speed: $\frac{14}{9\cdot25}$ kts. Oil Fuel: 19 tons. Radius: $\frac{1600}{85}$ miles at $\frac{14}{9}$ kts. Diving limit, 28 fathoms. Complement, 34.

1 Gunboat.

1926 *Official Photo.*

VIRSAITIS (ex-German Minesweeper *M* 68, Neptun Werft, Rostock, 1917). Reconstructed at Riga, 1921-22, after being sunk during War. Displacement : 525 tons. Dimensions : 182 (*w.l.*) × $23\frac{1}{2}$ × 7 feet. Guns : 2—2.9 inch (Canet), 1—2 pdr. AA., 2 M.G. 1 S.L. H.P. 1600 = 17 kts. Coal : 120 tons. Complement, 69.

2 Minesweepers.

IMANTA.　　1927 *Photo, Messrs. Normand (Builders).*

VIESTURS (Chantiers Dubigeon, Nantes, May 27th, 1926), **IMANTA** (Normand, Havre, Aug. 11th, 1926). Displacement : 255 tons. Dimensions : $160 \times 21 \times 5$ feet. Guns : 1—3 inch AA., **4** M.G. Provision for 30 mines. Machinery : 2 sets triple expansion. H.P. 750 = 14 kts. Fuel : 30 tons. Complement, 39.

Note.—These two vessels were designed for the Latvian Navy by Ch. & At. Augustin Normand.

Surveying Vessel.

HIDROGRAFS (ex-*Weichsel*, J. W. Klavitter, Danzig, 1918). 285 tons *gross*. Dimensions : $126\frac{1}{4} \times 23\frac{1}{4} \times 13\frac{1}{2}$ feet. Triple expansion engines. Speed : 10 kts.

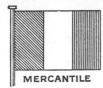

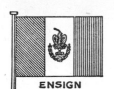
ENSIGN

MERCANTILE

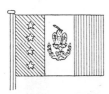
SECRETARY OF WAR AND
NAVY DEPTS.

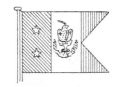
OFFICER COMMANDING
A DIVISION.

Minister of War and Marine : General Joaquin Amaro.

Docks.

At Vera Cruz (Atlantic Coast), Government floating dock, 262 × 46 × 18 feet (1600 tons).

At Salina Cruz (Pacific Coast), Government dry dock, 664 × 79⅓ × 35½ feet (leased to Tehuantepec National Railway Co.)

Mercantile Marine.

(From "Lloyd's Register," 1931 figures), 41,820 tons *gross*.

RECOGNITION SILHOUETTES.

Scale : 1 inch = 80 feet.

MAYO.
YAQUI.

Scale : 1 inch = 160 feet.

A. PRIETA.
(Has no fore topmast at present.)

ANAHUAC.

N. BRAVO.

(Revised by courtesy of the Secretary of the War and Navy Depts., 1927.)

Coast Defence Vessel (classed as *Crucero*.)

(Appearance similar to *Floriano* in Brazilian Navy.)

ANAHUAC (ex-*Deodoro*, ex-*Ypiranga*, purchased from Brazil, 1924). Built at La Seyne, 1898. Displacement : 3162 tons. Complement, 200. Length (*p.p.*) 267¼ feet. Beam, 48 feet. *Max.* draught, 13¼ feet. Guns : 2—9.4 inch, 45 cal.; 4—4.7 inch, 50 cal. Armour (Harvey-nickel): 13¾″ Belt (amidships), 4″ Belt (ends), 1½″ Deck (reinforcing belt), 8″ Casemates, 5″ Conning tower. Machinery : 2 sets triple expansion. 2 screws. Boilers : Babcock (converted to burn oil). Designed H.P. 3400 = 15 kts. Oil fuel : 440 tons. *Gunnery control* : A few voice pipes only.

Armed Transport (*Transporte*).

1925 Photo, by courtesy of Captain Julio Morales Coello, C.N.

PROGRESO (Odero, 1907). 1590 tons. Dimensions : 230 × 36½ × 11 feet. Guns : 4—6 pdr. H.P. 1400 = 13 kts. Coal : 209 tons.

---

2 Gunboats (*Cañoneros*).

NICOLAS BRAVO (Odero, 1903). 1227 tons. Dimensions : 242 × 34 × 9¾ feet. Guns : 2—4 inch, 4—6 pdr. H.P. 3000 = 12.25 kts. 2 screws. Oil fuel : 226 tons. Complement, 130.

Gunboats—*continued.*

Photo wanted.

AGUA PRIETA (ex-*U.S.S. Machias*, Bath I.W., 1891). Purchased 1921. 1293 tons. Dimensions : 204 × 32 × 12¼ feet. Guns : 6—4 inch, 2—6 pdr. H.P. 1800 = 15.5 kts. Coal : 285 tons. Complement, 157.

Note.—*Zaragoza* has been condemned as non-effective, and is no longer in service.

---

8 Patrol Vessels (*Guardacostas.*)

MAYO (ex-*U.S. S.C.*38, 1917) and **YAQUI** (ex-*U.S. S.C.* 1917). 77 tons. Dimensions : 105 × 14¾ × 6½ feet. Guns : 1—3 inch, 23 cal. Engines : 3 sets Standard motors. B.H.P. 660 = 18 kts. nominally. Fuel : 3,000 gallons petrol.

TAMPICO, COVARRUBIAS, MAZATLAN, GUAYMAS, ACAPULCO (ex-*Salinas*), **VERA CRUZ.** All are ex-trawlers purchased in Canada 1920. Built 1918. 486 tons. Dimensions : 133 × 24 × 13½ feet. Guns : 1—6 pdr., 2 M.G. I.H.P. 557 = 8 kts. Coal : 208 tons.

---

9 Vessels under control of Free Ports Department.

BOLIVAR (ex-*Floraba*), **WASHINGTON** (ex-*Gonzaba*). Both built 1920 by Dominion S.B. Co., Toronto. 1655 and 1670 tons *gross*.

MOCTEZUMA (ex-*Lake Fisher*) (Globe S.B. Co., Superior, Wis., 1919). 2713 tons *gross*.

COAHUILA, JALISCO (Cramps, Philadelphia, 1916). 2585 tons *gross*.

MEXICO (Hamilton, Port Glasgow, 1913). 2548 tons *gross*.

TABASCO, TAMAULIPAS (McMillan, Dundee, 1901). 1022 tons *gross*.

TEHUANTEPEC (McMillan, Dundee, 1896). 751 tons *gross*.

Note.—Above ships are available for transport service when required.

ROYAL NETHERLANDS NAVY.
Revised 1931, by courtesy of the Chief of the Naval Staff, Ministry of Defence, The Hague.

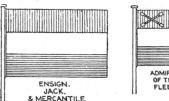

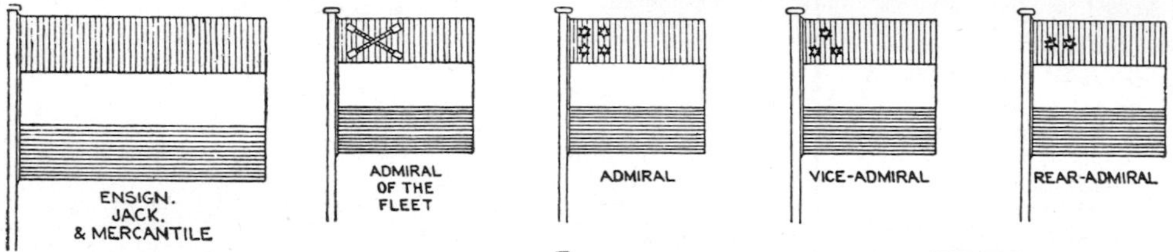

ENSIGN.
JACK.
& MERCANTILE

ADMIRAL
OF THE
FLEET

ADMIRAL

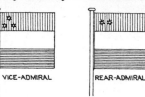

VICE-ADMIRAL

REAR-ADMIRAL

CAPTAIN COMMANDING
DIVISION FLIES THIS ➤➤
FROM THE MASTHEAD
SENIOR NAVAL OFFICER
FLIES THE SAME ➤➤
FROM SIGNAL YARD.

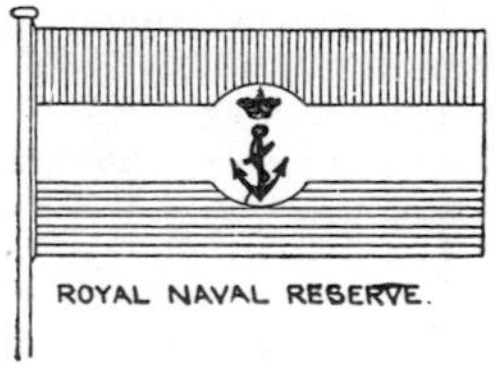

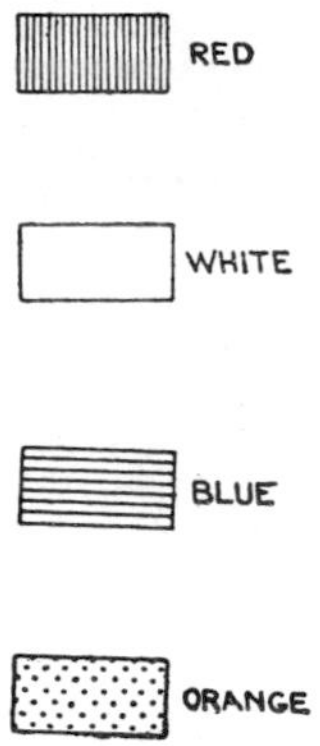

Officers commanding Flotillas fly a yellow
pendant with black letter D in centre,
from signal yard.

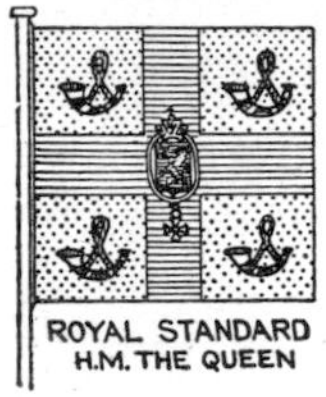

ROYAL NAVAL RESERVE.

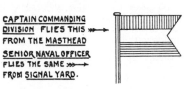

ROYAL STANDARD
H.M. THE QUEEN

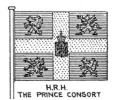

H.R.H.
THE PRINCE CONSORT

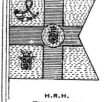

H.R.H.
THE CROWN
PRINCESS.

RED

WHITE

BLUE

ORANGE

Notes to Flags.

Royal Standard⎫
H.R.H. The Prince Consort⎬ Colours of these are *royal* blue and *dark* orange.

Governor of the East Indies :—A broad pendant (Red, White, Blue) above Ensign.
Governors of Colonies—As ensign, but with following distinguishing marks on red stripe near
staff ; Governors of Suriname and of Curaçoa : Three white balls.

Netherlands Uniforms. 7

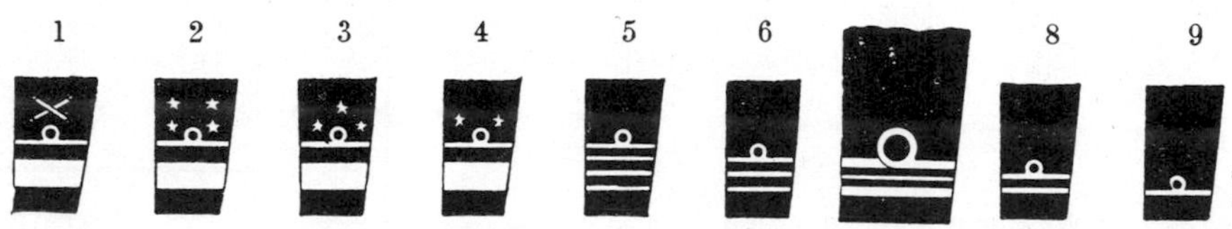

1	2	3	4	5	6	7	8	9
Admiraal	Luitenant-Admiraal	Vice-Admiraal	Schout-by-nacht	Kapitein ter Zee	Kapitein Luitenant ter Zee	Luitenant ter Zee 1e Kl.	Luitenant ter Zee 2e Kl.	Luitenant ter Zee 3e Kl

Corresponding ⎰ *Admiral*   *Admiral*   *Vice-*   *Rear-*   *Captain*   *Commander*   *Lieut.-*   *Lieutenant*   *Sub. Lieut.*
to British ⎱ *of the Fleet*   *Admiral*   *Admiral*   *Commander*

In relative ranks—
Doctors have insignia 5 to 9 without the curl.
Paymasters „ 5 to 10 „ in silver.
Engineers „ 5 to 10 with the curl, and are to be distinguished by the badge of a torch
crossed by two arrows on the collar, instead of the usual anchor.

The broad stripes in ranks 1—4 are 2 inches wide (5 c/m) ; 5—8, $\frac{2}{5}$ inch (1 c/m) ; No. 9, $\frac{1}{5}$ inch.
Distance between stripes is $\frac{1}{5}$ inch (5 m/m).
Flying Officers are of ranks 7, 8 and 9, and are to be distinguished by the badge of an aeroplane
propeller on collar instead of the usual anchor.
R.N. Reserve Officers are of ranks 6, 7, 8, and 9.

Notes

All displacements are "Standard." Regarding the two sets of figures given for complements
on later pages, (H) denotes complement when serving in home or European waters ; (A) denotes
complement when serving in Dutch East Indies or abroad.

Personnel : About 7,550 all ranks, navy and marine infantry , including Officers.
Oversea Possessions : Dutch East Indies (Sumatra, Java, Borneo, etc.); Dutch Guiana (Suriname)
Curaçoa, Bonaire, Aruba, Saba, etc.
Minister of Defence : Dr. L. N. Deckers. *Chief of the Naval Staff :* Vice-Admiral Dr. J. C. Jager.
Colour of Ships : Grey to green, except Submarines.
Tonnage = Standard displacement.

Mercantile Marine.

From "Lloyd's Register" 1931 figures.

Total gross Tonnage, 3,118,170 including 14 vessels of 16 Knots and over.

Defence Estimates, 1931.

Naval Construction	10,408,000	florins.
Ordinary	85,370,920	„
Non-military Expenses	5,952,987	„
	101,731,907	„

military and naval expenses.

Naval Guns (Krupp and Bofors Models). (Officially revised, 1931.)

Notation.	Calibre.		Official Mark.	Long.	Weight of Gun.	Weight of Shell.	Initial Velocity.	Max. penetration with A.P. capped against K.C.		
	in.	cm.		cals.	tons.	lbs.	ft. secs.	8000 in.	5000 in.	3000 in.
HEAVY	11	28	...	42½	31	595	2920	8	13	15½
	9·4	24	"No. 2"	40	24⅜	375	2788	3½	7½	10½
	9·4	24	"No. 1"	40	24¼	375	2690	4	8½	10¾
MEDIUM	5·9	15	"No. 8"	50	7⅓	101½	2953	—	—	—
	5·9	15	"Nos. 6 & 7"	50	5⅞	101½	2953	—	—	—
	5·9	15	"No. 5"	40	5	90¼	2788	—	—	—
	5·9	15	"No. 3"	40	4¾	90¼	2444	—	—	—
	5·9	15	"No. 2"	40	4¼	100	2231	—	—	—
	4·7	12	"Nos. 4 & 5"	50	4	53	2950	—	—	—
	4·7	12	"No. 3"	40	2	52½	2231	—	—	—
	4·7	12	"No. 2"	40	2	52½	2231	—	—	—
	4·7	12	"No. 1"	40	2	52½	2231	—	—	—
LIGHT	4.1	10.5	Semi. Aut.	50	—	39⅔	2897	—	—	—
	3·5	8·8	"Nos. 1—3"	45	—	22	2625	—	—	—
	3·0	7·5	"No. 9"	40	1½	13	2936	—	—	—
	3·0	7·5	"Nos. 6, 7 & 8"	50	—	13	2936	—	—	—
	3·0	7·5	"No. 5"	18	—	13	1148	—	—	—
	3·0	7·5	"No. 4"	30	—	13	2034	—	—	—
	3·0	7·5	"No. 3"	40	—	13		—	—	—
	3·0	7·5	"No. 2"	40	—	13	⎱ 2231	—	—	—
	3·0	7·5	"No. 1"	40	—	13		—	—	—
	3·0	7·5	Semi Aut. 5	55	—	—		—	—	—
	3·0	7·5	Semi Aut. 4	55	—	13	2936	—	—	—
	3·0	7·5	„ 3	55	—	13	2936	—	—	—
	3·0	7·5	„ 2	55	—	13	2936	—	—	—
	3·0	7·5	„ 1	55	—	13	2936	—	—	—
	2·0	5·0	"No. 2"	40	—	3·9	2231	—	—	—
	2·0	5·0	"No. 1"	40	—	3·9	2231	—	—	—
	2·0	5·0	Semi Aut.	55	—	3·9	2936	—	—	—
	1·5	4·0	Aut.	40	—	2	1975	—	—	—
	1·5	3·7	„	30	—	1·0	1358	—	—	—

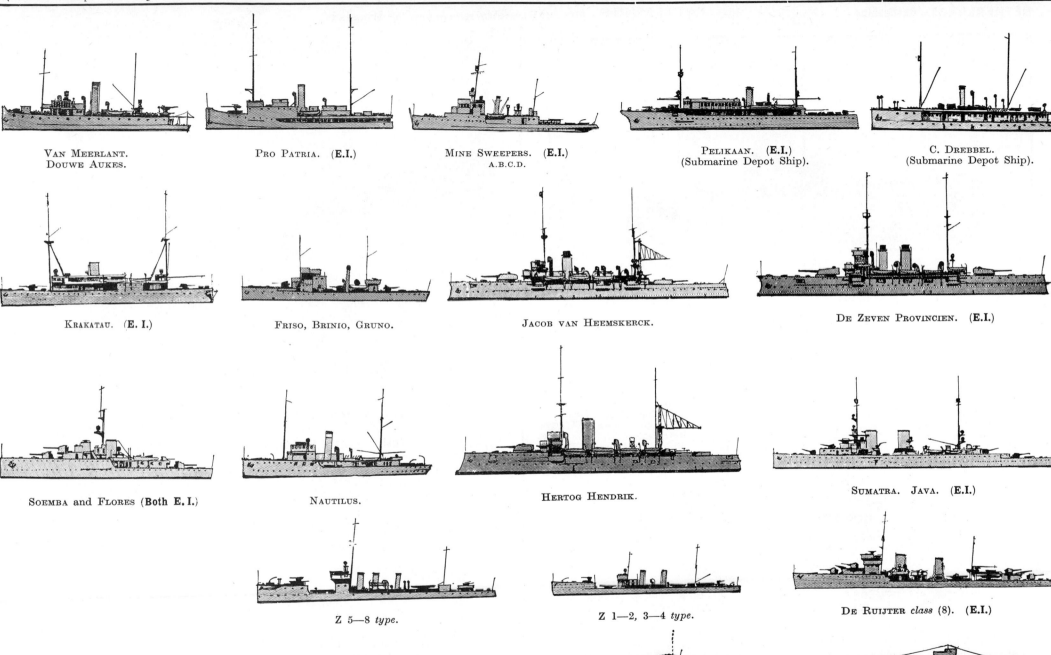

VAN MEERLANT.
DOUWE AUKES.

PRO PATRIA. **(E.I.)**

MINE SWEEPERS. **(E.I.)**
A.B.C.D.

PELIKAAN. **(E.I.)**
(Submarine Depot Ship).

C. DREBBEL.
(Submarine Depot Ship).

KRAKATAU. (E. I.)

FRISO, BRINIO, GRUNO.

JACOB VAN HEEMSKERCK.

DE ZEVEN PROVINCIEN. **(E.I.)**

SOEMBA and FLORES **(Both E. I.)**

NAUTILUS.

HERTOG HENDRIK.

SUMATRA. JAVA. **(E.I.)**

Z 5—8 *type.*

Z 1—2, 3—4 *type.*

DE RUIJTER *class* (8). **(E.I.)**

K 11—K 13. **(E.I.)**

O 9—11.

1924 *Photo, R. F. Scheltema, Esq.*

East Indies Station.

DE ZEVEN PROVINCIEN (March, 1909).

Displacement, 5644 tons. Complement, 447 (A), 409 (H).

Length (*o.a.*), 333 feet. Beam, 56·1 feet. *Maximum* draught, 20·2 feet.

Guns (Krupp):
2—11 inch, 42½ cal.
4—5·9 inch, 40 cal. "No. 5."
10—13 pdrs., 55 cal. S.A. "No. 1"
1—9 pdr. mortar "A."
4—1 pdr. (2 are AA. ?)
2 machine.
Torpedo tubes:
None.

Armour (Krupp):
6" Belt (amidships) ......
4" Belt (ends) ....
2" Deck (on slopes) ......
9¾" Main Barbettes (N.C.)
9¾" Shields ....
4" Small Barbettes
7¾" Conning tower (N.C.)

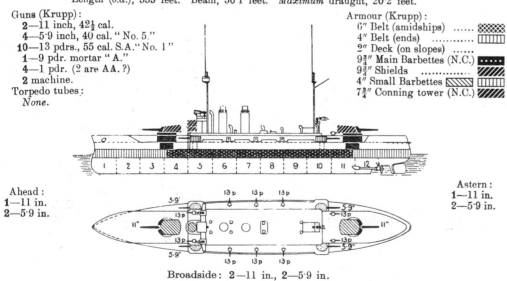

Ahead:
1—11 in.
2—5·9 in.

Astern:
1—11 in.
2—5·9 in.

Broadside: 2—11 in., 2—5·9 in.

Machinery: 2 sets triple expansion. 2 screws. Boilers: 8 Yarrow. Designed H.P. 8000 = 16 kts. (Trials: 8516=16·3 kts.) Coal: *normal*, 700 tons; *maximum*, 1030 tons. Radius of action, 2100 miles at 15·3 kts.; 5100 miles at 8 kts. Amm. hoists improved 1920.

Notes.—Main belt is 7 feet wide. Laid down Feb. 1908 at Amsterdam D.Y.

1930 *Photo, courtesy of Ministry of Defence.*

JACOB VAN HEEMSKERCK (September, 1906).

Displacement, 4445 tons. Complement, 351.

Length (*o.a.*), 321½ feet. Beam, 49·9 feet ; Beam outside sponsons, 55·4 feet. *Max.* draught, 18¾ feet.

Guns (Krupp):
2—9·4 in., 45 cal. "No. 2."
6—5·9 in., 40 cal. "No. 5."
6—13 pdrs. "No. 3."
1—9 pdr. mortar. "A."
4—1 pdr. (2 are AA. ?)
2 machine.
(Torpedo tubes removed.)

Armour (Krupp)
6" Belt (amidships) ...
4" Belt (ends) ....
2" Deck (reinforcing belt)
7¾" Main barbettes ...
4" Hoods to these ...
6" Small barbettes ...
7¾"Conning tower (K.C.)

Ahead:
1—9·4 in.
2—5·9 in.

Astern:
1—9·4 in.
2—5·9 in.

Broadside: 2—9·4 in., 3—5·9 in.

Machinery: 2 sets triple expansion. 2 screws. Boilers: 6 Yarrow. Designed H.P. 6400 = 16·5 kts. Coal: *normal* — tons; *maximum* 610 tons.

Notes.—Main belt is 6 feet wide and about 220 feet long. Begun at Amsterdam D.Y., 1905, and completed, May, 1908. *Trials*: I.H.P. 6396=16·54 kts. Radius of action : 3300 miles at 10 kts.

Aircraft Note.—Two seaplanes added to equipment, May, 1929.

Note.—Aft barbette is hidden behind lowering bulwarks.

1925 *Photo, W. A. Fuller, Esq.*

1928 *Photo, J. Vlieger, Amsterdam.*

MARTEN HARPERTSZOON TROMP (1904).

Displacement, 4371 tons.   Complement, 349 (H).
Length (*o.a.*), 330·7 feet.   Beam, 49·8 feet.   *Maximum* draught, 18·7 feet.

Guns—(Krupp):
  2—9·4 inch, 40 cal. "No. 2."
  4—5·9 inch, 40 cal. "No. 5."
  8—13 pdr. "No. 3"
  4—1 pdr. (2 are AA. ?)
  2 machine.
Torpedo tubes (removed).

Armour (Krupp):
  6″ Belt (amidships) ......
  4″ Belt (ends) ....
  2″ Deck (reinforcing belt)
  7¾″ Barbettes (N.C.) ......
  4″ Hoods to these ......
  3″ Small turrets ....
  7¾″ Conning tower ......

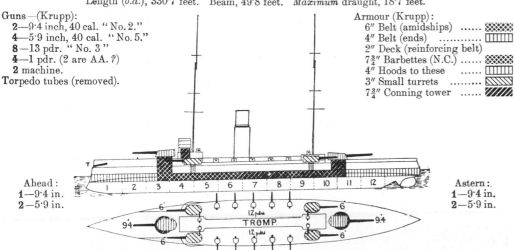

Ahead :
1—9·4 in.
2—5·9 in.

Astern :
1—9·4 in.
2—5·9 in.

Machinery : 2 sets triple expansion.   2 screws.   Boilers : 6 Yarrow.   Designed H.P. 6400 = 16 kts.   Coal : *normal* 680 tons ; *maximum* 830 tons.   Radius of action : 1600 miles at 14½ kts., 4100 miles at 9¼ kts.   *Trials* ('06).—6,405 I.H.P. = 16·7 kts.   Begun at Amsterdam D.Y., 1903, and completed 1906.

HERTOG HENDRIK (1902).

Displacement, 4560 tons.   Complement, 347 (H).

Length (*o.a.*), 316·9 feet.   Beam, 49·8 feet.   *Maximum* draught, 19 feet.

Guns (Krupp) :
  1—9·4 inch, 40 cal. "No. 1."
  4—5·9 inch, 40 cal. "No. 3."
  4—13 pdr. "No. 3."
  4—1 pdr.

Armour (Krupp) :
  6″ Belt (amidships) ......
  4″ Belt (ends) ....
  2″ Deck (reinforcing belt)
  9¾″ Barbettes..............
  4″ Hoods to these ....
  9¾″ Conning tower (fore)

Gunnery Notes—Armament reduced, 1926, by removal of 1—9.4 inch and several smaller guns, on appropriation as Cadets' Training Ship.

Armour Notes.—The belt is 5½ feet wide and four feet of it is below the waterline.   Gratings to engine room hatches are 4·7 inches thick.

General Notes.—2 planes added to equipment, 1928.

Machinery : 2 sets triple expansion.   2 screws.   Boilers : 6 Yarrow.   Designed H.P. 6300 = 16 kts.   Coal : *normal* 680 tons ; *maximum* 830 tons.   Same radius of action as *M. H. Tromp.*   Begun 1900 at Amsterdam D.Y.

(East Indies Station.)

JAVA (Aug. 6th, 1921) & **SUMATRA** (Dec. 29th, 1920).

Normal displacement, 6670 tons.
Complement, 480 (504 with E.I. personnel added).
Length (*o.a.*), 509·5 feet.   Beam, 52½ feet.   *Max.* draught, 18 feet.

Guns (Bofors) :
10—5·9 inch (50 cal.) "No. 6"
4—13 pdr. S.A., 55 cal. (anti-aircraft) "No. 4."
4 machine.
Torpedo tubes :
None.
Mines : 12.
Searchlights : 6—47".
Paravanes : 4.
Range Finders : 4.

Armour (Coventry) :
3" Belt ....
Deck { 1" flat
{ 2" slopes
4" Gun shield faces (much thinner at sides and roof)
2" Funnel bases ...
5" Conning tower

A Third Ship of this Type is projected, but details are not yet settled. (Oct., 1931):

JAVA.

1924 *Photo, by courtesy of the Ministry of Marine.*

Ahead :
4—5·9in.

Broadside : **7**—5·9 in.

Astern :
4—5·9 in.

Machinery : 3 sets Krupp-Germania turbines.   3 screws.   Boilers : 8 Schulz-Thornycroft.   Designed H.P., 65,000 = 30 kts.   Fuel, oil only : *normal*, 1070 tons ; *maximum*, 1200 tons.   Radius of action : 4800 miles at 12 kts, 3600 miles at 15 kts.

Armour Notes.—C.T. divided into gunnery control and navigation compartments.   3" belt is 392½ feet long.   Towards stern and over steering gear, belt is narrower for a length of 42½ feet, and is only 2" thick.

Name	Builder	Machinery	Laid down	Completed	Trials	Boilers	Best recent speed
Sumatra	Nederlandsche Scheepsbouw Maatschappij, Amsterdam	Krupp, Germania	July,'16	Nov. 1925	82.000 = 31 8	Schulz	30.3
Java	K. M. de Schelde, Flushing	Krupp, Germania	May,'16	1924	73,000 = 31.5 (St. Abbs, 7/7/25)	Schulz	

* Contracted for, June, 1917.
Aircraft Notes.—Each ship carries 2 Fairey III D type seaplanes, with 450 h.p. Napier "Lion" engines, crew 3 men. To handle these, 2 small cranes are now mounted abeam, to port and starboard, just abaft first funnel.
General Notes.—The German design of these ships is evident in their appearance.   A third ship of this type (*Celebes*) was authorised, but cancelled.   *Java*, though completed in 1924, did not enter into service until May, 1925.
Gunnery Notes.—5·9 inch guns elevate to 25-30°.   Electric hoists.

JAVA.

1924 *Photo, by courtesy of the Ministry of Marine.*

8 Destroyers *(Torpedobootjagers).*

PIET HEIN.   1928 *Photo.*

PIET HEIN.   1929 *Photo, by courtesy of Messrs. Burgerhouts (builders).*

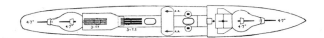

8 *Yarrow* type : **De Ruijter** (K. M. de Schelde, Flushing, Oct. 23, 1926), **Evertsen** (29 Dec., 1926), **Kortenaer** (June 30, 1927), **Piet Hein** (April 2, 1927), all by Burgerhouts, Rotterdam ; **Van Galen** (June 28th, 1928), **Witte de With** (Sept. 11th, 1928), both by M. Fijenoord. **Banckert, Van Nes,** both by Burgerhouts. Displacement: 1316 tons. Dimensions : 307 (*p.p.*), 322 (*o.a.*) × 31¼ × 9¾ feet *max.* draught. Armament: 4—4.7 inch (50 cal.), 2—3 inch AA., 6—20.8 inch tubes in triple deck mountings in first four. Other four carry AA., armament of 1– 3 inch and 4– 2 pdr. pom poms. Parsons geared turbines and Yarrow super heated boilers (250 lbs. pressure in first four, 400 lbs. in others). Designed H.P. 31,000 = 34 kts. in loaded condition, 36 kts. light. Oil : 330 tons. Complement, 126.

Notes.—These destroyers have been designed throughout by Messrs. Yarrow & Co., Ltd., and constructed under their supervision. The design was selected by the Dutch Government from several submitted by firms in England, France, Germany and the U.S.A. Included in the equipment of the vessels are a seaplane, bomb throwers and 24 mines. There is also a complete fire control system. *De Ruijter* and *Evertsen* both completed late in 1927, former said to have made 36 kts. with 90% full load. All are intended for East Indies Station. **Piet Hein** and **Kortenaer** completed 1928, **Van Galen** 1929, **Witte de With** 1930, **Banckert** 1930, **Van Nes** 1931.

New Construction.

1. Flotilla leader. Details not yet settled. Designed by Messrs. Yarrow.

16 Torpedo Boats (*Torpedobooten*).

No.	Type	Date	Dis-place-ment	H.P.	Max. Speed	Fuel	Comp-lement	T. tubes	Max. Dra'ght
	8 Sea-going class—		tons			tons			feet
4	Z 8—Z 5	'14—'16	204	5600	27	82	39	4	5½
4	Z 4—Z 1	'15—'21	277	5600 (t)	27	81½	39	4	
	8 1st class—								
3	G 16, 15, 13	'12—'14	180	2600	25	44	27	3	8
2	G 12, 2	'03—'06	140	1900	25	30	25	3	7¼
3	*Draak* All E.I.M.	'05—'07	103	1560	24	21	14+6*	2	6¾

All Yarrow types. (*t*)=Turbines. Z=*Zeegaand* (sea-going) type. G=*Groot* (large) type.

*Complements of these boats are 14 Europeans+6 East Indians.

The old *G* boats and *E.I.* boats now used for subsidiary duties.

Z 4.

Photo added, 1924.

4 boats, **Z 4—Z 1** (Ned. Scheepsb. Mij., Amsterdam, 1916-18.). 277 tons. Dimensions : 201 × 20¼ × 6 feet. Guns : 2—13 pdr., "No. 4," 2 machine. Torpedo tubes: 4—17·7 inch (one twin deck mounting + 2 single ditto). Designed S.H.P. 5500=27 kts. Curtis type turbines. Boilers fitted to burn coal or oil. Carry 72 tons coal+9·4 tons oil. Radius of action : 425 miles at 20 kts.

Note.—The original boats, Z 4—Z 1, building by the German Vulkan Co. in 1914, were appropriated by the German Navy, became the German Destroyers V108—105. German V 107 War Loss, while V 105, 106, 108 were partitioned between Poland and Brazil, 1920. These four " replace " boats were begun by the Nederlandsche Scheepsbouw Maatschappij, Amsterdam, in 1914, but owing to lack of materials they were not finished until 1919, or *after* the Z8—Z5 boats listed above. Z2 last boat of class to be delivered was not commissioned till 12/1/21.

Z 8. 1918 *Photo, Fotopersbureau " Holland," Amsterdam.*

4 boats, **Z 8, Z 7** (K. M. de Schelde, Flushing, 1915), **Z 6, Z 5** (Fijenoord Co., Rotterdam, 1915). 204 tons. Dimensions : 193 × 19¾ × 5½ feet. Guns : 2—13 pdr., "No. 4," 2 machine. Torpedo tubes : 4—17·7 inch (one twin deck mounting + 2 single ditto). Designed H.P. 5700 to 5500=27 kts. (made about 27·4 on trials). Machiner : Reciprocating. Boilers fitted to burn coal or oil. Carry 75 tons coal+7 tons oil. Radius of action : 425 miles at 20 kts. Completed 1916.

G13. 1919 *Photo, Fotopersbureau " Holland," Amsterdam.*
(*Now only used for Subsidiary Duties in Harbour.*)

3 *180 ton boats* ('12-'14): **G 16, G 15** (Fijenoord Co., Rotterdam, 1914), **G 13** (K. M. de Schelde, Flushing, 1913), 180 tons. Dimensions : 162·4 × 17 × 4·6 feet. Armament : 2—13 pdr. "No. 4," 3—17·7 inch deck tubes. Designed H.P. 2600=25 kts (26 kts. on trials). Coal : 44 tons.

G 14, Boiler explosion, February, 1919. Now sold.

Torpedo Boats—*continued.*

Photo, Fotopersbureau "Holland," Amsterdam.

(*Now only used for subsidiary duties in Harbour.*)

1 ('07–'09 boat):—**G 12.**
1 ('03–'06 boat):—**G 2.** } Armament: **2**—4 pdr., **3**—17·7 inch deck tubes. Radius: 1230 miles at 8 kts.

Note.—*G 11* mined and sunk off Vlieland, March, 1918. *G 2* mined Feb., 1918, salved in sections and rebuilt.

Torpedo Boats listed below belong to East Indies Marine.

3 *Draak* class:—**Draak, Krokodil, Zeeslang.** (1906–7). } Armament: **2**—1 pdr., **2**—17·7 inch tubes, (viz.— 1 bow *submerged*, 1 deck tube.)

(*Nominal* radius of all these boats about 1500 at 8¼ kts.)

(E. Indies Station), Coastal Motor Boats.

S.M. 1, S.M. 2, S.M. 3, S.M. 4. all by Messrs. John I. Thornycroft & Co., Ltd., 1927–1928. 55 × 11 feet. 2 Thornycroft motors, each 375 B.H.P. = 37 kts. contract speed, (trials 39 kts.). Auxiliary engine to give a cruising radius of 800 miles. Armament: **2** Lewis guns, **2**—18 inch torpedoes, **4** D.C., and an outfit of Thornycroft C.M.B. type Smoke Floats.

22 + *9* (building) Submarines.

Tabulated Details.

The following details are mainly from official data communicated by the Naval Staff. Dates refer to time when first boat was laid down and last boat completed. Displacement—Not Standard.

No.	Type	Date	Displacement tons.	H.P.	Max. speed kts	Extreme endurance.	Complement	T. tubes	Max. draug't feet
5	*K XVIII—XIV*	Bldg.	830 / 1020	3000 / 1000	17·5 / 15	35 0 miles at 10 kts.	35	8	12·8
4	*015—0 12* (ND)	Bldg.	562 / 700	1800 / 620	15 / 8	12 miles at 8 kts.		5	
3	*K XIII—K XI* (ND)	'22–'25	670 / 820	2400 / 725	15 / 8·8	3500 miles at 11 kts. / 13 miles at 8·8 kts.	31	6	12·2
3	*0 11—0 9* (ND)	'22–'26	515 / 645	900 / 610	12 / 8·5	3500 miles at 8 kts. / 11 at 7·5 kts.	29	5	11·5
3	*K X—K VIII* (H)	17–'23	570 / 715	1550 / 630	15 / 8	3500 miles at 11 kts. / 12 miles at 8·5 kts.	29	4	12·1
3	*K VII—K V* (HD)	'15–'20	560 / 610	1200 / 500	15 / 8	3500 miles at 11 kts. / 12 miles at 8·5 kts.	29	6	12·5
2	*K IV—K III* (H)	14–'20	560 / 710	1200 / 630	15 / 8	3500 miles at 11 kts. / 25 miles at 8·5 kts.	29	6	11·5
1	*M 1* (W) (ex *UC 8*)	1915†	160 / 180	96 / 175	5·6 / 5·7	900 miles at 5 kts. / 50 miles at 2·5 kts.	15	6*	9·8
1	*0 8* (H) (ex *H 6*, Brit.)	1915†	370 / 440	480 / 320	13 / 8·5	1350 miles at 12 kts.	26	4	12·8
1	*K II* (HD)	14–'20	566 / 610	1800 / 500	13 / 8·5	3500 miles at 11 kts. / 12 miles at 8·5 kts.	29	6	12·5
1	*0 7* (HD)	13–'16	180 / 210	350 / 185	11·5 / 12	750 miles at 10 kts. / 12 miles at 8·5 kts.	15	3	9·8
1	*0 6* (H)	'13–'16	190 / 230	350 / 180	12 / 8·5	750 miles at 10 kts. / 12 miles at 8·5 kts.	15	3	9·8
4	*0 5—0 2* (HW)	'09–'13	130 / 150	350 / 200	12 / 8·5	500 miles at 10 kts. / 26 miles at 8·6 kts.	10	2	9·5

* Mine-laying tubes. † Taken over in 1917.

Notes on above Table.

All boats with letter *K* (*Koloniën*) and *Roman* numerals are East Indies Marine. All boats with letter *O* (*Onderzeeboot*) and *Arabic* numerals are for service in home waters. ND boats are *Navy Design*. (H) submarines are "Holland" type, built by the Koninklijke Maatschappij de Schelde, to plans by Electric Boat Co., U.S.A. (HD) submarines are of the Hay-Denny type, built by the Maatschappij Fijenoord, Rotterdam, to plans by Marley F. Hay and Messrs. Denny & Co., Dumbarton. (HW) submarines are of the Holland type, built by the K. M. de Schelde, to plans by Messrs. Whitehead & Co., Fiume; no further boats of this design are now being built. W = Werner design (German Navy).

In H.P. column, B.H.P. of *M 1, 0 7, 0 6, 0 5—0 2* are for one set of engines. All other boats show total B.H.P. for two sets of engines. B.H.P. 1500 for *K IV, K III* is *average* for this class, as one boat has 2 sets of 600 B.H.P. (total 1200) engines and the other 2 sets of 900 B.H.P. (total 1800) engines.

Submarines on the East Indies Station are fitted with special cooling plant to render them more habitable.

New Construction.

4 *Navy* (*Home Service*) type: *O 12, O 13, O 14*, ordered December, 1927 (first) and June, 1928 (other two) from the Schelde Yard. Displacement: 562/700 tons. H.P. 1800/620 = 15/8 kts. Armament: **2** guns, —20·9 inch tubes, (**4** bow, **1** stern). Diving limit, 33 fathoms. *O 15* ordered 1929 at Fijenoord.

5 *Navy* (E.I.) type: *K XIV, K XV, K XVI.* Ordered 1929. *K XVII, K XVIII*, ordered 1930 at Fijenoord.

(*Continued on next page.*)

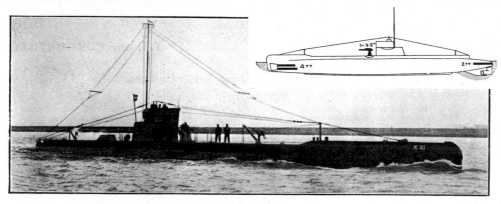

(East Indies Marine.)   1925 *Official Photo, by courtesy of Chief of Naval Staff, The Hague.*

K X.   1926 *Photo, R. F. Scheltema, Esq.*

3 *Navy* type : **K XIII** (Dec., 1924), **K XII** (Nov., 1924), **K XI** (April, 1924), all by M. Fijenoord, Rotterdam. Displacement : 670 tons *on surface*, 820 tons *submerged.* Dimensions : 231 × 20½ × 12½ feet. Engines : 2 sets M.A.N. Diesels, each 1200 B.H.P. = 15 kts. *surface* speed (17 kts. reached on trials). *Submerged* speed : 8 kts. Armament : **1**—3.5 inch AA. and **2**—21 and **4**—17.7 inch tubes (of which 4 are in bow and 2 at stern). **12** torpedoes carried. Complement, 31. Provided for under 1918 Naval Programme.

Note.—K XIII completed the voyage from Amsterdam to Surabaya, via the Panama Canal, unescorted, without mishap. Period occupied was from May 27 to Dec. 12, 1926.

O 9.   1926 *Photo, R. F. Scheltema, Esq*

K VIII, IX, X.   **(East Indies Marine.)**   1925 *Photo, by favour of R. F. Scheltema, Esq.*

O 11.   1926 *Photo, by courtesy of Chief of Staff, The Hague.*

3 *Navy* (Home Service) type : **O 11** (M. Fijenoord, 19th March, 1925), **O 10** (Nederlandsche Scheepsbouw, 30th July, 1925), **O 9** (K. M. de Schelde, 1925). Displacement : 515 tons *on surface*, 645 tons *submerged.* Dimensions : 180 × 19 × 11½ feet. Engines : 2 sets Sulzer Diesels, each 450 B.H.P. = 13 kts. *on surface.* *Submerged* speed : 8.5 kts. Armament : **1**—3.5 inch AA. and **5** torpedo tubes (of which **2**—21 inch are in bow, **2**—17.7 inch bow, and **1**—17.7 inch stern). **10** torpedoes carried. Provided for under 1917 Programme.

3 *Holland* type : **K X** (May, 1923), **K IX** (1923), and **K VIII** (1922), all by K. M. de Schelde. Displacements : 570 tons *on surface*, about 715 tons *submerged.* Dimensions : 211 × 18½ × 12 feet. Armament : **1**—3.5 inch AA. and **4**—17.7 inch tubes. Machinery : K VIII has two sets of 900 B.H.P. Diesel engines, M.A.N. type while K IX, and K X have 2 Schelde-Sulzer Type of 800 h.p. each for a *surface* speed of 15 kts. (16 reached *on trials*). Electric motors B.H.P. 630 = 8 kts. *Submerged* speed. Endurance about 3500 miles at 11 kts. *on surface.* Complement, 29. Provided for by the 1916 Naval Programme. Note arrangement of hydroplanes and anchor recesses.

K V in East Indies.   **(East Indies Marine.)**   1921 *Photo by courtesy of the Chief of Naval Staff, Batavia.*

3 *Hay-Denny* type: **K VII** (launched Mar. 8th, 1921), **K VI** (launched 1921) and **K V** (launched 1920), All by M. Fijenoord, Rotterdam. Displacements. dimensions and armament as *K II* in next column. Machinery: 2 sets of 600 B.H.P. Sulzer Diesel engines=16 kts. *max.* speed on surface. *Submerged* speed 9 kts., endurance as *K II.* Exceptingminor modifications and type of engines, these boats are identical with *K II.* Originally intended they should have M.A.N. engines but as the German firm was entirely engaged on engine building for German submarines, contract was declined. Sulzer engines of less B.H.P. were accordingly used in these boats. Begun 1915. *K V* completed 1921, *K VI* completed 1921, *K VII* completed 1922.

K 2, 5—8

K III on trials.   **(East Indies Marine.)**   1920 *Photo, by courtesy of M. F. Hay, Esq.*

2 *Holland* type: **K IV** (1920) and **K III** (1919). Both by K. M. de Schelde, Flushing. Displacement: about 560 tons *on surface,* 715 tons *submerged.* Dimensions: 211¼ × 18⅓ × 11¼ feet. Armament: 1—13 pdr. and 6—17·7 inch torpedo tubes. Designed *surface* speed 16 kts. Machinery: *K III* has 2 sets of 900 B.H.P. M.A.N. (completed by K. M. de Schelde) and *K IV* has 2 sets of 600 B.H.P. Sulzer engines. Electric motors B.H.P. 1200=8 kts. Endurance: 3500 miles at 11 kts. *on surface.*

M.1

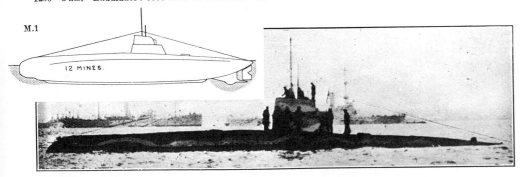

12 MINES.

M 1. Appearance generally as above.   *War Photo, Alfieri.*

1 *Werner* type: **M 1** (ex-German mine-laying submarine *UC 8,* Vulkan, Hamburg, 1915, stranded on Terschelling Island, Nov., 1915, salved, interned and purchased by Dutch Government, 1917). Displacements: 160 tons *surface,* 180 tons *submerged.* Dimensions: 111½ × 10½ × 9¾ feet. Guns: **1** machine. No torpedo tubes but carries 12 mines in 6 mine-laying tubes before conning tower. Machinery: 1—4 cyl. Daimler oil engine=5·6 kts. (7·5 kts. for short periods with electric motors), on *surface:* max. *submerged* speed: 5·7 kts. (1 hour). Endurance: 1050 miles at 5 kts. *on surface;* 50 miles at 2½ kts. *submerged.*

O 8.   1918 *Photo, Fotopersbureau " Holland."*

1 *Holland* type: **O 8** (ex-British submarine *H 6*), built by Canadian Vickers Co., Montreal, 1915, wrecked on Schiermonnikoog Island, Jan., 1916, salved Feb., 1916, interned at Nieuwediep, and subsequently purchased by Dutch Government. Displacements: 370 tons on *surface,* 440 tons *submerged.* Dimensions: 150½ × 15¾ × 12¼ feet. Armament: 4—18 inch torpedo tubes. Machinery: 2 sets 8 cyl. Nelseco* Diesel engines=13 kts. on *surface;* *submerged* speed 8·5 kts. Fuel: 16 tons oil carried.

*"Nelseco" is trade mark for engines manufactured by the New London Ship & Engine Co., Groton, Conn., U.S.A. Their engines are the German M.A.N. (Nuremberg) type built under licence.

K II.   **(For East Indies Marine.)**   1921 *Photo, by courtesy of R. F. Scheltema, Esq.*

1 *Hay-Denny* type: **K II** (launched 1917.) By M. Fijenoord, Rotterdam. Displacements: 560 tons *on surface,* 610 tons *submerged.* Dimensions: 177 × 16⅓ × 12·5 feet. Armament: 1—13 pdr. (anti-aircraft) and 6—17·7 inch torpedo tubes, of which two are on revolving twin deck mount within superstructure and before C.T., and are normally closed by sliding doors covering tube ports. Machinery: 2 sets, 8-cyl. 900 B.H.P. M.A.N.* Diesel engines=16 kts. *on surface.* Max. *submerged* speed 8½ kts. Endurance: 3500 miles (*normal*), 5500 miles (*extreme*), at 11 kts. *on surface;* 3 hours continuous running at 8½ kts. *submerged.* Begun 1914, completed 1921.

O. 7.

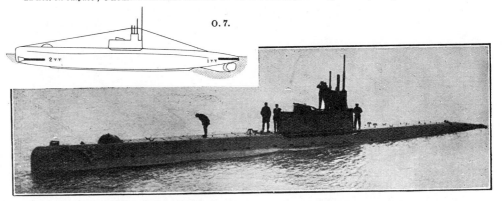

1918 *Photo, Fotopersbureau " Holland."*

1 *Hay-Denny* type: **O 7** (M. Fijenoord, Rotterdam, 1916). Displacements: about 180 tons *on surface,* 210 tons *submerged.* Dimensions: 105 × 12 × 9½ feet. 3—17·7 inch torpedo tubes (2 bow, 1 stern). Machinery: 1 set 6· cyl. M.A.N. Diesel engines=11½ kts. *on surface.* Max. *submerged* speed 9 kts. Endurance: 750 miles at 10 kts. *on surface;* 3 hours continuous running *submerged* at 8½ kts.

Appearance Note.—Has mast attached to a big stirrup which straddles C.T. and rises as high as periscope head. Has jumping wires fitted fore and aft.

Submarines—*continued.*

1918 *Photo, Fotopersbureau " Holland."*

¹ *Holland* type: **O 6** (K. M. de Schelde, Flushing, 1916). Displacements: about 190 tons *on surface*; 230 tons *submerged.* Dimensions: 112¼ × 12 × 9¼ feet. 3—17·7 inch torpedo tubes. 1 set of 6-cyl. M.A.N Diesel engines = 12 kts. *on surface*; *submerged* speed, 8·5 kts. Endurance as *O 7.*

O 6.

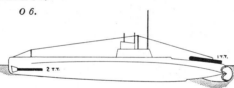

1930 *Photo, by courtesy of Ministry of Defence.*

⁴ *Holland* type: **O 2** (1911), **O 3** (1912, **O 4** and **O 5** (both 1913). All built by K. M. de Schelde, Flushing. Displacements: 130 tons *on surface*, 150 tons *submerged.* Dimensions: 98·4 × 9½ × 9 feet. Armament: 2—17·7 inch tubes (a spare torpedo carried for each). Machinery: 1 set 6-cyl. M.A.N. Diesel engines = 12 kts. *on surface.* *Max. submerged* speed 8¾ kts. Endurance: 500 miles at 10 kts. *on surface*; 3 hours continuous running at 8¾ kts. *submerged.*

Note.—*O 2* will be scrapped shortly.

Sloops (*Flottieljevaartuigen*).

SOEMBA. **East Indies Marine**. *1926 Photo. by courtesy of Chief of Naval Staff.*

FLORES (15th Aug., 1925), **SOEMBA** (24th Aug., 1925). Built at Rotterdam by M. Fijenoord and Wiltons, respectively, *JOHAN MAURITS VAN NASSAU*, Schelde Yard, Flushing. Displacement: 1457 tons. Dimensions: 248 × 37½ × 11¾ feet. Guns: 3—5.9 inch, 1—3 inch AA., 6 M.G. Machinery: 2 sets triple expansion, H.P. 2000 = 15 kts. 4 Yarrow boilers. Oil: 195 tons. Complement, 132.

Note.—These Vessels, which are intended for the defence of the Minefields at Surabaya, have 1″ armoured deck and C.T. They are fitted with Flettner rudders, and have accommodation for a seaplane.

Mine Layers (*Mijnenleggers*).
East Indies Marine.

KRAKATAU refitted.   1929 *Photo, by courtesy of Chief of Naval Staff.*

KRAKATAU (Surabaya D.Y., 1924). Displacement, 982 tons. Dimensions: $213 \times 34\frac{1}{2} \times 10\frac{1}{2}$ feet. Guns: **2**—3 inch AA., 4 M.G. H.P. 2500=17 kts. (*trials*). Complement, 80. Can carry 150/200 Mines. Reconstructed 1928, after funnel being removed.

PRO PATRIA.   1926 *Photo, by courtesy of Chief of Naval Staff.*

PRO PATRIA (Surabaya D.Y., July 21, 1922). Displacement, 612 tons. Dimensions: $154 \times 28\frac{1}{4} \times 9\frac{1}{4}$ feet. Guns: **1**—3 inch AA., 2 M.G. H.P. 650 = 10 kts. Reported to carry 80 mines of the latest type.

Mine Layers—*continued.*

DOUWE AUKES.   1926 *Photo, R. F. Scheltema, Esq.*

VAN MEERLANT.   1926 *Photo, by courtesy of Chief of Naval Staff.*

VAN MEERLANT (Nov. 24th, 1920), **DOUWE AUKES** (Feb. 23rd, 1922). First built under 1917 Naval Programme and the second under 1918 Naval Programme, by Werf Gusto, Schiedam. 687 tons. Dimensions: $180.5 \times 28.5 \times 10.4$ feet. Guns: **3**—13 pdr. semi-auto. "No. 4." Twin screws. Engines: 2 sets triple exp. surface condensation. I.H.P. 1200=13 kts. Coal: 80 tons. Complement, 60.

Of the same type as *Hydra* and *Medusa* (see next column), but faster and carry 60 mines. 2 steam winches for handling mines and double laying gears.

Mine Layers—*continued.*

1918 *Photo, Fotopersbureau "Holland."*

HYDRA (1911) & **MEDUSA** (1913). Both built at Amsterdam D.Y. 593 tons. Complement, 53. Dimensions: $163 \times 29.5 \times 9$ feet. Guns: 3—13 pdr. S.A. "No. 2" **1**—1 pdr., **1** M.G. Designed H.P. 800= 11.5 kts. Coal: 72 tons. Radius of action: 1440 miles at 6 kts. Each carries double laying gears for 70 mines.

Note.—*Hydra* sank off the "Wielingen" Light Ship by collision with T.B. Z 3, Feb., 1921; salved April, 1921 and again in service.

Special Note.

Fishery Protection Vessel *Nautilus* (described on a subsequent page) is fitted for minelaying.

(*Continued on next page.*)

Mine Layers—continued.

(East Indies Marine.)

HERKULES (Surabaya D.Y., 1909). Tug of 234 tons. Dimensions: 102·8 × 13·4 × 8·4 feet. Guns: **1**—1 pdr. 20 mines carried. I.H.P. 400 = 10·2 kts. 1 screw. Oil fuel : 45¼ tons = 2218 miles at 10 kts. Complement, 17.

Siboga.   (East Indies Marine.)

ASSAHAN* (1900), 685 tons ; **SERDANG*** (1897), 680 tons ; **SIBOGA*** (1898), 790 tons. About 173·2 × 31·2 × 12 feet average. Armament : **1**—4·1 inch, **1**—9 pdr. mortar, **4**—1 pdr. I.H.P. 1300 to 1400 = 13 to 14 kts. Coal : 130–150 tons. Complement : 100 (55 Europeans, 45 natives).
* Originally sisters to *Koetei* but on conversion to Mine Layers appearance of above three ships was considerably altered. Recently these vessels have also been employed as seaplane tenders.

Mine Layers—continued.

VULCANUS (Grimsby, 1902). Ex-steam trawler *Dolfijn*, 410 tons. Complement, 34. 123·7 × 21·6 × 10·5 feet. Guns : **3**—1 pdr., **1** M.G. H.P. 275 = 10 kts. Coal : about 140 tons. Double laying gear for 30 mines.

1920 *Photo, R. F. Scheltema, Esq.*

THOR (1877), **BALDER** (1878), **VIDAR, BULGIA** and **HADDA** (1879), ex-gunboats of 270-280 tons. Complement, 34-36. Carry 19 mines each (double mine-laying gear.) Guns : **2**—4 pdr. (semi-auto.) in *Balder* and *Hadda*, **2**—1 pdr. in *Vidar* and *Thor* ; **1** M.G. in all four. Speed : 7 kts. Coal : 30 tons. Double mine laying gears in all for 30 mines ;

And of similar appearance :

HAVIK (1875). Ex-gunboat of 210 tons. Guns : **2**—1 pdr., **1** M.G. Speed : About 6½-7 kts. Complement, 32. Coal : 18 tons. All these old vessels used for Harbour Training Service. Can carry 24 mines.

(East Indies Marine.)

Building.

PRINS VAN ORANJE, GOUDEN LEEUW, building at Rotterdam (" Maas "). Displacement : 1,206 tons. Dimensions : 230 × 36 × 11 feet. Guns : **2**—3″ AA. H.P. 1,750 = 15 kts.

Mine Sweepers. (*Mijnenvegers.*)
New Construction.

1921 *Illustration.*

I (Kuyck en van der Ree, Rotterdam), about 300 tons. **II** (Koopman Dordrecht), 300 tons. **III, IV** (v.d. Schuigt, Papendrecht), both 275 tons. Completed and taken over in 1918. Steel. Dimensions : (*I*) 92·5 × 20·6 × 9·6 feet ; (*II*) 100·7 × 20·5 × 10·2 feet ; (*III & IV*) 90·2 × 20 × 8·2 feet. Guns : **1** machine. Complement, 16. No more details available.

(East Indies Marine.)

1930 *Photo, by courtesy of Ministry of Defence.*

A, B, C, D. Completed 1930. Displacement : 190 tons. Dimensions : 148 × 20 × 5 feet. H.P. 700 = 14·5 kts. Complement, 30.

"Armoured" Gunboats (Pantserbooten).

BRINIO. Ventilators used as stanchions to forebridge. Small uncapped funnel.

1921 *Photo, R. F. Scheltema, Esq.*

FRISO. Thin and tall funnel.

GRUNO. Capped funnel and ensign gaff to mainmast.

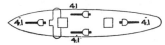

BRINIO (1912), **FRISO** (1912), **GRUNO** (1913). All built by Amsterdam D.Y. 540 tons. Complement, 52. Dimensions: 172·2 (*o.a.*) × 27·9 × 9·1 feet *max*. draught. Armament: 4—4·1 inch semi-automatic, 2 machine. Armour: 2″ Belt, ⅔″ Deck, 2″ Conning tower. Machinery: 2 sets Diesel engines (Germania, M.A.N., or Werkspoor types). B.H.P. 1200 = 14 kts. Oil, 34 tons.
These vessels are intended to guard mine fields.

Submarine Depot Ships (Depotschepen voor Onderzeebooten).

1925 *Photo, R. F. Scheltema, Esq.*

PELIKAAN (Nederland S. B. Co., Amsterdam, Dec. 31st, 1921). 2165 tons. Dimensions: 307 (*o.a.*) × 42½ × 13 feet. Guns: 4—3 in. (semi-auto) "No. 4," 4 M.G. M.A.N. Diesel Engines. H.P. 1400 = 12 kts. (electric drive). 2 screws. Oil fuel: 500 tons. Complement, 92. Provided for by 1918 Naval Programme. To carry 2 aeroplanes, stores for 6 submarines, and crews for 4 submarines. Workshops fully equipped for all ordinary repairs. Laid down, 1919; completed, 1922. 4 planes added to equipment since completion.

1918 *Photo, Fotopersbureau, "Holland."*

CORNELIS DREBBEL (1915). 668 tons. Dimensions: 166·8 × 32·8 × 6·8 feet. Guns: 1—1 pdr. Diesel engines. B.H.P. 170 = 6 kts. Oil fuel: 71 tons. Complement, 73.

Fishery Protection Vessel.

1930 *Photo, by courtesy of Ministry of Defence.*

NAUTILUS (Oct. 30th, 1929). Built by Rotterdam Dry Dock Co. Displacement: 800 tons. Dimensions: 180½ (*p.p.*), 191½ (*o.a.*) × 31 × 11½ feet. Guns: 1—3 inch, 2—40 m/m pom-poms. H.P. 1350 = 14 kts. Oil: 138 tons. Complement, 45. (This vessel can be equipped for minelaying. The 3″ gun is not mounted at present.)

Customs Patrol Vessels.
(East Indies Marine.)

1930 *Photo, by courtesy of Ministry of Defence.*

AREND (May 21st, 1929), **VALK** (Oct. 19th, 1929). Laid down 1928 by Fijenoord Co., for opium smuggling prevention in E. Indies. Displacement: 748 tons. Dimensions: 236½ × 29½ × 9 feet. H.P. 3350 = 18 kts. Guns: 2—3 inch. May carry a seaplane each.
Note.—Meaning of these names is "Eagle" and "Falcon."

Surveying Ship.

1930 *Photo, by courtesy of Ministry of Defence.*

(East Indies Marine.)

WILLEBRORD SNELLIUS (Fijenoord Co., Aug. 14th, 1928.)
Displacement: 930 tons Dimensions: 190 (*p.p.*), 203½ (*o.a.*) ×
31¾ × 11¼ feet. H.P. 525 = 10.5 kts. Oil: 170 tons. Guns:
1—3.5 inch, **2** M.G. Complement, 85.

Surveying Vessels (*Opnemingsvaartuigen*).

Photo Wanted.

EILERTS DE HAAN (25th June, 1919). Fijenoord Co. Rotterdam.
312 tons. Dimensions: 147·3 × 21·9 × 7 feet. No guns.
Designed H.P. 600 = 12 kts. Coal: 44 tons. Complement, 18.
Begun under 1915 Naval Programme. Completed May, 1921.

HYDROGRAAF (1911). 300 tons. Dimensions: 132·7 × 21·9 ×
9·6 feet. Guns: none. I.H.P. 360 = 9 kts. Coal: 30 tons.
Complement, 18.

Photo Wanted.

(East Indies Marine.)

TYDEMAN (Surabaya D.Y., 1916). 1320 tons. Dimensions: 226·4
× 32·8 × 11·8 feet. Guns: none. I.H.P. 814 = 10 kts. 1 screw.
Coal: 194 tons. Complement, 104.

Old Gunboats.
(Mostly employed as Harbour Tenders, or for Training purposes.)

HEFRING.   1921 *Photo, R. F. Scheltema, Esq.*

BRAGA, HEFRING, NJORD, TYR, FREIJR. Are old iron
twin-screw Gunboats, built 1876-79. 280 tons (*Hefring* and
Njord = 270 tons). Complements, 34-30. Dimensions: 91·5 to 91·8
(*o.a.*) × 26·9 × 7·8 to 8·1 feet (*max.* draught). Guns: In *Braga,
Hefring, Tyr*, **1**—4·7 inch "No. 3" or "No. 1," **2**—1 pdr., **1**
machine; in *Njord*, **1**—5·9 inch "No. 2," **3**—1 pdr. In *Freijr*,
1—5·9 inch "No. 1." H.P. 100 to 170 = 7½ to 8⅓ kts. Coal: 30
tons.

Training Ships.
(For Gunnery.)

Ex-Cruiser **GELDERLAND** (1898). 4030 tons. Guns: **8**—4·7 inch.
Is officially rated among "Training, Accommodation and Guard-
ships" and considered as non-effective for war duties.

Also

Sperwer (old Gunboat, 1875). 210 tons. Guns: **1**—13 pdr., "No. 2,"
3—1 pdr., **1** M.G. Speed: 7 kts.

Vessels in Dutch East Indies.

It should be carefully noted that there are three separate Naval Forces
on this Station, viz.:—

1. East Indies Squadron. Consists of ships sent out from Netherlands
   for service on this Station. Now on Station:—*De Zeven Provincien*,
   Sumatra, Java, and destroyers of *De Ruijter* class.
2. East Indies Marine (Indische Militaire Marine). This, as well as
   the vessels of the East Indies Squadron, comes under the orders
   of the Naval C.-in-C., East Indies Squadron, and sometimes combines with that Squadron for exercises and training. Consists
   of the sloops, *Flores, Soemba*, 4 Minesweepers, *A. B. C. D.*,
   6 Minelayers: *Herkules, Pro Patria, Krakatau, Assahan,
   Serdang, Siboga*, 3 torpedo boats of the *Draak* class, Depot
   Ship *Pelikaan*, all Submarines bearing index letter *K*, C.M.B's,
   and surveying ships *Tydeman, van Doorn, W. Snellius*.
   All these ships described on this and preceding pages.
3. East Indies Government Vessels, the property of the East Indies
   Government. Are used for Customs and Police Duties, &c.
   Some vessels armed with **4** and 1 pdr. guns. No full list of
   these craft available to date, but they include Cable Ships
   Telegraaf (1899), of 1500 tons gross, and *Zuiderkruis* (1923),
   2200 tons gross.

ROYAL NORWEGIAN NAVY.

(Revised, 1930, from information supplied by courtesy of H. E. the Minister of Defence.)

ENSIGN

JACK

MINISTER OF DEFENCE

COMMANDER IN CHIEF (ADMIRAL)

ADMIRAL

VICE ADMIRAL

REAR ADMIRAL

Red

White

Blue

Yellow

SQUADRON COMMR. (NOT OF ADMIRAL'S RANK)

DIVISION COMMANDER

NON.COM.OFFICER   PENNANT OF SENIORITY

COASTAL DEFENCES (FORTRESS ARTILLERY)

COM. IN CHIEF

COLONEL *

SUBORDINATE COMMANDING OFFICERS
MINING DIVISION

ROYAL STANDARD

✵ FORTRESS ARTILLERY
COLONEL . . . . 3 STARS
LT. COLONEL . . . . . 2 —
MAJOR ︷ WHEN IN ︷ 1 —
CAPTAIN ︷ COMMAND ︷ NO STAR

Modern Guns (Armstrong and Bofors). (Details officially revised 1930.)

Nota-tion.	Designation		Length in calibres	Model. •	Weight of Gun.	Weight of A.P. shot.	Initial velocity	Max. penetration firing A.P. capped at K.C.		Danger Space against average warship, at			Nom. Rounds per minute.
								5000 yards.	3000 yards.	10,000 yards.	5000 yards.	3000 yards.	
MEDIUM.	c/m. 20·9	inches. 8·2	44	A	tons. 18½	lbs. 309	ft. secs. 2300	6½	9¼	100	405	594	4
	14·91	5·9	46	A	7	100	2625	3	4½	67	215	440	8
	12	4·7	44	A	2¾	44	2570	...	...	...	...	...	10
LIGHT.	10·16	4	40	B	2	32	2545	...	...	...	...	...	20
	7·6	3	50	B	1	12	2820	...	...	...	...	...	...
	7·6	3	40	A	⅗	12	2210	...	...	...	...	...	...
	7·6	3†	25	B	⅖	12	1640	...	...	...	...	...	...
	7·6	3†	21	B	⅓	12	1500	...	...	...	...	...	...

* B = Bofors.   A = Armstrong.   † Anti-Aircraft.   There is also a 3 pdr. AA. gun and a 9 pdr. gun.

Minister of Defence.—Mr. M. A. Ryst. *Chief of Naval Staff.*—Rear-Admiral Jac. v. d. Lippe.
Naval Attaché, London.—Commander H. F. Dons.
Colour of Ships : Coast Defence Ships, Destroyers, Torpedo Boats, Gunboats, &c., all light grey.

British equivalents

Amiral.	Vice-Am.	Kontre-Am.	Komman-dör.	Kommandör-Kaptein.	Kaptein.	Premier-Löitnant.	Sekond-Löitnant.
Admiral.	Vice-Ad.	Rear-Ad.	Commodore.	Captain.	Commander.	Lieut-Com. & Lieut.	Sub-Lieut.

In relative rank Engineers have the same *without curl.*
  „   „   Doctors   „   „   „   and a *red* passe poil above upper stripe.
  „   „   Paymasters   „   „   „   „   *blue*   „   „   „

General Notes.—Personnel : About 1050 permanent, 1000 yearly conscripts, all seafaring men in reserve.

Mercantile Marine.—(From "Lloyd's Register," 1931). Total *gross* tonnage, 4,065,506.

GLOMMEN. LAUGEN.

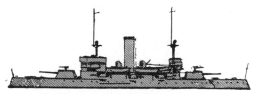

H. HAARFAGRE. TORDENSKJOLD.

FRIDTJOF NANSEN.

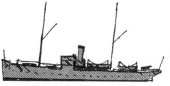

HEIMDAL.

FROYA.

NORGE. EIDSVOLD.

SNOGG. STEGG. TRYGG.

LAKS CLASS (8).

KJELL. SKARV. TEIST.

GARM. TROLL. DRAUG.

NORGE (March, 1900), EIDSVOLD (June, 1900).

Displacement, 4166 tons.　　Complement, 270.

Length (*p.p.*), 290 feet.　Length (*over all*), 301¼ feet.　Beam, 50½ feet.　*Max.* draught, 17⅔ feet.

Guns :
2—8·2 inch, 44 cal.
6—5·9 inch, 46 cal.
8—12 pdr.
2—3 pdr. AA.
Torpedo tubes (18 inch) :
2 *submerged.*

Armour (Krupp) :
6″ Belt...............
2″ Deck slopes ...
8″ Turrets ....
6″ Bases ....
5″ Casemates (NC)
6″ Conning tower

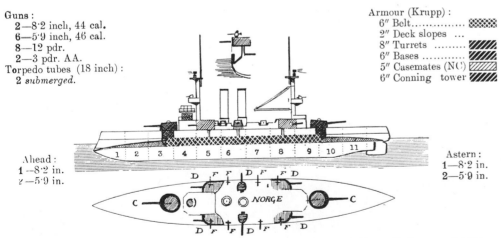

Ahead :
1—8·2 in.
2—5·9 in.

Astern :
1—8·2 in.
2—5·9 in.

Machinery : 2 screws.　Boilers : 6 Yarrow.　Designed H.P. 4500=16·5 kts.　Coal : *normal* 440 tons ; *maximum* 550 tons.

Notes.—Built by Armstrong.　Completed 1900–1901.　Machinery by Hawthorn, Leslie & Co.　Excellent seaboats, and still good for 15 kts.　On plans C=8·2 inch guns ; D=5·9 inch ; F=12 pdr. guns.

HARALD HAARFAGRE (Jan., 1897), TORDENSKJOLD (March, 1897).

Displacement, 3858 tons.　Complement, 249.

Length (*p.p.*), 279 feet.　Length (*over all*), 304 feet.　Beam, 48½ feet.　*Maximum* draught, 17⅔ feet.　*Mean* draught, 16½ feet.

Guns (Armstrong) :
2—8·2 inch, 44 cal.
6—4·7 inch, 44 cal.
6—12 pdr.
2—3 pdr. AA.
2—1 pdr. (Hotchkiss)
Torpedo tubes* :
2 *submerged.*

Armour (Harvey) :
7″ Belt (amidships)
4″ Belt ends ......
2″ Deck (flat on belt)
8″ Bulkheads ......
8″—5″ Turrets ...
6″ Bases of turrets
6″ Conning tower

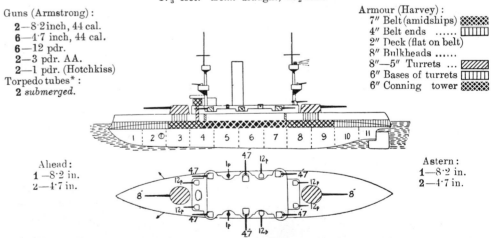

Ahead :
1—8·2 in.
2—4·7 in.

Astern :
1—8·2 in.
2—4·7 in.

Machinery : Boilers : 3 cylindrical.　2 screws.　Designed H.P. 4500=16·9 kts. (made 17·2 on *trial*, 1897-8).　Coal : *normal* 400 tons ; *maximum* 540 tons.

Notes.—Built by Armstrong, and completed 1897–8.　Engines by Hawthorn, Leslie & Co.　Belt is 174 feet long by 6½ feet deep.　Excellent seaboats, good for 14 kts. still.

* Tubes are 18 inch in H. Haarfagre and 17·7 inch in Tordenskjold.

Note.—*Tordenskjold* is employed as Cadets' Training Ship.

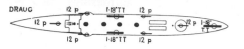

3 Destroyers (*Torpedobaatsjagare*).

"Large Torpedo Boats" (*Större Torpedobaater*).

TROLL.   *Photo added 1930, by favour of "Flottes de Combat."*

Garm (1913), **Draug** (1908), and **Troll** (1910). All built at Horten. 540 tons. Dimensions : 227 × 23½ × 8¾ feet. Armament : **6**—12 pdr., **3**—18 in. tubes. H.P. 7500 (8000 in *Garm*)=27 kts. Reciprocating engines in last two, turbines in *Garm*. Coal : 95 tons. Complement, 76.

Photo, by favour of "Flottes de Combat."

3 boats : **Snogg, Stegg, Trygg** (Horten, 1916-17). 220 tons. Dimensions : 173·9 × 18 × 5·2 feet. Guns : **2**—12 pdr. Tubes : **4**—18 inch. Designed H.P. 3500=25 kts. Fuel capacity : 30 tons coal *and* oil. Complement, 33.

GARM.   *1930 Photo, by courtesy of the Ministry of Defence.*
(Funnels raised and graded.)

SNOGG.   *1930 Photo, by courtesy of the Ministry of Defence.*

2nd Class Torpedo Boats *(Torpedobaater av II Kl.)*.

SKARV.   1925 *Photo, by favour of the Ministry of Defence.*

3 boats: **Kjell** (1912), 94 tons; **Skarv, Teist** (Karljohansvern, Horten. 1907-08). 92 tons. *Skarv, Teist*, **2**—3 pdr. guns. *Kjell* **1**—12 pdr. In all three boats, **3**—18 inch tubes, one bow and two deck aft. Speed of all three boats, 25 kts. H.P. 1700. Coal: 16 tons. Complement, 21.

8 boats: **Laks, Sild, Sael, Skrei** (1900). 90 tons and 21 kts.
Brand, Storm, Trods (1899). 20 kts. } 79 tons.
Hval (1896). 19 kts.

1918 *Photo, Wilse, Oslo.*

All armed with **2**—1 pdr. guns and **2**—18 inch tubes on deck. Complement, 19. Last two built by Schichau, Elbing. Others by Karl-Johansverns Verksted, Horten. H.P. 1000. Coal: 17 tons.

2nd Class Torpedo Boats—*continued.*

GRIB, JO, LOM, ORN, RAVN, as above photo.   1918 *Photo, Wilse, Oslo.*

5 boats: **Grib, Jo, Lom** (1906) and **Orn, Ravn** (1904). All 70 tons, and about 22—23 kts. Guns: **2**—1 pdr. but *Lom* has **2**—3 pdr. Complement, 16.

Note.—All above 5 boats have **2**—18 inch tubes, viz., 1 bow and 1 deck. All built in Norway.

1918 *Photo, Wilse, Oslo.*

4 boats: **Hauk, Falk** (1903), 63 tons; **Hvas, Kjœk** (1900), 64 tons. All have **2**—1 pdr. and 2 tubes (1 bow and 1 deck). First two 20 kts., others 19 kts. Complement, 14. Built in Norway.

(Same appearance as "Hauk," &c., above, but shorter funnels—v. Silhouettes.)

3 boats: **Kvik** (1897-98), 67 tons. **Blink, Lyn** (1896), 45 tons. All three boats 19 kts. speed. Guns: **2**—1 pdr. and **2**—18 inch tubes (1 bow, 1 deck). Complements, 14 for all. Built in Norway.

Note.—*Djerv* and *Dristig*, of this class, have been removed from Effective List.

9   Submarines   (*Undervandsbaater*).

B 2.   1925 *Photo, by favour of the Ministry of Defence.*

6 *Holland* type: **B 1** (1923), **B 2** (1 Oct.), 1924), **B 3** (1926), **B 4** (1 May, 1927) **B 5** (17 June, 1929), **B 6** (August, 1929) (all built at Horten).   420 tons *on surface* 545 tons *submerged.*   H.P. 900 = 14¾ kts. *on surface*, 700 = 9¾ kts. *when submerged.*   Dimensions: 167¼ × 17½ × 11½ feet.   Sulzer type Diesel engines, built at Horten.   Electric motors built in Norway. · Armament: 1—12 pdr., 4—18 inch torpedo tubes (2 bow, 2 stern).   Complement, 23.   Laid down 1915. *B 1* completed 1923, and reported to have been very successful, maintaining a speed of 14·5 kts. on trial. *B 2* completed in 1924, *B 3* in 1926, *B 4* in 1927. *B 5*, *B 6* both laid down in Dec. 1925, and will be completed in 1929 and 1930 respectively.

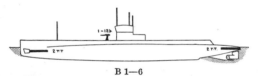

B 1—6

A 4.   *Photo added 1924.*

3 *Krupp-Germania* type: **A4-A2** (all 1914).   250 tons *on surface*, 335 tons *submerged.*   H.P. 700 = 14½ kts. *on surface*, 380 = 9 kts. *submerged.*   Complement, 15.   Dimensions: 152¼ × 16½ × 9¼ feet.   Surface engines: Krupp-Diesel. 3—18 inch tubes, 1 bow, 2 stern. 4 torpedoes carried.

Note.—*A5* completing at Kiel, was appropriated by Germany on outbreak of war and became the German *UA.*   Was surrendered at Harwich with other German Submarines; ceded to France for experiments, and demolished at Toulon, 1920-1.

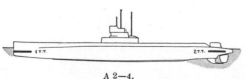

A 2—4.

Mine Layers.

FROYA.   1930 *Photo, by courtesy of the Ministry of Defence.*

FROYA (1916).   755 tons.   Complement, 79.   Dimensions : 248·7 × 27 × 8·2 feet.   Guns : 4—4 inch.   Tubes : 2—18 inch deck.   Designed H.P. 7000 = 22 kts.   Coal : 95 tons + 60 tons oil.   Carries about 200 mines.

To be built: **Mine Layer**—*2000 tons.*

GLOMMEN, LAUGEN.   1921 *Photo, by courtesy of the Ministry of Defence.*

GLOMMEN (1917), **LAUGEN** (1917).   Both built at Akers Yard, Oslo.   335 tons.   Complement, 39.   Dimensions : 137·8 × 27·9 × 6·2 feet.   Guns : 2—12 pdr.   Designed H.P. 170 = 9·5 kts.   Coal : 21 tons.   Each carries about 50 mines.

Fishery Protection Gunboat.

1931 *Photo, Lt. Comm. Steen Steensen.*

FRIDTJOF NANSEN. To be completed at Horten, 1931. Displacement: 1,300 tons. Complement, 70. Dimensions: 239·3 × 34·7 × 16·7 feet. Guns: 2—4″, 2—3 pdr. AA. I.H.P. 2,000 = 15 kts. Coal: 150 tons × 95 tons oil.

2nd Class Gunboat (*Kanonbaat av. 2 Kl.*).

Photo, Wilse, Oslo.

AEGER (1893). 383 tons. Complement, 43. Guns: 1—8·2 inch, 1—10 pdr., 2—4 pdr. H.P. 370 = 9·8 kts. Coal: 25 tons. *Max.* draught: 7¾ feet.

Old Gunboats.

Name.	Date.	Tons.	Crew.	Guns.	Speed kts.
Tyr ...	1888	281	44	1—4·7 in., 1—12,+2—1 pdr.	10·5
Gor ...	1885	276	44	1—4·7 in., 1—12 +2—1 pdr.	10·5
Vidar ...	1881	254	41	1—4·7 in., 1—3,+2—1 pdr.	9·5
Brage	1876				8·5
Nor ...	1878	254	38		8·5
Vale ...	1878	233	41	1—4·7 in 3—1 pdr.	8
Uller	1874				

(All fitted as Minelayers).

VALE (as Minelayer) on right. 1918 *Photo, S. Anderson, Esq.*

Fishery Protection Vessel.

Photo, Wilse, Oslo.

HEIMDAL (1892). 610 tons. Complement, 62. Length, 181 feet. Draught, 13 feet. Guns: 4—12 pdr. H.P. 625 = 12 kts. Coal: 92 tons.

Transport (*Transportskib.*)

1918 *Photo, Wilse, Oslo.*

FARM (1900). 300 tons. Complement, 32. Guns: 2—9 pdr., 2—1 pdr. Speed: 10 kts.

Submarine Depot Vessel.

SARPEN (1860). (Rebuilt, 1918). 187 tons. Guns: 2—9 pdr., 1—1 pdr. Speed: 9 kts.

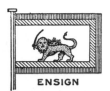

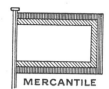

ENSIGN   MERCANTILE

7 Motor Gunboats.

1931 *Photo*.

CHAROKH (July 26, 1931), **SIMORGH** (August 3, 1931), **KARKAS** (August 3, 1931), **RAKER** (August 3, 1931). + 3 Building. Laid down 1930 at Cant. Nav. Riuniti (Palermo and Ancona) and Cant. Partenopei (Naples). Displacement : 331 tons. Dimensions : 170 (*p.p.*) × 22 × 5·75 (*mean*) feet. Guns : 2—76 mm. and 2 pompoms AA. Machinery : 2—450 B.H.P. Fiat diesels=15·5 kts.

1931 *Photo, favour of the Builders.*

BABR (Tiger) **PALANG** (Panther). Built by Cantieri Navali Riuniti. Palermo, 1930-31. Displacement : 950 tons. Dimensions : 204·7 (*p.p.*) × 29.5 × 9.8 feet. Guns : Machinery : 2 Diesels of 950 H.P.=1900 H.P.=15 kts.

Gunboats.

1924 *Photo, R. G. Strugnell, Esq.*

MOZAFFER (Nantes, 1899). Dimensions : 135 (*o.a.*) × 26 × 13 feet. 379 tons. No other details known. Served with and in H.M. Navy during the War. Re-conditioned by H.M. Dockyard, Bombay before return to Persian Navy.

PAHLAVI. This vessel is believed to be an ex-Minesweeper of German F.M. type, built 1917, and purchased 1923, for £4000. Displacement : (*normal*) 135 tons. Dimensions : 132½ (*w.l.*) × 19⅔ × 4 feet *normal* draught. Guns : 1—3 pdr. Machinery : 2 sets triple expansion. Oil fuel : 35 tons. I.H.P. 800 = 16 kts. (after alterations). Complement, 14.

Note.—There was formerly a gunboat on the Caspian, which was captured by Soviet Forces in May, 1920, and is believed to have been retroceded to Persia.

Gunboats—*continued.*

Photo, Lieut. Frewen, R.N.

PERSEPOLIS (1885). Dimensions : 207 × 32¾ × 19½ feet. 1200 tons. H.P. 450 = 10 kts. Guns : 4 old 2.7 inch, 2 machine. Still in service, 1921.

PERUVIAN FLEET.

Officially Revised by courtesy of the Director del Material, Ministry of Marine, Lima, 1929.

PERU ENSIGN

Rear-Admirals' flag similar to ensign but has a sun in place of arms in centre.

PERUVIAN CAPTAIN

Mercantile flag the same but without centre device.

Colour of Ships: Grey.

Minister of Marine: Señor Nuñez Chavez.
Naval Attaché (London): Commander Manuel D. Faura.

There is at present an American Naval Mission in charge of the re-organisation of the Peruvian Fleet, under Captain William S. Pye, U.S.N., with rank of Rear-Admiral (Peruvian).

Uniforms. (Device within circle is a radiant sun.)

As Contra-Almirante but with 2 thin stripes

Vice-Almirante.	Contra-Almirante.	Capitan de Navio.	Capitan de Fragata.	Capitan de Corbeta.	Teniente 1°.	Teniente 2°.	Alferez de Fragata.
Vice-Admiral.	*Rear-Admiral.*	*Captain.*	*Commander. Senior.*	*Commander. Junior.*	*Lieut. Comm'r.*	*Lieut.*	*Sub. Lieutenant.*

All branches have the same stripes, but Doctors have a torch with entwined snakes in place of a radiant sun, and red material between stripes.

Mercantile Marine.

(From "Lloyd's Register," 1931 figures). Total *gross* tonnage, 64,686.

PERUVIAN RECOGNITION SILHOUETTES.

Scale : 1 inch = 160 feet.

C. BOLOGNESI.

A. GRAU.

LIMA (funnels now shortened).

T. RODRIGUEZ t.b.d.

Submarines :—

R 1—R 4.

Cruisers.

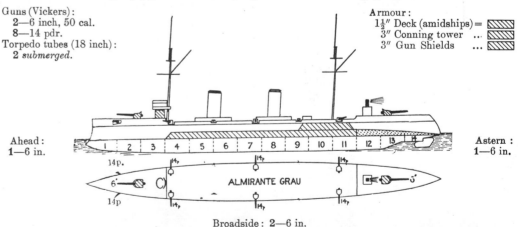

CORONEL BOLOGNESI. The A. Grau is identical *except* that she has a poop.

ALMIRANTE GRAU (March, 1906) & **CORONEL BOLOGNESI** (Nov., 1906).

Displacement : 3,200 tons. Complement, 315.

Length (*p.p.*), 370 feet. Beam, 40½ feet. *Maximum* draught, 14¼ feet.

Guns (Vickers) :
  2—6 inch, 50 cal.
  8—14 pdr.
Torpedo tubes (18 inch) :
  2 *submerged.*

Armour :
  1½" Deck (amidships) =
  3" Conning tower ...
  3" Gun Shields ...

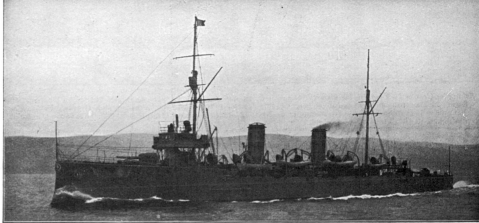

Ahead :
1—6 in.

Astern :
1—6 in.

Broadside : 2—6 in.

Machinery : 4 cylinder vertical triple expansion. 2 screws. Boilers : 10 Yarrow (converted to oil burning). Designed H.P. 14,000 = 24 kts. Oil : *normal*, 500 tons ; Endurance : 3,700 miles at 10 kts.

General Notes.—Built and engined by Messrs. Vickers, Ltd., about 1905-7. Refitted at Balboa, boilers being re-tubed and modified for oil burning, 1923-25. Both ships are now good for 23·5 kts. at sea. *Grau* is at present employed as fleet flagship.

Gunnery Notes.—Italian Giradelli type training indicators are believed to have been added to gunnery equipment.

Destroyer.

Photo by courtesy of Messrs. Schneider et Cie.

1 *Schneider-Creusot* :—**Teniente Rodriguez** (1909, ex-*Actée*). 490 tons. Dimensions: 212×21·3×14¾ feet. H.P. 8,600 = 28 kts. (present best speed 25 kts.). Schneider-Zoelly turbines, du Temple boilers (retubed 1922) Coal: 100 tons = 1200 miles at 10 kts. Armament: **6**—3 pdr., **2**—18 inch tubes. Complement 60. This vessel is regularly employed in the Training of Cadets.

Submarines.

R 1.

1927 Photo, by courtesy of Electric Boat Co.

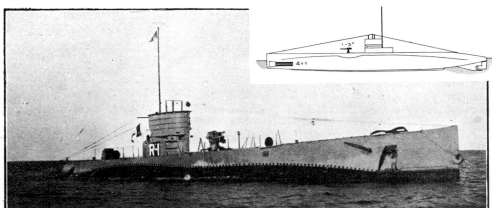

R1.   *Official Photo, 1927.*

6 *Electric Boat Co.* type : **R 1** (April, 1926), **R 2** (May, 1926), **R 3** (April 21st, 1928), **R 4** (May 10th, 1928). Built for contractors (Electric Boat Co.) by New London Ship & Engine Co., of Groton, Conn. *Surface* displacement, 576 tons. *Submerged* displacement, 682 tons (exclusive of non-watertight parts), 755 tons (inclusive of such parts). Length, 200 feet. 2 Nelseco Diesel engines, together 880 H.P. = 14.5 kts. Electric motors of 1000 B.H.P. = 9.5 kts. Radius of action : 8000 miles. Guns : **1**—3 inch. Tubes : **4**—21 inch. (bow). Complement, 30.

Note.—R 1, R 2, on delivery, completed an unescorted trip from New London to Callao, without mishap, arriving in good order. R 3, R 4 delivered in summer of 1928 : R 5, R 6 are projected, having been authorised in 1926.

Training Ship.

CONTRAMAESTRE DUEÑAS (ex-*Hebe*, ex-*Vortigern*). Steel 4-masted barque, built by R. Williamson & Son, Workington, 1891. 2469 tons gross. Dimensions : 305½ × 42⅛ × —feet.

Submarine Depot Ship.   (Classed as Cruiser.)

LIMA (Ex-*Socrates*, Kiel, 1880). 1790 tons. H.P. 2000 = 14 kts. Coal : 300 tons. Guns : **3**—4 inch, **4**—3 pdr. Complement, 150.

Note.—This Ship was completely refitted 1927-8 and can now make her designed speed. Radius is 3,000 miles at 10 kts.

LIMA.   *Photo added 1927.*

River Gunboats. (UPPER AMAZON FLOTILLA).

AMERICA.   *1927 Photo, by courtesy of Ministry of Marine.*

AMERICA (1904). Steel. 240 tons. Dimensions : 133 × 19½ × 4½ feet. Guns : **4**—3 pdr., **2** M.G. I.H.P. 350 = 14 kts. Coal : 42 tons. Complement, .

NAPO (1925). Steel. 57 tons. Dimensions : 100×18×5 feet. Guns : **3**—3 pdr. Speed : 12 kts.

IQUITOS (1875). Rebuilt 1896. 50 tons. Dimensions : 77×12×7½ feet. Guns : **1**—3 pdr.. **2** M.G. Speed : 7·5 kts.

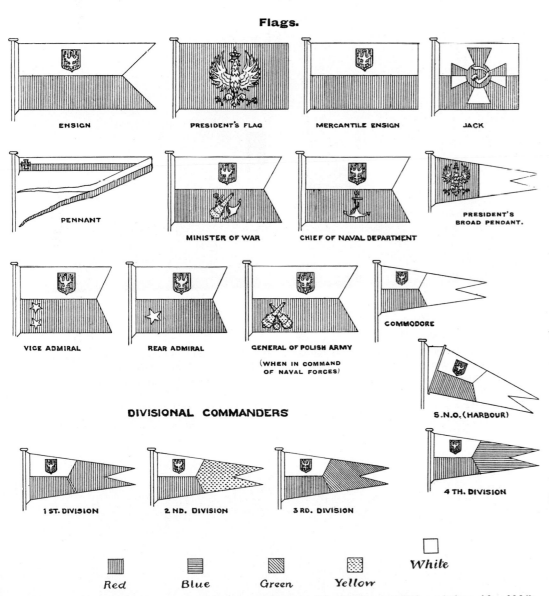

Flags.

ENSIGN

PRESIDENT'S FLAG

MERCANTILE ENSIGN

JACK

PENNANT

MINISTER OF WAR

CHIEF OF NAVAL DEPARTMENT

PRESIDENT'S BROAD PENDANT.

VICE ADMIRAL

REAR ADMIRAL

GENERAL OF POLISH ARMY
(WHEN IN COMMAND OF NAVAL FORCES)

COMMODORE

S.N.O. (HARBOUR)

DIVISIONAL COMMANDERS

1 ST. DIVISION

2 ND. DIVISION

3 RD. DIVISION

4 TH. DIVISION

Red   Blue   Green   Yellow   White

Note.—The Emblem in the centre of the Jack is a flesh-coloured arm holding a steel-blue scimitar with gold hilt. The covering over shoulder of the arm is pale blue and has a gold-tasselled fringe.

Minister of War.—Marshal Pilsudski.

Chief of the Naval Department.—Acting Rear-Admiral G. Swirski.

Military and Naval Attaché (London).—Major Count R. Michalowski.

Personnel.—250 officers, 2500 men; total, 2750.

Colour of Warships.—Pearl grey; of *Naval River Craft*, grey-green.

Uniforms.

a)=Polish Rank.   (b)=Equivalent British Rank.

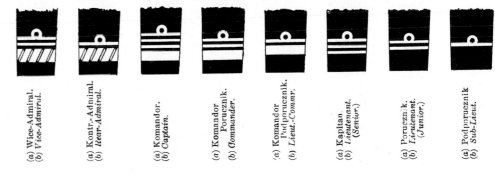

(a) Wice-Admiral. (b) Vice-Admiral.	(a) Kontr-Admiral. (b) Rear-Admiral.	(a) Komandor. (b) Captain.	(a) Komandor Porucznik. (b) Commander.	(a) Komandor Podporucznik. (b) Lieut.-Commr.	(a) Kapitan. (b) Lieutenant. (Senior.)	(a) Porucznik. (b) Lieutenant. (Junior.)	(a) Podporucznik. (b) Sub-Lieut.

Arsenals, Shipbuilders, &c.

A new naval base and dockyard is under construction at Gdynia, to be completed 1930.

MODLIN. Arsenal. Repair shops and plant for building hulls up to 100 tons.

PINSK. War port. Repair shops.

Unofficially reported that Naval Training Colleges have been established at Tczew (Dirschau) and Thorn, the Gunboat *Gen. Haller* carrying out instructional cruises for latter school.

At Pulawy, Warsaw, Plock and Thorn, establishments belonging to the Ministry of Public Works.

Private Establishments.—(a) Paruszewski, at Wloclawek; (b) Gornicki, at Plock; (c) Ateliers du Commerce et de la Navigation, at Warsaw; (d) Zieleniewski, at Cracow, for building machinery; (e) Lloyd Bydgoski, at Bromberg.

Mercantile Marine.

Official Polish figures, 1927.

32 Steamers of 33,775 tons; 90 Sailing Vessels, with auxiliary motors, of 3,600 tons. (There are besides 127,568 tons of shipping under the flag of Danzig). River Craft amount to 8,350 tons steam, 109,300 tons various.

"Lloyd's Register" 1931: 66,156 *gross* tonnage.

RECOGNITION SILHOUETTES.

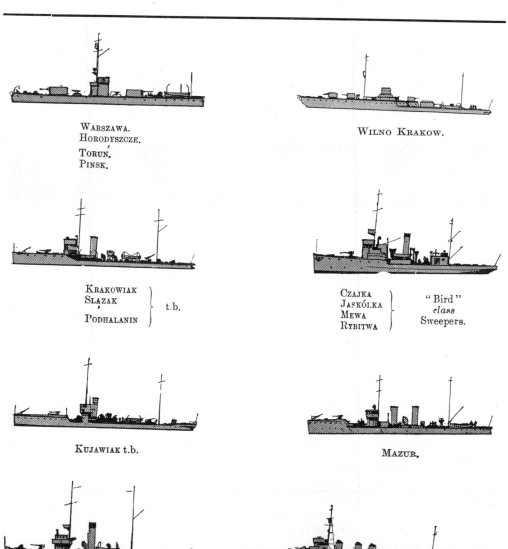

WARSZAWA.
HORODYSZOZE.
TORUN.
PINSK.

KRAKOWIAK
SLAZAK
PODHALANIN } t.b.

KUJAWIAK t.b.

KOMENDANT PILSUDSKI
GENERAL HALLER } Gunboats.

WILNO KRAKOW.

CZAJKA
JASKÓLKA
MEWA
RYBITWA } "Bird" class Sweepers.

MAZUR.

BURZA.
WICHER. } Destroyers.

Gunboats (*Lodzie Kanonierskie*).

1922 Photo, Comm. Filanowicz, P.N.

KOMENDANT PILSUDSKI } (Crichton, Abö, Finland, 1918-19.) } Completed Jan., 1921.
GENERAL HALLER } „ 1920.

Displacement: 342 tons *normal*, ? tons *full load*. Complement, 60. Length, (*p.p.*) 154·2 feet, (*o.a.*) 164½ feet. Beam, 22¾ feet. Designed load draught, 7 ft. 7 ins. Guns: 2—12 pdr., 2—3 pdr.

Machinery: 2 sets triple expansion. 2 screws. Boilers: Normand. Designed I.H.P., 1000=15 kts. at 120 r.p.m. Coal capacity: 50 tons *normal*=700 miles at full speed.

Notes.—Belong to a Class of four vessels originally ordered for the Russian Navy, and designed by General Borowski late Chief of Naval Construction, Russian Baltic Fleet. The above two purchased from Finland; the remaining two added to Finnish Navy as *Karjala* and *Turunmaa* (*q.v.*). The above two Gunboats are for service in the Baltic, and for showing the Polish Flag in distant seas.

2 Destroyers.

WICHER.

1930 *Photo, by favour of M. Le Masson.*

Burza (April 16th, 1929), **Wicher** (July 10th, 1928). Both laid down by Chantiers Navals Français, Blainville, Nov. 1st, 1926, and Feb. 19th, 1927. respectively. Displacement : 1500 tons. Dimensions : 344 (*w.l.*), 351 (*o.a.*) × 29 × 9¾ feet. draught. Guns : **4**—5.1 inch, **2**—1.5 inch AA. Torpedo tubes : **6**—20.8 inch, in triple deck mountings. Machinery : Geared turbines (supplied by At. & Ch. de la Loire). H.P. 35,000 = 33 kts.

Notes.—Design of these vessels follows closely that of French *Simoun* class. Meanings of names are : *Burza*, Squall ; *Wicher*, Hurricane. Completed 1930.

5 Torpedo Boats (*Torpedouce*).

Transferred to Poland, Nov. 4th, 1920.

1922 *Photo, Commr. Filanowicz, P.N.*

1 "*A III*" *type* : **Kujawiak** (ex-German *A 68*). Built by Schichau, Elbing, during 1917. Displacement : 335 tons *normal*, 355 tons *max.* load. Dimensions : 196·9 (*o.a.*) × 21 × 7·4 feet. Guns : **2**—12 pdr., **2** M.G. Tubes : **1**—17.7 inch. H.P. 5800=27·1 kts. *on trials.* Fuel : 76 tons (*on trials*) 82 tons *max.* capacity = 725 miles at 20 kts. Complement, 69.

Notes.—*A 68* re-fitted by H.M. Dockyard, Rosyth, 1921. *A 69* was in so bad a state as to be not worth re-fitting ; ex-German *V 105* (ceded to Brazil, but not required by that country) was taken over in place of *A 69*.

KRAKOWIAK.

1922 *Photo, Commr. Filanowicz, P.N.*

3 "*A III*" *type* : **Krakowiak** (ex-German *A 64*), **Podhalanin** (ex-*A 80*), **Slazak** (ex-German *A 59*). Built by Vulkan, Stettin, 1916-17. Displacement : 365 tons *normal*, 380 tons *max. load*. Dimensions : 196·8 (*o.a.*) × 21 × 6 feet. Guns : **2**—12 pdr., **2** M.G. Tubes : **1**—17.7 inch. H.P. *about* 6050=28·38 kts. *on trials.* Fuel : 85 tons (*on trials*), 91·67 tons *max.* capacity. Complement, 69.

Notes.—*A 64* re-fitted 1921, by H.M. Dockyard, Rosyth.

1922 *Photo, Comm. Filanowicz, P.N.*

1 *ex-German* boat : **Mazur** (ex-German *V 105*). Built by Vulkan, Hamburg, 1914-15. Displacement : 349 tons *normal*, 421.2 tons *max.* load. Dimensions : 205.6 (*o.a.*) × 20.4 × 7.4 feet. Guns : **2**—12 pdr., **2** M.G. Tubes : **2**—17.7 inch. H.P. 6000 = 30 kts., *on trials* 5500 = 28 kts. Fuel : 59.7 tons coal + 16.2 tons oil = 640 miles at 20 kts. Complement, 74.

Notes.—Original four boats of this class begun for Netherlands Navy as *Z 1—Z 4* ; taken over by Germany, August, 1914, re-numbered *V 105—108*. *V 107* War Loss. *V 106* of this class assigned to Brazil, but sold to England. *Kaszub* (ex-*V 108*) sunk by explosion in July, 1925, and subsequently discarded as not worth repair.

Armed River Steamers.

HETMAN CHODKIEWICZ.　　　　1924 Official Photo.

ADMIRAL SIERPINEK, GENERAL SOSNKOWSKI, GENERAL SIKORSKI, HETMAN CHODKIEWICZ, ADMIRAL DICKMAN, GENERAL SZEPTYCKI. 100-200 tons. 8-9 kts. Guns: 2—14 pdrs., and 4 M.G. "Armour plated." Complement, 38.

River Motor Boats.

30 boats. 7-13 tons. 10 kts. Guns: **1**—1 pdr., **2 M.G.**

Mine Sweepers (Traulery).

RYBITWA.　　　　Photo 1922, Comm. Filanowicz, P.N.

CZAJKA (Plover), **JASKÓLKA** (Swallow), **MEWA** (Seagull), **RYBITWA** (Sea Swallow). Built by various German shipyards. First two completed 1919. Last two completed 1917. Normal Displacement: 170·98 tons (203 tons full load). Dimensions: (p.p.) 131¼, (w.l.) 132½, (o.a.) 140¾ × 19⅔ × 4 feet normal draught, 5 feet "medium load" draught. Guns: 1—3 pdr., 2 M.G. Machinery: 2 sets triple expansion and one Normand or Schulz-Thornycroft boiler. I.H.P. 700 = 12 to 13 kts. speed. Coal: 20 tons normal; 34·6 tons full load. Oil: 4 tons. Complement, 44.
Notes.—Ex-German "F. M. Boote," i.e. flat-bottomed Mine "searchers." Performed very little service in German Navy. Purchased by Poland, 1921.

Surveying Ship (Statek Hydrograficzny.)

1924 Official Photo.

POMORZANIN (ex-German S.S. Vulkan, built by Boücke & Sieg, 1890). Displacement: 275 tons. Dimensions: 117½ × 20¾ × 8½ feet. Guns: 2—3 pdr., 2 M.G. Machinery: 2 sets triple expansion, I.H.P. 250 = 8 kts. 2 screws. 1 cyl. boiler. Coal: 46 tons. Complement, 34.

Transports (Transportowce).

Photo wanted.

WILJA. Displacement: 8400 tons. Dimensions: 342¼ × 46 × 19½ feet. Speed: 10 kts. Complement, 53.

Training Ships.

KRAL WLADISLAW IV.　　　　1929 Photo.

KRAL WLADISLAW IV (La Seyne, 1896). Displacement: 8000 tons. Dimensions: 393½ × 58½ × 23½ feet. Guns: Not reported. Designed H.P. 13,500 = 19 kts. (now much less). Depot and Training Ship at Gdynia.
Notes.—This vessel is ex-French Cruiser d'Entrecasteaux, which, having been presented to Belgium for use as a Training Ship, was retroceded to France on the suppression of the Belgian Navy, and acquired by Poland, in July, 1927.

ISKRA (1917). Auxiliary 3-masted Schooner, purchased in Netherlands, 1927. Displacement: 300 tons. Dimensions: 127¾ × 25 × 9¾ feet. H.P. 130 = 　 kts. Sea-going Tender to Kral Wladislaw IV.

River Monitors (Monitory).

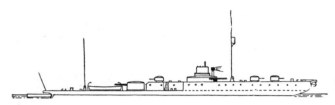

WILNO (1925), **KRAKOW** (1925), and 2 others (not yet named), building by Zieleniewski, Cracow, for completion in 1928. Displacement: 70 tons. Dimensions: 115 × 20 × 1.25 feet normal draught. Guns: 1—4.1 inch, 2—12 pdr., 3 M.G. Armour: Not reported. Machinery: 2 sets oil motors, each 70 H.P. = 9 kts. Complement, 35.

HORODYSZCZE and PINSK.　　　　Official Photo, 1922.

WARSZAWA (1920), **HORODYSZCZE** (1920), **TORUŃ** (1920), **PINSK** (1920). "Armoured Monitors" built by Gdansk Shipyard, 1920, for service on the Vistula. Displacement: 110 tons normal, 135 deep load. Dimensions: 113·2 (o.a.) × 16·56 × 2·3 feet normal draught, 2·6 feet deep load. Guns: 2—4·1 inch, 5 M.G. Armour: ⅓" side amidships, ½" turrets, —" C.T. Machinery: 3 sets 60 B.H.P. Daimler motors totalling 180 B.H.P. = 9·1 kts. Petroleum fuel, 5 tons normal, 10 tons max. capacity = 1500 miles at 8 kts. Complement, 34.

3 Submarines (*Minelayers*).

WILK.   1930 *Photo, by courtesy of Messrs. Augustin Normand.*

3 *Normand-Fenaux* type : **Rys** (At. & Ch. de la Loire, Nantes), April 22, 1929,   **Zbik** (Ch. Navals Français, Blainville),   **Wilk** (Ch. & At. Augustin Normand, Le Havre, April 12, 1929). Displacement: $\frac{980}{1250}$ tons. Dimensions : 216 × 10 × 13 feet. Guns : **1**—3.9 inch, **1**—1.5 inch AA.   Torpedo tubes : **6**—20.8 inch.   Mines carried: **32.** 2 sets Vickers-Normand Diesels, H.P. 1800 = 14 kts. on *surface*. Electric motors, B.H.P. 1200 = 9 kts. *submerged*.   Radius of action : 7000 miles on *surface*, 100 miles *submerged*. Diving limit : 44 fathoms.

Carry **10** torpedoes and **40** mines.

Notes.—Majority of above particulars are official.   Meanings of names are as follows : *Rys*, Lynx ; *Wilk*, Wolf; *Zbik*, Wild Cat.

Wilk is prototype of the class, and all were built to Normand plans.

PARAGUAY.

Armoured River Gunboats.

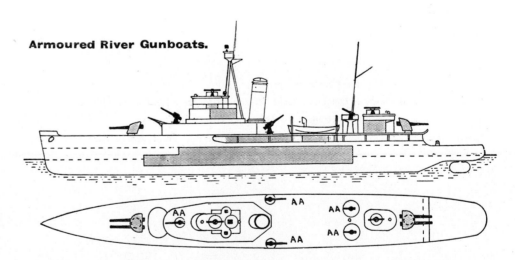

COMODORO DEZA, CAPITAN CABRAL: (both 1930). Built by Odero, Genoa. Displacement : 745 tons (865 tons full load).   Dimensions : 230 × 35 × 5½ feet draught. Guns : 4—4.7 inch, 3—3 inch AA, 2 pom-pom (40 *m/m*).   H.T. Armour: ½″ side amidships, ¼″ deck, ¾″ C.T.   Parsons turbines and oil-fired boilers.   H.P. 3,800 = 18 kts. 170 tons oil and feed water. Radius 1700 miles at 16 kts.   Complement, 86.   Completed 1930.

PORTUGUESE FLEET.

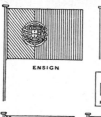

ENSIGN

JACK

MINISTRO DA MARINHA

KEY

RED   GREEN

CHEFE DE ESTADO MAYOR

VICE-ALMIRANTE COMMANDANTE EM CHEFE

CONTRA-ALMIRANTE COMMANDANTE EM CHEFE DIRECTOR GERAL DE MARINHA

MINISTROS

GENERAL COMMANDANTE DE DIVISÃO

CHEFE DO ESTADO

CONTRA-ALMIRANTE DEBAIXO D'ORDENS

CAPITÃO DE MAR E GUERRA COMMANDANDO DIVISÃO OU FORCAS ESTACIONADAS

COMMANDANTE SUPERIOR

Naval Uniforms.

British rank.

Almirante.*	Vice- Almirante.†	Contra- Almirante.‡	Capitão de Mare Guerra.	Capitão de Fragata.	Capitão Tenente.	Primeiro Tenente.	Segundo Tenente.	Guard Marinha.
Admiral.	*Vice- Admiral.*	*Rear- Admiral.*	*Captain.*	*Commander. (Senior.)*	*Commander. (Junior.)*	*Lieut.- Commander and Lieut.*	*Sub- Lieut.*	*Midshipman.*

* Admiral has four *gold* stars.   † Vice-Admiral has three *gold* stars.   ‡ Rear-Admiral has three *silver* stars.
Staff officers same but *without* executive curl. Colour between stripes—*Surgeons*: red; *Engineers*: violet; *Paymasters*: blue; *Constructors*: purple red.   On visor of cap, *Admirals*: 2 oak leaves; *Captains*: 1 oak leaf; *Commanders*: 1 narrow stripe.   Uniforms like British Navy.   Chin strap of gold cord, but officers of lieutenant's rank and below have black chin straps.

Minister of Marine: Captain Magalhaes Correa.

Chief of the Naval Mission (London): Capt. Fernando Augusto Pereira de Silva.

Personnel: 689 officers and 5670 men.   *Colour of Ships:* Dark grey.

Mercantile Marine: (From "Lloyd's Register," 1931 figures.)   Total *gross* tonnage, 276,357.

LIMPOPO.

ACOR.

BEIRA class (8).

CINCO DE OUTUBRO.

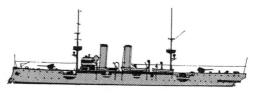

ADAMASTOR.

VASCO DA GAMA.

REPUBLICA.   C. ARAUJO.

TAMEGA.   GUADIANA.

Aircraft Tender.

(Building)

SACADURA CABRAL (Building).

Cantieri Riunii dell' Adriatico (Trieste).

Displacement (*normal*) : 5100 tons.

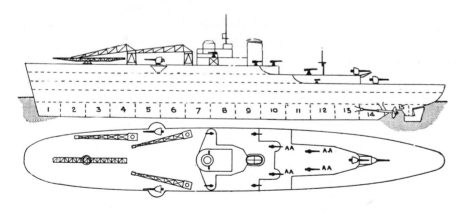

Dimensions : 406·8 × 57·3 × 32·8 feet.

124 × 17·5 × 10 meters.

Guns :

4—4·7 inch (120/50).

4—3 inch AA. (76/50).

4—Pompoms (40 mm.).

2—Bomb Throwers.

Capacity :

14 Hydroplanes.

Machinery : 2 geared turbines.　2 screws.　S.H.P : 14,000 = 22 kts.　Radius : 10,000 miles at 12 kts.　4 Yarrow boilers.　Oil : 830 tons.

Notes.—Design closely follows that of H.M.A.S. *Albatross.*

Cruisers.
1st class.

(Building)

ALFONSO DE ALBUQUERQUE (Building) *BARTOLOMEU DIAS* (Building).

Odero—Terni—Orlando (Genoa).

Displacement (*normal*) : 2,100 tons.

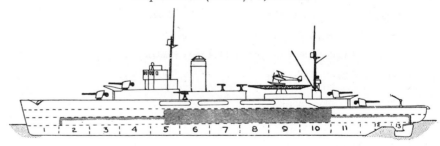

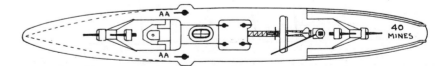

Dimensions : 326·4 × 44·2 × 22·9 feet.

99·6 × 13·5 × 7 meters.

Guns :

4—4·7 inch (120/50).

2—3 inch AA. (76/50).

4—Pompoms (40 mm.).

Fitted to carry 40 mines.

Machinery : Geared turbines.　S.H.P.: 8000 = 21 kts.　Radius : 8000 miles at 10 kts.　4 Yarrow boilers.

Notes.—Original design included two funnels and a light tripod mast forward.

2nd Class

2nd Class

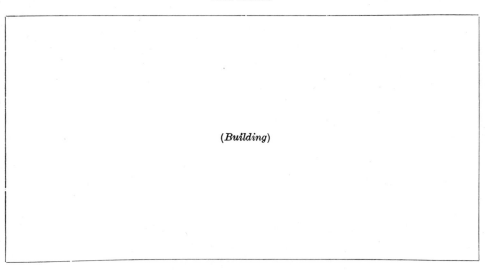

(*Building*)

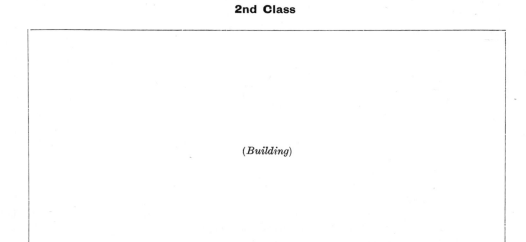

(*Building*)

PEDRO NUNES (Building), *GONÇALO VELHO* (Building).

R. & W. Hawthorne Leslie & Co.

Displacement (*normal*) : 1174 tons (metric).

Dimensions : 267·9 (*o.a.*) × 34·7 × 16·7 feet.
81·7 × 10·67 × 5·18 meters.

Guns :
3—4·7 inch (120/50).
2—Pompoms (40 mm.).

GONÇALVES ZARCO (Building)

Lisbon Arsenal

Displacement (*normal*) : 1017 tons (metric).

Dimensions : 231·5 (*o.a.*) × 32·8 × 16·4 feet.
70·5 × 10 × 5 meters.

Guns :
2—4·7 inch (120/50).
2—3 inch (76/50).
4—Pompoms (40 mm.).

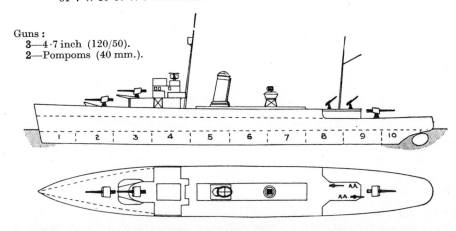

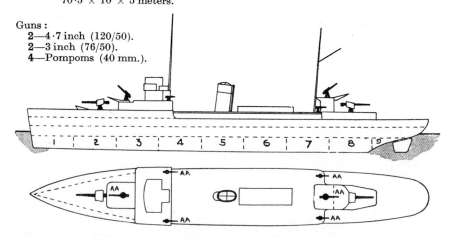

Machinery : Geared turbines. S.H.P.: 2000 = 16·5 kts. Radius : 6000 miles at 10 kts.
Oil : 335 tons.

Machinery : 2 Diesel motors. B.H.P.: 2400 = 16 kts. Radius : 8000 miles at 10·5 kts.
Oil :   tons.

REPUBLICA. C. ARAUJO of similar appearance. *1921 Photo, by courtesy of the Ministry of Marine.*

(Crowsnest now removed.)

1919 Photo.

VASCO DA GAMA (Blackwall, 1876, reconstructed and lengthened by Orlando, 1902). 2982 tons. Comp., 259. Dimensions: $232 \cdot 9 \times 40\frac{1}{4} \times 18\frac{1}{4}$ feet. Guns (re-armed 1922) **1**—8 inch (40), **1**—6 inch (45), **1**—4 inch (40), **6**—14 pdr. No torpedo tubes. Armour (iron): 9″—7″ Belt, $7\frac{3}{4}$″ (Terni) Barbettes. Machinery: 2 sets triple expansion. 2 screws. Designed H.P. (new): 6000=15·5 kts. Boilers: Cylindrical. Coal: 300 tons.
Note.—Doubtful if this ship can do 12 kts. now.

REPUBLICA (ex-British Fleet-sweeping Vessel, *Gladiolus*, launched Oct., 1915, by Messrs. Chas. Connell & Co., Scotstoun.) 1250 tons. Dimensions: $255\frac{1}{4}$ (*p.p.*), $267\frac{3}{4}$ (*o.a.*) $\times 33\frac{1}{2} \times 11$ (*mean*), $11\frac{3}{4}$ feet (*max.* draught). Guns: **2**—4 inch (British Navy Mk. IV.), **2**—3 inch A.A. (Elswick), **2**—9 pdr. (Hotchkiss), **4**—3 pdr. (Hotchkiss). Designed I.H.P. 1400=17 kts., but actually requires about 2200 I.H.P. for this speed. Machinery: 1 set 4-cyl. triple exp. Boilers: 2 cylindrical. 1 screw. Coal: 130 tons *normal*; 260 tons *max.*=about 2000 miles at 15 kts. Complement (79 as British ship). Built under British Emergency War Programme as a unit of the *Azalea* group of "Flower Class" Sloops. Sold to Portugal 1920.

CARVALHO ARAUJO (ex-British Fleet-sweeping Vessel, *Jonquil*, launched May, 1915, by Messrs. Chas. Connell & Co., Scotstoun.) 1200 tons. Dimensions: 250 (*p.p.*), $262\frac{1}{2}$ (*o.a.*) $\times 33 \times 11$ (*mean*), $11\frac{3}{4}$ feet (*max.* draught). Guns: as *Republica* above and also 2 Thornycroft type depth charge throwers. Designed I.H.P., speed, machinery, boilers, &c., as *Republica* opposite, but *max.* coal capacity 250 tons, and complement (as British ship) 77. Built under British Emergency War Programme as a unit of the *Acacia* group of "Flower Class" Sloops. Sold to Portugal 1920. Employed on Fisheries Protection Duties.

1931 Photo.

ADAMASTOR (Orlando, 1896). 1729 tons. Comp., 206. Dimensions: $242 \cdot 1 \times 35 \cdot 1 \times 15 \cdot 3$ feet. Guns: **2**—4·7 inch (Canet), **4**—4·1 inch (Krupp), **4**—3 pdr. (Hotchkiss), **3** machine. Torpedo tubes (14 inch): **3** *above water* (bow and broadside abreast of Q.D. gun). Armour: $1\frac{1}{4}$″ Deck, $2\frac{3}{4}$″ C.T. Machinery: 2 sets triple expansion. 2 screws. Boilers: 8 cylindrical. H.P. *forced* 4000 = 18·19 kts. Coal: 420 tons. Employed on Colonial service. (Re-fitted 1919-22).

4 Destroyers.

DOURO (Bldg.).   TÉJO (Bldg.).   Soc. de Const., Lisbon.

VOUGA (Bldg.).   LIMA (Bldg.).   Yarrows.

Displacement : (normal) 1,383 tons.

Dimensions : 321·8 × 31·1 × 11 feet.
98·15 × 9·5 × 3·4 meters.

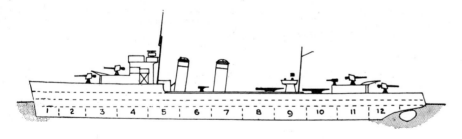

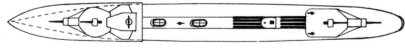

Guns :
    4—4·7 inch (120/50)
    3—Pom-poms (40 m/m)
    2—D.C. Throwers
Tubes :
    8—21 inch (530 m/m)
    in two quadruple
    mountings.

Machinery : Geared reaction turbines. S.H.P. 33,000 = 36 kts. Yarrow boilers (high pressure).
Oil : 296 tons. Radius : 5,400 miles at 15 kts.

2   Destroyers

GUADIANA.   1919 Photo.

2 Yarrow type.   **Tamega** (Jan. 1922) by Lisbon D.Y., **Guadiana** (1914). Built by Yarrow and assembled at Lisbon.
660 tons.   Dimensions: 240 × 23¼ × 7⅜ feet, *max.* draught.   Armament: **1**—4 inch, **2**—3 inch.   **2** pairs of 18 inch
Torpedo tubes.   Parsons turbines; H.P. 11,000—27 kts., 3 Yarrow boilers. Compl:—73.   Coal: 146 tons = 1600 miles
at 15 kts.

5   Torpedo Boats.   (*Torpedeiros*).

1921 Photo, by courtesy of the Ministry of Marine.

(*Assigned to Portugal for Police Duties only, Sept., 1920, and officially rated as Patrol Boats*).

4 Ex-Austrian boats: **Ave, Sado, Lis, Mondego** (Ganz-Danubius Co., Porto Ré, Fiume, 1913-15).
    Displacement: 266 tons.   Dimensions: 188·3 × 19 × 8 feet *max* draught.   Guns: **1**—11 pdr. (aft).   Tubes may have
    been removed.   Designed S.H.P. 5000 = 28 kts. (made 31 kts. when new).   Turbine engines and Yarrow boilers.
    Fuel: 20 tons coal + 34 tons oil.   Complement, 45.

1 old Yarrow type,   **No. 2** (Poplar, 1886).   66 metric tons. Dimensions : 119½ × 12½ × 3·4 feet.   Armament : **2** M.G. and
    2 tubes.   Designed H.P. 700 = 19 kts. (much less now).   1 screw.   Coal : about 18 tons.   Complement, 22.

5 Submarines. (Submerseveis).

Building

2 *Delfina* class : **Delfim** (   ), **Espadarte** (   ). Building by Cant. Riuniti dell'Adriatico (Monfalcone). Dims. : 206·7 × 22·5 × 19·3 feet = 770/975 m. tons. Armament : 1—4 inch, 6 21 inch ln tubes (4 bow, 2 stern). Machinery : 2 sets of Fiat Diesels. H.P. 2,300 = 16·5 kts. 2 motors. C.R.D.A. H.P. 1,000 = 9·25 kts. Radius : 5,200 at 10 kts and 110 at 4 kts *submerged*.

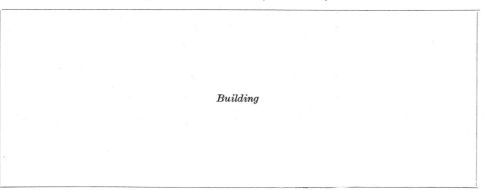

1919 *Photo.*

3 *Laurenti-Fiat* type : **Foca, Golfinho** and **Hidra** (Spezia, 1916–1917). Displ. : 260/389 tons. Dims. : 147¾ × 13·8 × 10¼ feet. Armament : 2—18 inch bow torpedo tubes. 4 torpedoes. Machinery : 2 sets of 275 B.H.P. 6-cylinder Fiat-Diesel engines *on surface* ; electric motors+batteries *submerged*. Maximum speeds : 14·2 kts. *on surface* and 8¼ kts. *submerged*. Radius of action : about 650 miles at full speed, and 3,500 miles at 8¼ kts. *on surface* : about 18 miles at 8¼ kts. and 100 at 4 kts. *submerged*. Complement : 21.

Gunboats (*Canhoneiras*).

DAMÃO (1925), **DIU** (Oct., 1929), **ZAIRE** (ex-*Goa*, 20th Feb., 1925), built at Lisbon D.Y. 500 tons. Details and appearance as *Beira* class below, with minor improvements.

Photo, R. E. Forrest, Esq.

BENGO (1917), **MANDOVI** (1917), **QUANZA** (1918), **BEIRA** (1910) and **IBO** (1910). All built at Lisbon D.Y. 463 tons. Dimensions : 147⅔ × 27¼ × 6 8 feet. Guns : in *Bengo*, 1—3·5 inch, 4—3 pdr. ; *Mandovi* and *Ibo*, 1—3 inch, 2—6 pdr., 2—3 pdr. ; in *Quanza*, 2—3 inch ; in *Beira*, 1—3·5 inch, 1—9 pdr., 2—3 pdr. H.P. 700 = 13 kts. Coal : 85 tons. Radius : 3200 miles at 9 kts. Boilers : Cylindrical. 2 screws. Complement, 71.

LIMPOPO.   1919 *Photo.*

LIMPOPO (Poplar, 1890). 288 tons. 124 × 21 × 6½ feet. Guns : **3** —6 pdr., **1** machine. H.P. 523 = 11·3 kts. Complement, 54.

(C) **DILY** 500 tons. 140 (*p.p.*) × 25 × 10·3 feet. H.P. 500 = 11 kts. 1 screw. Complement, 72.

Surveying Vessel.

1919 *Photo.*

CINCO DE OUTUBRO (ex-*Amelia*, ex-*Banshee*; Ramage & Ferguson, Leith, 1900). 1343 tons. 226·9 × 28·9 × 14 feet. Guns: 2—1 pdr. H.P. 1800 = 15 kts. 2 screws. Cylindrical boilers. Coal: 230 tons. Complement, 225.

Fishery Protection Gunboats.

FARO.   *Photo 1931, Tenente Manuel Rodriques.*

FARO, LAGOS. Built at Lisbon D.Y. Displ.: ? tons. Dims :—131·2 × 19·6 × 10·5 ft: Guns :—2—47 m/m. H.P. 650 = 13 kts. 1 Yarrow boiler. 1 Screw: Radius 2000 miles at 7·5 kts. Oil = 44 tons: Complement, 53.

Fishery Protection Gunboats—*continued.*

1919 *Photo.*

ACOR (ex-s.s. *Gomes VII*, 1874). 330 tons. 136·1 × 19 × 9 feet. Guns: Nil. I.H.P. 360 = 9 kts.; could make 11 with sail out. Complement, 53. Has been employed on fisheries and surveying duties, and may be condemned shortly.

RAUL CASCAES. 188 tons. Employed on Fishery Protection duties.

Mining Vessel.

Note.—This vessel is attached to school and service for laying out defensive minefields and is under control of War Office.

1919 *Photo.*

Has no distinctive name or number: is referred to as "Mineiro," *i.e.*, Mining Vessel. (Built 1892). 78 metric tons. 58·5 × 13·4 × 7 feet. I.H.P. 150 = 8 kts. 2 screws. 1 cylindrical boiler. Coal: 10 tons.

Mine Layer.   (*Vapores lanca minas.*)

1919 *Photo.*

VULCANO (1910). Built by Thornycroft. 151 tons. 110 × 19½ × 4½ feet. 2 dropping gears forward. H.P. 412 = 12 kts. 2 screws. Cylindrical boiler. Complement, 24.

Armed Launches.

Note —Are attached to Aviation Services.

No. 3.   *1921 Photo, by courtesy of the Portuguese Naval Attaché.*

2 boats: **No. 2, No. 3.** Are ex-British M.L. *557* and M.L. *574*, built 1915, purchased for Portuguese Navy, 1920. Load, displacement: 37 tons. Dimensions: 80 × 12⅜ × 3 feet (*max.* load draught). Guns: not known. B.H.P. 440 = 17·5 kts. 2 sets Standard petrol motors. Fuel: 2050 gallons petrol. Complement, 9.

Small River Gunboats. (*Lancha Canonheiras.*)

Training Ship.

SAGRES.   1931 *Photo, Bar, Toulon.*

SAGRES (1904). Sailing Vessel of 2000 tons gross, acquired in 1924. Displacement: 3221 tons. Dimensions: $262\frac{3}{4} \times 40 \times 18$ feet. Complement, 47. No other details yet available.

& (C) **MACAU** (Yarrow, 1909). 133 tons. $119\frac{2}{3} \times 19.8 \times 2$ feet. Guns: 2—6 pdr., 3 machine. H.P. 250 = 11.8 kts. Boilers: Yarrow. Complement, 24.

Note.—On Zambesi River, there is also a Stern Wheel Gunboat *Tete*, built by Yarrows, 1918-19, but she is the property of the Colonial Department. Displaces 70 tons. Armed with 2—1 pdr. (Hotchkiss), and 2 M.G. Speed: 9 kts.

RIO MINHO (Lisbon D.Y., 1904). 38 tons. Paddlewheel. $80.7 \times 13.1 \times 1.9$ feet. H.P. 64 = $7\frac{1}{2}$ kts. Guns: 2—1 pdr. Complement, 68, are nominally borne on her books, the majority of these ranks and ratings being actually at various shore stations on the Portuguese bank of the river Minho, for fisheries, customs duties, &c.

(C) **FLECHA,** is also given in Official Navy List as **FLEXA** (1909). 44 tons. $68.8 \times 13.1 \times 2.2$ feet. Guns: 1—1 pdr. 1 screw. H.P. 45 = 10 kts. Complement, 7.

Salvage Vessel. (*Vapor de Salvação.*)

PATRÃO LOPES (ex-*Newa*, Rostock, 1880). Iron. 1100 tons. 157.5 (*p.p.*) × 26.2 × 14.6 feet. I.H.P. 378 = 10 kts. 1 screw. Coal: 130 tons. Complement, 53.

Coastguard Patrol Vessel.

TORRES GARCIA (Vigo, 1928). 250 tons. $91\frac{3}{4} \times 19\frac{1}{2} \times 10$ feet. Triple expansion engines. 1 screw.

Transport.

GIL EANES (1914). 1775 tons gross. 278 × 41 × 16.8 feet. H.P. 1300 = 11 kts. 1 screw. Cylindrical boilers. Employed as Fleet Collier at present.

RUSSIAN FLEET.

It is extremely difficult to secure accurate information regarding the Russian Navy, but the particulars given in these pages were revised and compared with data from a reliable source in 1931.

Minister of War and Marine.—(Navy is administered by *Komissar Muklevitch*.)

Naval Flags. RUSSIA.

COMMANDER IN CHIEF.

CHIEF OF STAFF.

OFFICER COMMANDING NAVAL FORCES.

SENIOR FLAG OFFICER.

JUNIOR FLAG OFFICER.

COMMANDER OF FLOTILLA.

SENIOR OFFICER AFLOAT.

FORTRESS.

ENSIGN.

JACK.

NATIONAL.

PENDANT.

Mercantile Marine.

From "Lloyd's Register," 1931 figures (Ships under 100 tons *gross* excluded): Total *gross* tonnage, 603,836.

UNIFORMS.—Shoulder markings abolished, and rank is now indicated by stripes on cuff. *All* ranks now have gold buttons. Officers' caps have an anchor badge, on a red ground. Ranks are distinguished thus :—

Admiral : $\frac{3}{4}$-inch top stripe with curl and three stars round curl; two 1-inch lower stripes.

Vice-Admiral : Same as Admiral but only *two* stars.

Kontre-Admiral : Same as Admiral but only *one* star, above curl.

Kapitan (*I Ranga*) : Same as Admiral but *no* stars. (British, Captain.)

Kapitan (*II Ranga*) : Two 1-inch gold stripes, top with curl. (British, Commander.)

Starshi Leitenant : One 1-inch or $\frac{3}{4}$-inch top stripe with curl, and *three* $\frac{1}{2}$-inch gold stripes below. (British, Lieutenant-Commander.)

Leitenant : Same as above but only *two* $\frac{1}{2}$-inch gold stripes below. (British, Lieutenant.)

Mitchman : Same as above but only *one* $\frac{1}{2}$-inch gold stripe below. (British, Sub-Lieutenant.)

Pra'porchik : This is an acting rank, about equivalent to Acting Sub-Lieut., in British Navy. One $\frac{1}{2}$-inch gold stripe *without* curl.

> **Note.**—The above particulars relate to changes introduced by the Kerensky Government. Under later Administrations most of these marks of rank in the Fleet and Army were abolished, but have since been restored to a certain extent.

Personnel : 23,600 (about 10,000 seagoing).

Modern Naval Guns (Obukhoff).

Designation.		Length in Calibres.	Weight of Guns.	Weight of A.P. Shot.	Initial Velocity (approximate).	Maximum Penetration with A.P. Capped Shell against K.C. Armour.			Danger Space against average warship at			Usual Rounds per minute.
						10,000 yds.	5000 yds.	3000 yds.	10,000 yards.	5000 yards.	3000 yards.	
C.M.	inch.	calibres	tons.	lbs.	f.s.	in.	in.	in.	yards.	yards.	yards.	
30·5	12	52	48·2	714	3000	...	$14\frac{1}{2}$	20	...	...	...	...
	6	45	$7\frac{1}{2}$	89	2900	...	$4\frac{1}{4}$	6	60	250	485	3
	6	45	7	89	2600	...	$3\frac{1}{4}$	5	50	200	430	3
13·0	5·1	55/60	...	...	...	...	...	...	...	...	...	...
12·0	4·7	50	$2\frac{1}{4}$	46	2600	...	...	...	...	...	...	about 4
10·0	4	60	...	...	...	...	...	...	...	...	...	
7·5	3	60	14 cwt.	$13\frac{1}{2}$	2700	...	...	...	...	...	...	...
6·3	3	35	12 ,,	$13\frac{1}{5}$	2600	...	...	...	...	...	...	...

ADDENDA.

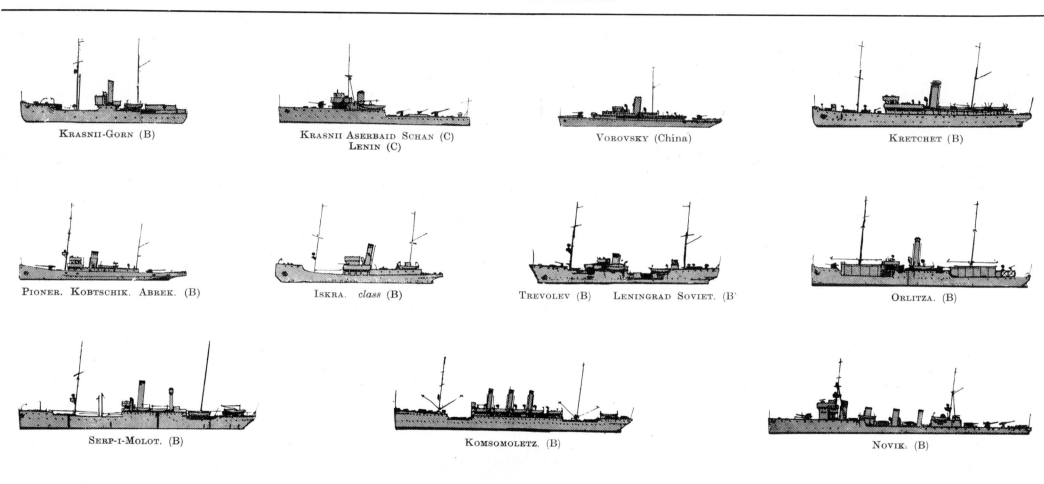

KRASNII-GORN (B)

KRASNII ASERBAID SCHAN (C)
LENIN (C)

VOROVSKY (China)

KRETCHET (B)

PIONER. KOBTSCHIK. ABREK. (B)

ISKRA. *class* (B)

TREVOLEV (B)   LENINGRAD SOVIET. (B)

ORLITZA. (B)

SERP-I-MOLOT. (B)

KOMSOMOLETZ. (B)

NOVIK. (B)

KOMMUNA. (B)

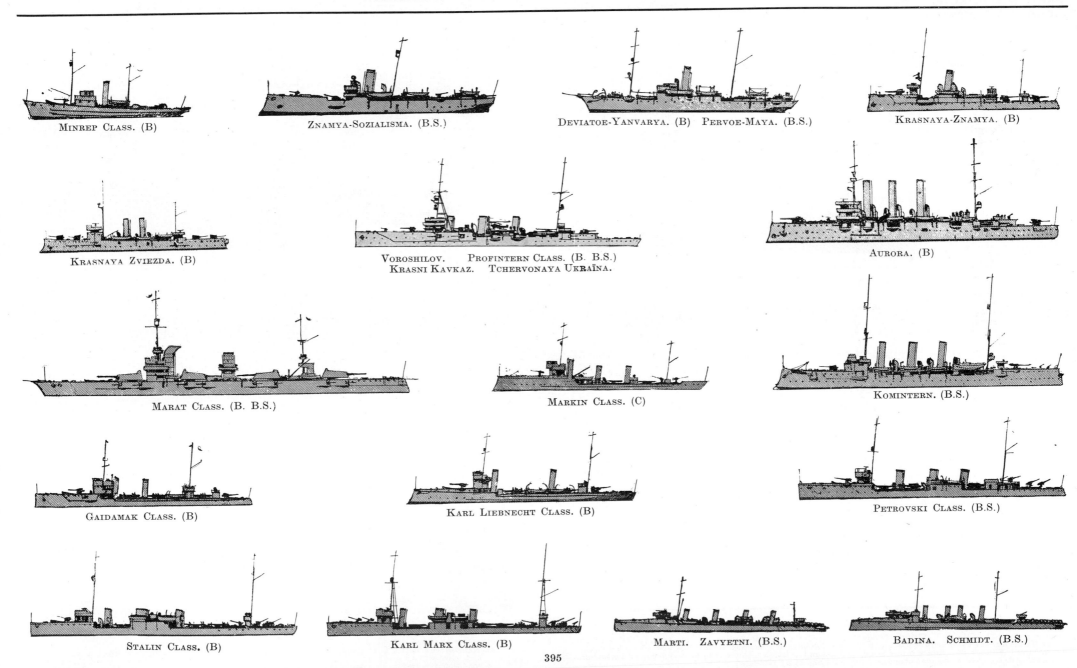

MINREP CLASS. (B)

ZNAMYA-SOZIALISMA. (B.S.)

DEVIATOE-YANVARYA. (B)   PERVOE-MAYA. (B.S.)

KRASNAYA-ZNAMYA. (B)

KRASNAYA ZVIEZDA. (B)

VOROSHILOV.   PROFINTERN CLASS. (B. B.S.)
KRASNI KAVKAZ.   TCHERVONAYA UKRAÏNA.

AURORA. (B)

MARAT CLASS. (B. B.S.)

MARKIN CLASS. (C)

KOMINTERN. (B.S.)

GAIDAMAK CLASS. (B)

KARL LIEBNECHT CLASS. (B)

PETROVSKI CLASS. (B.S.)

STALIN CLASS. (B)

KARL MARX CLASS. (B)

MARTI.   ZAVYETNI. (B.S.)

BADINA.   SCHMIDT. (B.S.)

PARISHSKAIA-KOMMUNA (ex-*Sevastopol*, June, 1911), **MARAT** (ex-*Petropavlovsk*, Sept., 1911),
OKTIABRSKAIA-REVOLUTIA (ex-*Gangut*, October, 1911), **MIHAIL FRUNZE** (ex-*Poltava*, July, 1911),

Normal displacement, 23,370 metric tons; *full load*, about 26,000 tons. Complement, 1125.

Length *over all*, 619 feet. Beam, 87 feet. *Mean* draught, 27½ feet.

Guns
12—12 inch, 52 cal.
16—4·7 inch, 50 cal.
2—3 inch (anti-aircraft).
1—3 pdr.
8 Machine.
Torpedo tubes (18 inch):
4 submerged.

Armour (Krupp):
8¾″ Belt (amidships) ...
5″-2″ Belt (ends)
3″-4″ Internal belt (*see notes*)
3″ Deck
12″-10″ Turrets
8″ Turret bases
6″ Battery
10″ Conning tower

OKT. REVOLUTIA.

Photo added 1929 (Dmitri Novik).

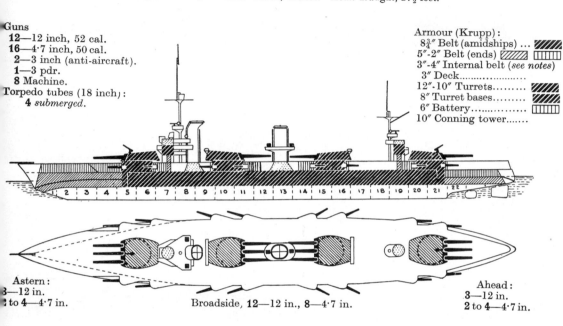

Astern:
3—12 in.
2 to 4—4·7 in.

Broadside, **12**—12 in., **8**—4·7 in.

Ahead:
3—12 in.
2 to 4—4·7 in.

Machinery: Parsons turbine. 4 screws. Boilers: 25 Yarrow. Designed H.P. 42,000 = 23 kts. Coal *normal*, 1000 tons; *maximum*, 3000 tons. Also 1170 tons oil. Radius of action. 900 miles at 23 kts., 4000 miles at 16 kts.

Gunnery Notes.—The port plate above each gun is in the form of a hinged flap, allowing each 12-inch gun to elevate to 30—40° *maximum*. Arcs of fire: End triple 12-inch barbettes, 310°; central barbettes, 130° *each beam*; aft group of 4—4·7 inch, 90°; other 4·7 inch, 85°.

Armour Notes.—Belt is about 15 feet wide, 5 feet of it below water, uniform thickness. There is a *secondary* 3″-4″ internal belt 11 feet inboard above protective deck, extending between the end barbettes. The space between main belt and internal belts is divided up into w.t. compartments.

Name	Builder	Machinery	Laid down	Completed	Trials: Full power	Boilers	Best recent speed
Marat P.Kommuna Okt. Revolutia M. Frunze	Baltic Works } Galernü	Baltic Works Franco-Rus. Works	June,'09 June,'09	Jan. '14 Jan. '15 Jan. '14 Jan. '15	About 50,000 = 23·4 = 23·6	Yarrow	20 16 18

General Notes.—The late Gen. Vittorio Cuniberti prepared the original designs for this type. The Ministry of Marine afterwards altered the plans to include Russian ideas of armouring, ice-breaking bows and other special features. Further, to obtain a higher speed, hull design is relatively lighter than in contemporary battleships of other fleets. Said to be most unhealthy, insanitary and badly ventilated.

PARISHSKAIA-KOMMUNA.

1930 *Photo*.

P. KOMMUNA during last general refit had fore-funnel raised and fitted with a cowl-like top, and bows extended and built with an overhang. Proceeded to Black Sea early in 1930 in company with "*Profintern*." General condition reported to be unsatisfactory, and official explanation of her remaining in Black Sea is that she could not face the return voyage.

Battleships.

Cruisers.

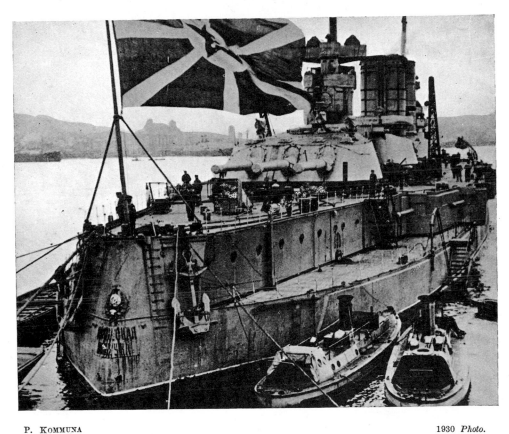

P. KOMMUNA

1930 *Photo.*

Old Battleship.
Reported converting into Aircraft Carrier.

LENIN (ex-Evstafi).

TCHERVONAYA UKRAÏNA.

1928 *Photo.*

PROFINTERN.

1931 *Photo.*

1913 Cruisers.

A { **PROFINTERN** (ex-*Sovnarkom*, ex-*Klara Zetkin*, ex-*Svietlana*, June, 1915. Reval).
VOROSHILOV (ex-*Ad. Butakov.* Reval).

B { **TCHERVONAYA UKRAÏNA** (ex-*Ad. Nakhimoff*, October, 1915. Nicolaiev).
KRASNI-KAVKAZ (ex-*Ad. Lazarev*, June, 1916. Nicolaiev).

A = 6,800 tons.   B = 7,600 tons.

Length, 507¾ feet.   Beam, 50⅓ feet.   Draught, 18⅓ feet (A)   20¼ feet (B)

PROFINTERN.   1930 *Photo.*

Guns :
15—5·1 inch, 55.
4—4 in. (anti-aircraft).
4—3 in.
4 machine.
Torpedo Tubes: (21 inch)
9 in Triple Mounts.
Can carry 100 mines.

Armour :
Belt...................
1″ Deck ....
3″ Gun shields ....
″ Conning tower .....

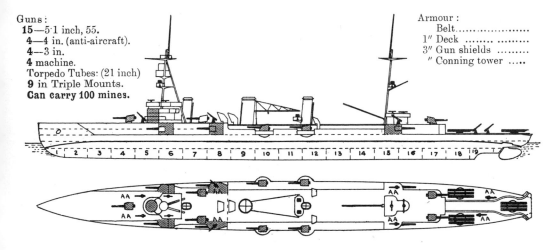

Machinery : Brown Curtis or Parsons turbines.   Boilers : A = 13 : B = 14 Yarrow.   H.P. 50,000 = 29·5 kts.   Coal : 540 tons.   Oil : 690 tons.   Radius of action : 470 miles at full speed, 3700 at 14 kts.

General Notes.—Built under the 1912 Naval Programme and laid down in 1913. Construction was held up for many years, *T. Ukraina* being the first to be completed in December, 1924, followed by *Profintern* in January, 1925. *Krasni-Kavkaz* was completed at the Imani Yard about February, 1930, and two more of the class remain under construction. It is reported that *Ad. Karnilov* was launched in October, 1929 and named *IIId Internationale :* present state of *Ad. Istonin* is uncertain. *Ad. Grieg* and *Ad. Spiridov* were turned into oilers and named *Azneft* and *Grozneft. Profintern* towed to Leningrad for completion 1918. Proceeded to Black Sea, 1930, staying for repairs at Brest and Naples, where it is reported that her condition was very unsatisfactory and that only minor repairs would be undertaken. Has always been described as having 3 inch armour for full length over main and lower decks, but from inspection it appears that there is no special side armour ; apparently the hull is built of thicker plating than usually obtains. Armour has therefore been deleted from above plan and exact protection is uncertain.

Gunnery Note.—It is reported that *K. Kavkaz* is armed with 10—5·1 inch and 4—4·7 inch guns. The two " B " type may have the extra protection allowed by difference in displacement.

PROFINTERN.   1930 *Photo.*

1900 Cruiser.

KOMINTERN.   *Photo added* 1925.

KOMINTERN (ex *Pamiat Merkuria*, ex-*Kagul*, June, 1905). 6750 tons. Dimensions : 436 × 54 × 20½ feet. Complement, 573. Guns : **14**—5.1 inch, **4**—3 inch AA., **2** M.G. Torpedo tubes : **2**—18 inch (*submerged*). Armour : 1″—3″ deck, turrets and casemates. Machinery : Triple expansion. 2 screws. Boilers : 16 Normand. Designed H.P., 19,500 = 23 kts. Coal : *normal* 700 tons, *maximum* 1,100 tons. Refitted and rearmed, employed as sea-going training ship.

It is reported from Moscow that a sister ship, *Oleg*, (torpedoed by a British C.M.B. in the Gulf of Finland in June, 1919) is to be raised and repaired. If salvage is undertaken it would seem that the ship would only have scrap value.

1896 Cruiser.

AURORA (ex-S.S.S.R.)   PROFINTERN.
                                  August, 1929, *Photo by favour of H. C. Bywater, Esq.*
(At present Seagoing Training Ship.)

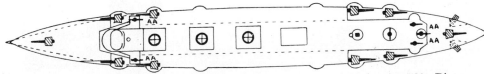

AURORA (ex-*S.S.S.R.**, ex-*Aurora*, May, 1900). 6,830 metric tons. Complement, 590. Dimensions : 410 (*w.l.*) × 55 × 21¼ feet (*mean draught*). Armament : **10**—5·1″, 45 cal., **5**—6 pdr. AA·, **2** M.G. Formerly carried 125 mines and **2** *submerged* torpedo tubes (*broadside*). Machinery : 3 sets horizontal 3-cylinder. Designed H.P. 11,600 = 20 kts. 3 screws. Boilers : 24 Belleville. Coal : *normal*, 960 tons ; *maximum*, 970 tons. Complement, 573. Laid down Oct. 31st, 1896 ; completed 1903. Still in nominally effective state, but speed reduced to 17 kts. Sister ship *Diana* has been sold for scrap.

*These initials stand for *Sonus Sovietskii Sozialistizeskii Respublik*, meaning "Union of Soviet Socialist Republics."
(*Note to Plan.*—Uncertain whether large ports at stern are for mine-laying or torpedo tubes, but the latter is reported.)

AURORA.   1930 *Photo.*

29 Destroyers. (*Eskadrenyi Minonosetz*).

(Other Destroyers still exist, but are no longer of any fighting value).

5 Petrovski type.

PETROVSKI.   1928 *Photo.*

5 boats : **Nezamojnik** (ex-*Feodinissi*, 1917), **Felix Dzerzhinski** (ex-*Kaliakria*, 1928), **Nezamojni** (ex-*Zante*, 1917), **Petrovski** (ex-*Korfu*, 1917), **Shaumyan** (ex-*Levkos*, 1917). All built at Nicolaieff. 1326 tons. Dimensions : 303½ × 29½ × 9 feet. Armament : **4**—4 inch, **4**—9 pdr., **1**—9 pdr. AA., **12**—18 inch tubes,* in triple deck mountings. Originally designed to carry 80 mines of pre-war pattern, but will now have 45 of heavier type. Turbine engines. Oil fuel only : 390 tons. S.H.P. 29,000 = 33 kts. Complement, 161. **Khadji** removed from list 1931.

* A fourth set of tubes may be mounted in some in place of deck house.

1 "Novik" type

1931 *Illustration.*

Jacob Sverdloff (?) (ex-*Novik*). Built 1910-12. Rebuilt and re-armed 1931. Dimensions : 336 × 31 × 9½ feet. Displ.: 1262 tons. D.H.P. 33,000 = 36 kts. Turbines. Oil 400 tons. Complement, 112. Guns : **4**—4 inch. **4** M.G. **8**—18 inch tubes in Turin mounts, (former armament : may now carry **3**—4·7 inch).

Note.—Recent alterations include enlarged bridge, tripod masts, extension of forecastle, and shifting of after, super-structure, and main mast. Employed on cruiser duties.

2 Karl Marx type (Mine Layers).

KARL MARX.   1930 *Photo, Lt.-Comm. R. Steen Steenson.*

2 *Reval Shipbuilding Co.* : **Karl Marx** (ex-*Isyaslav*), **Kalinin** (ex-*Priamislav*) (1914). 1350 tons. Dimensions : 344½ × 31½ × 9⅜ feet. Designed H.P. 32,700 = 33 kts. (Trials reported to have given 32 kts.) Parsons turbines and Normand boilers. Armament : **5**—4 inch, **2**—3 inch AA., **2** M.G. Torpedo tubes (18 inch) : **9**, in 3 triple deck mountings. Oil : 450 tons. 60 mines carried. Complement, 167. Commenced 1912. Completed 1923.

Note.—*Avtroil* captured by British, now Estonian *Lennuk*. These vessels were built to the designs of Chantiers et Ateliers Augustin Normand, Le Havre.

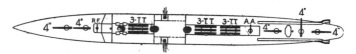

1930 *Photo.*

Frunze (ex-*Bistri*, 1915). (Refitted and rearmed 1928). 1100 tons. Complement, 156. Dimensions : 321½ × 30½ × 12½ feet. Armament : **2**—4·7 inch, **6** smaller. AA., **4**—21 inch tubes, 80 mines. Boilers : 4 Thornycroft. 2 screws. Oil : 350 tons. H.P. 23,000 = 34 kts.

8 Uritsky type (Mine Layers).

ENGELS.

Photo added 1929 (Dmitri Novik).

STALIN.

1930 Photo, Lt.-Comm. R. Steen Steensen.

LENIN (Voikoff behind).

1930 Photo.

6 *Leningrad Metal Works :* **Volodarsky** (ex-*Pooledilet*), **Uritsky** (ex-*Zabiaka*), **Zinoviev** (ex-*Azard*), **Engels** (ex-*Desna*), **Stalin** (ex-*Samsun*), **Rykov** (ex-*Leitun*) (all 1914).

2 *Putilov Works,* Leningrad : **Voikoff** (ex-*Trotsky,* ex-*Leit. Ilyin*), **Lenin** (ex-*Kap. 2 r. Isylmettiev*). (Both 1914.)

Displacement : 1260 tons. Dimensions : 314¾ × 30½ × 9¾ feet. Designed H.P. 30,000 = 35 kts. (Present best speeds vary between 28 and 32 kts.) All have turbines and oil fuel only. Thornycroft boilers. Armament : **4**—4 inch, **2**—9 pdr. AA., **2** M.G. Torpedo tubes (18 inch) : **9** in 3 triple deck mountings. Were designed to carry 80 mines of pre-war pattern ; believed that they now have only 45, of heavier type. Complement, 157. Oil : 400 tons. 1912 Programme. Built 1914—1918.

Note.—*Spartak,* ex-*Miklukha Maklej,* ex-*Kapitan Kinsbergen,* captured by British and now Estonian *Wambola.*

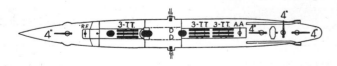

3 Markin type (Mine Layers).

BABINSKY RABOTCHY.   *Photo, Dmitri Novik (added 1929).*

3 "*Markin*" class, named *Alfater* (ex-*Turkmenetz-Stavropolski.*) *Markin* (ex-*Ukraina*) *Babinsky Rabotchy* (ex-*Voiskovoi*) (all 1904). Built by Lange's Yard, Riga. 580 tons. Dimensions : 240 × 23¾ × 7½ feet. Designed H.P. 6200=25 kts. Boilers : 4 Normand. Coal: 50 tons *normal*, 135 tons *full load*. Complement, 88-85. Armament : 3—4 inch, 1—1 pdr., 2 M.G., and 2 torpedo tubes (18"). Carry 16 mines.

Present Speeds : *Markin*, 23 kts. *Alfater* (Senior Officer of Caspian Flotilla), 20 kts. *Babinsky Rabotchy* probably less.

2 Sverdlov Class (Mine Layers).

Y. SVERDLOV.   *Photo, Association Navale Historique Russe (added 1929).*

Yakov Sverdlov (ex-*Emir Bukharski*), *Karl Liebnecht* (ex-*Finn*, Helsingfors, 1904-5.) 580 tons. Dimensions : 237¾ × 26¾ × 7½ feet. Complement, 94. Designed H.P. 6,200=25 kts., (less now). Coal: 150 tons. Armament : 2—4 inch, 3—18 in. tubes. Can carry 25 mines.

Note.—There are also 8 more destroyers as well as 3 submarines, in existence in Caspian ports, but none of them can be regarded as effective for fighting purposes.

3 Zhelesniakov type (Mine Layers).

3 *Zhelesniakov* class, named *Gaidamak,* (Krupp Germania Yard, Kiel, 1905), *Zhelesniakov* (ex-*Amuretz*, Riga, 1905), *Ussurietz* (Helsingfors, 1907). 570 tons. Dimensions : first ship, 233 × 24.2 × 7.5 feet, other two 233 × 23.6 × 7.8 feet. Designed H.P. 6500 and 6200 respectively=25 kts. Coal: 205 tons. Complement, 105. Guns : 2—4 inch, 1—3 pdr., 1—1 pdr. AA., 4 M.G. Tubes : 3—18 inch. Carry 25 mines.

Note.—Present best speeds : 22-24 kts. *Sladkov,* of this type, reported scrapped or non-effective.

4 Mine Layers (*Minonosetz.*)

2 *Laird* type: *Marti* (ex-*Zavidni*, 1905). *Zavyetni* (1905). 420 tons. Dimensions : 210 × 21 × 7 feet *mean* draught. H.P., 5,700=26 kts., originally. Boilers : 4 Yarrow. Fuel: 90 tons coal+oil. Armament : 2—11 pdr. 2 M.G., 2—18 inch tubes. 18 mines.

2 *Yarrow* type: *Badina* (ex-*Strogi*), *Schmidt* (ex-*Svirepi*, 1901). 376 tons. Dimensions : 190 × 18½ × 5 feet. Coal: 70 tons. Guns : 2—11 pdr., 2 M.G. Tubes : 2—15 inch. Carry 12 mines. H.P., 3,800=26 kts., originally. Employed as tenders at Sevastopol. *Schmidt* refitted 1923. *Badina* reported non-effective.
Note.—*Marti* also reported as ex-*Svirepi* and *Schmidt* as ex-*Zavidni.*

12 + 3 *(building or completing)* **Submarines** *(Podvodniya Lodki.)*

New Construction.

boats : *DEKABRIST, NARODVOIETZ* both 1929, and a third unnamed, reported to be under construction at the Baltic Yard, Leningrad. *Surface* displacement : 850 tons. Dimensions : 279 × 23 × 16½ feet. Guns : **1**—4 inch. Tubes : **10.** Speed : $\frac{15}{10}$ kts. Radius on *surface* : 7000 miles at 9 kts. ; *submerged* 105 miles at 5 kts. A fourth vessel of this type reported lost on trials, Sept., 1927.

.B.—It is possible these are identical with the *Bubnov* boats, *B* 1—4, ordered from the Baltic Works during the War.

Photo added 1930.

1 *Improved Bubnov* type : **Politruk** (ex-*Nerpa*, 1911-15). Displacement : 650/784 tons. Dimensions : 220 × 14½ × 12¾ feet. H.P., 560=10 kts. *on surface*, 1400=11.7 kts. *submerged.* Fuel : 21 tons. Guns : **2**—3 inch, **1**—6 pdr. Tubes : **4.** Dropping gears : **4.**

1 *ex-British* **"L.55."** Displacement : 845/1150 tons. Dimensions : 220½ (*p.p.*), 235 (*o.a.*) × 23½ × 13½ feet. Guns : **1**—4 inch, **1** M.G. Tubes : **6**—21 inch, all in bows. Machinery : 2 sets 12-cylinder solid injection. Vickers type Diesel engines. Oil : 78 tons. D.H.P. 2400/1600—17·5/10·5 kts. Lost in the Baltic, 1919, and subsequently raised, repaired, and put into service 1931. Reported lost during Oct., 1931.

8 Bubnov Type.

TOVARISHTCH (No. 3).

KRASNOARMEYETZ (No. 4).   *Both 1930 Photo, Lt.-Comm. R. Steen Steenson.*

(Dimensions of all : 223 × 14⅞ × 12¾ feet. Displacement : 650/784 tons.)

Special boat : **Rabotchi** (ex-*Yersh*) (Nobel & Lessner, Reval, 1912-17). Minelayer. Guns : May carry **1**—14 pdr. AA., **1** M.G. Tubes : **4.** Carries 42 mines. H.P. 2640/900. Speed : 16/9 kts. Oil : 40 tons.

Edinorog type : **Proletari** (ex-*Zmieya*) (Nobel & Lessner, Reval, 1912-17). Guns : **1**—14 pdr. AA., **1** M.G. Tubes : **4.** Dropping gears, **8.** (Reported no longer effective.) H.P. 2640/900. Speed : 16/9 kts. Oil : 40 tons. Compl. 50.

Bolshevik type : **Bolshevik** (ex-*Ryss*), **Komissar** (ex-*Pantera*), **Kommunar** (ex-*Tigr*), **Krasnoflotetz** (ex-*Yaguar*), **Krasnoarmeyetz** (ex-*Leopard*), **Tovarishtch** (ex-*Tur*). All built by Nobel & Lessner, Reval, 1915-16. Guns : **1**—14 pdr. AA., **1** M.G. Tubes : **4.** Dropping gears : **8.** H.P. 500/900. Speed : 10/9 kts.

Special boat : **Batrak** (ex-*Volk*), 1917. Guns : **4** small. Tubes : **4.** H.P. 2600/900 = 16/9 kts.

ote—One boat No. IX (name unknown) was sunk in the Baltic May 26th, 1931. She has not been deleted from the above totals.

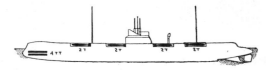

4 Holland Type.

1930 Photo.

(All boats now carry identification numbers.)

4 *Holland* type : **Politrabotnik** (ex-*AG* 26) 1916—1924; **Shakhter** (*AG* 23, ex-*Nezamuzhnyaya*) 1916—1920, **Kommunist** (*AG* 24) 1916—1922; **Marxist** (*AG* 25 ex-*Kamenev*) 1916—1922. Displacement : 375—467 tons. H.P. 480= 13 kts. *on surface*, 320=11 kts. *submerged.* Guns : **1**—6 pdr., **4**—18 inch tubes. Dimensions : 150½ × 15¼ × 15½ feet.

Armoured Gunboat.

KRASNAYA ZNAMYA (ex-*Khrabri*, 1895). 1740 tons. Complement, 197. Guns : **5**—5·1 inch. **1**—3 inch. **3**—3 pdr. Armour : 5″ Harvey, waterline belt amidships, 3″ ditto aft. Designed H.P. 2000 = 14 kts. Niclausse boilers. Coal : *maximum*, 160 tons. Built by Burmeister & Wain, Copenhagen.

Note.—Re-fitted and re-armed for service as Gunnery School Tender, 1916.

Gunboat.

Employed for Training purposes).

KRASNAYA ZVIEZDA (ex-*Khivinetz*) (1905). Displacement, 1340 tons. Comp. 161. Guns : **4**—5·1 inch, **2**—3 pdr. AA. Machinery : Triple expansion. 2 screws. Boilers : 8 Belleville. Designed H.P. 1400 = 13½ kts. Coal : *normal*, 100 tons ; *maximum*, 190 tons. (Re-fitted 1916.)

Despatch Vessels.

AZIZ BEKOV (ex-*Astrabad* 1900). 325 tons. 125 × 22 × 7½ feet. Guns : 5—3 pdr. H.P. 500 = 11 kts.

TRUD (ex-*Geok Tepe*, 1883). 1000 tons. Guns : **4**—4 pdr. Speed : 11 kts. Employed as Station Ship.

Miscellaneous.

A number of other vessels such as Sloops and Despatch Vessels, are also in commission in Black Sea ports, though of no fighting value. These include the ex-Torpedo Boat **LIETCHIK** (employed as Aircraft Tender), **KRASNII KOMANDIR** and **KRASNII MORIAK**. The last-named is serving as the Yacht of the Commander-in-Chief of the Black Sea Fleet.

Gunboats.

Photo added, 1922.

ZNAMYA SOZIALISMA (ex-*Teretz*, 1887), 1295 tons. Complement, 135. Guns : **3**—5·1 inch, **2**—3 inch. H.P., 1500 = 11 kts. Boilers (new in 1904-6): Belleville. Coal : 220-237 tons. Employed as Submarine Tender and School Ship.

Photo : "Motor Ship & Motor Boat."

LENIN, KRASNIIVOSTOK (ex-*Trotsky*) (1910). 950 tons. Complement, 104. 233 × 42½ × 4½ feet. Guns : 4—4.7 inch, 6 M.G. Armour : 4½ inch turrets. Machinery : Nobel-Lessner Diesel motors. H.P. 1000 = 11 kts. (Amur Flotilla.)

KRASNOYE ZNAMYA, TRUD (ex-*Biednota* 1907). 190 tons. 164 × 27 × 2 feet. Guns : 2—4.7 inch, 2 M.G. Designed H.P. 500 = 11 kts. Fuel : 145 tons. (Amur Flotilla).

Mine Layer.

KRASNII-ASERBAIDSCHAN.   1931 *Photo.*

KRASNII-ASERBAIDSCHAN (ex-*Trotsky*, ex-*Ardagan*). **LENIN** (ex-*Kars*). (Both 1909). Dims : 200 × 28 × 8 ft. 630 tons. Guns : 2—4.7 inch, 2—4 inch, 4 M.G. Diesel : 1000 H.P. = 11 kts. Compl. 126. Radius = 2270 miles at 10 kts.

Mine Layers.

DEVIATOË YANVARYA (ex-*Volga*, 1905). 1711 tons. Complement, 266. H.P. 1600 = 13 kts. Babcock boilers. Armament : 4—3 pdr. Carries 236 mines. Coal : 160 tons. Present best speed, 10 kts.

PERVOE MAYA (ex-*Dunai*, 1891). 1620 tons. Complement, 234. Guns : 3—3 inch, 2 M.G. Speed : 13⅓ kts. Coal : 130 tons. Carries 250 mines. Present efficiency questionable.

25 OCTABRIA (ex. *Narova*) **BARRIKADA** (ex. *Piet Veliky*) Both formerly *Volga* steam packets. 400 tons very light draught. Carry 90 mines. Guns : 2—47 mm., 1 M.G.
YAUSSA, BERESINA, KUBANJ. 400 tons. Guns : 2—75 mm. 2 M.G. 90 tons.

Seaplane Tender.

1931 Illustration.

ORLITZA (ex-*S.S. Imp.-Alexandra*), 1903. Displ.: 3000 tons. Speed : 17 kts. on trial, now about 10 kts. Guns : 8—3 inch. 2—M.G. 4 planes.

Mine Sweepers.

KAPSUL, KLIUZ, KRAMBOL, NEVOD, SCHTIT, STRELA, UDARNIK, YAKOR, ZMEYA.

ISKRA, IJORA (ex-*Plamya*). **TRETII INTERNATIONAL** (ex-*Patron*, Middlesbrough, 1913-14). 500 tons. Dimensions : 146 × 24½ × 10 feet. Guns : 2—11 pdr. H.P. 650 = 11 kts.

MINREP. (Now has a main mast.)

FUGAS, MINREP, PROVODNIK, ZAPAL (1911). 150 tons. Guns : 2—3 pdr. H.P. 300 = 10 kts.
Also about 14 Trawlers and other small craft, including ex-Torpedo Boats, *Artemiev* (ex-*Vinoslivi*), *Martinov* (ex-*Vnushitelni*), *Roshal* (ex-*Dmitriev*) *Zhemshuzni* (ex-*Sverev*), are fitted as Sweepers.

Despatch Vessels.

RAZVYEDCHIK and **DOZORNII** (both 1904). 100 tons. Complement, 23. Guns : 1—1 pdr., 1 machine. Speed, 16 kts. Both re-fitted 1915-1916.

KRETCHET (ex-S.S. *Polaris*, of Finnish S.S. Co.) (Dundee, 1899). 2011 tons gross. Guns : 4—3 inch AA. H.P. 2500 = 12 kts. Cylindrical boilers.

Note.—*Kretchet* at present serves as Administrative Flagship and Staff Headquarters for Baltic Fleet.

SHESTNADZATAVO OKTABRYA (ex-*Yastreb*). 150 tons. Speed 10 kts. No details available.

PIONIR ABREK, KOPCHIK. 500 tons. Speed : 12 kts. Guns : 2—4 inch.

A number of motor patrol boats also exist, but details are uncertain. 15 new vessels of C.M.B. type are projected, but it is not known definitely whether any have been begun.

BAKAN 900 tons. 11 kts. Guns : 2—3 inch. 4 M.G.
NEVA, MINJER KOPANETZ. 350 tons. 11 kts. Guns : 2—4 inch.
KUSNETSCHICHA (1910). 105 tons. 10 kts.

1924 Photo, Abrahams, Devonport.

VOROVSKY (ex-*Yaroslavna*, ex-yacht *Lysistrata*, built by Denny, Dumbarton, 1900). 2089 tons (yacht measurement), 1900 tons (registered). Dimensions: 285 (*p.p.*), 319 (*o.a.*) × 40 × 18 feet. Engines : Triple expansion. 2 screws. H.P. 3500 = 18 kts. Guns : 2—4·7 inch., 2—3 pdr., 2 M.G. Complement: 127. (In Far East).

Engineers' Training Ship.

(And Transport.)

KOMSOMOLETZ (ex-*Okean*, Howaldt, 1902). 11,900 tons. Guns: 4—3 pdr. H.P. 11,000 = 18 kts. Coal: 1600 tons. Boilers: 6 Belleville, 6 Niclausse, 3 Yarrow, 2 Thornycroft. Complement, 700.

Training and Depôt Ships.

TREVOLEV.   *1931 Photo, Herr T. Hallonbead.*

TREVOLEV (ex-*Voin*, 1893, rebuilt 1930). 1280 tons. Guns: 4—3 inch. Speed, 9 kts. Training and s/m depôt ship.

LENINGRADSOVIET (ex-*Vierny*, 1895, rebuilt 1926). Similar to *Voin* in main features. Training Ship for cadets.

Submarine Depôt Ships.

KHABAROVSK (1895). 2830 tons. H.P. 1800 = 12·5 kts. Guns: 2—11 pdr., 2—3 pdr., 2 M.G. Coal: 390 tons. Complement, 132. (Present best speed is 10 kts.)

SMOLNY (ex-*Tosno*) (Hull, 1907). 3200 tons. Dimensions: 318 × 41 × 18 feet. H.P. 1,200 = 13 kts. (only good for 10 kts. now). Guns: 4—3 pdr. Coal: 390 tons.

1931 Photo.

KOMMUNA (ex-*Volkhov*, Putilov, 1913). 2400 tons. Dimensions: 315 × 69 × 11¾ feet. Diesel engines. H.P. 1200 = 10 kts. Radius 3600 miles. Can raise 1000 tons.

Note.—Carries all essential stores for submarines (oil fuel, reserve accumulators, &c.), and has compressed air, distilling and charging plant, workshops, &c.

SOVIETSKAYA ROSSIA (ex-*Beresan*). 5096 tons. H.P. 2700.

Depôt Ships.

KRASNII-KOUBANETZ (ex-*Koubanetz*, 1887). 1295 tons. Sister to *Znamya*:

Sozialisma (p. 494).

KRASNII-KOMANDIA (ex-*General Broussilov*.)

Repair Ships.

KRASNII GORN (ex-*Kama*, 1911). 1982 tons. Dimensions: 237¾ × 36 × 12 feet. I.H.P. 1250 = 10 kts. Coal: 170 tons.

Photo added 1929.

SERP-I-MOLOT (ex-*Angara*, ex-*Anegawa Maru*, ex-*Angara*, ex-*Moskva*) (Clydebank, 1898). 11,700 tons. Dimensions: 508 × 58¼ × 24 feet. Guns: not known. H.P. 12,500 = 20 kts. Boilers: Original 24 Bellevilles have long been worn out and are probably replaced. Coal: 800 tons.

Transport.

(Appearance as Krasnii Gorn.)

KRASNII LENINGRAD (ex-*Sukhona*, 1911). 1982 tons. Dimensions: 237¾ × 36 × 12 feet. I.H.P. 1250 = 10 kts. Coal: 170 tons.

ROYAL ROUMANIAN NAVY.

Revised 1931, by courtesy of the Royal Roumanian Legation.

FLAGS

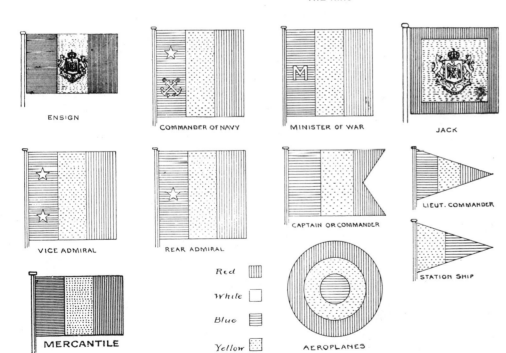

THE KING

ENSIGN

COMMANDER OF NAVY

MINISTER OF WAR

JACK

VICE ADMIRAL

REAR ADMIRAL

CAPTAIN OR COMMANDER

LIEUT. COMMANDER

STATION SHIP

MERCANTILE

Red

White

Blue

Yellow

AEROPLANES

Uniforms.

Vice-Amiral.	Comandor.	Capitan-Comandor.	Locotenent-Comandor.	Capitan.	Locotenent.	Sub-locotenent.	Elev din Scoala de Marina.
(British Vice-Admiral.)	(British Captain.)	(British Commander.)	(British Lt.-Com.)	(British Senr.-Lieut.)	(British Lieutenant.)	(Sub-Lieut.)	(Midshipman.)

In addition to above, there is rank of Contr' Amiral (British, Rear-Admiral) as Vice-Amiral but without lower thin stripe.

Stripes are gold (except Paymasters, who wear silver) with curl for all branches. Colour of silk between, above and below stripes :—Executive, black ; Engineers, violet ; Surgeons, dark red, almost purple in colour : Constructors, Light blue.

ADMINISTRATION

Inspector General of the Navy : Vice-Admiral H.R.H. Prince Nicholas of Roumania.

Director of Navy : Rear-Admiral Corneliu Bucholtzer.

Commander in Chief : Vice-Admiral Vasile Scodrea.

Naval Attaché, London : Commander Gheorghe Nieulescu.

Mercantile Marine : Total gross tonnage (from Lloyd's Register) 1931, 65,921 tons.

Colour of Ships : Light grey.

Personnel : 289 officers, 3,702 men.

Silhouettes

LT. L. REMUS class (4).

AREAL.

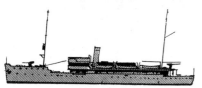

CONSTANTA.

I. C. BRATIANU class (4).

VIFOR class (4).

BASARABIA.

NALUCA. SMELI.

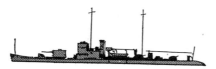

BUCOVINA.

REGELE FERDINAND I.
REGINA MARIA.

MIRCEA.

MARASTI. MARASESTI.

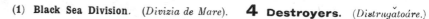

REGINA MARIA.   1930, *Dr. Mendl.*

2 *Thornycroft type:* **Regele Ferdinand I** (Dec. 2nd, 1928). **Regina Maria** (March 2nd, 1929).   Laid down at Pattison Yard, Naples, in June, 1927, to design of Messrs. Thornycroft.   Displacement 1900 tons.   Dimensions : 334½ × 31½ × 11¼ feet.   Parsons geared turbines by Stabilimento Tecnico Triestino. H.P. 40.000 = 34 kts.   Radius : 3000 miles at 15 kts.   Armament : **5**—4·7 inch, 50 cal., Bofors, **1**—3 inch, AA., Bofors, **2**—2 pdr. pom-pom, **6**—21 inch torpedo tubes (tripled), 50 mines.   Firing Director of Siemens type.   Cost per ship, without armament £205,000.   Completed 1930.

1919 *Photo.*

2 *Pattison type:* **Mărăsti** (ex-Italian *Sparviero*, 1919), and **Mărăsesti** (ex-Italian *Nibbio*, 1918). 1391 tons *normal* (1723 tons *full load*). Dimensions : 309½ (*p.p.*) × 31 × 11½ feet. Guns : **5**—4·7 inch, **4**—14 pdr., 40 cal. AA. **2** M.G. Tubes : **4**—17·7 inch in twin deck mountings. Searchlights : **1**—36 inch, **1**—13 inch. Designed S.H.P. 45,000= 34 kts. Trials : *Marasesti*, 48,020 S.H.P.=38·04 kts., 2 Tosi turbines. 2 screws. 4 Thornycroft oil burning boilers. Oil : 260 tons=1700 miles (15 kts.), 380 miles (full speed). Complement : 139.

Notes.—Belong to class of 4 Destroyers, *Vifor, Viscol, Vârtej, Vijelia*, ordered for Roumanian Navy about 1913. Were requisitioned for Italian Navy during war and re-named *Aquila. Falco, Nibbio, Sparviero.* Last two re-purchased by Roumania 1920, and renamed after actions fought in 1917.   Refitted and rearmed at Galatz and at Naples, 1925-26. Now has paired guns on forecastle, on after shelter deck, and a single gun between second and third funnels.

6 Torpedo Boats.* (*Torpiloare.*)

No.	Type	Date	Displacement tons	H.P.	Max. speed kts.	Fuel tons	Complement	Tubes	Max. draug't feet
4	*Vifor* (ST)	1914	262	5000	24	42	—	2 in some.	5
2	*Naluca* (GD)		266	t	...	54		15″ or 17·7″	

(GD)=Ganz-Danubius, Fiume.   (t)=Turbines.   (ST)=Stab. Tecnico Triestino, Trieste.

*Ex-Austrian boats taken over at Venice, 1920. Another of these boats (*Fulgerul*) was lost on the voyage from Italy to the Black Sea.

(Black Sea.)   1922 *Photo, M. Klein.*

4 Ex-Austrian boats: **Vifor** (ex-*74T*), **Vârtej** (ex-*75T*), **Vijelia** (ex-*80T*), **Sborul** (ex-*81T*), (Stab Tecnico Triestino, Trieste, 1913-14). Displacement: 262 tons. Dimensions: 189½ × 19 × 5 feet. Guns: *Sborul* and *Vifor*, 2—11 pdr.; *Vârtej* and *Vijelie*, 2 M.G. Torpedo tubes: 2—17.7 inch in *Sborul*, 2—15 inch in *Vârtej*, none in others. Searchlights: 1—16 inch in all. Designed S.H.P. 5000=28 kts. (24 best speed now). Turbine engines and Yarrow boilers. Fuel: 18 tons coal + 24 tons oil.

Note—Vifor means Snowstorm ; Vârtej, Whirlwind ; Sborul, Flight ; Vijelia, Thunderstorm.

NAULCA.   (Black Sea.)   1923 *Photo, Captain A. Tiufiaeff, late I.R.N.*

2 Ex-Austrian boats: **Naluca** (ex-*82F*), **Smeul** (ex-*83F*), (Ganz-Danubius Co., Porto Ré, Fiume, 1913-14.) 260 tons. Beam, 19 feet. Guns: 2—11 pdr., 2 M.G. No tubes. 1—16·5 inch S.L. Fuel: 20 tons coal + 34 tons *oil*, other details as *Vifor* class above. Smeul=Dragon. Naluca=Phantom.

Submarine

Quarnaro boat: **Delfinul.** Laid down at Fiume, August, 1927. Displacement: 650 tons. Dimensions : 225 × 19½ × 12 feet. Speed 14/9 kts. Armed with 1– 4 inch gun and 8—21 inch tubes. Completed 1931.

(Black Sea) Gunboats. (*Canoniere.*)

1919 *Photo.*

LOCOTENENT LEPRI REMUS (ex-French *Chiffone*, Lorient D.Y. launched 1917).

LOCOTENENT-COMANDOR STIHI EUGEN (ex-French *Friponne*, Lorient D.Y., launched 1916).

SUBLOCOTENENT GHICULESCU (ex-French *Impatiente*, Brest D.Y., launched 1916).

CĂPITAN DUMITRESCU Ç. (ex-French *Mignonne*, Brest D.Y., launched 1917).

Displacement: 400, 450, 350, 390 tons respectively.   Length : 189½ to 199¾ ft.   Beam : 22 ft. 7 in.   Draught : first pair, 9¼ ft. ; second pair, 7¾ ft.   Guns : 2—3·9 inch.   2 M.G.   S.L. : 2—15·7 inch.   Engines : 2 sets of Sulzer Diesel motors.   B.H.P. 900 = 15 kts   Fuel carried : 30 tons oil = 3000 miles (10 kts.), 1600 miles (15 kts.)   Complement, 50.

Notes.—Purchased from French Navy, 9th January, 1920. Entered service 15th Jan., 1920. Are differentiated by coloured rings around crowsnest. Names are those of naval officers killed in action, 1916-18.

(Black Sea.) **Training Ship** (*Vas Scoală*).

MIRCEA.

1928 *Photo, Dr. Mendl.*

MIRCEA (1882) London.　Brig, with auxiliary engine.　350 tons.　118 × 25 × 8¾ feet.　Guns : 2—1 pdr., 2 M.G.　I.H.P. 160 = 8·5 kts.　Coal : 32 tons.　Complement, 80.

Note.—Refitted 1923-24.　*Mircea* is said to have been one of the fastest sailing ships of her time, having made up to 16—17 kts.　At one time the Russians proposed to exchange her for a gunboat of the " Kubanetz " class, but the Roumanians refused, as all the traditions of their Navy resided in the *Mircea*. She is named after a Prince who flourished 1386—1418, defeating the Turks and occupying the territory on both banks of the Danube down to the Black Sea.

(2) **Danube Division** (*Divizia de Dunăre*).

Monitors (*Monitoare*).

Note.—With exception of *Bratianu* class, all are named after Roumanian provinces.

(Has flush deck forward.)

BUCOVINA (ex-Austro-Hungarian *Sava*, launched 1915).　Displacement, 550 tons.　Dimensions : 190¼ × 33·8 × 4¼ feet.　Guns : 2—4.7 inch, 45 cal. Skoda (paired in single turret forward) + 2—4.7 inch, 10 cal. howitzers (fortress type, singly mounted in pits with cupola protection), 2—66 m/m. (AA., twin-mounted in turret), 4—47 m/m., and 6 M.G.　1—24 inch searchlight. Armour : 1½″ Belt and Bulkheads, 1″ Deck, 2″ C.T., 2″ Turret and Cupolas.　3 magazines with water-jackets and electric-controlled refrigerators.　Designed H.P. 1600 = 12 kts. Boilers : Yarrow.　Fuel : 75 tons, oil *only*.　Complement, 90 to 100.　Built under 1914-15 Austro-Hungarian Naval Programme, completed 1915.　Interned at Novi Sad 1919-20 and handed over by Yugo-Slavs at Orsova early in 1921.　Sister ship, *Vardar*, now unit of Yugo-Slav Danube Flotilla.

BASARABIA (ex-Austro-Hungarian *Inn*, launched 1915).　Displacement, 550 tons.　Dimensions : 203¼ (*o.a.*) × 34½ × 4¼ feet.　Guns : 2—4.7 inch, 45 cal. + 3—4.7 inch, 10 cal. howitzers, 2—47 m/m., 4 M.G.　Armour : 1½ Belt and Bulkheads, 1″ Deck, 2″ Turret and Cupolas, 2″ C.T. Designed I.H.P. 1500 = 12 kts.　Boilers : Yarrow.　Fuel : 70 tons, oil *only*.　Complement, 100.　Built under Austro-Hungarian 1912 Naval Programme ; interned at Novi Sad 1919-20, handed over by Yugo-Slavs at Orsova early in 1921.　Sister ship, *Drava*, now unit of Yugo-Slav Danube Flotilla is shown above.

(Danube) **Monitors**—*continued.*

M. KOGALNICEANU.

1931 *Photo, Dr. Mendl.*

IOAN C. BRĂTIANU (1907), **MIHAIL KOGĂLNICEANU** (1907), **ALEXANDRU LAHOVARI** (1908), and **LASCĂR CATARGIU** (1907). Displacement : 680 tons. Complement, 110. Dimensions : 208¼ × 33¾ × 5¼ feet. Guns (Skoda) : 3—4.7 inch, 35 cal. (2—4.7 inch howitzers removed during the War), 1—3 inch. AA., 2—47 m/m., 2 M.G. S.L.: 1—30.7 inch, 1—28.3 inch. Armour : 3″ Belt, 3″ Deck, 3″—2″ Turrets. H.P. 1800 = 13 kts. Coal : 60 tons. Built by Stabilimento Tecnico Triestino, at Trieste, in sections, re-erected at Galatz. Deck cabins and military masts removed during the War. All named after 19th century Roumanian statesmen.

(Danube.)   1922 *Photo,. M. Klein.*

7 *Major Sontu* class : **CĂPITAN NICOLAE LASCAR BOGDAN, CĂPITAN ROMANO MIHAIL, LOCOTENENT CĂINESCU DIMITRIE, MAJOR CONSTANTINL ENE, MAJOR DIMITRIE GIURESCU, MAJOR NICOLAE GRIGORE LOAN, MAJOR SONTU GHEORGHE** (Thames Iron Works, 1906), Displacement, 50 tons. Dimensions : 100 × 13 × 2¾ feet. Armament : 1—47 m/m. Skoda, 1 machine. 1—20 inch S.L. Some have a light steel c.t. with s.l. on top. H.P. 590 to 620 = 17·7 to 18 kts. Oil fuel : 7½ tons. Complement, 20. Differentiated by large coloured numerals on funnels, Their two twin funnels, ram bows and round tunnel sterns make their recognition easy. *Capt. V. Mărăcsneau* mined 1916.

Submarine Depot Ship, (*Nava Baza.*)

1922 *Photo.*

ARDEAL (ex-Austro-Hungarian *Temes*, 1904). Displacement : 450 tons. Complement, 80 to 90. Dimensions : 183½ × 31¼ × 3¾ feet. Guns : 2—4.7 inch, 35 cal., 1—3.4 inch AA., 2—47 m/m., 2 M.G. Armour : 1½″ Belt, 3″ and 1½″ Turrets, 1½″ Bulkheads, 1″ Deck. H.P. 1400 = 10 kts. Fuel capacity : 60 tons. Was originally built as a sister-ship to *Sava*, of Yugo-Slav Navy. While serving on Danube as Austro-Hungarian *Temes*, she was sunk in October, 1914, but was raised in June, 1916, and entirely rebuilt 1916-17 ; she is thus, compared with others of the same original design, a practically new Monitor. Re-entered service April, 1917. Interned at Novi Sad, 1919-20 ; handed over at Orsova by Yugo-Slavs early in 1921. Easily identified by her tall, thin funnel and raised gun aft, mounted during reconstruction, 1916-17. No other Monitor exists with this arrangement, except Yugo-Slav *Morava*, and her guns are not in turrets.

Photo 1931, Dr. Mendl.

CONSTANTA (November 8, 1928). Laid down at the Quarnara Yard, Fiume, August 15, 1927, completed in 1931. Displacement : 2,300 tons. Dimensions : 255¾ × 37 × 13¼ feet. 2 Diesel motors = 1,000 H.P. = 13 kts. Radius : 12,000 miles. Guns : 2—4 inch, 2 M.G. 3 electric generating sets H.P. 136. Fitted with engineering and torpedo shops ; bakery : torpedo loading room : salvage, diving and submarine signalling apparatus.

(3) (Danube.)

Royal Yacht. (*Iachtul Regal*).

STEFAN CEL MARE (ex-river passenger steamer *Orient*, 1870.) Built by Donau-Dampfschiffahrts Gesellschaft Yard, Altofen, Budapest. Dimensions : 250 × 27·5 × 4.6 feet. Paddle engines, H.P. 670 = 18 kts. Painted white, with two thin yellow funnels.

Note.—Named after the famous Moldavian Prince (1457–1504), who was victorious over the Turks and Poles.

(Danube.)

Miscellaneous Vessels.

MĂCIN (Stab. Tecnico Triestino, Linz, 1912). 200 tons. Dimensions : 138·9 × 20·3 × 4·9 feet. 2 sets Diesel engines, B.H.P. 500 = 12 kts. 2 screws. Guns : Nil. Complement, 30.

Note.—This vessel, originally a river tug, has had a deckhouse built forward, and serves as administrative flagship of the Roumanian Danube Flotilla. Painted white, with a yellow funnel.

Măcin is a small town in the Dobrudja.

The Danube flotilla also includes 2 Armed Paddle Steamers, *General Maican* and *Capitan-Comandor Paun* ; two others, *Locotenent Stoicescu* and *Locotenent Vârtosu*, fitted for minesweeping ; 6 ex-Russian floating batteries ; and a number of tugs, lighters and other small vessels.

Motor Launches. (*Vedete Anti-Submarine.*)

VAS 1—VAS 4. Purchased from Italy, 1920. Displacement : 43 tons. Dimensions : 85¼ × 12 × 3¾ feet. H.P. 430 = 15 kts. Are ex-Italian M.A.S., type C, with 1 Machine Gun.

---

(4) FRONTIER GUARD VESSELS.

In addition to the Regular Navy, the vessels detailed below compose a separate force, with personnel detached from the regular service, under a Commander, R. Roumanian Navy. These craft are known as *Grupul de Vase ale Granicerilor* (Group of Frontier Guard vessels). They are under the Army, but uniforms worn by personnel are the same as those of Navy, except for aiguillettes corresponding to those of Frontier Guard troops. Headquarters and base are at Braila.

(Danube.)

Police Gunboats. (*Nare de Politie.*)
(Painted grey.)

BISTRITA.

BISTRITA, OLTUL, SIRETUL (Blackwall, 1888). 95·2 tons. Dimensions : 100 × 13 × 6½ feet. Guns : 1—6 pdr., 1—1 pdr. H.P., 400 = 12 kts. Oil : 12 tons. Complement, 20.

Police Launches (*Salupe de politie*).*
(All painted grey.)

Rândunica (Galatz, 1900). 10 tons. 46 × 7·9 × 3·3 feet. H.P. 25 = 8 kts. Oil : 1½ tons. Complement, 5.

Argesul, Teleorman, Trotus, Vedea (Schichau, Elbing, 1894). 30 tons. 65·6 × 9·8 × 4·9 feet. Guns : 1—1 pdr. Hotchkiss, 1 Nordenfelt M.G. I.H.P. 148 = 10 kts. Coal : 8 tons. Comp., 16.

Granicerul, Pandurul, Poterasul, Santinela, Vegheatorul (London, 1882). 10 tons. 50 × 7¾ × 3½ feet. I.H.P. 25 = 10 kts. Oil : 1 ton. Complement, 5.

Porumbita
Silistra } Built at Galatz Navy Yard.
Soimulet

* All except *Argesul* class are at present unarmed and used as Communication Tenders.

Motor Launches.

(1) *For service on Lower Danube and Black Sea :*—

4 boats (built by Pattison, Naples, 1921) : *Maior Caracas Petre, Capitan Popescu Constantin, Capitan Constantinescu Traian, Capitan Pantulescu Eugeniu.* Displacement, 9 tons. 43 × 9 × 3 feet. H.P., 150— 175 = 15 kts. Guns : 1—37 m/m. on fore deck. Built of steel. Painted white.

(2) *For service on the Danube :*—

8 boats : *Gr. D1, 2, 3, 4, 5, 6, 7, 8.* (Gr. = Graniceri., *i.e.* Frontier Guard. D = Dunare, *i.e.*, Danube.) Displacement, 3½ tons. 31½ × 6 × 2¼ feet. H.P., 150— 175 = 20 kts. Guns : 1 M.G. Built of wood. Painted white.

(3) *For service on the Dniester :*—

3 boats : *Gr. N.1, 2, 3.* (N = Nistru, *i.e.* Dniester.) Displacement, 2·2 tons. 26·2 × 5·9 × 1·9 feet. H.P., 24—35 = 10 kts. Built of wood. Painted white.

(These are Patrol Boats of no military importance).

Harbour Launches.

Opanez, Rahova, (London, 1882). 45 tons. 55¾ × 11½ × 5¼ feet. Guns : 1—1 pdr. Hotchkiss, 1 M.G. I.H.P. 100 = 8½ kts. Oil : 8 tons. Complement, 10. *Smârdan* a war loss, 1917.

General Note.

Of the names on this page, *Bistrita* and *Argesul* classes and *Silistra* are geographical ; *Granicerul* class are named after various military types ; *Porumbita* = Pigeon, *Soimulet* = Sparrowhawk, and *Rindunica* = Swallow ; motor launches bear the names of officers killed in action, 1916-18 ; and *Opanez* and *Rahova* were actions in the war of Independence, 1877.

Flags

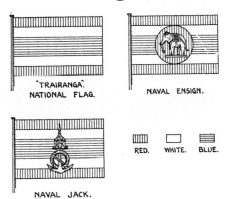

"TRAIRANGA". NATIONAL FLAG.

NAVAL ENSIGN.

NAVAL JACK.

RED. WHITE. BLUE.

ADMIRAL OF THE FLEET'S FLAG.—A blue flag with a white elephant, and in the upper canton next the staff two yellow anchors crossed surmounted by the Siamese crown.

ADMIRAL'S FLAG.—A blue flag with a white elephant in the centre.

VICE ADMIRAL'S FLAG.—The same as the Admiral's flag but with a white "Chakra" in the upper canton next the staff.

REAR ADMIRAL'S FLAG.—The same as the Admiral's flag but with two white "Chakras" near the staff.

Personnel: 5000. Reserve : 20,000.

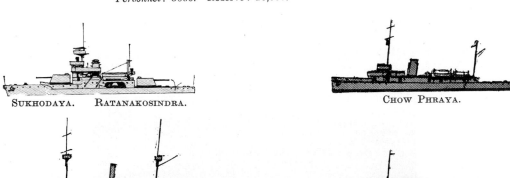

SUKHODAYA. RATANAKOSINDRA.

SAW, SUGRIB, MONGKUT.

CHOW PHRAYA.

T.B. 1, 2, 3, 4.

PHRA RUANG.

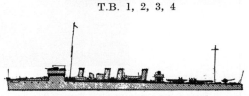

SUA TAYARNCHOL No. 4th funnel.
SUA KHAMRONSINDHU.

413

SUKHODAYA (p. 413).

1930 *Photo, by courtesy of Messrs. Vickers-Armstrong.*

1926 *Photo, by courtesy of Messrs. Armstrong.*

SUKHODAYA (Vickers Armstrong, Nov. 19,1929).

RATANAKOSINDRA (Armstrong, April 21, 1925). 1000 tons. 160 (*p.p.*), 175 (*o.a.*) × 37 × 10¾ feet. Guns : 2—6 inch, 4—3 inch AA. Protection : Side 2½″ (amidships), 1¼″ ends, nickel steel. Barbette rings, 2½″ nickel steel. C.T. 4¾″ cast steel armour. Upper deck, ¾″ to 1½″ high tensile steel. 2 screws. Vertical triple expansion engines. H.P. 850 = 12 kts. 2 oil-burning water-tube boilers. Oil : 96 tons. Complement, 103.

Ratanakosindra laid down 29th Sept., 1924, and completed August, 1925. *Sukhodaya* completed 1930.

3 Destroyers.

Phra Ruang.

1921 *Photo, by courtesy of J. Bailey, Esq.*

PHRA RUANG

Phra Ruang (ex-British *Radiant*, launched by Thornycrofts, Nov., 1917. Purchased by Siam, July, 1920). 1035 tons. Dimensions : 274 (*o.a.*), 265 (*p.p.*) × 27½ × 11 feet (*max.* draught) and 8½ feet (*mean*). Guns : 3—4 inch, 1—3 inch AA, 1—2 pdr. 1 M.G. Tubes : 4—21 inch, in two twin deck mountings. Machinery : Brown-Curtis (all geared) turbines. Designed S.H.P. 29,000 = 35 kts. (39.67 trials). 3 Yarrow boilers. Oil fuel : about 285 tons *max.* Complement, 100.

1919 *Photo, J. Bailey, Esq.*

Sua-Khamronsindhu (1912), 385 tons, and **Sua-Tayarnchol** (1908), 375 tons. Both built by Kawasaki Co. Kobé, Japan. Dimensions : 227 (*p.p.*) × 21½ × 6 feet. H.P. 6000 = 27 kts. Oil : 75 tons = 850 miles at 11 kts. Armament : 1—12 pdr., 5—6 pdr., 2 M.G. ; 2—18 inch tubes. Complement : 71.

Notes.—Same type as the Japanese "*Arare*" class Destroyers. *Sua-Tayarnchol* has only three funnels.

4 Torpedo Boats.

No. 3.

1919 *Photo, J. Bailey, Esq.*

4 *Kawasaki* boats :—No. *1, 2* and *3* (1908), and No. *4* (1913), 120 tons. 131·6 × 16·2 × 3·6 feet. H.P. 1200 = 22 kts. Armament : **1**—6 pdr., **1**—3 pdr., **2**—18 inch tubes. Complement : 24.

C. M. B.

C.M.B. 1925 *Photo, by courtesy of Messrs. Thornycroft.*

One 55-ft. type, (1922) by Messrs. Thornycroft. 11 tons. B.H.P. 750 = 37 kts. (40 kts. *extreme*). Petrol carried : 300 gallons *normal*, 500 *max.* **4** Lewis guns, 2 torpedoes, **2** D.C. Complement, 5.

Training Ship.

CHOW PHRAYA.   *1924 Photo, by courtesy of Messrs. Thornycroft.*

CHOW PHRAYA (ex-British Twin Screw Minesweeper *Harant*, built by Eltringhams, S. Shields, Nov., 1918, purchased 1923 and reconstructed by Messrs. Thornycroft). Displacement, 840 tons. Dimensions: $220 \times 28\frac{1}{2} \times 7\frac{1}{2}$ feet. Machinery: Vertical triple expansion. Boilers: Yarrow, converted to burn oil. I.H.P. 2200 = 16 kts. Oil: 160 tons. Complement, 65.

Despatch Vessel.

PI-SUA-NAM. Displacement 165 tons   Dimensions: $100 \times 20 \times 8\frac{1}{2}$ (*mean* draught) feet. H.P. $210 = 9\frac{1}{2}$ kts.   Complement, 25.

Royal Yacht.

1919 Photo, J. Bailey, Esq.

MAHA CHAKRI (Kawasaki Co., Kobé, Japan, 1918). About 2,400 tons *gross*. Complement, 199. Length, 298 feet (*w.l.*), 335 feet (*o.a.*). Beam, 40 feet. Draught, feet. Guns: Not known. Machinery (*see Notes*): 2 sets triple exp. Boilers: 4 (type unknown) coal and oil burning. I.H.P. about 2000 = 15 kts. Oil fuel: 200 tons = 2000 miles endurance. 2 screws.

Notes.—The hull of the old Royal Yacht *Maha Chakri* was sold to the Kawasaki Co. in 1917, but the engines and other fittings were removed, overhauled and renovated for installation in the new *Maha Chakri* described above.

Coastguard Vessel.

1921 Photo, J. Bailey, Esq.

SRIYA* MONTHON (Thornycroft, 1908).   Displacement: 225 tons.   Dimensions: 137 (*p.p.*) $\times$ 18 $\times$ $6\frac{1}{2}$ (*mean* draught) feet. Guns: 2—6 pdr. I.H.P. 700 = 14·5 knots speed. Coal: 66 tons. No. of Screws: 2.   Boilers: 1 (type unknown).   Complement, 34.

* Usually known by first name only.

Also 3 ex-N.D.L. steam lighters, re-named *Chen Thale, Han Thale, Leu Thale,* built by Hongkong and Whampoa Dock Co. About 160 $\times$ 27 $\times$ feet, 440 tons *gross*. Nom. H.P. 60 = 8 kts. speed. Seized during the war and now used for various purposes, including occasional surveying duties.

There are various small craft used for River Duties of which no precise details are available.

MONGKUT RAJAKUMARN (ex-*Filipinas*, Hongkong and Whampoa Dock Co., 1887; purchased 1891). 700 tons. $175 \times 23\frac{1}{2} \times 11$ feet. Guns: 2—4·7 inch, 2—6 pdr., 3—3 pdr. Speed 11 kts. 2 screws. Complement: 100. In reserve.

Transports.

1921 Photo, J. Bailey, Esq.

VIDES* KICHKAR (ex-*Buk*, ex-*Lycidas*, Ritson & Co., Maryport, 1902). 850 tons. $176 \times 27\frac{1}{8} \times 10\frac{1}{2}$ feet. H.P. 780 = 9 to 10 kts.
* Usually known by first name only.

PRA-YOM. Displacement 190 tons.   Dimensions: $110 \times 18 \times 8$ (*mean* draught) feet. H.P. 225 = 10 kts.   Complement, 30.

BALI.   *1921 Photo, J. Bailey, Esq.*

BALI (1901), **SUGRIB** (1901).   580 tons. $162 \times 23 \times 10$ feet. Guns: 1—4·7 inch, 5—6 pdr.   Designed H.P. 500 = 11·4 kts. Complement, 75.

Appearance Note.—Tops on *both* masts;   2 yards above top on foremast.

SPANISH NAVY.

Revised 1931 by courtesy of the Ministry of Marine.

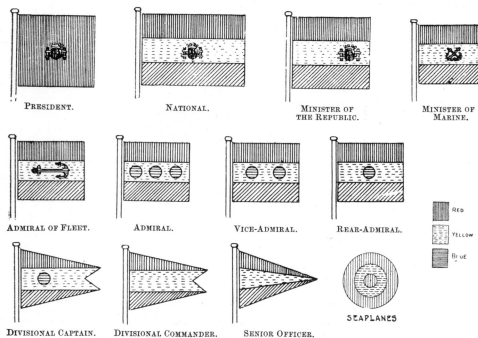

I—Flags.

| PRESIDENT. | NATIONAL. | MINISTER OF THE REPUBLIC. | MINISTER OF MARINE. |

| ADMIRAL OF FLEET. | ADMIRAL. | VICE-ADMIRAL. | REAR-ADMIRAL. |

RED
YELLOW
BLUE

| DIVISIONAL CAPTAIN. | DIVISIONAL COMMANDER. | SENIOR OFFICER. |

SEAPLANES

II—Administration.

Minister of Marine—
Naval Attaché, (London)—Capitan de Corbeta Don Juan Pastor.

III—Naval Programme and Budget.

A new Programme of Naval Construction was authorised by the Law of July 4th, 1926, to include the following vessels, all of which are to be completed in six years' time:—

3 Cruisers, of about 10,000 tons.
3 Flotilla Leaders, of *Churruca* type.
12 Submarines, of "C" type.
3 Fishery Protection Gunboats, of 250 tons.
2 Oilers (of 6,000 tons capacity).

IV—Fleet Organisation.

No exact details available: is reported to vary according to the season of the year. The latest statement available is as follows:—

(a) "In third Condition" (*i.e.* fully manned):—Training Squadron, *Espana, Jaime I,* 6 Cruisers and 3 destroyers of *Alsedo* class.

(b) *Juan Sebastian de Elcano* on Foreign Cruises, for Training Duties.

(c) For service on African Coast and in territorial waters, &c.:—
1 gunboat, 6 patrol vessels, 1 tug, and sundry small craft.

V—Personnel.

Officers: 1729 (including Departmental Corps). Reserve: 374. 14,000 seamen; 2813 marines.

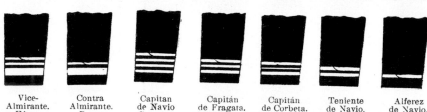

| Vice-Almirante. *Vice-Admiral.* | Contra Almirante. *Rear-Admiral.* | Capitan de Navio *Captain.* | Capitán de Fragata. *Commander.* | Capitán de Corbeta. *Lieutenant-Commander.* | Teniente de Navio. *Lieutenant.* | Alferez de Navio. *Sub-Lieutenant* |

Other branches, *without the curl,* have distinguishing colours as follows:—

Engineers	...	*green.*	Astronomical	...	*green brown.*
Constructors	...	*blue.*	Pharmaciens	...	*yellow.*
Doctors	...	*red.*	Chaplains	...	*violet.*
Paymasters	...	*white.*			

VI—Training Establishments.

For Training Squadron and Division, &c., v.§ IV (a) (b) (c).

Shore Establishments are:—For Executive Officers, Gunnery Officers, Naval School (*Escuela Naval Militar*), San Fernando. For Engineering Branch and Cadets, Ferrol. The old corvette, *Nautilus,* serves as a depot ship. For Accountant Officers, Cartagena.

In future, naval constructors and gunnery officers will be selected from executive branch by means of special courses. In order that officers may extend their studies in these and other directions, a Naval War College has been established in Madrid.

VII. Naval Ordnance.

Nota-tion.	Nominal Calibre.		Model.	Length in calibres	Weight of Gun.	Weight of A.P. shell.	Initial velocity	*Max.* penetration A.P. capped direct impact at K.C. at		Danger Space against average ship. at			Rounds per minute.
								5000 yards.	3000 yards.	10,000 yards.	5000 yards.	3000 yards.	
HEAVY	c/m. 30·5	inches. 12	V'09	50	tons. 66	lbs. 850	ft. secs. 3010	inches. 17	inches. 20	...	...	...	2
	28	11	H.	35	32½	837	2034	5½	8	...	...	...	...
	20 3	8	...	50	...	...	...	...	...	...	...	...	...
MEDIUM	15	6	*V.	50	7¾	100	3100	...	8¾	...	...	...	10
	15	5·9	R.	45	4½	88	2625	...	3	25	200	430	5—6
	14	5·5	H.	35	...	86	2001	...	...	...	...	...	...
	14	5·5	C.	35	...	86	2034	...	...	...	...	...	...
LIGHT	12	4·7	V.	45	...	48·5	2788	...	...	...	...	...	...
	10·5	4·1	K.	35	...	35·2	...	...	...	...	...	...	...
	10·2	4	V.	50	2·1	31	3030	...	...	...	...	...	15

V=Vickers.   H=Hontoria.   G=Guillen.   R=Rueda.   C=Canet.   K=Krupp.

✲ Arsenal de Carraca.

VIII. Colour of Ships.

Light grey.

IX. Mercantile Marine.

(From "Lloyd's Register," 1931 figures. Total *gross* tonnage, 1,227,370, including 12 vessels of 16 kts. and over.

MacMahon.

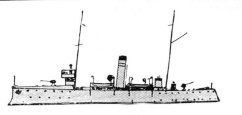

Antonio C. del Castillo.
Josě Czaralejas.
Eduardo Dato.

Lauria.   Laya.
Bonifaz.   Recalde.

Dedalo.

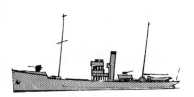

" Uad Lucas" and "Arcila" Types.

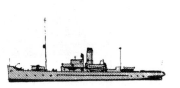

Alcazar.   Larache.   Tetuan.

Republica.

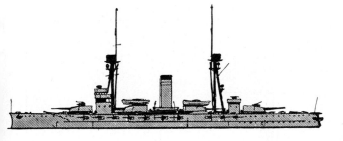

España.   Jaime 1.

Libertad.
Almirante Cervera.
Miguel de Cervantes.

Blaz de Lezo.
Mendez Nunez.

Bustamante.

T.B's.

Barcaiztegui class

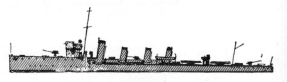

Alcedo.
Velasco.
Juan Lazaga.

ESPAÑA (ex-*Alfonso* XIII) (May, 1913), & **JAIME PRIMERO** (Sept., 1914).

Normal displacement, 15,452 tons (*max.* 15,700 tons).   Complement, 854.

Length (*waterline*), 435 feet.   Beam, 78¾ feet.   *Max.* draught, 25½ feet.   Length (*over all*), 459⅙ feet.

Guns (Vickers and Skoda) :
 8—12 inch, 50 cal. (**Dir. Con.**)
 20—4 inch, 50 cal.
 2—3 pdr. (Vickers)
 2—3 pdr. (Skoda)
 2 Maxims.
 (**2** landing).
Torpedo tubes :
 none.

Armour (Krupp) :
 8″ Belt (amidships) ......
 3″ Belt (bow) ....
 4″ Belt (aft) ....
 1½″ Deck
 6″ Lower deck side ......
 8″ Turrets (N.C.) ....
 10″ Turret bases (N.C.) ...
 3″ Battery (N.C.) ......
 10″ Conning tower ....
 6″ After C.T. (Hadfield)
Special protection :
 1½″ H.T. internal screens over
 Sections 4—15 on plans.

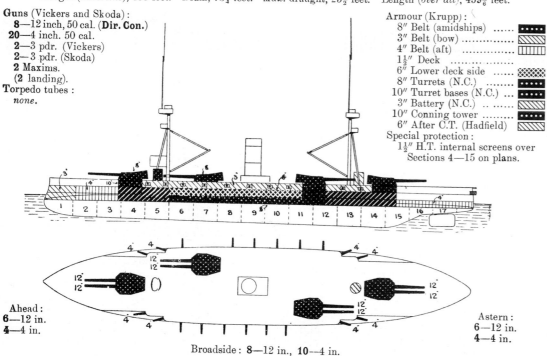

Ahead :
6—12 in.
4—4 in.

Astern :
6—12 in.
4—4 in.

Broadside : **8**—12 in., **10**—4 in.

Machinery : Parsons turbine.   4 screws.   Boilers : 12 Yarrow.   Designed H.P. 15,500=19·5 kts.   Coal : *normal* 900 tons ; *maximum* 1900 tons + 20 tons oil fuel = nominal radius of 5000 miles at 10 kts., and 3100 miles at 16¾ kts.

Gunnery Notes.—Vickers type 12 inch gun directors in lower top on each mast.   12 inch manœuvred by hydraulic power ; all-round loading at any angle of elevation.   Magazine capacity is 80 rounds per 12 inch gun, but there is ample storage for more than this.   Arcs of fire : end 12 inch, *about* 270° ; echelon 12 inch, 180° on own beam (*nominal*) and about 80° far beam.   Heights of guns over normal waterline : 12 inch, 24¼ feet ; 4 inch, 13¾ feet.   Total weight *about* 2550 tons.   (These notes are not from any official source.)

Armour Notes.—Main belt is 6 feet 7 inches deep, 4 feet 7 inches of this being below waterline and 2 feet above.   On plans 8 inch belt amidships should extend to bases of end barbettes.   Hull without armour = 5600 tons.

Machinery Notes.—Engines = 1320 tons.

Torpedo Notes.—Bullivant net defence.   No torpedo tubes installed.

Name	Builder	Machinery	Laid down	Completed	Trials (Full Power)	Boilers	Best recent speed
España *Jaime I*	} Ferrol Yard	S. E. C. N.	{ Feb.'10 Feb.'12	1915 1921	23,357 = 20·36 = 20·028	} Yarrow	

General Notes.—Built under Navy Law of 7th January, 1908.   Construction of *Jaime I* was greatly impeded by delivery of materials from England being stopped during the war up to 1919.   A third ship of this type, *España*, wrecked on Riff coast of Morocco, August, 1923, and became a total loss.

JAIME I (two white bands round funnel).

1925 *Photo, Capitan M. Mille.*

ESPAÑA (only one white band round funnel).

1926 *Photo, Capitan M. Mille.*

1st Class Cruisers

(*Cruçeros de 1a Clas*).

(BALEARES CLASS—2 SHIPS.)

BALEARES (Apl., 1932).
CANARIAS (May 28th, 1931).

Displacement: 10,000 tons *standard* (12,230 tons *full load*). Complement,

Length, 636 feet.

Beam, 64 feet.

Draught, 17⅓ feet (*mean*).

1931 *Illustration*.

Guns:
8—8 inch.
6—4.7 inch.
4—4.7 inch AA.
8—2 pdr. pom-pom AA.
Torpedo tubes (21 inch):
12 (*above water*, tripled).

Armour:
Probably on similar lines to British *Kent* type.

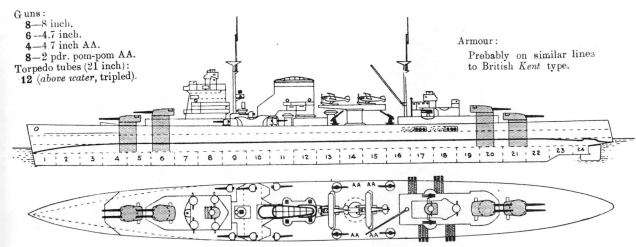

Machinery: Parsons geared turbines.   Boilers: Yarrow.   Designed S.H.P. 90,000 = 33 kts.

Notes.—Both ships laid down at Ferrol, August 15th, 1928.   A third cruiser of this type is to be constructed.   These ships are exceedingly well thought out, and now embody the latest developments in design according to British practice.   Above plan has been prepared from the official drawings, and shows modifications to the two funnelled design (1930 edition F.S.) which are under consideration.   The illustration is based on a later alternative design in which the AA. armament will consist of eight 4·7″ AA.; four twin 2 pdrs. and multiple ½ inch. M.G. grouped at the base of the funnel.   *Canarias* is to be completed by February, 1932.   *Baleares* is to be launched in April, 1932.

EE

LIBERTAD (ex-**Principe Alfonso**) (Jan. 3rd, 1925), **ALMIRANTE CERVERA** (Oct. 16th, 1925), and **MIGUEL DE CERVANTES** (May 19th, 1928).

Normal Displacement, 7,850 tons.   Full load, abt. 9,000 tons.

Length, 575 feet, (p.p.)   579½ feet, (o.a.)   Beam, 54 feet.

Draught, mean 16½ feet, deep load ? feet.

Complement, 545.

Guns :
- **8**—6 inch, 50 cal. (**Dir. Con.**)
- **4**—4 inch, 45 cal. A.A.
- **2**—3 pdrs. A.A.
- **1** Machine.

Tubes :
- **12**—21″ in four triple U.D. rev. mounts.

Armour :
- 3″ Side (amidships.) ....
- 2″ Side (forward.) ....
- 1½″ Side (aft.) ....
- 1″ Deck. ....
- 2″ (H.T. ?) over rudder. ? ....
- 6″ Conning tower. ? ....

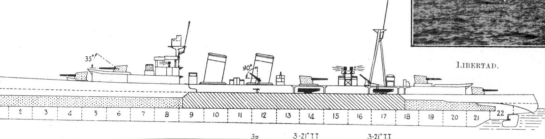

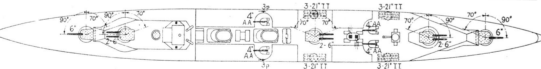

Ahead :
3—6 in.

Broadside : 8—6 in., 6—21 in. T.T.

Astern :
3—6 in.

Machinery : Parsons Geared Turbines.   4 screws.   Boilers : 8 Yarrow (large tube). Designed S.H.P. 80,000 = 33 kts.   Fuel capacity : 500 tons oil, normal ; 1650 tons oil, maximum. Endurance : 5000 at 15 kts., 1200 at full power.

Name	Builder	Machinery	Laid down	To be Completed	Trials	Boilers
Libertad Alm. Cervera M. de Cervantes	Ferrol D.Y.	S. E. C. N.	Aug. '22 25 Nov '22 Apr. '26	Dec. '25 May '27 1931	83000 = 34.7.	Yarrow

Notes.—Laid down by S.E.C.N. at Ferrol D.Y., under Navy Law of 17th Feb., 1915. Originally projected that only one Cruiser should be begun, but redistribution of funds has permitted the construction of two more of this type. Cost estimated at about 8122 pesetas a ton.

Designed under direction of late Sir Philip Watts, K.C.B., Director of Sir W. G. Armstrong, Whitworth & Co., Ltd., for Spanish Government. Are practically enlargements of British "E" class, with second third and fourth gun positions paired.

LIBERTAD.

1927 Photo, Capitan Mateo Mille.

LIBERTAD.

1929 Photo, Renard, Kiel.

420

Cruiser (*Cruçero Ligero de 2ª Clas*).

REPUBLICA (ex-**Reina Victoria Eugenia**) (21st April, 1920).

Displacement, 5590 metric tons.   Complement, 404.

Length (*p p.*) 440 feet, (*o.a.*) 462 feet.   Beam, 49⅔ feet.   *Mean* draught, 15¾ feet.

Guns (Vickers) :
  9—6 inch, 50 cal.
  4—3 pdr. AA.
  1—12 pdr. (Field)
  4 Machine
Torpedo tubes : (21 inch).
  4 *above water*
    (twin mountings).

Armour (Nickel and H.T.) :
  3″ Side ....
  2½-1¼″ Ends ......
  3″ Deck ....
  6″ Conning tower

1925 Photo, Capitan M. Mille.

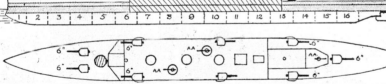

Ahead :
4—6 in.

Astern :
3—6 in.

Broadside : **5**—6 in., **1**—21 in. tube.

Machinery : Parsons turbines. 2 screws. Boilers : 12 Yarrow (coal and oil burning), in 3 rooms.
Designed H.P. 25,500 = 25·5 knots. Coal : *normal* 660 tons (inclusive of oil fuel).

Gunnery Notes.—6 inch are Vickers models, built at La Carraca.   Those on Forecastle have 180° arc of training, *i.e.*,
30° inboard and 150° on own beam.

Torpedo Notes—Above water tubes are behind lidded ports on main deck above section numbered 5.

Name	Builder	Machinery	Ordered	Laid down	Completed	Trials	Boilers	Best recent speed
Republica	Ferrol D.Y.	S. E. C. N.	Aug. '14	Mar. '15	15 Jan., '23	8 hours : 26049 = 25·77 4 hours : 28,387 = 26·9	Yarrow	25·7

General Notes.—Built under Navy Law of 30th July, 1914.

1923 Official Photo.

BLAS DE LEZO.

1926 *Photo, Capitan M. Mille*

MENDEZ NUÑEZ.

1925 *Photo, Capitan M. Mille*

BLAS DE LEZO (27th July, 1922).
MENDEZ NUNEZ (3rd March, 1923).

Normal Displacement : 4725 *metric* tons.   Complement, 343.

Length, (*p.p.*) 440 feet, (*o.a.*) 462 feet.   Beam, 46 feet.   Draught, $14\frac{1}{3}$ feet *mean*.

Guns :

6—6 inch, 50 cal. **Dir. Con.**
4—3 pdr. AA.
4 machine.
(1—12 pdr. landing.)
Torpedo Tubes (21 inch) :
12 *above water* (triple mountings).

Armour :

3″ Side amidships ....
$2\frac{1}{2}$-$1\frac{1}{4}$″ Side (ends) ....
1″ Deck ....
6″ C.T. ....
 ″ Director tower............ ....

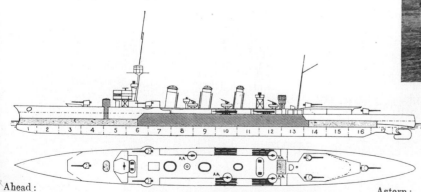

BLAS DE LEZO.

1930 *Photo, C. de C. Mateo de Mille, R.S.N.*

Machinery : Parsons (geared) turbines. 4 screws. Boilers : 12 Yarrow (6 oil burning, 6 mixed
firing). Designed H.P. 45,000 = 29 kts. Coal : *normal,* 250 tons ; *maximum,* 787 tons + 492 tons oil
Radius : 5000 miles at 13 kts.

Ahead :
3—6 in.   Broadside: **4**—6 inch, **6**—21 inch tubes.   Astern :
3—6 in.

Name	Builder	Machinery	Laid down	Completed	Trials	Boilers
B. de Lezo	Ferrol D.Y.	} S. E. C. N.	9 April '17	Mar.' 25	45,093 = 29.25	} Yarrow
M. Nuñez	Ferrol D.Y.		28 Sept.'17	1924	43,776 = 29.28	

Old Cruiser.

(Harbour Training Ship.)

1920 Photo, Capitan M. Mille.

CARLOS QUINTO (1895). 9993 tons. Comp., 583. Dimensions: 404¾ (o.a.) × 67 × 27⅔ feet *max.* draught; *mean* draught, 25 feet. Armament: **2**—11 inch (35 cal. Hontoria), **8**—5·5 inch (35 cal. Hontoria), **4**—4·1 inch (Krupp), **2**—12 pdr. (Vickers), **8**—6 pdr. (Nordenfelt), **8**—1 pdr. (Hotchkiss). Torpedo tubes (14 inch): **2** *above water.* Armour: 2½″ Deck, 10″ Barbettes with 4″ Hoods and 8″ Hoists, 2″ over Battery, 12″ C.T. Boilers: 8 Yarrow (fitted 1925). Designed H.P. 15,000, made 19 kts. on trial. Coal: *max.* 2040 tons. Begun at Cadiz, 1892. At present serves as Depot Ship for seamen under training at Ferrol and no longer goes to sea. May be discarded in near future.

19 **Flotilla Leaders and Destroyers**
Flotilla Leaders.

1926 *Photo, by courtesy of the Ministry of Marine.*

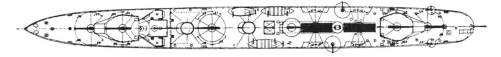

14 CHURRUCA class. All built at Cartegena D.Y. (S.E.C.N.).

				Bow Initials.
SANCHEZ BARCAIZTEGUI 1926.	..	..	..	SB
ALMIRANTE JUAN FERRANDIZ (May 21, 1928)		..	..	AF
JOSÉ LUIS DIEZ (August 25, 1928)	..	..	..	JD
LEPANTO (November 7, 1928)	..	..	..	LP
ALCALÁ GALIANO (April 12, 1930)	..	..	..	AG
CHURRUCA ( )	..	..	..	CH
ALMIRANTE VALDÉS (September 8, 1930)	..	..	AV
ALMIRANTE ANTEQUERA (December 29, 1930)	..	..	AA
ALMIRANTE MIRANDA ( )	..	..	AM

+ 5 others building.

Displacement: 1,650 tons *normal,* 1,800 tons *full load.* Dimensions: 320 × 31¾ × 10½ feet. Designed H.P. 42,000 = 36 kts. Two sets Parsons turbines. Guns: **5**—4·7 inch, **1**—14 pdr. AA. Torpedo tubes: **6**—21 inch tripled. **2** D.C. carried. Oil: 540 tons. Radius: 4,500 miles at 14 kts.

Note.—Built under 1915 Programme. Design generally similar to British Leaders of *Scott* class. Former *Churruca* and *Alcala Galiano*, of this type, were sold to Argentine Navy, 1927. New vessels bearing these names were laid down in 1929.

SANCHEZ BARCAIZTEGUI

1931 *Photo*

3 Alsedo Class

ALSEDO.   *1928 Photo, Abrahams & Sons, Devonport.*

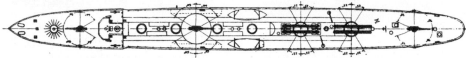

3 *Alsedo* class: **Alsedo** (26th Oct., 1922), **Velasco** (1923), **Juan Lazaga** (March, 1924). All built at Cartagena. Displacement: 1145 tons (*normal*) 1325 tons (*full load*). Dimensions: 275 × 27 × 10½ feet. (*max.*) Parsons geared turbines and 4 Yarrow boilers. Designed H.P. 33,000 = 34 kts. (36 kts. reached on trials.) Fuel 265 tons oil only. Radius: 2500 miles at 15 kts. Guns: 3—4 inch (40 cal.), 2—2 pdr. anti-aircraft. Torpedo tubes: 4—21 inch in 2 twin deck mountings.

Notes.—Provided under Law of 1915. First of class laid down about June, 1920. Design resembles British *Nimrod* type.

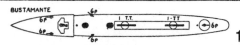

Note.—T.T. now in twin mounts.

1 Bustamante Class.

1925 Photo, Capitan Mateo Mille.

1 *Bustamante* class: named **Bustamante** (1913). Built at Cartagena D.Y., 527 to 548 tons. Dimensions: 221½ × 22 × 5¼ feet. Armament: 5—6 pdr. Tubes: 4—18 inch. S.H.P. 6250 = 28 kts. Yarrow or Normand boilers. Parsons turbine. 3 screws. Coal: 80 tons = 900 miles at 15 kts. Complement, 70. Built under Navy Law of 7th January, 1908. Fitted for min elaying. *Cadarso* of this class scrapped 1930, *Villamil* 1931.

1 Audaz Class.

(Now employed on Fishery Protection duties.)   *1920 Photo, Capitan M. Mille.*

Proserpina (Clydebank, 1897; rebuilt 1916). 467 tons. 229 × 22½ × 9¾ feet. I.H.P. 7200 = 30 kts. Guns: 2—14 pdr., 2—6 pdr., 2—1 pdr. Torpedo tubes: 2—15 inch. Coal: 96 tons = 1020 miles at 15 kts. Complement, 74.

18 1st Class Torpedo Boats

(*Torpederos de 1ª Clas*).

No. 11   *1931 Photo, Capitan M. Mille.*

18 *Vickers-Normand.* **2** (1911). **3**, **6** (1912), **7, 8, 13** (1914), **9, 12, 14** (1915), **10, 15, 16** (1916), **17, 18, 19, 20** (1918), **21, 22** (1919) 177 tons. Dimensions: 164 × 16½ × 4⅘ feet (*max.* draught). Armament: 3—3 pdr., 3—18 in. tubes, twin amidships and single aft. H.P. 3750 = 26 kts. Parsons turbines and Normand boilers. Coal: 33 tons. 3 screws (Nos. 1—7). 2 screws (Nos. 8—22). Complement, 31. 24 boats sanctioned under Law of the 7th January, 1908, but Nos. 23 and 24 were abandoned 1919. *No. 22* completed 1921. All are fitted for minelaying. Nos. **1, 4, 5, 11,** scrapped 1931.

C. M. B.

1 boat. *Thornycroft* 40 feet type (1922). 1 V/12, 250 B.H.P. motor = 30 kts. No armament. Used as a Vedette boat. Complement, 3.

15 + 1 *(building)* Submarines *(Submarinos.)*

Note.—The details given on this and next page are only partly based on official information.

No.	Type	Date	Dis-place-ment	H.P.	Speed	Radius of Action.	T. tubes	Com-ple-ment	Max. draug't
6	*C 1—6* (H)	'23-'30	tons 915 ——— 1290		kts. 16 —— 10		6		feet
6	*B 1—6* class (H)	'16-'25	556 ——— 836	1400 ——— 850	16 —— 10¼	...	4	28	11¼
3	*A 1—3* class (FL)	'15-'17	260 ——— 382	600 ——— 450	13 —— 8¼	1600 miles at 8·5 kts 85 miles at 4 kts.	2	18	10½
1	*Peral* (H)	'15-'16	488 ——— 750	1000 ——— 480	15 —— 10	2100 miles at 11 kts. 70 miles at 4·5 kts.	4	24	11

(H) = Holland type.   (FL) = Fiat-Laurenti type.

The 1915 Naval Programme provided for 28 submarines, out of which 16 boats will have been completed by 1930

New Construction.

E.1. Laid down 1930. Displ. 780/— tons.

C 1.

1927 *Photo, Capitan Mateo Mille.*

6 *Holland* type, built at Cartagena : **C1** (1925), **C2** (1926), **C3** (1927), **C4** (1927), **C5** (1928), **C6** (1928). Displacement : 915 tons *on surface*, 1290 tons *submerged*. Dimensions : *about* 247 × 20¾ × 13½ feet. Machinery : 2 sets 8-cylinder Nelseco Diesel engines. Speed : 16 kts. *(surface)*, 8½ kts. *(submerged)*. Guns : 1—75 m.m. AA. Torpedo tubes : 6—21 inch (4 bow, 2 stern). Diving limit, 45 fathoms, (reached by *C1*, on trials in 1928).

Note:—About Sept. 1930 C1 was named "ISAAC PERAL". The number is to be retained.

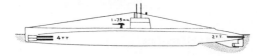

1922 *Photo, Capitan M. Mille.*

6 *Holland* type : **B1** (1921), **B2** (1922), **B3** (1922), **B4** (1922), **B5** (1923), **B6** (1923). Begun at Cartagena, July, 1916. Are an improved and enlarged *Isaac Peral* type. Displacements : 556 tons *on surface*, 836 tons *submerged*. Dimensions about 205 × 17·9 × 11½ feet. Machinery ; *on surface*, 2 sets 8-cyl. Nelseco Diesel engines, totalling 1400 B.H.P. = 16 kts. ; *when submerged* electric motors and batteries of 850 H.P. = 10-10¼ kts. Trial results for class averaged $\frac{16.8}{10.7}$ kts. Guns : 1—3 inch. Torpedo tubes : 4—18 inch. Provided for by Law of 17th February, 1915.

Note.—B6 was submerged for 72 hours without inconvenience during experiments

Photo (1919), *Capitan M. Mille.*

MONTURIOL (A1).   These boats now carry a tall mast for W/T. abeam of after periscope on port side of C.T.

3 *Laurenti-Fiat* type : **Narciso Monturiol (A1), Cosme Garcia (A2)** and **A3,** (all built by Fiat San Giorgio Co., Spezia. 1915-17). Displacements : 260 tons *on surface*, 382 tons *submerged*. Dimensions : 149·6 × 13·8 × 10·2 feet. Machinery : *on surface*, 2 sets of 300 H.P., 6-cylinder, 2-cycle Fiat Diesel engines = 600 H.P. ; when *submerged*, 2 electric motors of 225 H.P. + batteries = 450 H.P. Maximum speeds : 13 kts. *on surface* and 8½ kts. *submerged*. Radii of action : *on surface*, 650 miles at full speed and 1600 miles at 8½ kts. ; when *submerged*, 18 miles at 8 kts. and 85 miles at 4 kts. Torpedo tubes : 2—18 inch in bows. Complement, 18. Built under Law of 17th February, 1915.

Note : Each boat is internally sub-divided into 8 w.t.c. Maximum diving depth 130 feet (about 22 fathoms). Detachable lead keel, weighs 9½ tons. Fitted with telephone buoy, Fessenden submarine signalling and receiving apparatus, and Marconi W/T. For rescue and salvage work there are 6 lifting rings outside hull, and 3 escape hatches within hull, for crew. 2 Periscopes about 3½ inches diameter.

"A.O." (ex. *Isaac Peral*) retained as hulk at Cartagena for motor training.

1st Class Gunboats.
(*Cañoneros de 1a Clas*).

E. Dato.

1925 *Photo, Capitan M. Mille.*

ANTONIO CANOVAS DEL CASTILLO (21st Jan., 1922), **JOSÉ CANALEJAS** (1st Dec., 1922), **EDUARDO DATO** (1923). Built by S.E.C.N., at Cartagena. Displacement, 1335 tons. Complement, 132. Dimensions: 236·3 (*p p.*) 253·6 (*o.a.*) × 33·9 × 11·2 feet. Guns: 4—4 inch, 2—3 pdr., AA., 2 pom-poms (for landing). No T.T. or armour. Machinery: 2 sets, triple exp. Boilers: 2 Yarrow. Designed I.H.P. 1700. Speed, 18 kts. Fuel: 324 tons coal *or* oil = 6500 miles at 10·5 kts. Provided for by Law of 17th February, 1915, and ordered January, 1920. *C. de Castillo* and *J. Canalejas* completed 1923, *E. Dato* completed 1924. Differentiated by number of funnel bands.

1st Class Gunboats - *continued.*

Laya.

1925 *Photo, W. A. Fuller, Esq.*

BONIFAZ (1911), **LAURIA** (1912), **LAYA** (1910). 800 tons. **RECALDE** (1910). 811 tons. Complement, 126—129. Dimensions: $213\frac{3}{4} \times 30 \times 9\frac{1}{2}$ feet (*max.*) draught. Guns: 4—14 pdr. 2 machine. Designed H.P. 1100 = 14 kts. Made 13·8 to 14·6 kts. on trial. Yarrow boilers. Coal: 148 tons. Radius, 3000 at 10 kts. Built under Navy Law of 7th Jan., 1908, at Cartagena.

Third Class Gunboat. (*Cañonero de 3a class.*)

1916 *Photo Capitan M. Mille.*

MACMAHON (1887). 114 tons. $91\frac{1}{2} \times 16 \times 5$ feet. Guns: 2—$2\frac{1}{2}$ pdr., 1—1 pdr. I.H.P. 150 = 7 kts. Coal: $10\frac{1}{2}$ tons. Complement, 32.

9 Armed Trawlers.

(Purchased in England and France, 1922.)

Photo added 1925 by courtesy of Messrs. Cochrane & Sons, Ltd.

2 "*Mersey type*" **ARCILA**, (ex-*William Doak*, Goole S.B. & Rep. Co., 1918), **XAUEN** (ex-*Henry Cramwell*, Lobnitz & Co., 1918). Displacement: 665 tons. (324 tons *gross*). Dimensions: 138½ (*p.p.*), 148 (*o.a.*) × 23¾ × 13½ feet. I.H.P. 550 = 11 kts. Coal: 204 tons.

1 *Special type*: **UAD QUERT** (ex-*Rother*, ex-*Anthony Aslett*, Cochrane & Sons, Ltd., Selby, 1917). Displacement about 600 tons (305 tons *gross*). Dimensions: 130 (*p.p.*) × 23½ × 13 feet. I.H.P. 550 = 10.5 kts. Coal: 140 tons.

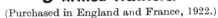
UAD LUCUS type.

1925 Photo, W. A. Fuller, Esq.

3 "*Castle type*": **UAD LUCUS** (ex-*Ness*, ex-*Alexander Palmer*, Smith's Dock Co., Ltd., 1917), **UAD MARTIN** (ex-*Erne*, ex-*John Chivers*, Bow, McLachlan & Co., 1917), **UAD MULUYA** (ex-*Waveney*, ex-*James Conner*, W. Harkness & Co. Ltd., 1917).

Armed Trawlers – (*continued*).

ALCAZAR.

1925 *Photo, W. A. Fuller, Esq.*

LARACHE.

1922 *Photo.*

3 "*French type*" (builders not reported): **ALCAZAR** (ex-*Rengagé*), **LARACHE** (ex-*Poilu*), **TÉTUAN** (ex-*Grognard*). 370 tons *gross*. Dimensions: 124 × 22½ × 11 feet. I.H.P. 400 = 10 kts.

Note.—All the above vessels built 1917-18, and understood to be armed with 1—3 inch gun, though some (including *Arcila* and *Xauen*) mount **2**.

Surveying Vessel. (*Comisión Hidrografica.*)

Note.—2 new surveying vessels are projected.

GIRALDA (Govan 1894, bought 1898) 2450 tons. 300 × 35 × 16½ feet. Guns: 2—6 pdr. (Nordenfelt). I.H.P. 2000 (*n.d.*), 3500 (*f.d.*) = 20 kts. Coal: 436 tons = 4671 miles at 20 kts. Complement, 147. Refitted 1921, and specially fitted out for oceanographic research.

Coastguard and Fisheries Vessels. (*Guardapescas.*)

To be built during 1929-32 : 3 Fishery Protection Vessels of 250 tons displacement.

GAVIOTA.

1920 *Photo, Capitan M. Mille.*

GAVIOTA (1910-11). 158 tons. Guns: **1**—5 pdr. Speed, 11 kts. Complement, 26.

Training Ships.

1931 *Photo.*

JUAN SEBASTIAN DE ELCANO. (Echevarrieta Yard, Cadiz, 5th March, 1927), completed 1928. Four-masted Schooner. Displacement at ¾ load : 3420 tons. Dimensions : 269¼ (*p.p.*) 308½ (*o.a.*) × 43 × 21½ feet (draught at ¾ load). 1 Sulzer Diesel motor of 800 H.P. = 9.5 kts. 1 screw. Oil: 230 tons. Endurance: 10,000 miles at 9.5 kts. Complement, 310 + 80 cadets.

Training Ships—continued.

GALATEA.   *Photo, Manuel I. Codoner, Esq., 1927.*

GALATEA (ex-Barque *Clarastella*, 1896). Purchased in Italy, 1922. 2085 tons. 2 auxiliary Diesel motors of 450 h.p. each = 9 kts. T.S. for boys.

Sea-going Tugs. (*Remolcadores.*)

(Appearance as British "Saint" class.)

CICLOPE (ex-*St. Clement*, purchased 1922.) Built by Crichton & Co., 1918. Displacement: 800 tons. 136 × 29 × 16½ feet. Guns: 1—3 inch. H.P. 1200 = 12¼ kts. Coal: 240 tons. Complement:

GALICIA (ex-*R.5*). Displacement: 350 tons. 100½ × 21 × 11 feet. H.P. 550 = 10 kts. Guns: 1—3 inch.

CARTAGENERO (ex-*H.S. 78*), **FERROLANO** (ex-*H.S. 80*), **GADITANO** (ex-*H.S. 82*). Built by Crichton & Co., South Saltney, Chester, 1918. Displacement: 300 tons. 83½ × 21½ × 10½ feet. Guns: 1—6 pdr. H.P., 420 = 10 kts.

Note.—Above 5 vessels mainly employed in Morocco Coast patrol and examination service.

Photo (1919), Capitan M. Mille.

ANTELO (1903). Ocean-going Tug, Mine Layer, Mine Sweeper and Training Ship for Mining Service. 342 tons. 131·2 × 21·6 × 6·8 feet. I.H.P. 650 = 11 kts. Coal: 32 tons. Carries 40 mines.

Submarine Salvage Vessel.

(*Buque para salvamento de submarinos.*)

1921 Photo, Capitan M. Mille.

(*Attached to S/M. Station, Cartagena.*)

KANGURO (1917). Double hulled type, with interior docking space. Built by Werf Conrad, Haarlem, Netherlands. 2550 tons. Length, 275·4 feet; beam, 65·4 feet; draught (empty) 14·4 feet; (with submarine docked), 20 feet. Can dock submarine up to 151 feet long. Salvage power: Can raise 650 tons, from 27⅛ fathoms. H.P. 1000 = 10 kts. (9·53 trials). Fuel: 150 tons = 2448 miles at economical speed. Guns: 4—42 mm.

Aircraft Carrier.

(*Estacion Transportable de Aeronautica Naval.*)

1925 Photo, Capitan M. Mille.

DÉDALO (ex-*Neuenfels*), built by Swan Hunters, 1901; afterwards *España No. 6*. Transformed 1922. 10800 tons. Dimensions: 420 × 55 × 20½ feet. Engines: Quadruple expansion. 3 S.E. boilers. H.P., 3000 = 12½ kts. Guns: 2—4·1 inch, 2—1 pdr. Complement, 324. Coal: 940 tons.

Forward is space for one small airship, 42 metres long (shown in photo attached to mooring mast), and there is a complete hydrogen plant. Aft is the seaplane accommodation, workshops, &c., nominal capacity = 25 planes, 2 dirigibles, and 2 balloons. Observe anti-flare device on funnel top in above photo.

Transport. (*Transporte.*)

Photo (1919), Capitan M. Mille.

ALMIRANTE LOBO (1909). 2545 tons. Guns: 2—5 pdr. Designed H.P. 4300 = 12 kts. *Nominal* radius, 4540 miles at 10 kts. Complement, 76.

Fleet Oilers.

2 Oilers, each of 6000 tons capacity, are to be built during 1929-32.

Fleet Collier.

CONTRAMAESTRE CASADO.

1929 Photo, Capitan M. Mille.

CONTRAMAESTRE CASADO. (Armstrong Naval Yard, launched 26th October, 1920). 2042 tons net register, 3282 tons *gross*; 5000 tons *d.w.c.* Dimensions: 320 (*p.p.* and *w.l.*), 332 (*o.a.*) × 45⅓ × 23 feet. Guns: 4—42 mm. Machinery: 1 set triple exp. Boilers: 3 Cyl. (Howden f.d.). 1 screw. I.H.P. 1950 = 10·5 kts. Own coal: about 310 tons. Complement, 107.

Motor Launches.

Official Photo, 1921.

H.1, H.2, H.3. Are ex-British Motor Launches purchased 1921 and employed as tenders to Naval Aviation Centre. Built 1916-18. 40 tons. Dimensions: 80 × 12⅙ × 6¼ feet. Guns: 1—5 pdr. B.H.P. 440 = 19 kts. 2 sets of petrol motors. Fuel: 7500 litres petrol. Complement, 11.

Note.—To replace above vessels, which are more or less worn out, it is proposed

ROYAL SWEDISH NAVY.

Revised 1931 by courtesy of the Chief of the Naval Department, Ministry of Defence.

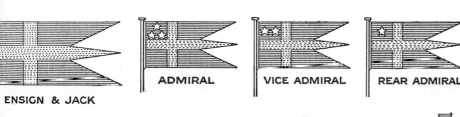

ENSIGN & JACK   ADMIRAL   VICE ADMIRAL   REAR ADMIRAL

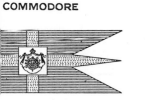

COMMODORE

MERCANTILE

☐ *Blue*

☐ *Yellow*

ROYAL STANDARD   MINISTER OF MARINE

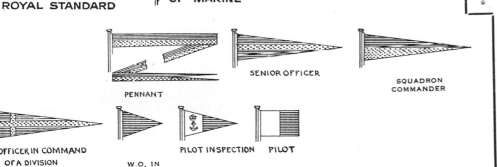

PENNANT   SENIOR OFFICER   SQUADRON COMMANDER

OFFICER IN COMMAND OF A DIVISION   W.O. IN COMMAND OF A SHIP   PILOT INSPECTION   PILOT

Note.—The blue is azure in every case but last 3 flags

Mercantile Marine.

From " Lloyd's Register," 1931 figures.

Total *gross* tonnage, 1,704,669 including 7 vessels of 16 kts and over.

Administration.

Minister of Defence : A. W. Rundqvist.

Chief of the Naval Staff : Rear-Admiral. O. E. Lybeck.

The Naval Staff is divided into Mobilisation, Operations, Communication, Organisation and Intelligence and Historical Divisions.

Naval Attaché (London) : Capt. E. A. Öberg.

INSIGNIA OF RANK ON SLEEVES.

     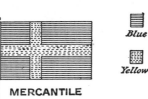

British equivalent.

Amiral.	Vice-Am.	Konter-Am.	Kommendör.	Kommendörkapten. 1 graden.	2 graden.	Kapten.	Löjtnant.	Under-Löjtnant.	Fänrik
Ad-miral.	Vice-Ad.	Rear-Ad.	Commodore.	Captain. (Senior)	Captain. (Junior)	Commander & Lieut.-Com.	Lieutenant.	Sub-Lieut.	Acting Sub-Lieut.

All civilian officers have stripes with triangular curl, and colour between stripes as follows : Constructors and Engineers, *violet blue* ; Doctors, *red* ; Paymasters, *white*.

Personnel : Active List, *about* 4300 officers and men. Total for Reserves cannot be estimated, as it is dependent on conscription, but includes 500 officers.

Modern Swedish Guns (Bofors).
(All details are unofficial).

Nota-tion	Designation		Length in calibres	Model	Weight of Gun	Weight of A.P. shot	Initial velocity	Max. penetration firing A.P. capped at K.C.			Danger Space against average warship, at			Nom. per minute
								8000 yds.	5000 yds.	3000 yds.	10,000 yards	5000 yards	3000 yards	
	c/m	inches			tons	lbs.	ft.secs.	in.	in.	in.				1·2
A5	28	11	45	'11	41	760½	2576†	10½	15	18	..	..	..	1
AA	25.4	10*	42	'94	29	450	2362	..	8	11	125	340	675	2
A	21	8.3	44	'98	17	275½	2460†	..	7	9½	100	425	600	6
C	15.2	6	50	'03	7½	100	2789†	..	..	7	75	230	460	6
E	15.2	6	45	'98	6	100	2460	..	..	6	60	200	410	8
	12	4.7	50	'11	3½	46½	2822	..	..	..	..	..	..	8
F	12	4.7	45	'94	2	46½	2430	..	..	3½	..	..	..	

Guns marked † in the velocity column fire Bofors special nitro-compound.

* Also a Schneider Canet 10-inch Mark of which details are not available.

Torpedo.

Whiteheads. *Submerged* tubes (Armstrong pattern). Torpedoes, 21 in., and 18 in. Since 1911 torpedoes have all been manufactured at Karlskrona.

Colour of Ships.
Light Grey all over.

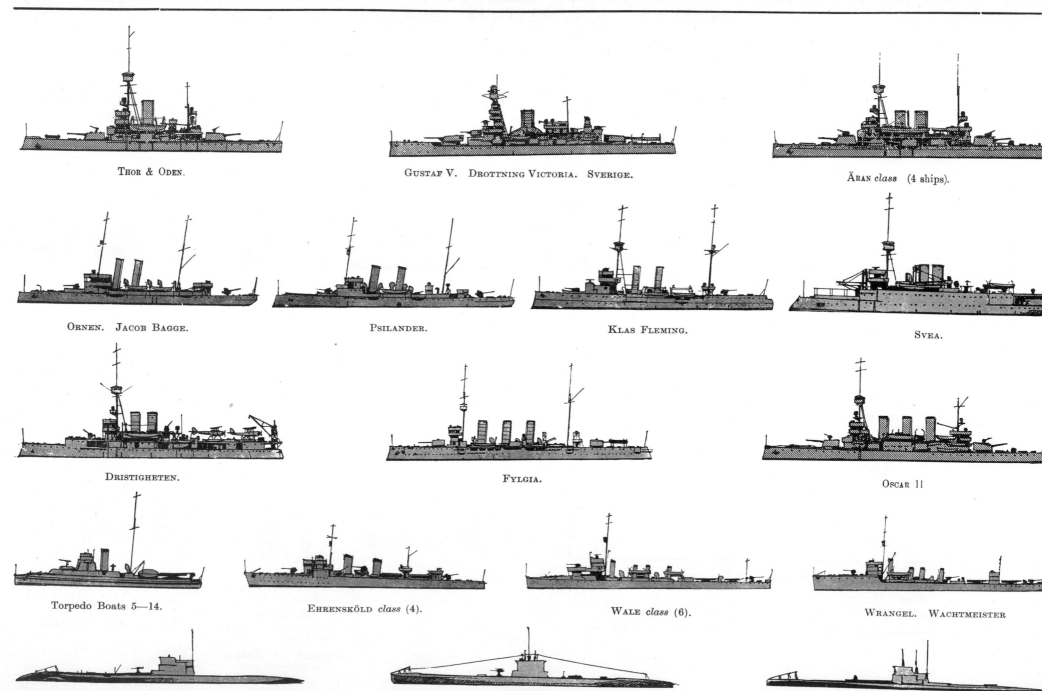

THOR & ODEN.

GUSTAF V. DROTTNING VICTORIA. SVERIGE.

ÄRAN class (4 ships).

ORNEN. JACOB BAGGE.

PSILANDER.

KLAS FLEMING.

SVEA.

DRISTIGHETEN.

FYLGIA.

OSCAR II

Torpedo Boats 5—14.

EHRENSKÖLD class (4).

WALE class (6).

WRANGEL. WACHTMEISTER

BÄVERN class.

DRAKEN class.

HAJEN class.

COAST DEFENCE BATTLESHIPS. (*Kustpansarfartyg*).

From *Sverige* class, down to and including *Oden*, officially rated as *Pansarskepp* (Ironclads).

(SVERIGE CLASS—3 Ships.)

SVERIGE (May, 1915), **DROTTNING VICTORIA** (Sept., 1917) and **GUSTAF V** (Jan., 1918).

Displacement : 7,600 tons (*Sverige*), 7,900 tons (*other two*).   Complement, 450.

Length (*w.l.*) { *Sverige*, 392·8 feet.
 D.V. & *G.V*, 396·6 feet. } Beam, 61 feet.   *Max.* draught, 22 feet.

Guns (Bofors) :
- 4—11 inch 45 cal. **Dir. Con.**
- 8—6 inch, 50 cal.
- 4—14 pdr.
- 2—14 pdr. AA.
- 2—6 pdr.
- 2 machine.

Torpedo tubes removed.

Armour : (Carnegie and Bofors).
- 8″ Belt (amidships)......
- 6″—3″ Belt (ends)...
- 1⅝″ Deck (slopes) ......
- 4″ Redoubt..............
- 8″ Big gun turrets......
- 6″ Barbettes ....
- 5″—2½″ Small turrets
- 7″ Conning tower .. ...

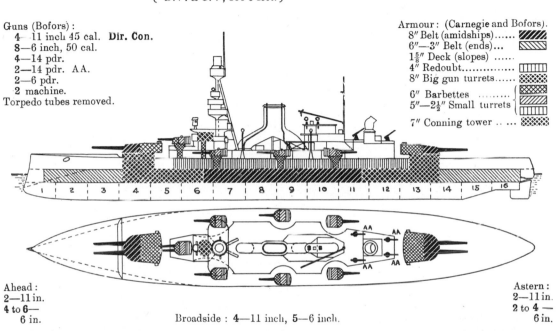

Ahead :
2—11 in.
4 to 6—
 6 in.

Broadside : **4**—11 inch, **5**—6 inch.

Astern :
2—11 in.
2 to 4 —
 6 in.

GUSTAF V

1930 *Photo, Var Flotta.*

Machinery : In *Sverige*, Curtis turbines by Kockum Co., 4 screws ; in *Gustaf V* and *Drottning Victoria*, Westinghouse geared turbines by the Motala Company. 2 screws. Boilers : 12 Yarrow. Designed S.H.P. 20,000 in *Sverige*, 22,000 in *D. Victoria* and *Gustaf V* = 22·5 kts. Trials : 23 to 23·6 kts. Coal : *Normal* 350 tons ; *maximum* 700 tons + 100 tons oil.

Engineering Notes.—In *D. Victoria* and *Gustaf V*, Westinghouse turbines consist of 2 sets on each shaft, each containing two turbines of the "divided-flow" type, driving propellers through double-pinion reduction gears (total weight of turbines and reduction gears about 160 tons) :

Shaft H.P.	24,800	11,045	2,228
R.P.M. (turbines)	3,760	2,939	1,810
R.P.M. (propellers)........	210	167	101
Speed (knots)	23·6	19 2	12·3

Gunnery Notes.—11 inch guns elevate to 25°. Load in 17 seconds. Turrets somewhat cramped ; are divided by partition bulkheads.

Armour Notes.—Shields to 11″ guns are 8″ on fore side, 4″ on side, 4¾″ rear. Smaller gunshields are 5″ front, 3″ sides.

General Notes.—*Sverige* was sanctioned 1911 ; but upon a change of Government was cancelled by the Liberals. The nation then voluntarily subscribed a sum which at the end of April, 1912, amounted to nearly £970,000 for the building of this ship, which was estimated to cost £670,000 ; the balance was devoted towards commencement of *D. Victoria* and *Gustaf V* under the 1915-19 Naval Programme. Work on *D. Victoria* and *Gustaf V* was stopped during the war, owing to non-delivery of armour plates from the U.S. Building was resumed in 1919. *Sverige* and *D. Victoria* built by Gotaverken, Gothenburg, and engined by Kockum Co., Malmo, and Motala Co., respectively. *Gustaf V* (in full, Gustaf den Femte) built and engined by Kockum Co., Malmo. Bows of all this class are strengthened for icebreaking. They have proved excellent seaboats. Are being altered as *Gustaf V* with trunked funnel, new bridges, upperworks and control positions.

GUSTAF V

1930 *Photo, Official.*

431

OSCAR II. (main topmast removed 1930). 1930 *Photo, by courtesy of Ministry of Defence.*

OSCAR II (1905).

Displacement, 4600 tons.   Complement, 339.
Length (*w.l.*) 313⅔ feet.   Beam, 50½ feet.   *Maximum* draught, 18 feet.

Guns (Bofors) :
  2—8·3 inch, 44 cal.
  8—6 inch, 50 cal.
  10—6 pdr.
  1—1 pdr.
Torpedo tubes (18 inch) :
  2 *submerged* (Armstrong).

Armour (Krupp) :
  6″—4″ Belt (amidships)
  2″ Deck (slopes)
  6″ Bulkheads
  4″ Lower deck redoubt
  7½″—5″ Big gun
     ″ turrets (N.C.)
  7″ Hoists to these
  5″—2½″ Small tur-
     rets (N.C.)
  7″ Conning tower

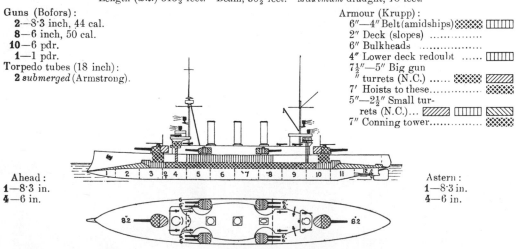

Ahead :
  1—8·3 in.
  4—6 in.

Astern :
  1—8·3 in.
  4—6 in.

Broadside : **2**—8·3 in., **4**—6 in.

Machinery : 2 sets 4 cylinder triple expansion. 2 screws. Boilers : 10 Yarrow. Designed H.P. 9000 = 18·3 kts. Coal : *normal* 350 tons ; *maximum* 500 tons = 2950 miles at 10 kts.

Notes.—Four searchlights carried—one on each bridge, and one on each mast. Built by Lindholmen Co., 1905-07 On *trial* : 9400 = 18·96 kts. *Oscar II* is written in full *Oscar den Andre.* Main mast cut down 1930.

MANLIGHETEN. 1926 *Photo, Cribb.*

(ÄRAN CLASS—4 SHIPS).

ÄRAN (Aug., 1901), **WASA** (Sept., 1901), **TAPPERHETEN** (Nov., 1901) & **MANLIGHETEN** (Dec., 1903).

Length, (*w.l.*) 287 feet.   Beam, 49¼ feet.   *Maximum* draught, 16¾ to 17¾ feet.
Displacement, 3800 tons.   Complement, 301.

Guns (Bofors) :
  2—8·3 inch, 44 cal.
  6—6 inch, 45 cal.
  8—6 pdr.⁎
  1—1 pdr.
Torpedo tubes (18 inch) :
  2 *submerged* (Armstrong).
⁎*Tapperheten* only has
  10—6 pdr.

Armour (Krupp) :
  7″ Belt (amidships)
  1″ Deck (flat on belt)
  7″ Bulkheads
  7½″—5″ Turrets
  7½″ Supports
  5″—2½″ Small turrets (N.C.)
  4″ Hoists, etc.
  7″ Conning tower

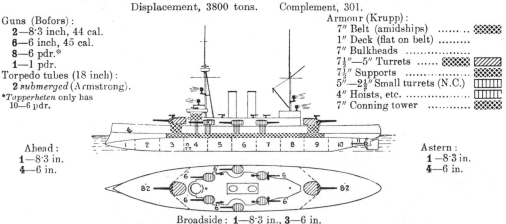

Ahead :
  1—8·3 in.
  4—6 in.

Astern :
  1—8·3 in.
  4—6 in.

Broadside : **1**—8·3 in., **3**—6 in.

Machinery : 2 sets triple expansion. 2 screws. Boilers : 8 Yarrow. Designed H.P. 7400 = 17 kts. Coal : *maximum*, 300 tons. Endurance : 2000 at 10 kts.

Notes.—Where built : *Äran*, Lindholmen ; *Wasa*, Bergsund ; *Tapperheten* and *Manligheten*, Kockum. Completed : *Äran*, 1902 ; *Wasa* 1903 ; *Tapperheten*, 1904 ; *Manligheten*, 1906.

THOR, as rebuilt, 1916.

1918 Photo, Karlsson, Karlskrona.

THOR (1898).

Displacement : 3690 tons.   Complement, 263.

Length (*w.l.*), 278¼ feet.   Beam, 48⅕ feet.   *Maximum* draught, 18 feet.

Guns (Canet) :
2—10 inch, 42 cal.
6—4·7 inch, 45 cal.
8—6 pdr.
1—1 pdr.

Armour (Harvey-nickel) :
9½″ Belt ....
1″ Deck (flat on belt)......
8″ Turrets ....
8″ Supports and hoists ...
3¾″ Battery.................
8″ Conning tower ....

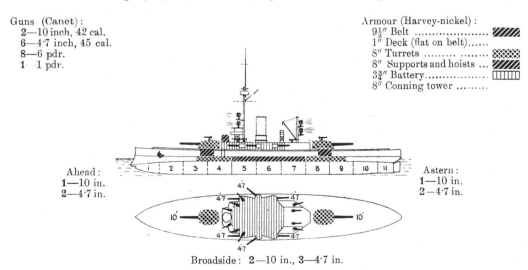

Ahead :
1—10 in.
2—4·7 in.

Astern :
1—10 in.
2—4·7 in.

Broadside : 2—10 in., 3—4·7 in.

Machinery : 2 sets, vertical triple expansion. 2 screws. Boilers : 6 Cylindrical. Designed H.P., 5000 = 16 kts. Coal : *normal*, 280 tons ; *maximum*, 300 tons = 2530 miles at 10 kts.

Notes.—4 searchlights. *Thor* was rebuilt in 1916, appearance being greatly altered. As originally built, she had two masts and two funnels. *Thor* built and engined by Bergsund Co., 1896-99.

1918 Photo, Karlsson, Karlskrona.

ODEN as re-built 1915. To distinguish from *Thor*, observe that chart house is slightly deeper fore and aft, and small topmast to stump of old mainmast is much higher. As will be seen by comparing photos and plans the 4.7 inch guns are differently arranged. Has plain top on tripod mast. *Thor* has a ringed top.

ODEN (March, 1896).

Normal displacement, 3700 tons.   Complement, 267.

Length (*w.l.*), 278¼ feet.   Beam, 48½ feet.   *Maximum* draught, 18⅓ feet.

Guns (Canet and Bofors) :
2—10 inch, 42 cal. Canet.
6—4·7 inch, 45 cal. Bofors.
8—3 pdr.
1—1 pdr.

Armour (Harvey-nickel)
9½″ Belt (amidships)......
1″ Deck (flat on belt)
8″ Turrets ....
10″ Supports and hoists
3¾″ Battery.................
9¾″ Conning tower ......

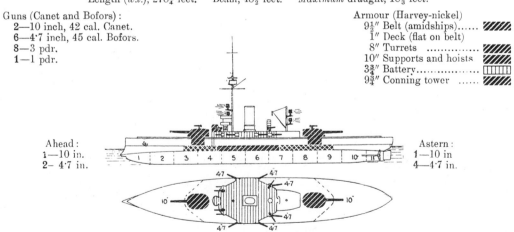

Ahead :
1—10 in.
2—4·7 in.

Astern :
1—10 in.
4—4·7 in.

Machinery : 2 sets vertical triple expansion. 2 screws. Boilers : 6 cylindrical. Designed H.P. 5000 = 16 kts. Coal : *normal* 275 tons ; *maximum*, 282 tons. Endurance : 2530 miles at 10 kts.

Laid down by Bergsund Co., 1894. Completed 1897. 4 searchlights. Re-constructed 1915, when appearance was greatly changed. As originally completed she had military and main masts and two funnels.

Aircraft Cruiser (*Flygplankryssare*).

GOTLAND (as re-designed).   1930 *Illustration.*

GOTLAND.   (Laid down 1930.)

Full load displacement : 5,260 tons.   Complement, 480.

Length, (*w.l.*) 426½ feet.   Beam, 47¾ feet.   *Max.* draught, 16 feet.

Guns :
6—6 inch, (M. 25).
4—14 pdr. AA. (M. 28).
4—Machine guns (M. 2).
Torpedo tubes :
(in triple deck mounting).
6—21 inch
(Abreast of after conning
tower).

Will have 1 catapult only in centre line.

Armour :
⅝″—1⅛″ vertical Bulkheads.
1⅛″ Uptakes ....
1⅛″—2″ Hoists and supports
2″ Conning Tower ....

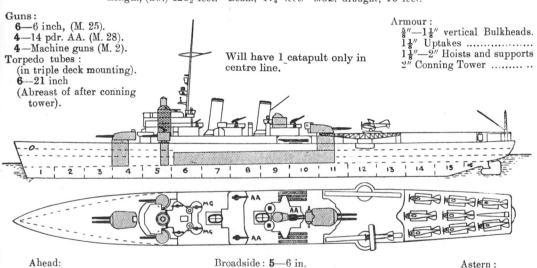

Ahead :
4—6 in.

Broadside : **5—6 in.**

Astern :
2—6 in.

Machinery : 2 sets De Laval geared turbines.   2 screws.   Boilers : 4.   Designed S.H.P. 33,000 = 27 kts.

Note.—The first cruiser designed to act as an aircraft carrier, and represents a well thought out and exceedingly useful type of warship. As originally designed (see 1929 edition) there was a superfiring twin turret forward, but in order to save topweight this has been replaced by two single wing turrets athwart the conning tower. Speed has also been reduced a knot and displacement lowered some 300 tons, when design was re-cast, to reduce cost.

Armoured Cruiser (*Pansarkryssare*).

FYLGIA.   1931 *Official Photo.*

FYLGIA   (Dec., 1905).

Displacement, 5000 tons.   Complement, 341.

Length (*w.l.*), 377⅔ feet.   Beam, 48½ feet.   *Max* draught, 20⅔ feet.

Guns (M. '03) :
8—6 inch, 50 cal.
10—6 pdr.
2—1 pdr.
Torpedo tubes (18 inch) :
2 *submerged.*
(Abreast of foremast.)

Armour (Krupp) :
4″ Belt ....
2″ Deck (slopes) ......
5″—2″ Turrets
4″ Hoists and supports
4″ Conning tower......

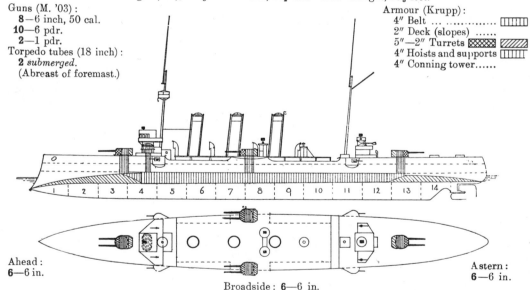

Ahead :
6—6 in.

Astern :
6—6 in.

Broadside : **6—6 in.**

Machinery : 2 sets 4 cylinder triple expansion.   2 Screws.   Boilers : 12 Yarrow.   Designed H.P. 13,000 = 21·5 kts.   Coal : *normal* 350 tons ; *maximum* 900 tons = 5770 miles at 10 kts.

General Notes.—Laid down by Bergsund Co., at Finnboda, in 1903, and completed 1907. Trials : 12,440 H.P. = 22·7 kts. Machinery by builders. Bow and stern sponsons removed 1926-27.

No.	Type	Date	Displacement	H.P.	Max. speed	Fuel	Complement	T. tubes	Max. draug't feet.
			tons		kts.	tons			
4	*Ehrensköld*	'24—31	1050	24000*t*	35	150 (oil)	81	6	10½
2	*Wrangel*	'15—'18	560	12000*t*	34	105 + 6 oil	71	6	9¼
2	*Hugin*	'11—'12	460	10000*t*	31	90 + 1½ oil	71	4	8½
4	*Wale*	'08—'10	460	8800	30	90	71	4	8¾
1	*Magne* (T)	1905	460	7200	30	80	67	2	8¾

T=Thornycroft.   *t*=turbines.

VIDAR.   *1928 Photo, Herr O. Janson.*

EHRENSKÖLD.   *1930 Photo, Herr Ossi Janson.*

2 *Hugin* class : **Hugin** (1911), **Munin** (1912). 460 tons. Dimensions : 215¾ × 20⅝ × 8¼ feet. Guns : **4**—14 pdr., **2** machine. Torpedo tubes : **4**—18 inch. 4 Yarrow boilers. Curtis turbines. S.H.P., 10,000 = 31 kts. Fuel: 90 tons coal + 1½ tons oil. Endurance : 800 miles at 15 kts. *Hugin* built by Götaverken Co., and *Munin* by Kockum Co., Malmö.

4 *Wale* class :—**Wale** (1907), **Ragnar** (1908), **Sigurd** (1908), **Vidar** ('09). 460 tons. Dimensions : 215½ × 20¾ × 9 feet. Armament : *Wale*, **2**—14 pdr., **4**—6 pdr., **2** machine ; other boats, **4**—14 pdr., **2** machine ; **4**—18 inch tubes in all. 4 Yarrow boilers. Hull on Thornycroft lines. Coal : 90 tons. Radius of action : 920 miles at 15 kts. *Sigurd* built by Lindholmen Co , other three by Kockum Co.

Note.—*Hugin* and *Wale* as *Magne* but :—A. T.T. in pairs ; B. Guns 14 pdr. ; C. No guns abeam 2 and 4 funnels.

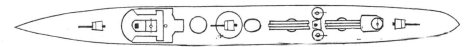

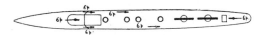

4 *Ehrensköld* class : **Ehrensköld** (Sept. 25, 1926), **Nordenskjöld** (June 19, 1926). Built by Götaverken, Gothenburg and Kockum Co., Malmö, respectively. **Klas Horn** (June 17th, 1931), **Klas Uggla** (June 13th, 1931). Laid down 1928— by Kockum Co., and at Karlskrona D.Y., respectively. Displacement : 974 tons (*light*), 1050 tons (*full load*). Dimensions : 293 (*w.l.*), 300 (*o.a.*) × 29¼ × 10½ feet. Armament : **3**—4.7 inch and **2**—1 pdr. AA. guns ; **6**—20.5 inch torpedo tubes in triple deck mountings. De Laval Geared turbines. H.P. 24,000 = 35 kts. Fuel (oil only) : 150 tons. Radius of action : 600 miles at full speed : 1600 miles at 20 kts. Complement, 125. Estimated cost : Kr.7,150,000 each. First pair completed in 1927.

Has mainmast now as *Wale* class above.

WRANGEL.   *1928 Photo, Herr Ossi Janson.*

2 *Wrangel* class : **Wrangel** and **Wachtmeister** (Lindholmen Co., Gothenburg, both launched 1917.) 560 tons. Dimensions : 232¾ × 22 × 9¼ feet. Armament : **4**—14 pdr., **2** machine guns, **6**—18 inch torpedo tubes in two twin-deck mountings and two single mountings, P. and S. in forecastle. Designed S.H.P., 11,000 (*n.d.*), 13,000 (*f.d.*) =34 kts. Reported to have attained 34.8 kts. on trials. Have De Laval geared turbines. Fuel : 105 tons coal +6 tons oil. Complement, 81. Completed, early 1918.

1 *Thornycroft* : **Magne** (1905). Dimensions : 215½ × 20¾ × 8¾ feet. Armament: **6**—6 pdr., **2** machine, **2** single 18 inch tubes aft. 4 Thornycroft boilers. Endurance : 920 miles at 15 kts.

6 Torpedo Boats.

(*Torpedbåtar.*)

No 14.

1918 Photo.

N:r 5, 6, 7, 8, 9, 14 (1906-08). Displacement, 60 tons. Dimensions: $106 \times 12\frac{3}{4} \times 6\frac{1}{2}$ feet. Armament: 1—1 pdr., 2—18 inch tubes. H.P. 800 = 21 kts. Coal : 22 tons. Complement, 14.

Motor Torpedo Boats (*Motor Torpedbåtar*).

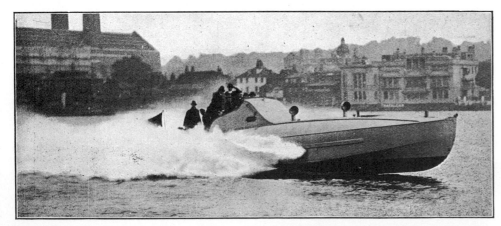

No. 3.

1925 Photo, by courtesy of Messrs. Thornycroft (Builders).

N: r. 3, N: r. 4. Built by Messrs. Thornycroft, at Hampton-on-Thames, 1925. Usual 55 ft. type C.M.B., with smoke screen apparatus.

14 (+ *2 building*) Submarines.

1st Class Submarines.

2 Building. Details confidential.

DRAKEN.

1929 Photo.

3 *Draken* class : **Draken** (20th Oct., 1926), **Gripen** (1927), **Ulven.** Laid down at Karlskrona, 1924, 1925 and 1928 respectively. Few particulars yet available, but believed to be enlarged and improved *Baverns*, of comparatively high *surface* speed, for working in conjunction with the Fleet. Unofficially stated to be armed with **1—3 inch** gun and **4—21 inch** tubes. Displacement: 700/850 tons. H.P. 2,800/? = 15/9 kts. Radius 5,600 miles to 10 kts. *on surface.*

Valen (May 6th, 1925). Fitted for laying mines on the Normand-Fenaux system. Design generally follows that of *Uttern* class.

BAVERN *class.*

UTTERN.

1930 Photo, "Var Flotte."

3 *Bävern* class : **Bävern, Illern, Uttern** (1921—1922), built by Karlskrona D.Y. and Kockum Co., Malmö. H.P.: 2,800 = 15 kts. *on surface,* —— = 9 kts. *submerged* Guns : **1—6 pdr. AA., 1 M.G.** Tubes : **4—20.8 inch** (bow). 8 torpedoes carried. Displacement : 500/650. Radius 300 miles at 15 kts. *surface,* 54 miles at 6 kts. *submerged.*

1st Class Submarines—*continued.*

HAJEN.

1924, *Official Photo.*

3 *Hajen* class: **Hajen** ('20), **Sälen** ('20), **Valrossen** ('20), built by Kockum Co., Malmö. Guns: **1**—6 pdr. AA.
Tubes: **4**. Displacement: **450/580** tons.

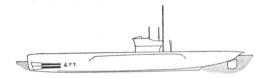

ABBORREN *class*

1931 *Photo, Official.*

DRISTIGHETEN (Lindholmen Co., 1900). 3,600 tons. Dimensions: $285 \times 48\frac{1}{2} \times 17$ feet. Guns:
4—14 pdr. H.P. 5,000=16 kts. Coal: 310 tons. Is an old battleship converted into an
Aircraft Tender and Depot Ship.

BRAXEN.

1928 *Photo, O. Janson, Esq.*

4 *Abborren* class: **Abborren** ('17), **Braxen** ('18), **Gäddan** ('18), **Laxen** ('18), built by Karlskrona D Y.
Displacement: **450/580** tons. 4 Torpedo Tubes.

Torpedo Gunboats,

Officially classed as Cruisers (*Torpedkryssare*).

PSILANDER.   1926 *Photo, Herr Ossi Janson.*

J. BAGGE.   1928 *Photo, Herr Ossi Janson.*

ÖRNEN (distinguished by cut-away stern).

PSILANDER (1900), 813 tons, **JACOB BAGGE** (1899), 835 tons, **ÖRNEN** (1896), 844 tons. Designed H.P. 4,000=20 kts., *natural draught.* Coal, 100 tons. Armament : 2—4·7 inch, 4—6 pdr., 1—15 inch *submerged* bow tube.

General Notes : To distinguish between these ships compare relative positions of foremast, bridges, and fore funnel.

Minelayer (*Minfartyg*).

(Officially classed as a Cruiser).

KLAS FLEMING.   1926 *Photo, Herr Ossi Janson.*

KLAS FLEMING (1914). 1,800 tons. Dimensions: 263 × 34 × 14 feet. Guns : 4—4·7 inch (50 cal.), 4 machine. Parsons turbines. H.P. 7000=20 kts. Complement, 175.

Depot Ships (*Depafartyg*).

Note :—Other old Vessels used as Receiving Ships are *Vanadis, Freja*, attached to Flying Station, and *Norrköping*.

Photo wanted.

NIORD (Lindholmen Co. 1898). Ex-Battleship. 3700 tons. Dimensions 278¼ × 48½ × 18 feet. Guns : mostly removed. Appearance and other particulars generally similar to *Thor*, on an earlier page, of which ship she was originally a sister.

GÖTA.   1927 *Photo, Herr Ossi Janson.*

GÖTA (Lindholmen Co., 1889). Old Battleship, somewhat similar to *Svea*, but 3350 tons. Dimensions : 258½ × 48 × 17¼ feet. Guns : now mostly removed. Depot for seaplanes.

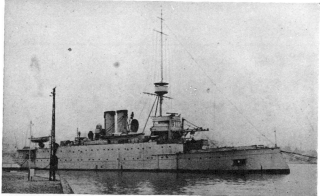

SVEA.   1930 *Photo, Herr Ossi Janson.*

SVEA. Old Coast Defence Battleship, built by Lindholmen Co., 1886, re-built 1904 and 1920. 3,050 tons. Dimensions: 248·4 × 48·5 × 16·4 feet. Guns : 4—4·7 inch, 2—6 pdr. (*AA*), 2 M.G. Armour : 11¼″ –8″ Belt, 2″ Decks. 2 screws. 6 cyl. boilers. I.H.P. 4,650=15 kts. Coal : 220 tons. Fitted as a depot ship for Submarines.

Flags.

Note.—Mercantile flag is same as Ensign.

RED 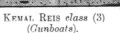 WHITE ☐

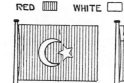 

| ENSIGN & JACK. | MINISTER of MARINE. | COMMODORE. |

Minister of National Defence :—Abdul Halik Bey.
Under-Secretary for Navy :—Captain Mehamet Ali Bey.
Colour of Ships :—Khaki.

General Notes.—A programme of new construction is to be undertaken when funds are available, and the present naval base at Ismid will be converted into a modern dockyard. A 25,000 ton floating dock has been installed (in 1926), but sustained considerable damage when the *Yawuz Sultan Selim* was placed in it. It has been proposed to invite a foreign naval mission to undertake training and reorganisation of Turkish Navy.

Shipbuilding Programme, as amended 1929, includes : 6 Flotilla Leaders ; 12 Submarines ; and 6 Motor Launches.

Uniforms.

| CAPTAIN | LIEUT. CAPTAIN. | COMMANDER | LIEUT. COMMANDER. | LIEUTENANT | SUB.-LIEUTENANT. |

BRITISH.		TURKEY.
Captain	=	Galion Capitani.
Commander	=	Fregate Capitani.
"	=	Corvette Capitani.
Lieut. Commander	=	Birindji Yuzbachi.
Lieutenant	=	Yuzbachi.
Sub.-Lieut.	=	Mulazim.
Midshipman	=	Mehendis

Mercantile Marine.

(From " Lloyd's Register," 1931 figures.

Total *gross* tonnage, 179,287.

RECOGNITION SILHOUETTES

KEMAL REIS *class* (3)
(*Gunboats*).

AIDAN REIS.
(*Gunboat*).

(similar to *Hamidieh* but two funnels only.)

MEDJIDIEH.

PEIK-I-SHEVKET.
(*Torpedo Gunboat.*)

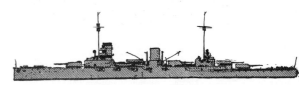

YAWUZ SULTAN SELIM.

ERTOGRU.
(*Presidential Yacht.*)

HAMIDIEH.

TINAZTEPE. ZAFIR.

ADATEPE. KACOTEPE.

SAMSOUN *class.*

YAWUZ SULTAN SELIM (ex-German *Goeben*, March, 1911).

Displacement, 22,640 tons. Complement, 1013.

Length (*w.l.*), 610¼ feet. Beam, 96 ft. 10 in. Draught (*max. load*), 26 ft. 11 in.

Guns (*see Notes*) :
10—11 in. 50 cal.
10—5.9 in. 45 cal.
8—3.4 in. 45 cal.
2 M.G.
(**1** landing)
Torpedo tubes (19.7 in.) :
2 *submerged.*

Anti-Torp. Pro. :—
2″—1″ deep H.T. Steel B.H., between extreme barbettes : Minute internal subdivision.

Armour (Krupp) :
10½″ Belt (amidships) tapers
to 6″ at top and 5″ below
3¾″ Belt (bow and stern) . . . . . .
9″—8″ Barbettes . . . .
8″ Gunhouses . . . .
5″ Battery . . . .
10″ Fore C.T. . . . .
8″—3″ Double com. tube . . . .
8″ After C.T. . . . .
6″—3″ Com. tube . . . . . .
″— ″ R.F. towers . . . . .
3″—1″ Decks . . . .
″ Roofs to gunhouses . .
3″ Roof, fore C.T. . . . . . .

YAWUZ SULTAN SELIM.

1924 *Photo, Tarik Hussein, Esq.*

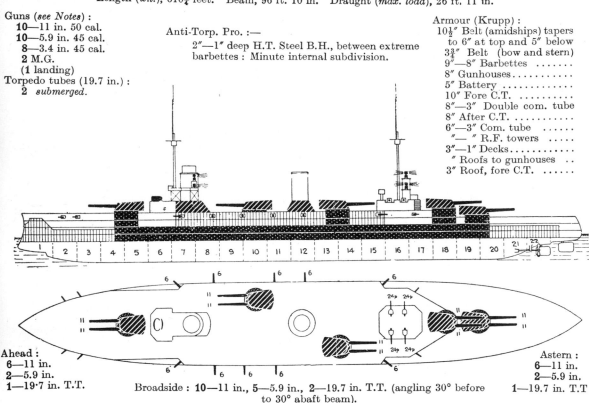

Ahead :
6—11 in.
2—5.9 in.
1—19.7 in. T.T.

Broadside : **10**—11 in., **5**—5.9 in., **2**—19.7 in. T.T. (angling 30° before to 30° abaft beam).

Astern :
6—11 in.
2—5.9 in.
1—19.7 in. T.T

Machinery : Parsons turbine, 4 shaft, direct drive. Boilers (see *General Notes*) : 24 Schulz-Thornycroft = German "Marine Type." Designed H.P. nominally 52,000 = 25.5 kts., but on trials she developed 70,000 H.P. = 28 kts. Coal : *normal* about 1000 tons ; *maximum* 3050 tons. Oil fuel : 200 tons.

Gunnery Notes.—All guns German Navy Models, 5.9 inch range up to 16,500 yards. Two R.F. towers are sunk into the deck, near amidships (echelon) barbettes. All range-finding and fire-control instruments were rendered useless by Germans before Armistice, 1918. Under the Penhoët Yard's contract for refit, a French fire control system has been installed.

Torpedo Notes.—Torpedoes and torpedo tubes German Navy type. Torpedoes probably German G VII*** (23-ft. steam heater type) with 430 lbs. charge, and *max.* ranges of (*a*) 11,700 yards at 28 kts., (*b*) 5,500 yards at 35 kts. Stern *submerged* torpedo tube is on starboard quarter. 8—60″ controlled S.L. Torpedo nets removed during War.

Armour and Protection Notes.—Like all German built Battle Cruisers, this ship is heavily armoured and minutely sub-divided. Main belt between extreme barbettes is about 350 feet long, 11″ at w.l., tapering to about 8″ on upper edge, and 6″ on lower edge. Barbette bases only 1″ where covered by belt.

Engineering Notes.—Endurance is (*a*) 5,350 miles at 10 kts., (*b*) 2,370 miles at a continuous *max.* sea-going speed of 23 kts. She made 29¼ knots on Trials in 1931.

General Notes.—Laid down, August, 1909, by Blohm & Voss, Hamburg, under 1909 German Navy Programme, as a sister to German *Moltke*. Completed, July, 1912. Transferred to the Turkish Navy in 1914, and during the war was mined five times and severely damaged. A contract was signed in December, 1926, with the Chantiers de St. Nazaire (Penhoët), for the repair and refit of this battle cruiser at Ismid ; the work was considerably delayed owing to a floating dock proving unequal to her weight, and completion was not reached till autumn of 1929.

Torpedo Gunboats (*Torpedo Muhribi*).

BERK-I-SATVET (1906). **PEIK-I-SHEVKET** (Nov., 1906). Built at Krupps' Germania
Yard, Kiel. 1014 tons. Dimensions : 262½ × 27⅔ × 9½ feet. Guns : **2**—2.9 inch, **4**—6
pdr. Torpedo tubes : **3**—18 inch. Designed H.P. 5100 = 22 kts. Coal : 240 tons. 25 mines
carried. Complement, 105.

Note.—Torpedoed by British Submarine *E* 14, during 1915, but beached and salved.

Cruisers (*Muhafasali Kruvasor*).

1924 *Photo, Tarik Hussein, Esq.*

HAMIDIEH (ex-*Abdul Hamid*, Armstrong, Sept., 1903). 3830 tons. Complement, 302. Dimensions : 368 × 47½ × 16 feet (*mean* draught). Guns : **2**—5.9 inch, 45 cal. Krupp, **8**—3 inch
(75 m/m) 50 cal. Schneider. Torpedo tubes (18 inch) : **2** *above water*. Armour : 4″ Deck.
Machinery : 2 sets 4-cylinder triple expansion. 2 screws. Boilers : Cylindrical. Designed
H.P. 12,000 = 22 kts. (*forced* draught). Present best speed about 16–18 kts. Coal : *normal*,
275 tons ; *maximum*, 750 tons. Endurance : 5550 miles at 10 kts. At present serves as
Training Ship for Naval Cadets. Fitted as a Mine-layer. 70 mines.

Appearance similar to *Hamidieh* without tops
on masts, and with only two funnels.

MEDJIDIEH (ex-Russian *Prut*, ex-Turkish *Medjidieh*, July 25th, 1903). Mined and sunk in
Black Sea, 1915. Salved, repaired and re-fitted at Nicolaieff for Russian Navy, 1915-16.
Seized by Austro-German Armies at Sevastopol, 1918, and returned to Turkish Navy. 3300
tons. Complement, 365. Dimensions : 330 × 42 × 17½ feet. (*max.* draught). Guns (as re-
armed) : **6**—5.1 inch (Vickers 1914), **4**—3 inch 50 cal. (Schneider). Deck, 1″. H.P. 12,000 =
About 18 kts., now. Babcock and Wilcox boilers. Coal : 600 tons. Endurance : 4700
miles at 10 kts. Built by Cramps, Philadelphia. (Refitted and reboilered 1930).

DESTROYERS.
(*Torpedo Muhriby*)

2 Destroyers.

2 Destroyers.

2 *Ansaldo* boats : **Kacotepe** (7-2-31) and **Adatepe** (19-3-31).   Laid down at Sestin Ponente, Jan. 15th, 1930.
Displacement : 1,250 tons (*standard*),
　　　　　　　1,350 tons (*normal*),
　　　　　　　1,650 tons (*full load*).
Dimensions : 328·6 × 30·4 × 18·6 (height of hull) feet.
　　　　　　100·20 (97·7) × 9·36 × 5·7 (height of hull) metres.
Geared Parsons turbines. S.H.P. 40,000 = 38 kts.
3 Thornycroft boilers with superheaters.
Guns : 4—4·7", 50 cal., 3—40 m/m AA. and 2 pom-poms.
Tubes : 6—21" in triple mountings.
Oil, 360 tons. Complement, 149.
These boats are of Ansaldo design and are named after mountains near Smyrne associated with Turkish
　　military glories.

ZAFER.

1931 *Photo.*

2 *C.N. del Tirreno* boats : **Tinaz Tepe** (27-7-31). **Zafer** (20-9-31). Contracted for on May 15th, 1930, and laid
　　down in the Summer of 1930.
Displacement : 1,350 tons (*normal*).
　　　　　　　1,610 tons (*full load*).
Dimensions : 307(*p.p*) × 30½ × 10¾ feet.
Geared Parsons turbines. S.H.P. 35,000 = 36 kts.
3 Thornycroft boilers with superheaters.
Guns : 4—4·7", 50 cal., 2—40 m/m AA., 2 M.G.
Tubes : 6—21" in triple mountings.
Oil : 350 tons. Complement, ?
These boats are of Italian design and generally resemble the Italian " Turbine " class.

KACOTEPE.

1931 *Photo.*

4 Submarines.

3 *French type* boats: **Samsoun, Basra,** (both launched at Bordeaux (1907), and **Tashoz** launched by Creusot, Chalons, (1907). 290 tons. Dimensions: 185×21×9¼ feet. Armament: **2**—9 pdr., **6**—1 pdr., **2**—18 inch tubes. I.H.P. 6000 =29 kts. Coal: 70 tons. Endurance: 975 miles at 15 kts. Complement, 67. *Tashoz* re-fitted, 1923-24. *Samsoun :*—**1**—75 mm. gun. Present speed about 20 kts.

DUMLUPYNAR.

1931 *Photo.*

1 *Bernardis* type: **Dumlupynar** (4-3-31) laid down 1929 by Cantiere Navale Triestino, Monfalcone. Displacement $\frac{830}{1050}$ tons. Dimensions: 223×19×14 feet. Machinery: 2 sets Diesels, H.P. 3000 = 17·5 kts. on surface. Electric motors of 1000 H.P. = 9 kts. *submerged.* Armament: **1**—4 inch gun, **6**—21 inch tubes.

1 *Bernardis* minelaying type: **Sakarya** (2-2-31) laid down 1929, at same yard. Displacement, $\underline{950}$ tons. Dimensions: × × feet. Speed: $\frac{12}{7}$ kts. Armament: **1**—3 inch gun, **2**—21 inch tubes. 48 mines carried.

No. 1.

1927 *Photo, R. F. Scheltema, Esq.*

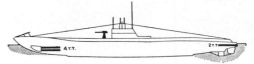

2 *Fijenoord* type: **No. 1** (February 1, 1927) **No. 2** (March 12, 1927). (In Turkish these numbers are rendered as BIRINDJI-IN-UNI and IKINDJI-IN-UNI). Both built by Fijenoord Co., Rotterdam. Displacement $\frac{505}{620}$ tons. Dimensions: 192½ × 19 × 11½ feet. 2 sets M.A.N. Diesels. Speed: $\frac{13.5}{8.5}$ kts. Guns: **1**—37 mm. Tubes: **6**—17.7 inch (4 bow, 2 stern). Both arrived in Turkish waters in early summer of 1928.

Gunboats (*Ganbot*).

1 *St. Nazaire* type : **AIDAN REIS** (June, 1912). Refitted in 1925. 502 tons. Dimensions : $178\frac{1}{2} \times 27\frac{5}{6} \times 8$ feet. Boilers : Babcock. H.P. 1025 = 14 kts. Guns : **2**—3 inch, **2**—6 pdr.

1 *La Seyne* type : **HIZIR REIS** (Feb., 1912), 413 tons. Dimensions : $154\frac{1}{4} \times 25\frac{3}{4} \times 4\frac{1}{4}$ feet. Guns : **3**—3 inch (12 pdr.), **2**—3 pdr., **2** M.G. H.P. 850 = 14 kts. Refitted, 1923. The **2** forward 3 inch guns, shown above in sponsons, are now mounted on forecastle.

Note.—HIZIR REIS is tender to Gunnery School; and above armament is varied.

Minelayer.

NUSRET (1912). 365 tons. Dimensions : $132 \times 22 \times 8\frac{1}{4}$ feet. Speed : 15 kts. Can carry 25 mines. Now fitted with deep sea diving apparatus, and 210 meters has been attained.

Sea-going Tug.
(Both fitted for Minelaying.)

INTIBAH (ex-*Warren Hastings*, Port Glasgow, 1886). Iron. 616 tons *gross*. Dimensions : $202 \times 30 \times 12$ feet. H.P. 1670 = 12 kts. 2 screws. Carries 20–25 mines.

1931 *Photo.*

3 *S.V.A.N.* boats, built at Venice, 1930-31. 32 tons. 34 kts. **2** torpedoes, **1**—3 inch gun.

8 New Boats (1926). 25 tons. 4 depth charges carried.

Photo, Messrs. J. I. Thornycroft & Co.

5 boats : *Nos. 11, 14, 15, 18, 21.* Are Thornycroft type motor patrol boats, built 1911, for customs, police and coastguard duties. Dimensions : $\times \times 2\frac{1}{2}$ feet. Guns : **1** M.G. or **1** small Q.F. 140 H.P. Thornycroft petrol motor = 11 kts. Bullet-proof steel over conning position and engines.

UNITED STATES FLEET.

Revised from Official Handbook, "Ships' Data, U.S. Naval Vessels," and from information furnished by courtesy of the Navy Department, Washington, D.C., 1931.
(The Navy Department accepts no responsibility whatever for the accuracy of the data as actually published herein.)

UNIFORMS.

As Rear-Admiral, but with two and one extra thin stripes respectively.

Admiral. Vice-Admiral. Rear-Admiral. Captain. Commander. Lieut-Commander. Lieutenant. Ensign.

The rank of Admiral has been provided for the Chief of Naval operations, Navy Dept., also the ranks of Admiral and Vice-Admiral for certain flag officers afloat.

Note.—Lieutenants, junior grade, have 1½ stripes. Chief Warrant Officers one stripe broken with blue. Line Warrant Officers star without any stripe. Staff Warrant Officers under Chiefs have no sleeve mark. Engineers same as Line Officers (interchangeable). Other branches than executive wear no sleeve star, but have badge of branch over top stripe.

FLAGS.

ENSIGN

JACK

ADMIRAL

VICE ADMIRAL

Red

Blue

White

Yellow

REAR ADMIRAL SENIOR

REAR ADMIRAL

PRESIDENT'S FLAG

NAVAL MILITIA

SECRETARY OF THE NAVY

Senior office when of or below rank of captain flies a blue triangular flag. Assistant-Secretary of Navy has a flag same as Secretary's with colours reversed, *i.e.*, white ground and blue anchor and stars.

Secretary of the Navy: The Hon. Charles F. Adams.
Assistant Secretary of the Navy: The Hon. Ernest L. Jahncke.
  Do.   (Aviation): David S. Ingalls.
General Board: Rear-Admiral Mark Bristol.
  Rear-Admiral J. V. Chase.
  Rear-Admiral E. B. McVay.
  Capt. J. W. Greenslade.
  Capt. E. S. Jackson.
  Commander T. C. KenKaid
  Commander E. M. Williams.
  Lt.-Col. L. C. Lucas (Ret.), U.S.M.C.
Naval Attaché, London: Captain A. L. Bristol.

Personnel U.S.N. and Marine Corps:
  Officers, 16,809.
  Men, 98,449
(Reserves): Officers, 4,256.
  Men, 18,179.

Principal Guns in the U.S. Fleet.

(Officially revised, 1929.)
Built at Washington Gun Factory, proved at Indian Head, Dahlgren, Va., and Potomac Range.

Notation.	Nominal Calibre.	Mark or Model.	Length in Calibres.	Weight of Gun.	Weight of A.P. Shot.	Service Initial Velocity.	Maximum penetration firing *capped* A.P. direct impact against K.C. armour.			Muzzle Energy.
							9000	6000	3000	
	inch.			tons.	lbs.	ft. secs.	in.	in.	in.	ft-tons.
HEAVY	16	II	50	128	2100	2800	...	...	...	...
	16	I	45	105	2100	2600	...	...	...	98,531
	14	IV	50	81	1400	2800	...	...	...	76,087
	14	I	45	63⅓	1400	2600	18	...	...	...
	12	VII	50	56·1	870	2900	11·0	13·9	17·5	50,783
	12	VI	45	53·6	870	2700	10·6	13·3	16·6	44,020
	12	V	45	52·9	870	2700	9·8	12·3	15·5	44,020
	10	III	40	34·6	510	2700	6·9	9·0	11·9	25,772
MEDIUM	8	IX	55	29.7	250	3000	...	...	8·6	16,240
	8	VI	45	18·7	260	2750	4·4	6·1	8·6	13,630
	8	V	40	18·1	260	2500	4·0	5·3	7·5	11,264
	6	XII	53	10	105	3000	...	...	...	6,551
	6	VIII	50	8·6	105	2800	2·3	3·2	5·2	5,707
	6	VI	50	8·3	105	2600	2·2	2·9	4·7	4,920
	6*	IX	45	7·0	105	2250	2·1	2·5	3·8	3,685
	6*	IV. VII	40	6·0	105	2150	2·1	2·4	3·6	3,365
LIGHT and AA.	5*	VII	51	5·0	50	3150	1·4	1·8	3·4	3,439
	5	VI	50	4·6	50	3000	1·4	1·7	3·2	3,122
	5	V & VI	50	4·6	60	2700	1·6	2·0	3·5	3,032
	5*	II, III, IV	40	3·1	50	2300	1·4	1·7	2·6	1,834
	4*	IX	50	3.0	33	2900	...	...	2·6	1,926
	4*	VIII	50	2·9	33	2800	1·2	1·5	2·6	1,794
	4*	VII	50	2·6	33	2500	1·2	1·4	2·2	1,430
	4*	III,IV,V,VI	40	1·5	33	2000	...	1·2	1·7	915
	3§	X	50	1·15	13	2700	...	...	...	657
	3	V, VI, S-A	50	1·0	13	2700	...	0·8	1·2	658
	3*	II, III	50	0·9	13	2700	...	0·8	1·2	658

* = Brass cartridge case.
Guns of 1899 and later have Vickers breech, etc. All guns use nitro-cellulose.
§ Anti-aircraft gun.
Naval Appropriation: 1931-1932, $360,101,593.

Mercantile Marine.

("Lloyd's Register," 1931, figures.)
Total *gross* tonnage, including Great Lakes and Philippines, 13,642,183 including 120 vessels of 16 knots and over.

NOTES ON ORDNANCE, TORPEDOES. &c.

Note.—Starred Paragraphs (*₊*) are official data, furnished to " Fighting Ships " by courtesy of the Navy Department.

I.—Ordnance, &c.

DIRECTORS.—In all Battleships, Newer Light Cruisers and Destroyers. Type of Director : Navy type. Range Clocks on masts and Deflection Scales on gunhouses, as in British Navy.

FIRE CONTROL.—Latest type is self-synchronising electric.

₊₊*RANGE FINDERS.*—Made in various sizes from short 3–feet base range finders for navigation to 30–feet base range finders for use in turrets. Standard practice in U.S. Navy is now to mount one range finder in each turret.

₊₊*HIGH EXPLOSIVES.*—T.N.T. and Explosive "D" are standard high explosives for U.S. Navy.

₊₊*NON-RICOCHET SHELLS.*—Flat-nosed type ; does not ricochet from surface when fired at elevation of over 2°. Made in 3 inch, 4 inch, 5 inch and 6 inch sizes for guns of equivalent bores. Delay action fuze commences on impact with water. Use of this shell converts gun into what is practically a long range depth charge thrower, the flat-nosed shell acting as depth charge.

₊₊*STAR SHELLS.*—Range, three to six land miles. Made for 3 inch, 4 inch, 5 inch and 6 inch guns. Time fuze lights lamp and expels parachute and burner through base of shell. Normally, shell detonates at 1000 feet. Burner, 800,000 candle power, burning for 30 seconds, and illuminating sea for one mile diameter.

II.—Torpedoes.

₊₊*Torpedoes in U.S. Navy are all turbine-driven. 21 inch is standard size used, though 18 inch still exist in older vessels. (No current official details available of marks, ranges, speeds, charges and types of heater.) Hammond radio-dynamic (distance-controlled) torpedo has been reported under test.

III.—Mines.

₊₊*Made in various sizes and of constructions particularly adapted for work they are expected to perform. Anchor similar to British type.

Unofficial Notes.—Mk. VI anti-submarine type of mine is reported to weigh 1400 lbs. and to have 300 lbs. T.N.T. charge. Body of mine, spherical, 3 feet diameter. Form of detonation uncertain ; said to consist of antennae fitted with the Earle Patent Magnetic Pistol. Sinker is box-shaped and has wheels to gauge of laying ship's mine-discharging rails. Mine and sinker float together immediately after laying, while a 90 lb. plummet (attached to ⅛ inch steel wire) sinks. The " plummet cord " is measured off to same depth at which mine is to float below surface. When plummet cord is spun full out, latch is unlocked and mine and sinker separate. Mine still floats on surface, while mine-mooring cable begins to spin off drum and sinker descends. Immediately the plummet touches bottom, the running-out of mine-mooring cable is stopped and cable is locked. Sinker (or anchor) then comes down to bottom, drawing down the mine to the desired depth below the surface. Soluble safety plug used. Antennae said to consist of thin conducting wires and magnetic pistols, floating out in a star pattern all round body of mine and giving a contact diameter of 50 feet. Has been found effective against large surface-ships. Being light and easily handled, it has been adopted for laying by Light Minelayers.

IV.—Aircraft Bombs.

₊₊*(a)   18 lb.   Explosive charge, T.N.T.
    (b)   25 lb.   Explosive charge, T.N.T.
    (c)   158 lb.*   Explosive charge, T.N.T.
    (d)   214 lb.*   Explosive charge, T.N.T.
    (e)   230 lb.   (British design).*   Explosive charge, Amatol.
    (f)   266 lb.*   Explosive charge, T.N.T.
    (g)   500 lb.   Explosive charge, T.N.T.
    (h) 1000 lb.   Explosive charge, T.N.T.

Note.—Types marked * for Anti-Submarine use.

V.—Anti-Submarine.

₊₊*DEPTH CHARGES.*—Mk. IV.—Charge 600 lbs. of T.N.T. Dimensions : 24 inch diameter, 28 inches long. 100 feet effective radius, hydrostatic firing valve, similar to Mks. II and III Depth Charges.

₊₊*Depth Charge, Mks. II and III. Charge : 300 lbs. of T.N.T. Dimensions : 18 inch diameter, 28 inches long. Effective within a radius of 70 feet from point of detonation. Limit of detonation adjustable between 36 and 300 feet. Safety device prevents detonation due to gun blast, etc., detonation above six fathoms, or when thrown overboard with firing device in the off position. Detonation by hydrostatic pressure only. During War, destroyers carried from 30 to 50 depth charges and vessels on submarine patrols up to 100 depth charges.

₊₊*Y-GUN OR DEPTH CHARGE PROJECTOR.*—Two barrels set at an angle of 90°, each barrel 3 feet long and 6 inch bore. 300 lb. depth charges fastened to arbors, inserted in barrels of Y and common powder charge exploded at junction of barrels ; range of about 30 yards obtained.

HYDROPHONES.—K-tube fish type, 30 miles acoustic radius, but operating vessel must stop engines and auxiliaries while listening. SC- and MB-tube types, 3 miles acoustic radius built into hull and insulated against noise ; can be used without stopping ship.

(Also *v.* Non-Ricochet Shells ; Aircraft Bombs, Sweeping Gear.)

VI.—Sweeping Gear.

PV's as British Navy of H.S.S.S. and H.S.M.S. types, but with slight modification of inhaul gear. Methods of attachment also same as British Navy.

VII.—Searchlights.

No details known, but in latest ships are of controlled type, as in British Navy. Battleships of later types carry 8 per ship ; those of older types, prior to *California*, only have 4 per ship.

VIII.—General.

All battleships carry 3 'planes and one or two catapults ; in most ships, latter are of new explosive type.

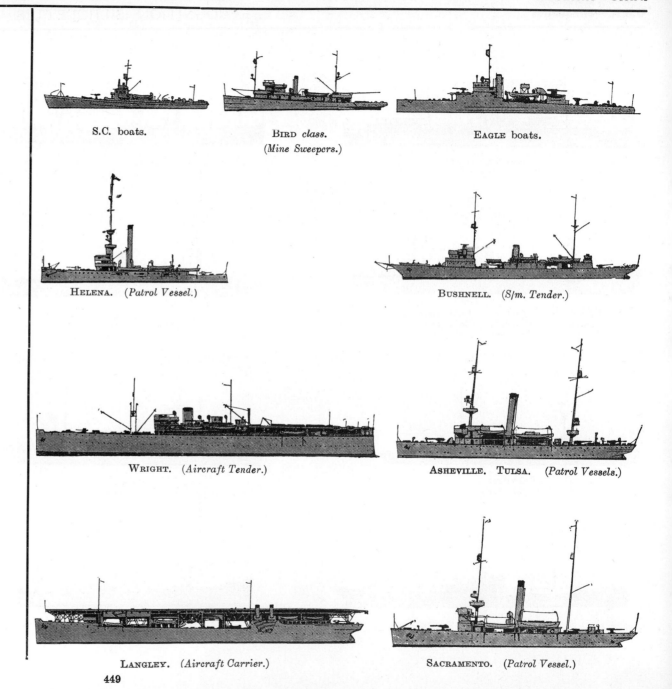

S.C. boats.

BIRD *class.*
(*Mine Sweepers.*)

EAGLE boats.

HELENA. (*Patrol Vessel.*)

BUSHNELL. (*S/m. Tender.*)

WRIGHT. (*Aircraft Tender.*)

ASHEVILLE. TULSA. (*Patrol Vessels.*)

LANGLEY. (*Aircraft Carrier.*)

SACRAMENTO. (*Patrol Vessel.*)

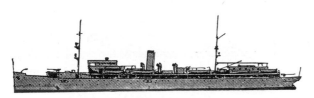

BEAVER.
(S/m. Tender.)

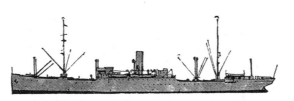

RAPPAHANNOCK.
(Store Ship.)

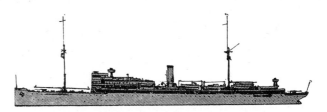

WHITNEY.   DOBBIN.
(Destroyer Tenders.)

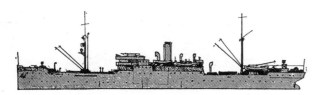

CAPELLA.   VEGA.   PROCYON.
SIRIUS.   REGULUS.   GOLD STAR.
SPICA.   ANTARES.   (Cargo Ships, etc.)

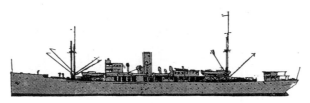

ALTAIR.   DENEBOLA.   RIGEL
(Destroyer Tenders.)

ARGONNE.   CHAUMONT.

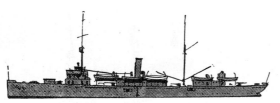

MELVILLE.
(Destroyer Tender.)

BRIDGE.
(Store Ship.)

BLACK HAWK.
(Destroyer Tender.)

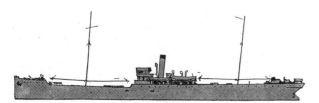

HANNIBAL.

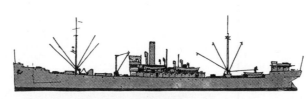

ARCTIC.   BOREAS.   YUKON.
(Store Ships.)

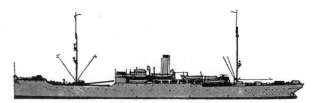

SAVANNAH.
(S/m. Tender.)

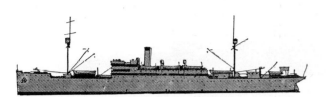

BRIDGEPORT.
(*Destroyer Tender.*)

BRAZOS.   NECHES.   PECOS.   CUYAMA.
(*Oilers.*)

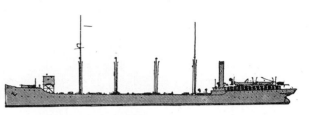

MAUMEE.
KANAWHA.
(*Oilers.*)

HOLLAND.
(*S/m. Tender.*)

RAPIDAN.   RAMAPO.   TRINITY.
SALINAS.   SAPELO.   KAWEAH.
TIPPECANOE.   SEPULGA.   LARAMIE.
MATTOLE.   (*Oilers.*)

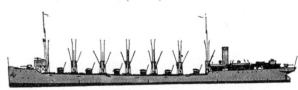

NEREUS.
PROTEUS.
(*Colliers.*)

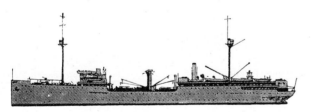

MEDUSA.
(*Repair Ship.*)

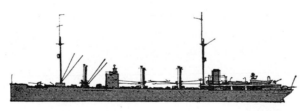

NITRO.   PYRO.
(*Ammunition Ships*)

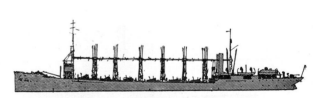

JASON.   ORION.   NEPTUNE.
(*Colliers.*)

HENDERSON.
(*Transport.*)

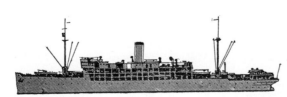

CANOPUS.
(*S/M. Tender.*)

CAMDEN.
(*S/m. Tender.*)

SARATOGA.   LEXINGTON.

OKLAHOMA.   NEVADA.

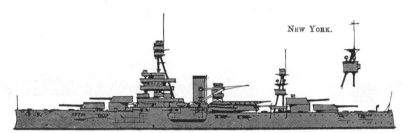

NEW YORK.

TEXAS.   NEW YORK.

ARIZONA.   PENNSYLVANIA.
(Note bridge height, tops and derricks.)

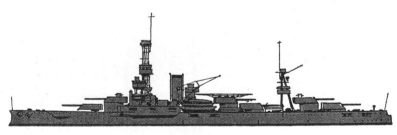

ARKANSAS.

(re-constructing).

NEW MEXICO.   IDAHO.   MISSISSIPPI.

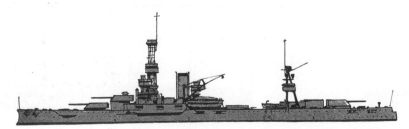

WYOMING (Training Ship.)

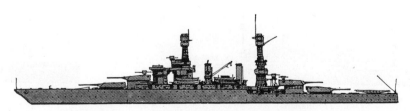

COLORADO.   WEST VIRGINIA.   CALIFORNIA.
MARYLAND.   TENNESSEE.

ROCHESTER.

OMAHA *class* (9 ships.)

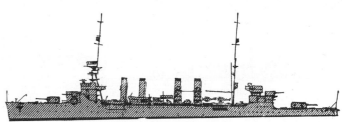

MARBLEHEAD only.

DESTROYERS.

PERKINS.   STERETT.   WALKE.
MAYRANT.   WARRINGTON.

Flush Deckers.

"1000 Tonners."

CONNOR.   STOCKTON.   GWIN.

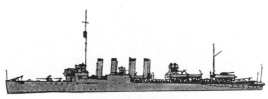

Light Minelayers.

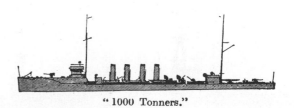

"1000 Tonners."

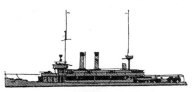

MONOCACY.
PALOS.
(River Gunboats.)

LUZON.
MINDANAO.
(River Gunboats.)

GUAM.
TUTUILA.
(River Gunboats.)

OGLALA.

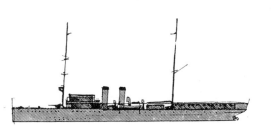

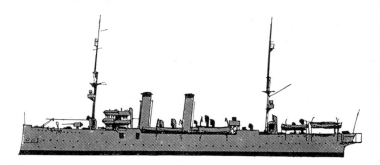

AROOSTOOK.
(Mine Layers.)

ISABEL.
(Patrol Vessel.)

YOSEMITE.
(Mine Layer.)

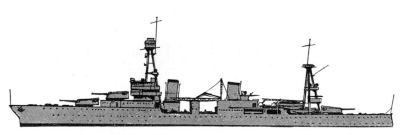

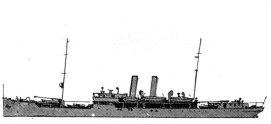

CHESTER.   LOUISVILLE.   NORTHAMPTON.

KITTERY.

BALTIMORE.
(Mine Layer.)

HOUSTON.   CHICAGO.   AUGUSTA.
(Flagships. Note extension of forecastle).

PENSACOLA.   SALT LAKE CITY.

R 1—20. (20).

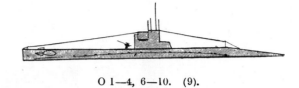

O 1—4, 6—10. (9).

S 42—47. (6).

S 4, 6—41. (36).

BARRACOUDA. BASS. BANITA.

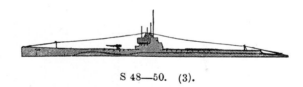

S 48—50. (3).

ARGONAUT.

NARWHAL. NAUTILUS.

WEST VIRGINIA.   1924 *Photo, Abrahams.*

W. VIRGINIA.—bow view.
1924 *Photo, Abrahams.*

W. VIRGINIA.   1924 *Photo, Abrahams.*   MARYLAND.   1926 *Photo, W. W. Stewart, Esq.*

(1919 & 1917) BATTLESHIPS—FIRST LINE (BB).

(MARYLAND CLASS—3 SHIPS.)

COLORADO (March 22nd, 1921), **MARYLAND** (March 20th, 1920),
and **WEST VIRGINIA** (Nov. 19th, 1921).

Standard displacement, 32,500 tons.* *Full load*, 33,590 tons. Complement, 1407.

Length (*w.l.*), 600 feet. (*o.a.*), 624 feet. ⎰ *Mean* draught, 30½ feet.
Beam, 97 feet 3½ inches. ⎱ *Max.* „ 31ft. 3½ in.

Complement of *W. Virginia* as fleet flagship, 1486.

Guns (**Dir. Con.**) :
  8—16 inch, 45 cal. Mk. I.
  12—5 inch, 51 cal.
  8—5 inch (A.A.) Mk. X.
  4—6 pdr. (saluting).
  2—1 pdr.
  2 M.G.
  2 landing
Torpedo tubes (21 inch) :
  2 *submerged.*

Armour :
  16″—14″ Belt..............
  8″ Belt (aft) ....
  3″ Deck (ends)............
  16″—9″ Funnel bases ...
  18″—9″ Turrets..........
  16″ Conning tower and
    tube...................

* *Maryland*, 31,500. *W. Virginia*, 31,800 tons.

MARYLAND   1926 *Photo, W. W. Stewart, Esq.*

Gunnery Notes.—16 inch are a new model, successfully proved at Indian Head, 1917. Maximum elevation, 30°; Maximum range at this elevation unofficially stated to be 33,300 yards. Turrets electrically manœuvred and with electric hoists. Excepting increase of calibre to 16 inch, otherwise as Notes for *Tennessee* Class on page 459. **2**—5 inch guns removed 1922, and **4**—3 inch guns added New director system installed, 1923. Main control is at a height of 120 feet above sea level.

Armour Notes. ⎱ As for *California* and *Tennessee.*
Appearance Notes. ⎰

Anti-Torpedo Protection.—Ferrati type triple hull and minute internal subdivision by longitudinal and transverse unpierced bulkheads.

Engineering Notes.—"Electric Drive" is identical with that for *California* Class (p. 459), but, in these ships, electric installation has been extended. Part of steam generated in boilers is diverted for running six auxiliary turbo-generators, supplying current to anchor gear, workshop lathes, refrigerating plant, bakeries, &c. Guns are also electrically manœuvred, ammunition hoists are electric. In fact, every possible item of equipment, even down to potato peelers and ice-cream freezers, is run by electric power. Estimated weight of machinery, 2002 tons. Heating surfaces as *Tennessee* on page 458.

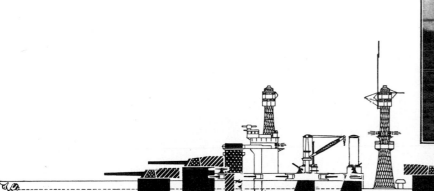

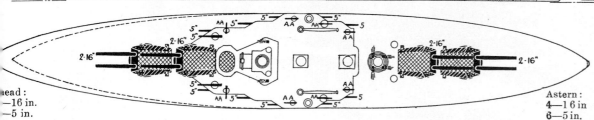

head :
—16 in.
—5 in.

Astern :
4—16 in
6—5 in.

Broadside : 8—16 inch, 7—5 inch, 1—21 inch torpedo tube.

Machinery : In *Colorado* Westinghouse turbines and electric drive ; in *Maryland* and *W. Virginia*, G.E. turbines with electrical drive. Designed S.H.P. 28,900 = 21 kts. cf. trials. 4 screws. Boilers : 8 Babcock & Wilcox. Fuel (oil only) : *normal* 2500 tons ; *maximum* 4000 tons (unofficial figures).

Name	Builder	Machinery	Laid down	Completed	Trials	Boilers	Best recent speed
Colorado	New York S.B. Co.	Westinghouse Co.	May '19	Aug..'23	37,400 = 22·06	Babcock	
Maryland	Newport News	Gen. Elec. Co.	Apl.,'17	July '21	36,167 = 21·07	Babcock	} 21
W. Virginia	Newport News	Gen. Elec. Co.	Apl., '20	Dec. '23		Babcock	

General Notes.—Authorised 1916 as *No. 45* (*Colorado*), *No. 46* (*Maryland*), and *No. 48* (*W. Virginia*). *W. Virginia* and *Maryland* both fitted as Flagships. Except for change in primary armament, and slight increase in displacement, they are identical in nearly all respects with *California* class. *Washington* scrapped under Naval Treaty. Catapult has been added to equipment of each of this class

CALIFORNIA.

1930 *Official Photo.*

CALIFORNIA.

1922 *Photo, O. W. Waterman.*

(CALIFORNIA class—2 ships).

CALIFORNIA (Nov. 20th, 1919) and **TENNESSEE** (April 30th, 1919).

Displacement $\begin{cases} Standard\ 32,600\ tons.§ \\ Full\ load,\ 33,190\ tons \end{cases}$ Complement, 1407.*

Length $\begin{cases} (w.l.)\ 600\ feet. \\ (o.a.)\ 624\ feet. \end{cases}$ Beam, 97 feet $3\frac{1}{2}$ inches. $\begin{cases} Mean\ draught,\ 30\frac{1}{4}\ feet \\ Max.\ \ ,,\ \ 31\ feet \end{cases}$

* As Flagship, 1469.
§ Tennessee 32,300 tons.

Guns (**Dir. Con.**) :
  12—14 inch, 50 cal., Mk. IV.
  12—5 inch, 51 cal.
  8—5 inch 25 cal. AA.
  4—6 pdr. (saluting).
  2 —1 pdr.
  2 M.G.
  2 landing.
Torpedo tubes (21 inch):
  2 *submerged*.

Armour :
  14″ Belt ....
  8″ Belt (aft) ....
  3″ Deck (ends) ....
  15″—9″ Funnel bases ...
  18″—9″ Turrets..........
  16″ Conning tower and
  tube ....

TENNESSEE.

1921 *Copyright Photo, O. W. Waterman.*

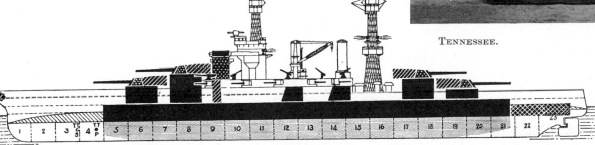

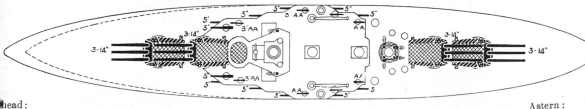

Ahead :
  —14 in.
  —5 in.

Astern :
  6—14 in.
  6—5 in.

Broadside : **12**—14 in. **6**—5 in. ; **1**—21 in. torpedo tube.

Machinery : *California*, G. E. turbines with electric drive. *Tennessee*, Westinghouse turbines with electric drive. 4 screws in both ships. Boilers : 8 Express Bureau type in *California*, 8 Babcock in *Tennessee*. Designed H.P. 28,500 = 21 kts. Fuel (oil only): *normal* 2200, *maximum* 3328 tons.

Gunnery Notes.—The 14 inch mounted in separate sleeves ; elevation, up to 30°. Maximum range stated to be over 35,000 yards. Main guns controlled from upper storey and 5 inch from lower storey of masthead tops.

Armour Notes.—Generally as *New Mexico, Pennsylvania* and *Nevada* classes on subsequent pages. Internal subdivision by unpierced bulkheads developed to the utmost degree below waterline.

Engineering Notes.—Generally as those relating to *New Mexico* on page 450, but (*a*) current generated is 3-phase, (*b*) turbine speed is controlled by hydraulic governors instead of mechanical, (*c*) controls are located in one small room. Four alternating current motors, one to each propeller shaft, supplied by current at 3400 volts, from 2 turbo-generators. Motors are wound for 36 and 24-pole connections, operating on former as squirrel-cage machines, and on latter as wound-rotor machines. Oil for trials : 1467 tons and 187 tons feed water. Estimated weight of machinery : *California*, 1805 tons ; *Tennessee*, 2045 tons. Heating surface : 50984 sq. ft. for Express Bureau boilers in *California* ; 41,768 sq. ft. + 4168 sq. ft. (superheated) for Babcock boilers in *Tennessee*. Each boiler is in a separate w.t. compartment. Boiler rooms are abeam of engine rooms (4 to port, 4 to starboard), and boilers are under central control. Turbines are in tandem on centre line. On *trials, Tennessee* brought to rest from full speed within 3 minutes ; tactical diameter : 700 yards (full helm, both screws turning forward).

Aircraft Notes.—These ships now carry a catapult on third turret.

Name	Builder	Machinery	Laid down	Completed	Refit	Trials	Boilers	Best recent speed
California	Mare Island Y.	G. E. Co.	Oct., 16	Aug.'21		21·75	Express	
Tennessee	New York Yard	Westinghouse Co.	May,'17	June'20		30,908 = 21·378	Babcock	

General Notes.—Authorised 1915 as *No. 43 (Tennessee)* and 44 *(California)*. The above design is practically identical with *New Mexico* class on next page. *California* fitted as Flagship.

(NEW MEXICO *class*—3 ships).

NEW MEXICO (ex-*California*, April 23rd, 1917), **IDAHO** (June 30th, 1917),

MISSISSIPPI (January 25th, 1917).

Displacement $\left\{ \begin{array}{l} \textit{New Mexico,} \quad ? \quad \text{tons.} \\ \textit{Idaho,} \quad ? \quad \text{tons.} \\ \textit{Mississippi,} \quad ? \quad \text{tons.} \end{array} \right\}$ Complement, 1434.
Standard

Length $\left\{ \begin{array}{l} \textit{waterline, 600 feet.} \\ \textit{over all, 624 feet.} \end{array} \right\}$ Beam, 97 ft. 4½ in. $\left\{ \begin{array}{l} \textit{Mean draught, 30 feet.} \\ \textit{Max.} \quad \text{,,} \quad 31\text{ft. }0\frac{1}{2}\text{in.} \end{array} \right\}$

Guns (Dir. Con.):
12—14 inch, 50 cal., Mk. IV.
12—5 inch, 51 cal.
8—5 inch (AA.), 25 cal.
4—3 pdr. (saluting).
2—1 pdr.
2 machine.
1 landing.
Torpedo tubes removed.

Armour :
14″ Belt (amidships) ......
8″ Belt (aft) ....
″ Deck ends ....
15″—9″ Funnel base ......
18″–9″ Turrets ....
16″ Conning tower & tube

Undergoing Modernization.

(Unofficial Plan).

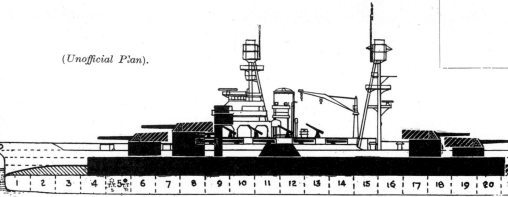

Ahead :
6—14 in.
8—5 in.

Astern:
6—14 in.
4—5 in.

Broadside : 12—14 in., 6—5 in.

Machinery : Westinghouse Parsons Turbines being fitted in all three ships. 4 screws.
Boilers : 9 Babcock & Wilcox. Designed H.P., *New Mexico* 27,500, others 32,000 = 21 knots. Fuel:
Oil only, 2200 tons (pre-alterations figures).

Armour and Gunnery Notes.—Generally as *Pennsylvania* and *Nevada* classes, but have still greater degree of inter[?]
protection. Belt reaches to 2 ft. above w.l. at stern. As designed, it was intended they should mount 14 in. 45 c[?]
guns, but while building, the more powerful 50 calibre model of the 14 inch gun was adopted. In this (and [?]
newer ships) triple turret guns mounted in separate sleeves. Elevation reported to be increased to 30°.

Name.	Builder and Machinery.	Laid down.	Completed	Trials. (4 hrs)	Tons Fuel per day.			Best recent speed.
					10—	15—	19–kts.	
New Mexico	New York Yard	Oct., '15	May, '18	31,197 = 21·08	—	132	263	21
Idaho	N. York S.B. Co.	Jan., '15	Mar.,'19	33,100 = 21·29	—/74	165/194	—/310	21·92
Mississippi	Newport News	Apl., '15	Dec.,'17	31.804 = 21·09	77	—/168	—/305	

General Notes.—Authorised 1914, as No. 40 (*New Mexico*), 41 (*Mississippi*) and 42 (*Idaho*). *New Mexico* fitted as Fleet Fla[?]
ship. Originally, only two ships were to have been built, but the sale of the old *Idaho* and *Mississippi* to Gre[?]
contributed two-thirds of the cost for a third unit. *New Mexico* was first named *California*. The type is deriv[?]
from the *Nevada* design through the *Pennsylvania* class, upon which all the above are improvements. T[?]
electrical transmission of *New Mexico* was adopted through the excellent results given by the Melville-Macalp[?]
electric-drive system in the Aircraft Carrier *Langley*. A Bill authorising the appropriation of $30,000,000 for modern[?]
ing these ships has been approved by the House Naval Committee. Displacement will be increased by about 3,[?]
tons. They are to undergo extensive alterations which include the fitting of bulges, increased protection, alterati[?]
to the secondary battery, changes in the elevation of the main armament, new masts, bridges and machinery. N[?]
Mexico was formerly fitted with turbo-electric drive, which proved entirely successful, but is being replaced by hig[?]
powered machinery identical with that which is being installed in her sisters, for the purposes of homogeneity a[?]
economy: Approximately 300,000 dollars will be saved by equipping all three ships with the same type of turb[?]
machinery.

(Pennsylvania Class—2 Ships).

PENNSYLVANIA (16th March, 1915) & ARIZONA (19th June, 1915)

Standard Displacement 32,100 tons.   Complement* 1439 as flagships.

Length $\begin{cases} \text{w.l. 600 feet} \\ \text{o.a. 608 feet} \end{cases}$ Beam, 97 feet, $0\frac{1}{2}$ in. $\begin{cases} \text{Mean draught, } 28\frac{5}{6}\text{ feet.} \\ \text{Max.} \quad \text{,,} \quad 29\frac{5}{6} \text{ ,,} \end{cases}$

War:—Penn. 1574. *Ariz.* 1620.

Guns (**Dir. Con.**) :
- 12—14 inch, 45 cal.
- 12—5 inch, 51 cal.
- 8—5 in. (A.A.), 25 cal.
- 4—3 pdr. (saluting).
- 2—1 pdr
- 2 M.G.
- 2 landing.

Torpedo tubes removed.

Armour :
- 14″ Belt (amidships) ....
- 8″ Belt (aft) ....
- 3″ Deck (ends) ....
- 15″—9″ Funnel base ....
- 18″—9″ Turrets
- 16″ Conning tower & tube ...
  (Total, 8072 tons.)

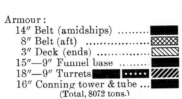

PENNSYLVANIA reconstructed.

1931 *Official photo.*

Plans revised 1930.

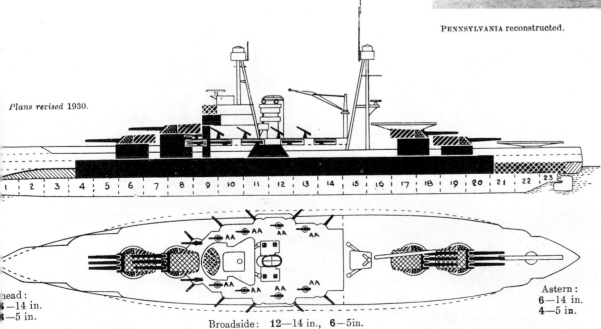

Head :
- 8—14 in.
- 3—5 in.

Astern :
- 6—14 in.
- 4—5 in.

Broadside: 12—14 in., 6—5 in.

Machinery : *Pennsylvania*, Curtis (geared cruising) turbines. 4 screws. *Arizona*, Parsons, (geared cruising) turbines. 4 screws. Boilers : 12 Babcock. Designed H.P. (*Pennsylvania*) 31,500 ; (*Arizona*) 34,000 = 21 kts. Fuel : oil only, *normal* 2,322 tons (694,830 gallons).

Armour Notes.—Generally as for *Nevada* class on page 463. Increase of armour weight due to increased internal protection against submarine explosions and greater length of belt. Armour for each triple barbette, $226\frac{1}{4}$ tons. *Arizona* has cement backing to belt, instead of teak, and armoured fire-control tops.

Gunnery and Fire Control Notes.—14 inch guns mounted in single sleeve, and can be fired as one piece. *Max.* range at 15° elevation reported to be 21,000 yards. Triple positions weigh about 650 tons each (guns, mountings and armour). Hoists deliver 1 round per 40 secs., which may be improved to 2 rounds per minute, but three rounds fired per turret per minute probably represents actual rate of fire in service. Breech blocks worked by hand power. Interior of the shields to 14 inch guns very roomy and well arranged.

Name	Builder	Machinery	Laid down	Completed	Trials Full Power : 12 hrs.	Tons Fuel per day†		
						10—	15—	19—kts
Pennsylvania	Newport News	Newport News	Oct.'13	June,'16	29,366 = 21·05	65/—	90/—	—/—
Arizona	New York Yard	New York Yard	Mar.'14	Oct. '16	34,000 = 21	76/—	167/174	—/30

General Notes.—*Pennsylvania* authorised 1912, as No. 38, *Arizona* 1913, as No. 39. Both ships are enlarged and improved *Nevadas.* They have proved excellent sea boats, very steady gun platforms, and have proved to be very economical ships. Their general design is marked by great simplicity and a very high standard of excellence. Living quarters are very roomy and well ventilated. Both are fitted as Flagships.

These ships have undergone extensive reconstruction which has cost $14,800,000. Battery raised a deck and A.A. armament increased ; tripods fitted, funnel moved further aft ; bulges and increased internal protection ; additional bridges, and catapults fitted.

In appearance differ from *Nevada* and *Oklahoma* in having higher conning tower and bridge which reaches funnel level.

ARIZONA.

1931 *Official photo*.

OKLAHOMA.

1931 *Photo*.

(NEVADA CLASS—2 SHIPS).

OKLAHOMA (March 23rd, 1914) & **NEVADA** (July 11th, 1914).

Standard Displacement 28,900 tons.   Complement, both 1384. *

Length $\left\{\begin{array}{l}\text{waterline, 575 feet.}\\ \text{over all, 583 feet.}\end{array}\right\}$ Beam, 95 ft. 2½ ins. $\left\{\begin{array}{l}\text{Mean draught 28½ feet.}\\ \text{Max.} \quad \text{,,} \quad \text{29 ft. 7 ins.}\end{array}\right.$

War : Nevada, 1598, Oklahoma, 1628.

Guns (Dir. Con.) :
- **10**—14 inch, 45 cal.
- **12**—5 inch, 51 cal.
- **8**—5 inch, 25 cal. AA.
- **4**—6* or 3† pdr. (saluting).
- **2**—1 pdr.
- **2** machine.
- **1** landing.

Torpedo tubes removed.

*In *Nevada*. †In *Oklahoma*.

Armour :
13½″ Belt (amidships)	
8″ Belt (aft)	
13½″ Bulkheads	
13½″ Funnel base	
3″ Deck (ends)	
18″—9″ Triple turrets .. $\Big\}$	
16″—9″ Double turrets... $\Big/$	
16″ Conning tower and tube	

(Total weight, 7664 tons.)

OKLAHOMA.

1930 *Official photo.*

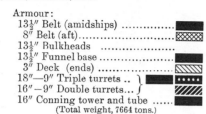

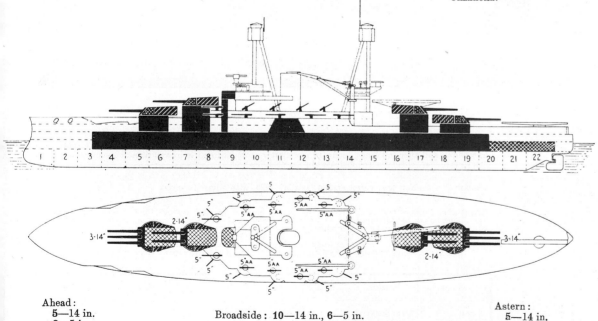

Ahead :
- 5—14 in.
- 8—5 in.

Broadside : 10—14 in., 6—5 in.

Astern :
- 5—14 in.
- 4—5 in.

Machinery: *Oklahoma,* Triple expansion, 4 cylinder; *Nevada,* Curtis (geared cruising) turbines. 2 screws in both. Boilers: O, 12 Babcock; N, 12 Yarrow. Designed H.P. 26,500=20·5 kts. Fuel: oil, 598,400 gallons (2000 tons), *maximum capacity.* Radius of action : 4000 miles at full speed, 10,000 miles at 10 kts.

Special Note:

The alterations effected to *Oklahoma* and *Nevada* include substitution of tripod for cage masts, and installation of a deck house, on which, **8**—**5** inch, 25 cal. guns are mounted. The 5 inch 51 cal. torpedo defence battery is raised from the main deck to the forecastle deck. The funnel is moved aft slightly. Cost of alterations $7,000,000 per ship.

Armour Notes.—Main belt is 400 feet long by 17½ feet wide; 8½ feet of it being below *l.w.l.* Lower edge is 8″. The ends are unarmoured; the battery also. Plates are applied in vertical strakes. Two protective decks upper 3″ flat, lower 1½″ flat, 2″ on slopes. Barbette bases are 13½″ thick, but turrets are only 4½″ where below protective deck and behind belt. Barbette shields: 18″ port plate for triple positions, 16″ port plate for twin positions, 10″ sides, 9″ back, 5″ roof. Sighting slits in conning tower closed by splinter-proof shutters. There is a signalling station protected by 16″ armour behind conning tower. These ships mark a new era in naval construction, being the first to embody the "everything or nothing" idea in the matter of protection. No bulkhead between 14 inch guns.

Gunnery Notes.—Guns in the triple turrets in one sleeve, can be fired as one piece. Elevation has been increased to 30°

Engineering Notes.—*Nevada* has 2 H.P. and 2 L.P. Curtis turbines.   Cylinders of *Oklahoma* are H.P. 36.5″, I.P. 59.5″, L.P. (2) 78″. Stroke, 48″. Total heating surface, 45,080 sq. feet. Weight of machinery, *Nevada,* 1860 tons : *Oklahoma,* 1933 tons. Electric installation in both is 4 generating sets of 300 k.w., 125 volts, 2400 amp. each. Boilers are in 6 compartments and occupy less than 80 feet of length. Boilers are large tube "Express" type, those specially designed by Messrs. Babcock & Wilcox for *Oklahoma* proving most satisfactory. No superheaters in either ship. Electric-driven f.d. blowers proved too unreliable, and were replaced by steam turbine-driven blowers. All oil fuel carried in double bottom ; no wing tanks.

Name	Builder	Machinery	Laid down	Completed	Trials : (Full Power—12 hrs.)	Tons fuel per day: 10 kts.	15 kts.	19 kts.
Oklahoma	N.York S.B.Co	N.Y. S.B. Co.	Oct. '12	May,'16	21,703=20·58	77	143	278
Nevada	Fore River Co.	Fore River	Nov.'12	Mar. '16	23,312=20·53	{50·5† 77§	132·5† 149§	210§

†Cruising turbines. §Main turbines.

General Notes.—Authorised 1911 as *No. 36 (Nevada),* 37 *Oklahoma).*   Each carries a catapult astern.

*Unofficial Notes.

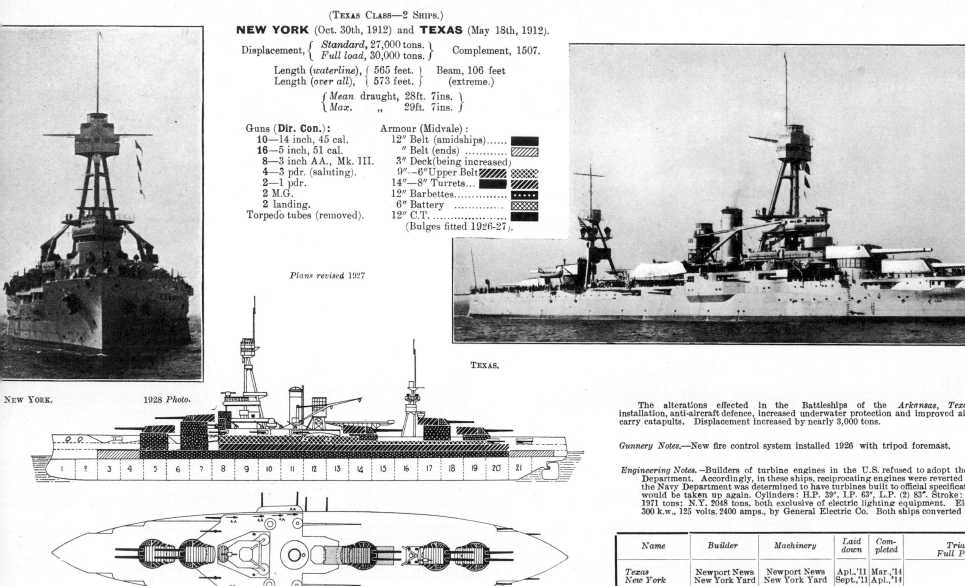

(Texas Class—2 Ships.)

NEW YORK (Oct. 30th, 1912) and **TEXAS** (May 18th, 1912).

Displacement, { Standard, 27,000 tons. / Full load, 30,000 tons. }   Complement, 1507.

Length (waterline), { 565 feet. }   Beam, 106 feet
Length (over all), { 573 feet. }   (extreme.)

{ Mean draught, 28ft. 7ins. / Max. „ 29ft. 7ins. }

Guns (Dir. Con.):   Armour (Midvale) :

10—14 inch, 45 cal.   12″ Belt (amidships)......
16—5 inch, 51 cal.   ″ Belt (ends) ....
8—3 inch AA., Mk. III.   3″ Deck(being increased)
4—3 pdr. (saluting).   9″—6″Upper Belt
2—1 pdr.   14″—8″ Turrets...
2 M.G.   12″ Barbettes..........
2 landing.   6″ Battery ....
Torpedo tubes (removed).   12″ C.T. ....

(Bulges fitted 1926-27.)

Plans revised 1927

TEXAS.

NEW YORK.   1928 Photo.

1927 Official Photo.

The alterations effected in the Battleships of the *Arkansas*, *Texas* classes, include oil burning installation, anti-aircraft defence, increased underwater protection and improved aircraft handling arrangements. A carry catapults. Displacement increased by nearly 3,000 tons.

Gunnery Notes.—New fire control system installed 1926 with tripod foremast.

Engineering Notes.—Builders of turbine engines in the U.S. refused to adopt the standards laid down by the Nav Department. Accordingly, in these ships, reciprocating engines were reverted to, to show the turbine builders th the Navy Department was determined to have turbines built to official specification, or else the older type of engin would be taken up again. Cylinders : H.P. 39″, I.P. 63″, L.P. (2) 83″. Stroke : 48″. Weight of machinery : *Tex* 1971 tons : N.Y. 2048 tons, both exclusive of electric lighting equipment. Electrical installation : 4 sets each 300 k.w., 125 volts, 2400 amps., by General Electric Co. Both ships converted to oil burning.

Name	Builder	Machinery	Laid down	Completed	Trials : Full Power.	Boilers	Best recent speed
Texas	Newport News	Newport News	Apl.,'11	Mar.,'14		Bureau	
New York	New York Yard	New York Yard	Sept.,'11	Apl.,'14		Express	...

General Notes.—Authorised 1910 as *No. 34* (N.Y.) and *35* (Texas). Both ships fitted as flagships. Are very economic ships and most successful steamers. *Texas* cost *about £2,194,000.*

Ahead:
4—14 in.
6—5 in.

Astern :
4—14 in.
6—5 in.

Broadside: 10—14 in., 8—5 in.

Machinery : Vertical triple expansion, 4 cylinder. 2 screws. Boilers : 6 Bureau Express (37,020 H.S. and 6096 H.S. superheat). Designed H.P. 28,100 = 21 kts. Oil : 5200 tons.

(ARKANSAS CLASS)

ARKANSAS (Jan. 14th, 1911).

Displacement, { *Standard,* 26,100 tons. } Complement, 1489.
{ *Full load,* 29,000 tons. }

Length { (*w.l.*), 554 feet. } Beam, 106 feet (extreme). { *Mean* draught, 28½ feet.
{ (*o.a.*), 562 feet. } { *Max.* „ 29 ft. 7in.

Guns (**Dir. Con.**):
- **12**—12 inch, 50 cal.
- **16**—5 inch, 51 cal.
- **8**—3 inch AA., Mk III.
- **4**—6 or 3† pdr. (saluting).
- **2**—1 pdr.
- 2 machine.
- 2 landing.

Torpedo tubes (removed).

Armour (Midvale):*
- 11"—9" Belt amidships }
- 5" Belt (ends) ....
- 12"—9" Turrets......... }
- 11" Turret bases ....
- 6½" Battery ....
- 12" Conning tower........
- (Bulges fitted 1926-27)

*See Notes.

ARKANSAS (**as modified by reconstruction**).

1927 *Official Photo.*

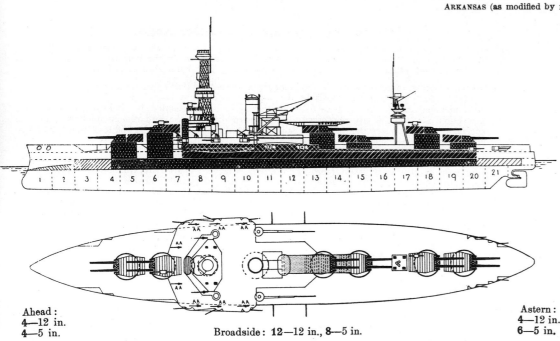

Ahead :
4—12 in.
4—5 in.

Broadside : **12**—12 in., **8**—5 in.

Astern :
4—12 in.
6—5 in.

Machinery : I.P. and L.P. Parsons turbines, H.P. geared Curtis. 4 screws. Boilers : 4
White-Forster. Designed H.P. 28,000 = 20.5 kts. Oil : 5100 tons.

A sister ship **WYOMING** has been de-militarised according to the terms of the Naval Treaty. No. 2, 3, 4 turrets removed. (see silhouette.) She is employed as a Training Ship.

*Gunnery Notes.—Height of guns above water: No. 1 turret, 28¼ feet; No. 2, 36¼ feet; No. 3, 33 feet; No. 4, 25 feet; No. 5, 31¼ feet; No. 6, 23¼ feet.

Arcs of training: (1) 300°, (2) 270°, (3) 280°, (4) 260°, (5) 330°, (6) 300°. Max. elevation, 15°; range, 24,500 yds.

*Armour Notes.—Main belt 400 feet long, 9" on bottom edge, 11" on upper edge. Upper belt is same, but is 11" on bottom edge and 6½" on upper. Internal protection is by 1½" high-tensile longitudinal bulkheads. Two protective decks over all machinery and magazine spaces, one deck at ends. 6½" armour and 1½" splinter bulkheads to funnel uptakes, up to main deck.

Engineering Notes.—Approximately 148 r.p.m.=10·5 kts., 215=15 kts., 300=20 kts., 320=22 kts. Heating surface: 45,000 sq. feet, superheat 4364. Weight of machinery: 2178 tons in *Arkansas,* 2095 tons in *Wyoming* (excluding electric lighting equipment). Electrical installation: 4 sets each 300 k.w., 125 volts, 2400 amps. by General Electric Co. Searchlights: 16. It was first intended that these ships should have combined turbines and reciprocating engines, but the plan was dropped in favour of complete turbine propulsion. Tactical Diameter, 800 yds. (See also Special Note under *Texas* class).

Name	Builder	Machinery	Laid down	Com-pleted	Trials (mean)	Boilers	Best recent speed
Arkansas	N.Y.Shipbld. Co	N.Y. Shipbld. Co.	Jan.,'10	Sept.,'12		White-	

General Notes.—Authorised 1909, as 33 (*Arkansas*). Contracts awarded Sept. and Oct., 1909. Freeboard : Forward, 25'; amidships, 19' 2" ; at No. 6 turret, 18' ; at stern, 16' 3". Underwent extensive alterations and refit, 1925-27, when displacement was increased by 3,000 tons.

*Unofficial Notes.

LEXINGTON (3rd Oct., 1925.)

SARATOGA (7th April, 1925.)

Standard Displacement, 33,000 tons.

Complement (including flying personnel) 169 Officers, 1730 men.

Length (*p.p.*), 850 feet ; (*o.a.*) 888 feet.   Beam, 106 feet (*extreme*).
Draught, 24 feet 1½ inches (*mean*).

SARATOGA.

(Additional views on following page).

1928 *Photo, by favour of H. C. Bywater, Esq.*

Guns :
8—8 inch, 55 cal.
12—5 inch AA., 25 cal.
4—6 pdr. saluting.

Plans revised 1930.

Armour :
Unofficially reported to have 6″ Belt, 600 feet in length, and 3″ deck.   Triple hull and bulge protection.

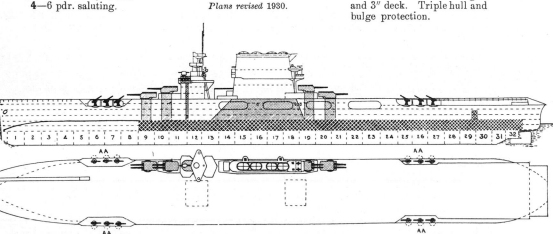

Notes on Lexington and Saratoga.

These two ships were originally authorised in 1916 for construction as Battle Cruisers of 35,300 tons, with *seven* funnels and boilers disposed on two deck levels.   After the War, and as a result of the lessons thereof, plans were to a large extent re-cast, v. F.S. 1919—1921 Editions.

As Aircraft Carriers, these ships show a reduction (from the second Battle Cruiser design) in displacement of about 8,500 tons, achieved mainly by the elimination of eight 16-inch guns in four twin turrets, with mounts, armour, &c.   It is believed the main belt protection is retained and that deck protection has been heavily reinforced.   The general lines of the hull remain unaltered, and the special system of underwater protection is also adhered to.   Flight deck is 880 feet long, from 85 to 90 feet in width, and 60 feet above waterline.

Handling of Aircraft.—The Landing Net is placed just before the recessed stern portion of the Flight Deck ; it is about 100 ft. long.   Before it is a large T-shaped lift for moving aircraft from Flight to Hangar Deck.   There is another and similar T-shaped lift abeam of the mast and C.T. At the bow is a catapult, 155 feet in length, capable of launching the heaviest aircraft into the air at flying speed with a travel of 60 feet.   Before the C.T. and abaft the Navigating Officers' Deck House, and right over to starboard beam, are powerful derricks for lifting seaplanes and flying boats from the water.   As a result of experiments with *Langley*, certain modifications have been made which should enable planes to land safely on deck in any weather.

Reported that 120 planes can be carried.   Photos show them with from 70 to 80 planes on deck ready for flight, but number varies as the type of plane employed.

Total cost of these ships, with aircraft, was over $45,000,000 each.

Engineering Notes.—Each boiler 11,250 H.P.   Steam pressure, 295 lbs. to sq. inch.   Fuel consumption estimated at 2000 tons daily under full power.   Machinery is the most powerful ever installed in a warship ; it is all controlled, so far as main engines are concerned, from one central position.   There are over 1000 auxiliary motors, ranging from 425 H.P. ventilating plant down to the small electric motors connected with the self-synchronising electric fire-control arrangements, which develop 1-200th of one H.P.   For general distribution through the ship, current is supplied by six turbo-generators of 750 K.W. each.   There are eight propelling motors of 22,500 H.P. (two to each of the four shafts), speed 317 R.P.M.   The combined illuminating power of the S.L. is equal to 3,260,000 c.p.   Altogether, these ships represent the climax of American practice in applying electric power to warship construction. On trials, it is stated that 97% of designed speed was obtained with 85% of designed power.   *Lexington* did the voyage from San Diego to Honolulu (2228 miles) at an average speed of 30·7 kts.   A speed of 34·5 kts. was maintained for one hour by the latter ship with S.H.P. 210,000.

Machinery : G.E. Turbines, electric drive.   Designed S.H.P. 180,000 = 33·25 kts.   Boilers : *Lexington*, 16 Yarrow ; *Saratoga*, 16 White-Forster.   4 screws.

Name	Builder	Machinery	Laid down	Completed	Trials	Boilers
Lexington	Fore River S.B. Co.	Gen. Elec. Co.	8/1/21	Dec.'27	153,600 = 33·04	Yarrow
Saratoga	New York S.B. Co.	Gen. Elec. Co.	25/9/20	Nov.'28	158,375 = 33·42	White-Forster

SARATOGA.

Photo, Nov., 1927, Topical.

SARATOGA.

1928 Photo, by favour of H. C. Bywater, Esq.

RANGER.

(*Newport News*).

Laid down 1930.   To be completed 1934.

Displacement : 13,800 tons.

Guns : **8**—5 inch.

Planes 76 reported.

Details and design confidential.

SARATOGA.

1928 Photo, by favour of H. C. Bywater, Esq.

SARATOGA.

1928 Photo, by favour of H. C. Bywater, Esq.

LANGLEY.

1925 *Photo.*

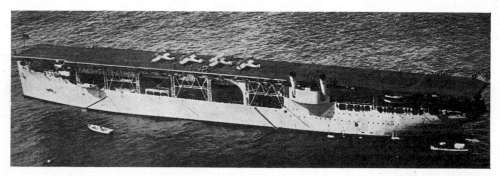

Photo added 1930.

LANGLEY (ex-Fleet Collier *Jupiter*, 1912, launched Aug. 24th, 1912, converted 1920-21).

Displacement, $\left\{\begin{array}{l}\textit{Normal, } 12,700 \text{ tons.}\\ \textit{Full load, } \text{tons.}\end{array}\right\}$ Complement, 341 (excluding flying personnel).

Length, $\left\{\begin{array}{l}\textit{p.p. } 520 \text{ feet.}\\ \textit{o.a. } 542 \text{ feet.}\end{array}\right\}$ Beam, 65 feet.   Draught $\left\{\begin{array}{l}\textit{Mean, } 18 \text{ feet } 10\frac{1}{2} \text{ in.}\\ \textit{Full load, } \text{feet.}\end{array}\right\}$

Guns :   Armour :
  4—5 inch, 51 cal.   *Nil.*
(Carries 275 bombs for aircraft,
  also 24 torpedoes).

Note to Plan.—Now has 2 funnels, which are arranged to lower as in
Japanese *Hosho*.

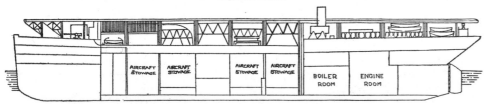

Machinery.—G.E. turbines and electric drive. 2 screws. Boilers : 3 double-ended cylindrical and 1 auxiliary. S.H.P. (on first trials as Fleet collier) 7152 $=$ 14·99 kts. *Max.* fuel capacity : oil only, 2300 tons.

Engineering Notes.—First large ship of U.S.N. built with electric drive and Melville-McAlpine reducing gear. This system of propulsion proved so successful, it has been adopted for Capital Ships. Two horizontal smoke ducts on port side with hinged extensions which can be lowered. Fitted with Sperry gyro-stabiliser.

Official photo added 1930.

W/T. Notes.—Masts stow flat along hangar deck. Auxiliary radio carried for communicating with 'planes when main W/T. masts are housed down.

Aircraft Capacity.—Maximum capacity reported as 55 'planes, but at present carries :—

  (a) 12 single-seater chasing 'planes (3 hours endurance at 100 kts.).
  (b) 12 two-seater spotting 'planes (4 hours endurance at 100 kts.).
  (c) 4 torpedo-dropping 'planes (2 hours endurance at 100 kts.).   (24 torpedoes carried for these).
  (d) 6 80-kt. torpedo-seaplanes.

Aircraft Stores, Repairs, &c.—For planes, all stores, spare parts, accessories, and magazines built for bombs, torpedoes, &c. Petrol capacity : 1130 tons, with elaborate plant for pumping petrol and lubricating oil to hangar and flying decks. Repair plant ; machine shop ; wing-repair shop ; metal working shop ; kite balloon filling station, etc.

Handling of Aircraft.—Original cargo holds altered to give max. space for housing 'planes. Runways below flight deck carry travelling cranes for hoisting 'planes from hold and moving them fore and aft, or to lifts for hoisting to flying deck. Electric lift raises 'planes from hangar to flying deck.

Flying-off.—Flight deck : 534 × 64 feet and 56 feet over w.l. Launching catapults fitted which can deliver torpedo 'planes into air at 60 m.p.h. with 60 feet run.

Flying-on and Landing Alongside.—Mantlets rigged to check speed. 2 cranes on each beam, with wide radii to pick seaplanes from water and place them on deck. Can receive 'planes at 60 m.p.h. and stop in 40 feet without injury to machine or pilot. It is considered safe for 'planes to alight on deck in a moderate sea.

General Notes.—Begun at Mare Island N. Yd., October, 1911, and completed as Fleet Collier, 1913. So served till March, 1920, when she was placed out of commission for conversion by Norfolk Navy Yd. For training purposes a complete and full-sized replica of LANGLEY'S flight deck, with landing net, has been erected at the Long Beach Aerodrome.

(See also Aircraft Tenders on a later page.)

CRUISER—SECOND LINE (OCA):

(Fore funnel removed, 1927.)

ROCHESTER (ex-*Saratoga*, ex-*New York*). (1891). (Reconstructed 1907-08 and 1927). Displacement: *normal*, 8150 tons*; *full load*, 8900 tons. Complement, 648. Dimensions: 384 × 64⅚ × 26⅓. Guns: 4—8 inch, 45 cal., 8—5 inch, 50 cal., 2—3 inch AA., 2—3 pdr. Armour (Harvey nickel): 4″ Belt, 6″ Deck (amidships); (Krupp) 6″—4″ Barbettes, 6½″ Turrets; 5″ Hoists, 7″ Conning tower. Boilers: 4 Babcock. Weight of machinery, 1317 tons. H.P. (estimated) 7700 = 21 kts. Coal: 750—1100 tons. Authorised 1888. Laid down by Cramp, Philadelphia, Sept., 1890. Completed 1893. Originally had three funnels and 12 boilers.

* Including full supply ammunition and stores.

Light Cruisers—First Line
(MINNEAPOLIS CLASS—3 SHIPS.)

NEW ORLEANS (**NO. 32**).　　*ASTORIA* (**NO. 34**).　　*MINNEAPOLIS* (**NO. 36**).

Standard displacement, 10,000 tons. Complement,
Dimensions : Not available for publication.　Armament : As *Portland* class.

Building.

Notes.—These three ships are not officially included in the *Portland* class and details are confidential. It is expected that they will exhibit a break-away from the earlier design. *New Orleans* building at Navy Yard, New York; *Astoria* building at Navy Yard, Puget Sound; *Minneapolis* building at Navy Yard, Philadelphia.

LIGHT CRUISERS—FIRST LINE (CL).

(PORTLAND CLASS—2 SHIPS.)

PORTLAND (**NO. 33**).　　*INDIANAPOLIS* (**NO. 35**).

Standard displacement, 10,000 tons. Complement,
Dimensions, 610 (*o.a.*), 592 (*p.p.*) × 64½ × 19 feet 5 inches.

Building.

Guns :
　9—8″, 55 cal.
　8—5″
　2—3″
Torpedo tubes :
　6—21″ in triple mountings.

Armour :
　 ″ side.
　 ″ deck.

Machinery : Parsons geared turbines. S.H.P. 10,500=32·5 kts. 8 White Forster boilers. 4 screws.

Notes.—Reported to follow the general lines of *Augusta* design, with improved protection and internal subdivision. Secondary battery increased to eight guns and speed slightly reduced. *Portland* laid down at Bethlehem S.B. Co., Quincy, Mass., Feb., 1930. *Indianapolis* at New York S.B. Co., Camden, N.J., March, 1930.

(TUSCALOOSA CLASS—5 SHIPS.)

TUSCALOOSA (No. 37). New York S.B. Co., Camden.)
SAN FRANCISCO (No. 38) (Mare Island D.Y.)
(No. 39)　To be commenced in 1933.
(No. 40)　To be commenced in 1934.
(No. 41)　To be commenced in 1935.
　Nos. 37 and 38 commenced in 1931.

Displacement : 10,000 tons.
Armament of 8-inch guns.

(Augusta *class* 6—ships).

AUGUSTA (Feb. 1st, 1930). **CHESTER** (July 3rd, 1929). **CHICAGO** (Apr. 10th, 1930).
HOUSTON (Sept. 7th, 1929). **LOUISVILLE** (Sept. 1st, 1930). **NORTHAMPTON**
(Sept. 5th, 1930).

Standard displacement, 9,050 tons.* Complement, 611.
Dimensions, 582 (*p.p.*), 600 (*o.a.*)×65×17 feet 7 inches (*mean*).

Guns :
10—8″, 55 cal.
4—5″ AA.
2—3 pdr.
Torpedo tubes (21″)
  6 in. 2 triple mountings
Catapults : **2**
  4 planes.

***Chester** 9,200 tons.
Chicago 9,300 tons.

Armour :
  3″ Belt.
  1″ Deck.
  1½″ Gunhouses.

HOUSTON.   1931 *Official Photo.*

(*Note extension of forecastle to catapult base.*)

Machinery : Parsons geared turbines. Designed S.H.P. 107,000=32·7 kts. 8 White-Forster
boilers, excepting in *Northampton* (8 Yarrow). 4 screws. Radius :

General Notes.—Authorised 1926–27 under Act of December, 1924, as Nos. 26–31. Although this class are considerably
improved editions of the *Pensacola*, they have not proved particularly successful. The previous class having worked
out at 9,100 tons only, the dimensions were increased and a forecastle deck added. Weight was saved by reducing
and re-grouping the armament, while a certain amount of extra protection was worked in. Because of vibration
in the *Pensacola* the hull was stiffened to try and overcome this defect. Owing to the centre of gravity being placed
too low, they roll considerably and *Northampton* has been fitted with bigger bulge keels. If the anti-rolling tanks
in *Pensacola* are more successful in overcoming this defect, these will be fitted to the remainder of the class. Some
have developed cracked stern posts due to weight-saving and/or vibration. Four planes are carried, two on top of
and two inside the large hangars amidships. *Houston, Augusta* and *Chicago* are fitted as flagships and extra accommodation has been secured by extending the forecastle aft to the catapult.

Gunnery Notes.—

Engineering Notes.—Heating surface, 95,040 sq. feet. Machinery weighs 2,161 tons. 4 Turbo-
generator sets ; 250 kilo-watts each ; 120—240 volts ; built by General Electric Co.
There are 4 boiler rooms

Name	Builders	Machinery	Laid down	Completed	Trials
Augusta	Newport News Co.		2/7/28	Jan., 1931	
Chester	Am. Brown Boveri Cpn.		6/3/28	June, 1930	
Chicago	Mare Island Navy Yard	G.E. Co.	10/9/28	March, 1931	
Houston	Newport News Co.		1/5/28	June, 1930	
Louisville	Puget Sound Navy Yard		4/7/28	March, 1931	
Northampton	Bethlehem S.B. Co., Quincy		12/4/28	May, 1930	

NORTHAMPTON.   1930 *Photo, favour of Bethlehem Steel Co.*

AUGUSTA.

1931 photo, Mr. L. Opdycke.

AUGUSTA.

1931 photo, Mr. L. Opdycke.

AUGUSTA (To show catapult and hangar).

1931 photo, Mr. L. Opdycke.

(PENSACOLA CLASS).

PENSACOLA (April 25th, 1929), **SALT LAKE CITY** (Jan. 23rd, 1929).

Standard displacement, 9,100 tons.   (Estimated *normal* displacement, 11,568 tons.)

Complement, 612.

Length (*p.p.*), 570 feet ; *o.a.*, 585½ feet.   Beam, 64 ft.

Mean draught (at *normal* displacement), 17 ft. 5 in.

Guns :
  10—8 inch, 55 cal.
  4—5 inch, 25 cal. AA.
  2—3 pdr.
Torpedo tubes (21 inch) : **6** (tripled).
Catapults, 2.
  4 planes.

Armour :
  3″ side.
  1″ deck.
  1½″ gunhouses.

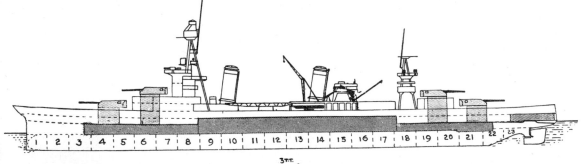

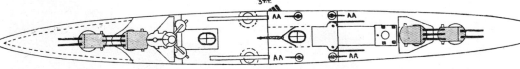

SALT LAKE CITY.

1930 *Photo.*

Machinery : 4 sets of Parsons geared turbines. Cramp type, with de Laval single reduction gearing. Designed S.H.P., 107,000 = 32.5 kts. (more expected), 8 White-Forster boilers, working pressure reported as 300 lbs. to square inch. 4 screws. Radius of action : 13,000 miles at 15 kts.

General Notes.—Laid down under Act of December 18, 1924. Tons per inch immersion, 60·7. Utmost economy in weights practised in design and construction. Aluminium alloy fittings replacing steel and aluminium paint is used internally. Welding has been employed wherever possible instead of rivetting. They suffer from lack of freeboard, vibration is excessive, mainly due to the shape of their sterns, and they roll considerably. Anti-rolling tanks are being tried out in *Pensacola.*

Gunnery Notes.—These ships are the first to carry 8 in. 55 cal. guns.   The fore control station at the mast head is about 120 feet above w.l. : the after control is abaft second funnel, and AA. control on fore bridge.

Engineering Notes.—Heating surface, 95,000 square feet. Machinery weighs 2,161 tons. Can steam at 30 kts. with 60 per cent H.P. There are 2 engine and 2 boiler rooms, the outboard shafts coming from the foremost engine rooms.

Name	Builders	Machinery	Laid down	Completed	Trials
Pensacola Salt Lake City	New York N. Yd. Am. Brown Boveri Cpn.	Am. B. B. Cpn.	Oct. 1926 June 1927	Nov. 1929	107,746 = 32·78

SALT LAKE CITY.

Official Photo, added 1930.

PENSACOLA.

1931 *Photo, Mr. L. Opdycke.*

PENSACOLA.

Official Photo, added 1930.

(OMAHA CLASS—10 SHIPS.)

OMAHA (Dec. 14th, 1920), **MILWAUKEE** (Mar. 24th, 1921), **CINCINNATI** (May 23rd, 1921),
RALEIGH (Oct. 25th, 1922), **DETROIT** (June 29th, 1922), **RICHMOND** (Sept. 29th, 1921), **CONCORD**
(Dec. 15th, 1921), **TRENTON** (April 16th, 1923). **MARBLEHEAD** (Oct. 9th, 1923), **MEMPHIS** (April 17th, 1924).
Standard displacement, 7050 tons ; *full load*, 9000 tons.   Complement, 458.

Length (*waterline*), 550 feet ; *over all*, 555½ feet.   Beam, 55 feet.   { Mean draught, 14' 3" }
{ Max.   ,,   ———— }

Armour :
3" Side................
1½" Upper Deck .....

ns : (Dir. Con.)
0—6 inch, 53 cal. Mk. XII.
11—6 inch in Marblehead.)
4—3 inch, 50 cal. AA.
2—3 pdr. (saluting)
rpedo tubes (21 inch) :
6 in two triple-
deck mountings.

DETROIT.

1927 *Photo, F. J. Parsons, Esq.*

In order to improve seaworthiness the lower after battery guns have been removed in *Marblehead* and replaced by a single gun on top of the battery, making her armament **11—6 inch guns.** In other vessels of the class the lower guns will be removed but the raised gun omitted for the present.

Ahead :
6—6 inch.

Astern :
4—6 inch.

Broadside : **7—6 inch.**

Machinery : Turbines (see Table for types), with reduction gears.   Designed S.H.P. 90,000 = 33·7 kts.
4 screws.   Boilers : see Table.   Fuel : oil only ; *about* 2000 tons (300,000 gallons).   Radius of action :
10,000 miles at 15 knots, 7200 at 20 kts.

Name.	Built and Engined by	Laid down	Completed	Trials	Turbines.	Boilers	Heating Surface (sq. ft.)
Omaha	Todd Co., Tacoma	6 Dec. '18	Feb. '23	94,290 = 34·87	Westgshs. Parsons	12 Yarrow	} 90600
Milwaukee	,, ,,	13 Dec. '18	June '23	90,060 = 34·64	,,	12 Yarrow	
Cincinnati	,, ,,	15 May '20	Dec. '23	94,290 = 34·44	,,	12 Yarrow	
Raleigh	Bethlehem Co., Quincy	16 Aug. '20	Feb. '24	97,722 = 34·63	Curtis	12 Yarrow	} 90084
Detroit	,, ,,	10 Nov. '20	July '23	97,375 = 34·63	,,	12 Yarrow	
Richmond	Wm. Cramp & Sons	16 Feb. '20	June '23	95,000 = 34·2	Parsons	12 White-F	
Concord	,, ,, ,,	29 Mar. '20	Nov. '23	92,772 = 33·48	,,	12 White-F	
Trenton	,, ,, ,,	18 Aug.'20	April, '24	33·91	,,	12 White-F	} 90840
Marblehead	,, ,, ,,	4 Aug. '20	Sept. '24	95,950 = 34·24	,,	12 White-F	
Memphis	,, ,, ,,	14 Oct. '20	Jan. '25	33·43	,,	12 White-F	

General Notes.—Estimated cost (without guns) in 1916, five to six million dollars each ; revised estimate 1919, 7½ million dollars each.   Reported that in some cases even this has been exceeded by over a million dollars.   Authorised (in order of names as given above) as *Nos.* 4—7 (1916), *Nos.* 8—10 (1916-17) and *Nos.* 11—13 (1916 and 1918).   All were light on trials.

Gunnery Notes.—The original design included eight 6" guns only, disposed in two groups fore and aft so as to allow four guns to bear axially or abeam—an arrangement never before attempted and not likely to be repeated.   The shortcomings of the design were so apparent that the two turrets were fitted subsequently and the armament raised to twelve guns with additional ammunition supply, on an increase in displacement of about 600 tons only.   The " turrets " are splinter-proof gunhouses and offer very limited protection.   There are 6 ammunition hoists, delivery rate 10 r.p.m. each.   3 inch AA. guns elevate up to 90°, and range up to 8200 yards.

Aircraft Notes.—2 Seaplanes stowed between 4th funnel and mainmast.   2 catapults fitted between 4th funnel and mainmast for launching planes, while running with, against or across wind.   These catapults are of a new type in which a charge of powder is substituted for compressed air as a propellant.   It is reported that planes can be thrown off by this means at a speed of 60 miles per hour.

Engineering Notes.   Curtis turbines of *Detroit* and *Raleigh* were modified in 1925 with the object of improving their efficiency.

OMAHA.

RALEIGH.   1929 *Photo, R. Perkins, Esq.*

RICHMOND. (Showing alterations to after battery.)   1931 *Photo, Mr. L. Opdycke.*

MARBLEHEAD. (Showing alterations to after battery.)   1930 *Photo, Mr. L. Opdycke.*

MEMPHIS.   1928 *Photo.*

184 ABBOT 1	131 BUCHANAN ... 3	215 DU PONT 2	183 HARADEN 12	63 LAUB 5	343 NOA 11	159 SCHENCK 6	212 THOMPSON, SMITH 2
211 ALDEN 2	222 BULMER 2	84 DYER 7	91 HARDING 10	250 LAWRENCE ... 6	177 O'BANNON ... 10	103 SCHLEY 10	270 THORNTON ... 5
258 AULICK 4	166 BUSH 7	219 EDSALL....... 2	231 HATFIELD 6	118 LEA 2	239 OVERTON 6	189 SEMMES 1	135 TILLMAN...... 13
128 BABBITT 6	69 CALDWELL ... 8	265 EDWARDS 5	107 HAZELWOOD .. 10	158 LEARY 6	161 PALMER 7	268 SHUBRICK..... 5	272 TINGEY....... 5
126 BADGER 6	104 CHAMPLIN 10	216 EDWARDS, JOHN D. ... 2	160 HERBERT 6	336 LITCHFIELD .. 8	218 PARROTT 2	346 SICARD 3	214 TRACY 2
185 BAGLEY 1	206 CHANDLER . 2	146 ELLIOT 2	178 HOGAN 10	79 LITTLE 7	238 PAULDING, JAMES K. .. 6	81 SIGOURNEY ... 7	339 TREVER 8
269 BAILEY 5	106 CHEW 10	154 ELLIS 2	181 HOPEWELL ... 1	209 LONG 2	226 PEARY 2	221 SIMPSON 2	229 TRUXTUN 2
246 BAINBRIDGE .. 6	241 CHILDS 6	78 EVANS 3	249 HOPKINS 6	175 MACKENZIE ... 10	340 PERRY 8	275 SINCLAIR 5	259 TURNER 4
267 BALLARD 5	140 CLAXTON 8	93 FAIRFAX 8	208 HOVEY 2	220 MACLEISH 2	76 PHILIP 3	207 SOUTHARD 2	127 TWIGGS....... 6
256 BANCROFT 4	186 CLEMSON 1	169 FOOTE........ 7	179 HOWARD 10	168 MADDOX 7	227 PILLSBURY .. 2	180 STANSBURY ... 10	144 UPSHUR 2
213 BARKER 2	155 COLE 2	228 FORD, JOHN D. 2	342 HULBERT 11	74 MANLEY 3	225 POPE 2	86 STEVENS 7	163 WALKER 7
149 BARNEY 2	85 COLHOUN 7	234 FOX.......... 6	236 HUMPHREYS .. 6	191 MASON 1	345 PREBLE 3	73 STOCKTON 2	139 WARD 8
248 BARRY 6	72 CONNER 2	260 GILLIS....... 4	255 INGRAM, OSMOND ... 4	253 McCALLA 4	344 PRESTON, WILLIAM B. 11	83 STRINGHAM ... 7	132 WARD, AARON. 3
251 BELKNAP 4	167 COWELL 7	233 GILMER....... 6	245 JAMES, REUBEN 6	252 McCOOK 4	347 PRUITT 3	240 STURTEVANT .. 6	338 WASMUTH ... 8
95 BELL 7	109 CRANE 10	247 GOFF 6	130 JONES, JACOB . 6	223 McCORMICK .. 2	120 RADFORD 1	115 WATERS 2	115 WATERS 2
153 BERNADOU ... 2	70 CRAVEN 11	188 GOLDSBOROUGH 1	230 JONES, PAUL . 2	262 McDERMUT ... 5	113 RATHBURNE... 2	273 SWASEY 5	257 WELLES 4
151 BIDDLE....... 2	164 CROSBY....... 7	266 GREENE 5	170 KALK 7	237 McFARLAND .. 6	176 RENSHAW..... 10	114 TALBOT....... 2	217 WHIPPLE 2
150 BLAKELEY ... 2	134 CROWNINSHIELD 3	145 GREER 2	235 KANE 6	90 McKEAN 10	89 RINGGOLD ... 10	156 TALBOTT, J. FRED 2	75 WICKES 2
136 BOGGS........ 8	187 DAHLGREN ... 1	82 GREGORY 7	138 KENNISON 8	87 McKEE 10	88 ROBINSON ... 10	142 TARBELL 2	108 WILLIAMS..... 10
215 BORIE 2	199 DALLAS....... 1	92 GRIDLEY 10	137 KILTY 8	264 McLANAHAN .. 5	254 RODGERS 4	125 TATTNALL ... 6	244 WILLIAMSON .. 6
197 BRANCH 1	341 DECATUR 8	71 GWIN 12	80 KIMBERLY ... 7	274 MEADE 5	147 ROPER 2	94 TAYLOR 8	143 YARNALL 2
148 BRECKINRIDGE 2	116 DENT 2	133 HALE 3	242 KING......... 6	165 MEREDITH 7	243 SANDS 6	162 THATCHER 7	337 ZANE......... 8
232 BROOKS 6	157 DICKERSON ... 6	141 HAMILTON 8	119 LAMBERTON .. 1	271 MORRIS 5	190 SATTERLEE.... 1	182 THOMAS 1	
210 BROOME 2	117 DORSEY 2			105 MUGFORD 10			

Numerals preceding name are the Official Number which is painted on the bows of each boat.

Number after name = Builder's Name (see list).

Builders :—

1 Newport News S.B. Co.	6 New York S.B. Co.	10 Union Iron Works.
2 Wm. Cramp & Sons.	7 Fore River S.B. Co.	11 Navy Yard, Norfolk.
3 Bath Iron Works.	8 Navy Yard, Mare Island.	12 Seattle Con. and D.D. Co.
4 Bethlehem S.B. Co., Quincy.		13 Navy Yard, Charleston.
5 ,, ,, Squantum.		

Transferred to Coast Guard:
GEORGE F. BADGER.
HERNDON
HUNT
ABEL P. UPSHUR
WELBORN C. WOOD

Employed as Target Ship:
STODDART.

New Construction.

1 Leader. Not yet ordered (October, 1931).

10 Destroyers.

No. (1) Boston, N.Y.; (2) N. York, N.Y.; (3) Bath I. Works; (4) Fore River; (5) Puget Sound, N.Y.; (6–10) Not yet ordered (October, 1931).

Displacement: 1,500 tons. To cost $4,700,000 each.

186 boats by various yards (Flush Deckers—"#186 Series.")

WILLIAMSON and boats Nos. 186—347 series.   *Photo, 5th March, 1921, Gieves, Ltd.*

General Notes.—*Normal* displacement: 1215 tons (1308 *full load*). Dimensions: 310 (*w.l.*), 314 ft. 4 in. (*o.a.*) × 30 ft. 11½ in. × 9 ft. 4 in. *mean* draught, 9 ft. 10 in. *full load.* Armament[*]: **4**—4 inch, 50 cal., **1**—3 inch, 23 cal. AA., **12**—21 inch tubes in 4 triple deck mountings. Oil fuel: 375 tons. Complement, 122. In these boats the after 4 inch gun is on deck-house and the AA. gun is on quarter deck—a modification which will be effected in all other "Flush Deck" destroyers. 16 D.C. carried in some.

[*] **8**—**4 inch** in *Hovey* (208), *Long* (209); **4**—5 inch in *Brooks* (232), *Fox* (234), *Gilmer* (233), *Hatfield* (231), and *Kane* (235). **5**—4 inch In *Semmes* (189).

Designed S.H.P. 26,000—27,000 = 35 kts. Parsons Westinghouse or Curtis turbines. 2 Screws. 4 Normand, Yarrow or White-Forster boilers.

Curtis-engined boats. Oil consumption: 280-290 gallons at 16 kts., over 1000 gallons at full speed. Can get up steam in less than 20 minutes if required, and can manage 5 kts. under exhaust steam only. R.P.M., 181 for 16 kts., 465 for 35 kts.

HOVEY & LONG HAVE TWIN 4 INCH MOUNTS. BROOKS CLASS HAVE 5 INCH GUNS

Nᵒˢ 186 TO 347.

HERBERT, and boats Nos. 75—185 series.   1920 *Photo, by courtesy of Builders.*

STOCKTON (CONNER & GWIN similar).   1919 *Photo.*

Oil fuel supply is about 288—294 tons in earlier boats # 75 series.

3 Allen class.

Note.—*Davis, Shaw* and *Wilkes,* of this class, have been transferred to Coast Guard.

1 *Bath I.W.*: **Allen** (1916). 1071 tons (1185 *full load*). Designed H.P. 17,500 = 30 kts. Parsons geared (cruising on port shaft only) turbines. Machinery weighs 320 tons. Boilers: 4 Normand—22,500 sq. ft. heating surface. Trials: 30.29 kts.

2 *Fore River*: **Rowan** (1916), **Sampson** (1916). 1111 tons (1225 *full load*). Designed H.P. 17,000 = 29.5 kts. Curtis geared (cruising on both shafts) turbines. Machinery averages 385 tons. Boilers: 4 Yarrow—21,500 sq.ft. heating surface. Trials: *Rowan*, 29.57 kts.; *Sampson*, 29.52 kts.

General Notes.—Dimensions: 310 (*w.l.*) × 29⅝ × 9½ to 9½ feet *mean* draught. *Full load* draught of first one: 9 ft. 9 in. Others, 10 ft. 9 in. Armament: 4—4 inch (50 cal.), 1—3 inch anti-aircraft, 12—21 inch deck tubes in 4 triple deck mountings. Designed H.P. 17,000 = 29.5 kts. Oil fuel: 290 tons (estimated). Complement: 122/136 war. Authorised 1914 as " Nos. 63—68."

SAMPSON.

1919 Photo, O. W. Waterman.

1 Wadsworth Class.

Note.—Remaining boats of this class (*Conyngham, Porter, Wainwright, Tucker*) have been transferred to Coast Guard.

1919 Copyright Photo, O. W. Waterman.

1 *Bath I.W.*: **Wadsworth** (1915). 1060 tons (1174 *full load*). Designed H.P. 17,000 = 29½ kts. Parsons geared turbines. Machinery weighs 323 tons. Boilers: 4 Normand—21,500 sq. ft. heating surface. Oil: 310 tons. Trials: 30.67 kts.

General Notes.—Dimensions: 310 (*w.l.*) × 29⅝ × 9⅛ to 9⅝ feet (*mean* draught). *Full load* draught 10 feet to 10 feet 8¼ inches. Armament: 4—4 inch (50 cal.), 1—3 inch AA., 8—21 inch tubes in 4 twin-deck mountings. Designed H.P. 17,000 = 29.5 kts. Unofficial endurance figures: 5640 miles at 14 kts. Complement: 106-109 (132 war). Authorised 1913 as " Nos. 57—62," *Jacob Jones* (*No.* 61) being a War Loss.

4 Cushing Class.

Note.—*Ericsson* and *McDougal* of this class, transferred to Coast Guard.

NICHOLSON.

1919 Copyright Photo, O. W. Waterman.

1 *Fore River*: **Cushing** (1915). 1050 tons (1171 *full load*). Curtis (geared cruising) turbines. Machinery: weighs 360 tons. Boilers: 4 Bureau Modified Yarrow—21,500 sq.feet heating surface. Trials: 29.18 kts.

3 *Cramp*: **Nicholson** (1914), **O'Brien*** (1914), **Winslow** (1915). 1050 tons (1171 *full load*). 2 Cramp-Zoelly turbines with 2 reciprocating. Machinery weighs 351 tons. Boilers: 4 White-Forster—21,600 sq. feet heating surface. Trials: *Nicholson* 29.08 kts., *O'Brien* 29.16 kts., *Winslow* 29.05 kts.

General Notes.—Dimensions are about 300 (*w.l.*) × 30½ × 9 feet 4 inches to 9 feet 9 inches (*mean*). *Full load* draught: 9 feet 8 inches to 10 feet 9 inches. Armament: 4—4 inch (50 cal.), 1—3 inch AA., 8—21 inch tubes in 4 twin-deck mountings. Designed H.P. 16,000 = 29 kts. Oil fuel: 305 to 311 tons. Complement: 104-106 (war 132). Built to guaranteed radius at 15 kts. Authorised 1912 as " Nos. 51—56."

* Has very low mainmast.

(Continued on next page.)

5 Aylwin Class.

(Unofficially known as "Thousand Tonners.")

Note.—Cassin, Cummings and *Downes,* of this class, transferred to Coast Guard or stricken.

DUNCAN.   1919 *Copyright photo, O. W. Waterman.*

BENHAM (*Aylwin* class).   1920 *Photo.*
Aircraft view showing disposition of guns and T.T.   Note stump mainmast.

8 Drayton Class.

Note.—Jouett, Trippe, Paulding, Ammen, Burrows McCall, Beale, Patterson, Henley, Fanning, Monaghan, Roe, Terry,
of this class, transferred to Coast Guard.

All 742 tons (883/893 *full load*).   Dimensions : 289 (*w.l.*) × 26¼ × 8¼ feet (*mean*).   Armament : § 5—3 inch, 50 cal. ;
6—18 inch tubes (in pairs).   Designed H.P.12,000 = 29½ kts.   *Full load* draught, from 9 ft. 5 in. to 10ft. 1in.
Complement 86, war 107.   Authorised 1908 (10 boats), 1909 (5 boats), 1910 (6 boats), as " Nos. 22—42."

§ This is authorised battery, but guns are not on board at present.   *Sterett, Warrington,* have only 4—3 inch, 50 cal.

1919 *Photo.*

2 *Bath I.W.* : **Drayton** (1910), **Jenkins** (1912).   Machinery : Parsons turbines.   Weight of machinery : 263 tons.
Boilers : 4 Normand.   Oil fuel : *Drayton,* 227 tons ; *Jenkins,* 222 tons.   Trials : *Drayton,* 30.83   *Jenkins,* 31.27 kts.

DRAYTON.

Note.—Sterett, Warrington, 4—3 inch only.   In a few boats TT. are between second and third funnels.

(*Continued on next page.*)

---

4 *Cramp* : **Aylwin, Balch, Benham, Parker** (1913).   1036 tons (1156 *full load*).   Cramp-Zoelly turbines
and reciprocating engines.   Machinery : 347 tons.   Boilers : 4 White-Forster—21,600 sq. feet heating surface.
Oil fuel : *Aylwin,* 307 tons ; *Balch,* 306 tons ; *Benham,* 311 tons ; *Parker,* 317 tons.   Trials : *Aylwin* 29·6,
Balch 29·62, *Benham* 29·59, *Parker* 29·55 kts.

1 *Fore River* : **Duncan** (1913).   1014 tons (1133 *full load*).   Curtis turbines and reciprocating engines.   Weight :
348 tons.   Boilers : 4 Yarrow—21,500 sq. feet heating surface.   Oil fuel : 308 tons.   Trials : 29·14 kts.

Note.— Dimensions *about* 300 (*w.l.*) × 30¼ × 9¼ to 9¾ (*mean*).   *Full load* draught 10¼ to 10¾ feet.   *Designed* H.P.:
16,000 = 29 kts.   Armament : 4—4 in. (50 cal.).   1—3 in. AA., 8—18 in. tubes in four twin-mountings.   Complement
122, War 134.   Built to specified radius at 15 kts.   Reciprocating engines not used over 15 kts.   Very economical
steamers.   Authorised 1911 as " Nos. 43—50."

(General details given on preceding page.)   **8 Drayton class**—*continued.*

14 Light Mine Layers—DM.
(ex-Flush Deck Destroyers of " # 75 Series.")

1924 Official Photo.

1 *New York S. B. Co.* **Jarvis** (1912). Parsons turbines.* 3 screws. Machinery: 296 tons. Boilers: 4 Thornycroft. Oil fuel: 223 tons. Trials: 30.01 kts.

*Geared cruising

MAHAN.   *1921 Photo.*

PERKINS (*Walke* and *Sterett* similar).   *1920 Photo.*

3 *Fore River*: **Perkins** (1910), **Sterett** (1910), **Walke** (1910). Curtis turbines (300 tons). 2 screws. Boilers: 4 Yarrow. Oil fuel: *Walke*, 238 tons: others, 230 tons. Trials: *Perkins*, 29.76; *Sterett*, 30.37; *Walke*, 29.78 kts.

LANSDALE.   *1921 Photo.*

5 *Fore River*: **Israel, Lansdale, Luce** (ex-*Schley*), **Murray, Stribling.**
5 *Union I. W.*: **Anthony, Hart, Ingraham, Rizal, Sproston.**
4 *Newport News B Co.*: **Ramsey, Gamble, Breeze, Montgomery.**
Displacements: 1191 tons *normal* (1284 *full load*).   Dimensions: 310 (*w.l.*), 314 ft. 4 in. (*o.a.*) × 30 ft. 11¼ in. × 9 ft. 2 in. (*mean* draught), 9 ft. 10 in. (*full load* draught aft).
Guns: 4—4 inch, 50 cal., 1—3 inch, 23 cal. AA.
Torpedo tubes: Removed on conversion.
Mines carried: Unofficially reported to carry 80 Mark IV mines, for which magazines, deck rails and chutes have been fitted.
Machinery (*about* 486 tons): Curtis geared turbines. 4 Yarrow boilers—27,540 sq. ft. heating surface. 2 screws. Designed S.H.P. 27,000 = 35 kts. (only *Lansdale* and *Mahan* made this *on trials*). Fuel: 283 tons oil. Complement, 128.
Notes.—Flush Deck Destroyers converted 1920-21. *Israel* has submarine bell.   *Rizal* built at expense of Philippine Government, and manned by Filipino crew.

```
No photo.
Have three funnels like Perkins.
```

MAYRANT, WARRINGTON.

2 *Cramp*: **Mayrant** (1910), **Warrington** (1910). *Mayrant* re-engined 1916-17 with Westinghouse turbines and mechanical reduction gear (284 tons). *Warrington* has Cramp-Zoelly turbines. 2 screws. Weight of machinery: 283 tons. Boilers: 4 White-Forster. Oil fuel: 236 tons. Trials: *Mayrant*, 30.22; *Warrington*, 30.12 kts.

81 (+ *3 bldg.* + *4 authorised*) **Submarines.**

Fleet Submarines—Cruiser Type (SC).

DOLPHIN (ex. *V.7*) Portsmouth N.Y. Laid down 1930.
CACHELOT (ex. *V.8*) Portsmouth N.Y. Laid down 1931.
CUTTLEFISH (ex. *V.9*) Electric Boat Co. Laid down 1931.

    Displacement : 1,560 /2,215 tons.   Dimensions : 319 × 28 × 14 feet.

    H.P. ? . Speed : 18 kts. *surface.*

    Armament : **1**—4 inch gun ;

    6—21 inch tubes.

    V.10 design not yet settled nor appropriation made.

1929 Official Photo.

Narwhal (ex. *V.5*.) (1929), **Nautilus** (ex. *V.6*) (1929). Laid down at Portsmouth and Mare Island Navy Yards, respectively, May 10th and August 2nd, 1927. Machinery for both vessels built at New York Navy Yard. Displacement : 2760/3960 tons. Dimensions : 371 × 33½ × 16 feet. Armament : 2—6 inch, 6—21 inch tubes. Diesels of 5447 S.H.P. Speed 17/8·5 kts. Complement, 88. Estimated cost : Hull and machinery, $5,350,000 ; armament, $1,020,000. Authorised 1916 as Nos. 167—168. Completed in 1930.

Fleet Submarines—Minelaying Type (SM).

V 4.

1928 Official Photo.

V 4.

1929 Official Photo.

Argonaut (ex *V*.4) (Portsmouth Navy Yard, Nov. 10th, 1927). Machinery by Brooklyn Navy Yd. Displacement : 2660/4080 tons. Dimensions : 381 × 33½ × 15½ feet. Armament : 2—6 inch gun, 4—21 inch tubes, 60 mines. Diesels of 3175 S.H.P. Speed 14·6/·8 kts. Complement, 86. Is an improved edition of *V*1 type in other respects. Estimated cost : Hull and machinery, $5,300,000 ; armament, etc., $850,000. Authorised 1916, as *No.* 166, and completed April, 1928.

Fleet Submarines—First Line (SF).

BASS.

1930 *Photo.*

BARRACUDA.

1925 *Official Photo.*

3 *Bureau Design* : **Barracuda** (ex. *V*.1) (July 17th, 1924), **Bass** (ex. *V*.2) (Dec. 27th, 1924), **Bonita** (ex. *V*.3) (June 9th, 1925). Authorised 1916-18 as *Nos. 163—165*, ordered March, 1920, and laid down at Portsmouth Navy Yard, Oct.-Nov., 1921. Dimensions : 300 (*w.l.*), 341½ (*o.a.*) × 27½ × 15½ feet. Guns : 1—5 inch (51 cal., HA. mount), 2 Lewis. Tubes (21 inch) : 6 (4 bow, 2 stern). 16 torpedoes carried. Engines : 2 sets of 2250 B.H.P. Busch-Sulzer for main drive and 2—1000 B.H.P auxiliary Diesel forward driving generators supplying current to electric motors ; these latter and smaller engines can be used for surface cruising with electric drive. Cruising radius believed to be 12,000 miles. This type is said to be capable of crossing the Atlantic and returning without refuelling or otherwise receiving attention. Authorised 1916-18 as *Nos. 163—165*. Understood that a small seaplane of special design is included in equipment of this class, being carried abaft C.T. Completed : *V* 1, Oct., 1924 ; *V* 2, Sept., 1925 ; *V* 3, May, 1926.

Fleet Submarines—First Line (SF).

Note on S Class.—An official report in 1925 stated that " experience in manœuvres indicates that these vessels cannot be considered as a satisfactory type of fleet submarines."

S50.

Photo, 1923.

1 *Bureau* design : **S48** (1921). By Lake T. B. Co. Dimensions : 240 × 21⅚ × 13½ feet. Guns : 1—4 inch, 50 cal. Tubes : 5—21 inch (4 bow, 1 stern). 14 torpedoes carried. Engines : 2 sets of 900 B.H.P. Busch-Sulzer except *S 48*, 2 sets M.A.N. (N.Y.) 4 cycle 6 cyl. = total B.H.P. 2000. Motors : 2 sets each 750 h.p. Speed 14·5/11 kts. Crash dive in 60 secs. *Max.* dive limit : 200 feet. Divided into 6 watertight compartments. Double hull amidships, single hull at ends. 3 periscopes. Oil : 23,411 gallons *normal*, 44,305 *max*. Rad : 8,000 at 10 kts. Authorised 1916. Compl : 38.

Note.—*S 48* is stated to have been re-engined in 1929 with two new motors of 1000 H.P. each, oil storage being increased at same time.

S 45.

1926 *Official Photo.*

6 *Electric Boat Co.* design : **S 42—S 47** (1923-24). All contracted for by Electric Boat Co. and built by Bethlehem S. B. Co., Quincy. Authorised 1916-18, as *Nos. 153—158*. Dimensions : 225½ × 20⅞ × 16 feet = 906/1126 tons. Guns : 1—4 inch, 50 cal. Tubes : 4—21 inch. 12 Torpedoes carried. Engines : Two sets 600 B.H.P., 8 cylinder, 4 cycle Nelseco. Motors : 2 sets each 750 H.P. Elect. Dy. Co. Speed 14.5/11 kts. Oil : 11,463—46,363 gallons. Compl : 38.

25 *Electric Boat Co.* design : **S 1** (1918), **S18—41** (1918-22), viz., *S 1* by Fore River S. B. Co., *S 18—S 29* by Bethlehem S.B. Co., Quincy *S 30*—S 41* by Bethlehem S. B. Co., San Francisco. Dimensions : 219½ × 20⅞ × 16 feet. Machinery : 2 sets of 600 B.H.P. Nelseco Diesel engines. Motors : 2 sets 750 H.P. Ridgeway or Electric Dynamic Co. (*S 1*). Oil : 11,511/41,921 gallons. Have large radius of action *on surface.* Armament : 1—4 inch gun and 4—21 inch bow tubes (**12** torpedoes carried). Authorised : *S 1* (1916, as No. 105), *S 18—21* (1916-17 as *Nos. 123—126*), *S 22—41* (1916-17, as *Nos. 127—146*). *S 1* experimentally fitted, 1923, to carry a small seaplane in a cylindrical tank abaft C.T.

General Note to all " S " boats.—Special attention given to constructional strength against depth charge attack. *S 37* was immersed to a depth of 208 feet for 65 minutes without inconvenience. *S 1—4, S 6—8, S 14—35*, all have Cutler-Hammer system of electric control. *S 9—13, S 36—51*, all fitted with Westinghouse or G. E. Co. pneumatic controllers, considered to be a decided improvement.

**Note.*—*S 30* built at expense of Philippines Government. *S 19* reached 33 fathoms during diving trials, Dec., 1925.

Submarines—First Line (SS).

S 14.

R 3—R 10.

1920 *Photo.*

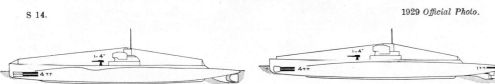

1929 *Official Photo.*

10 *" Bureau design "* boats : **S3,** (1918), **S4, S6—S13** (1919-21) ; all by Portsmouth Ny. Yd. Dims : 231 × 21⅝ × 13½ feet. Dispt. 876/1092 tons. Guns : **1**— 4 inch, 50 cal. Tubes : **4**—bow, 21 inch (**12** torpedoes carried). *S* 10—*S*13, **5** tubes (**14** torpedoes carried). Engines : *S* 3—9, 2 sets of 4-cycle Nelseco Diesels, each 700 B.H.P. (8 cyl.) *S* 10—13, 2 sets of 4-cycle " Bureau Design " M.A.N. (6 cyl.) type, each 1000 B.H.P. Motors : 2 sets 600 H.P. Westinghouse. Oil : 19,271/36,950 gallons. Speed 15/10·5 kts. Completed 1919-23. *S* 4 sunk by collision with Coast Guard Destroyer, *Paulding*, on December 17, 1927 ; salved and brought in to port March 1928. Is now used as a special vessel for experimental purposes, and has no propulsive machinery at present.

4 *Bureau* design : **S14—S17** (1919—20). All by Lake T.B. Co. Dimensions : 231 × 21⅝ × 13 feet = 876 /1092 tons. Guns : **1**—4 inch, 50 cal. Tubes : **4**—21 inch (**12** torpedoes carried). Engines : 2 sets M.A.N. (N.Y.) 4 cycle 6 cyl. = B.H.P. 2,000. Motors : 2 sets each 600 H.P. Westinghouse. Speed, 14/12.25 kts. Complement, 38. Oil, 19,271/36,950 gallons.

20 *Electric Boat Co. design :* **R 1—R 20** (1917-19), viz., *R 1—R 14* by Fore River S.B. Co., *R 15—R20* by Union I.W., San Francisco. Dims : 186 ×18× 14½ feet. 569/680 tons. **1**—3 inch, 50 cal. gun. **4** torpedo tubes (**8** torpedoes carried). Engines : 2 sets of 440 B.H.P. (400 r.p.m.) 6-cyl. 4-cycle Nelseco Diesel. Fuel : 7691/18,880 gallons. Motors : 2—467 H.P. Electric Dynamic Co., with Cutler-Hammer Co. magnetic controllers. Batteries : Electric Storage Co. Type 31-WLL. Authorised 1916 as Nos. 78—97. Completed 1918-19.

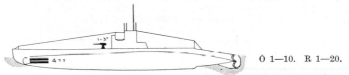

O 1—10. R 1—20.

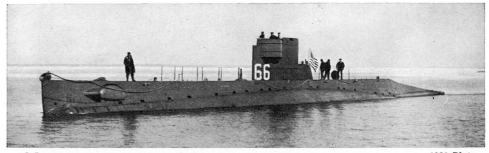

O 5.

1920 *Photo.*

9 *Electric Boat Co. design :* **O 1—O 4** and **O 6—O 10** (1917-18), viz., *O 1* by Portsmouth N.Y. ; *O 2* by Puget Sound Navy Yard ; *O 3, O 4* and *O 6—O 10* by Fore River Co. Dims. : 172½ × 18 × 14½ft. 520/623 tons. **1**—3 inch, 23 cal. AA. gun. **4** torpedo tubes (**8** torpedoes). Engines : 2 sets of 440 B.H.P. (400 r.p.m.) 6-cyl. 4-cycle Nelseco Diesel engines. 14·5/11 kts. 10,089/21,897 gallons. Motors : 2—370 H.P. in *O 1, O 2,* by New York Navy Yard ; in others, by Electric Dynamic Co., all with Cutler-Hammer Co. magnetic controller. Gould storage batteries, Type 29-WLL in *O 1* and *O 2.* Electric Storage Co., Type 49-WL in others. Electric batteries weigh 65 tons. Radius of action : 3500-3000 miles, at 11 kts. *on surface.* Authorised 1915, as Nos. 62—71. Completed 1918.

Note.—*O 5* wrecked, Oct. 28, 1923, and not considered worth repair after salvage.

Patrol Vessels—Eagles (PE).

EAGLE 17.   1919 *Photo, by courtesy of the Ford Motor Co., Detroit.*

Nos. 6 to 60.

53 "EAGLE BOATS" :—

Missing Numbers :—Transferred to Coast Guard : *16, 20, 21, 30.* Wrecked, *17, 25.* Sold, *31.*
Stricken—Nos: 1. to *9. 13. 14. 18. 23. 24. 28. 29. 33. 37. 40. 41. 42. 43. 45. 46. 49. 50. 53. 54.*
Nos. 6—12 launched 1918. *Nos. 14—60,* 1919.
Displacement, *normal* 500 tons, *full load* 615 tons. Complement, 61.
Dimensions : Length, 200 feet (*p.p.* and *o.a.*). Beam, 25½ feet. *Mean* draught, 7¼ feet ; *full load,* 8½ feet.
Armament : **2**—4 inch (50 cal.), **1**—3 inch AA., **2** M.G. Carry **12** depth charges.
Machinery : Poole geared turbine. 2 Bureau Express boilers. 1 screw. Designed H.P. 2500 = 18 kts. Fuel : 105 tons coal + 45 tons oil. Endurance : 3500 miles at 10 kts.
Notes.—Assembled by Ford Eagle Boat Plant, River Rouge ; machinery and fittings by Ford Plant, Highland Park, Detroit. Majority now assigned to Naval Districts and Ports ; to Naval Academy ; or for duty with U.S.N.R.F.

Patrol Vessels—Submarine Chasers (PC).

SC. 200.   1919 *Photo.*

24—110 ft. boats :—Numbered between **SC. 57** and **SC. 440.** Built 1917-19 by various Navy Yards and private contractors.
Displacement, 77 tons *normal,* 85 tons *full load.* Wooden hulls. Length, 105 feet (*p.p.*), 110 feet (*o.a.*). Beam, 14 feet 9 ins. *Mean* hull draught, 5 feet 6 ins., *full load* aft, 5 feet 8 ins. Machinery : three sets of 220 B.H.P. Standard petrol motors = 17 kts. 2400 gallons petrol = 900 miles at 10 kts. Complement, 26. Have small radius W/T.
Armaments : Majority have **1**—3 inch (23 cal.), and **2** Colt M.G. Carry depth charges.
Notes.—Quick rollers with period of about 5 secs.

C. M. B.

55 FT. C.M.B.   1922 *Photo by courtesy of Messrs. Thornycroft.*

1—55 ft. *type* (1922). **2** Thornycroft Y12 motors of 350 B.H.P. = 38 kts. Armament : **2** Lewis guns, **2**—18 inch torpedoes, **2** D.C. Complement, 5.

No name or number assigned. Built for U.S.N. by Thornycrofts for experimental purposes. Is similar to British models, *q.v.*

Patrol Vessels—Gunboats (PG).

TULSA.   1925 *Photo, by courtesy of the Navy Dept.*

TULSA (Charleston, N.Y., 25th August, 1922). **ASHEVILLE** (Charleston, N.Y., July, 1918). *Normal* displacement, 1575 tons (*full load*, 1760 tons). Complement, 185. Length (*p.p.*) 225 feet, (*o.a.*) 241⅛ feet. Beam, 41¼ feet. *Mean* draught, 11⅓ feet. Guns: **3**—4 inch, 50 cal., **2**—3 pdr., **3**—1 pdr. Machinery: Parsons turbine with reduction gear. 1 screw. Boilers: 3 Bureau (modified Thornycroft). Designed H.P. 800 = 12 kts. Fuel, 180 tons coal + 440 tons oil.

1919 *Photo.*

SACRAMENTO (Feb., 1914). *Normal* displacement, 1425 tons. Complement, 153. Length (*waterline*), 210 feet. Beam, 40⅝ feet. *Mean* draught, 11¼ feet. Guns: **3**—4 inch, 50 cal.; **2**—3 pdr.; **2**—1 pdr. Machinery: 1 set triple expansion. Boilers: 2 Babcock. H.P. (on trials), 1022 = 12·78 kts. Coal: *maximum*, 428 tons. Built by Cramps. Completed, 1914.

Patrol Vessels—Gunboats (PG)—*continued.*

(Height of funnel reduced by about one-third, 1923.)   1920 *Official Photo.*

(*Asiatic Fleet.*)

HELENA (1896). Displacement: 1392 tons. Complement, 193 to 196. Length (*waterline*), 250¾ feet. Beam, 39⅔ feet. *Mean* draught, 9 feet. Guns: **8**—4 inch, 40 cal.; **4**—3 pdr. Machinery: 2 sets vertical triple expansion. 2 screws. H.P. (*trials*) 1988 = 15·5 kts. Coal: *maximum*, 307 tons. *Nominal* radius 2200 miles at 10 kts.

Note.—*Wilmington*, sister to *Helena*, is still retained in service for training purposes under heading "Unclassified."

Patrol Vessels—River Gunboats (PR).

GUAM.   1928 *Official Photo.*

GUAM, TUTUILA. Displacement: 350 tons *standard*. *Mean* draught (fresh water), 5¼ feet. Freeboard at side (main deck): Forward, 6 ft. 3 in.; amidships, 3 ft. 5 in.; aft, 4 ft. 2 in. Triple expansion engines, $\dfrac{12 \times 18 \times 29}{16}$, revs. 320. H.P. 1950 = 14.5 kts. Guns: **2**—3 inch, 23 cal., behind shields, **10**—30 cal.

Patrol Vessels—River Gunboats (PR)—*continued.*

PANAY.   1929 *Official Photo.*

OAHU, PANAY. Displacement: 385 tons *standard*. *Mean* draught (fresh water), 5½ feet. Freeboard at side (main deck): Forward, 7 ft. 9½ in.; amidships, 3 ft. 9½ in.; aft, 4 ft. 6 in. Triple expansion engines, $\dfrac{13\frac{1}{2} \times 22 \times 34}{16}$, revs. 320. H.P. 2250 = 15 kts. (Trials, 17.73 kts). Guns: **2**—3 inch, 50 cal. AA., **10**—30 cal.

LUZON.   1929 *Official Photo.*

LUZON, MINDANAO. Displacement: 500 tons *standard*. *Mean* draught (fresh water), 6 feet. Freeboard at side (main deck): Forward, 10 ft. 7 in.; amidships, 5 ft. 7 in.; aft, 5 ft. 10 in. Triple expansion engines, $\dfrac{15 \times 23 \times 36\frac{1}{4}}{18}$, revs. 320. H.P. 3150 = 16 kts. Guns: **2**—3 inch, 50 cal. AA., **10**—30 cal.

The following characteristics are common to all six :—2 Thornycroft oil-burning boilers, 250 lbs. working pressure. 2 screws. Lengths of each pair are 150, 180 and 198 feet respectively.

Above 6 gunboats authorised 1924 as *PG 43—48*, and laid down 1926 by Kiangnan Dock and Engineering Works Shanghai. Completed, 1927-28.

(*Continued on next page.*)

Patrol Vessels—River Gunboats (PR)—*continued.*

MONOCACY   1927 *Photo.*

(Asiatic Fleet.)

MONOCACY (1914), **PALOS** (1914). 190 tons. Complement, 46. Guns: 2—3 inch 23 cal., 7—30 cal. Machinery: 2 sets vertical compound. Boilers: 2 Babcock. Designed H.P. 800 = 13¼ kts. Coal: 34 tons. Built at Mare Island Navy Yard and re-erected by Shanghai Dock and Engineering Co.

Patrol Vessels—Yachts (PY).

Note.—Down to and including *Niagara*, all purchased during World War. Remaining 3 purchased during war with Spain, 1898.

ISABEL.   1927 *Photo.*

ISABEL (Bath I.W., 1917, taken over 1917). 938 tons*. Dimensions: 230 (*w.l.*) × 26¼ × 10¼ feet. Guns: 2—3 inch, 50 cal., 2—3 inch, 23 cal. AA. S.H.P. 8400 = 26 kts. Parsons turbine and 2 Normand boilers. Fuel: 216½ tons oil. Complement, 112.

Note.—Was fitted and classed as a Destroyer during the World War.

* Full load.

Patrol Vessels—Yachts (PY)—*continued.*

NOKOMIS.   1925 *Photo, by courtesy of the Navy Dept.*
(On Surveying Service.)

NOKOMIS (ex-*Nokomis II*, 1917, taken over 1917). 1265 tons. Dimensions: 203 × 31⅚ × 13⅔ feet. Guns: 2—3 inch, 30 cal., 4—6 pdr. Boilers: 2 Babcock. I.H.P. 2000 = 16 kts. Coal: 350 tons = 1517 miles at 14.7 kts. Complement, 87.

1924 *Official Photo.*

ARAMIS (1916, taken over 1917). Motor Yacht of 375 tons. Dimensions: 153½ × 22⅓ × 7½ feet. Guns: *Nil.* S.H.P. 700 = 13 kts. Craig 4-cycle 6-cyl. Diesel engines. Fuel: 7500 gallons = 3750 miles at 9 kts. Complement, 53.
(Transferred to "District Craft Unclassified," 8th Sept., 1924.)

Photo, by courtesy of Rear-Admiral Twining, U.S.N.
(On Surveying Service.)

NIAGARA (1898, taken over 1917). 2600 tons. Dimensions: 245 × 36 × 17 feet. Guns: 4—4 inch, 50 cal., 2—3 pdr. Boilers: 3 Babcock. I.H.P. 1800 = 13 kts. Coal: 400 tons = 3500 miles at 12 kts. Complement, 185.

General Note to this and following pages.—Armaments of U.S. Tenders and Auxiliaries as given below are those authorised, but in a great many cases these are not actually carried under peace conditions.

Destroyer Tenders (AD).

DOBBIN.   1925 *Official Photo, U.S. Navy Dept.*

WHITNEY (Boston N.Yd., Oct. 12th, 1923), **DOBBIN** (Philadelphia N.Yd., May 5th, 1921). *12,450 tons. Dimensions: 460 (*p.p.*), 483⅝ (*o.a.*) × 61 × 24⅛ feet (*mean* draught). Guns: 8—5 inch, 4—3 inch AA., 2—6 pdr. Torpedo tubes, for testing purposes: 2—21 inch. Parsons geared turbines. Boilers: 2 Bureau Modified Thornycroft. 1 screw. Designed S.H.P. 7000 = 16 kts. Oil: 1107 tons. Complement, 452. Equipped to serve as Depot, Repair and Hospital Ship for 18 Destroyers. To have special anti-torpedo protection. Generally sister ships to *Holland*, Tender to Submarines. Both fitted as flagships.

* Full load.

ALTAIR.   1927 *Official Photo.*

ALTAIR (1919), **DENEBOLA** (1919), **RIGEL** (1918). 13,925 tons. Dimensions: 423¾ × 54 × 20 feet. Guns: 4—5 inch, 51 cal., 4—3 inch AA., 2—6 pdr. Curtis geared turbines. Boilers: 3 single-ended. S.H.P. 2500 = 10.5 kts. Oil: 1097 tons. Complement, 481 (*Rigel*, 531). All three built by Skinner & Eddy Corporation, Seattle.

Destroyer Tenders (AD)—*continued.*

1919 *Photo, C. E. Waterman.*

(*Battle Fleet.*)

MELVILLE (1915). 7150 tons. Complement, 473. Dimensions: 400 (*p.p.*) × 54⅓ × 20 feet (*mean* draught). Guns: 8—5 inch (51 cal.), 1—3 inch AA., 2—3 pdr. Torpedo tubes: 1—18 inch. Machinery: Parsons geared turbines. 2 Thornycroft boilers. H.P. (estimated) 4006 = 15.09 kts. Fuel: 930 tons *oil*

1920 *Photo.*

(*Asiatic Fleet.*)

BLACK HAWK (Cramp, 1913, ex-Grace Steamship Co. S.S. *Santa Catalina*, taken over 1917). 8,900 tons. Dimensions: 404½ (*p.p.*) × 53¾ × 19¾ feet. Guns: 4—5 inch, 2—3 pdr., 2—1 pdr. Boilers: 3 single-ended. I.H.P. 3400 = 13 kts. Oil: 2108 tons. Complement, 471.

Destroyer Tenders (AD)—*continued.*

1920 *Photo, Seward, Weymouth.*

(*Scouting Fleet.*)

BRIDGEPORT (Vegesack, Germany, 1901, ex-North German Lloyd S.S. *Breslau*, seized 1917). 11,750 tons. Dimensions: 429¼ (*p.p.*) × 54⅓ × 24⅔ feet. Guns: 8—5 inch, 4—3 inch 50 cal. AA. Boilers: 2 double-ended and 2 single-ended. I.H.P. 3600 = 12.5 kts. Coal: 1060 tons. Complement, 552.

Auxiliaries—Submarine Tenders (AS).

Note.—Obsolete Cruiser *Alton*, ex *Chicago*, Submarine Barracks at Pearl Harbour. Various Minesweepers of "Bird" class serve as Submarine Tenders at New London, Hampton Roads; Coco Solo, and Pearl Harbour.

1926 *Official Photo.*

HOLLAND (Puget Sound N. Yd., 1926. Begun Apl. 11th, 1921, completed 1926). 11,570 tons. Dimensions : 513 (*o.a.*) × 61 (*extreme*) × 22⅔ feet (*mean* draught). Guns : **8**—5 inch, **4**—3 inch AA., **2**—6 pdr. Torpedo tubes : **1**—21 inch, *submerged*. Parsons geared turbines. 1 screw. Boilers : 2 Bureau Modified Thornycroft. Designed S.H.P. 7000 = 16 kts. Oil : 1050 tons. Complement, 398. Generally sister ship to *Whitney* and *Dobbin*, Destroyer Tenders.

1926 *Official Photo.*

CANOPUS (New York S.B. Co., 1919). 8000 tons. Dimensions: 373¾ × 51½ × 21½ feet. Guns : **2**—5 inch, 51 cal., **4**—3 inch AA., **2**—3 pdr. Machinery: Quadruple expansion. 1 screw. Boilers : 4 single-ended. H.P. 3858 = 13 kts. Oil: 1277 tons. Complement, 317.

Auxiliaries—Submarine Tenders (AS)—*continued.*

BUSHNELL. 1919 *U. S. Navy Photo.*
(*Atlantic Fleet.*)

BUSHNELL (Seattle Constrn. and D.D. Co., 1915). 3580 tons. Complement: 217. Dimensions : 350½ × 45⅔ × 15 feet (*mean* draught). Guns : **4**—5 inch (51 cal.). Machinery : Parsons turbines with reduction gear. Boilers : 2 Yarrow. H.P. (*on trials*) 2617 = 14·15 kts. Fuel : 728 tons *oil*.

(*Pacific Fleet.*) 1920 *Photo.*

BEAVER (Newport News, 1910, purchased 1918). 6250 tons. Dimensions : 380 (*o.a.*) × 47 × 22⅔ feet (*max.* draught), Guns : **4** —5 inch, **2**—1 pdr. 1 screw. Boilers : 6 single-ended. I.H.P. 4500 = 16·5 kts. Fuel : 530 tons oil fuel. Complement, 350.

Note.—Has only one funnel now. 1922 *Official Photo.*
(*Atlantic Fleet.*)

CAMDEN (Flensburger S. B. Co., 1900, ex-German-Australian s.s. *Kiel*, seized 1917). 9000 tons (estimated). Dimensions : 403⅔ (*o.a.*) × 48 × 22⅓ feet. Guns : **4**—4 inch, **2**—3 pdr., **2**—1 pdr. Boilers : 4 Babcock. I.H.P. 2550 = 12 kts. Coal : 975 tons. Complement, 378.

Auxiliaries—Submarine Tenders (AS)—*continued.*

(*Atlantic Fleet.*) 1920 *Photo.*

SAVANNAH (Flensburger S. B. Co., 1899, ex-Hamburg-American S.S. *Saxonia*, seized 1917). 8570 tons. Dimensions : 414½ × 46 × 21⅔ feet. Guns : **4**—5 inch, **4**—3 inch AA., **4**—30 cal. Boilers : 4 Babcock. I.H.P. 2000 = 10·5 kts. Coal : 743 tons + 531 tons additional stowage = 1274 tons. Complement, 383.

ARGONNE. 1930 *Photo, Lt.-Com. H. A. Gosnell, U.S.N.*

ARGONNE (Hog Island, 1920). 11,100 tons. Dimensions : 448 × 58 × 24⅔ feet *max.* draught. Guns : **4**—5 inch 51 cal., **4**—3 inch, 50 cal. AA., **2**—6 pdr. Curtis geared turbines. 1 screw. Boilers : 6 Babcock. S.H.P. 6000 = 15 kts. Oil fuel : 1473 tons. Complement, 344.

Aircraft Tenders (AV).

Note.—Minesweepers *Gannet, Pelican, Teal* and *Sandpiper*, have been serving for some time past as Seaplane Tenders.

1924, *Official Photo.*

WRIGHT (ex-Emergency Fleet Corporation Hull *No. 680*, "Type B," launched at Hog Island, April 28th, 1920). Conversion effected by Tietjen & Lang Dry Dock Co., Hoboken, 1920-21. 11,500 tons. Dimensions : 448 (*p.p.* and *o.a.*)×58×27⅝ feet *max.* draught. Guns : 2—5 inch, 51 cal., 2—3 inch, 50 cal. AA., 4—30 cal. Designed S.H.P. 6000 = 15 kts. G.E. Curtis geared turbines and 6 Babcock & Wilcox boilers. Oil: 1629 tons. Complement, 311. Fitted as flagship,

1924 *Official Photo, U. S. Navy.*

PATOKA (1919). For details see *Rapidan* class, p. 491.

Patoka, though classed as an oiler, is fitted with a mooring mast for aircraft and a landing platform for planes. Equipment includes workshops for repair of aircraft and storage for petrol.

JASON (1912). Converted to Aircraft Tender 1930-31. For details (see *Orion*, p. 490).

Mine Layers—Second Line (OCM)—*continued.*

AROOSTOOK.   1920 *Photo.*

(*Atlantic Fleet.*)

OGLALA (Cramps, 1907. Ex-*Shawmut*, ex-S.S. *Massachusetts*, of Eastern Steamship Corpn., purchased 1917 and converted by Boston N.Yd. into Mine Planter). 4950 tons. Dimensions : 395 (*o.a.*) × 52⅙ × 14½ feet (*mean*). Guns : 1—5 inch, 51 cal., 2—3 inch AA., 2—6 pdr., 4—1 pdr. Reciprocating engines and 4 S. E. boilers. 2 screws. H.P. and speed uncertain. Oil: 607 tons. Complement 373.

(*Pacific Fleet.*)

AROOSTOOK (Cramps, 1907. Ex-S.S. *Bunker Hill*, of Eastern Steamship Corpn., purchased 1917 and converted by Boston N.Yd. into Mine Planter). All details as *Oglala* Boilers: 8 S.E. H.P. 7000 = 20 kts. Has been employed as Aircraft Tender. Now out of commission.

Photo, *U. S. Navy.*

(*Atlantic Fleet.*)

YOSEMITE (ex-*San Francisco*) (Union Iron Works) (1889). Displacement, 4683 tons. Complement, 349. Dimensions : 324½ (*o.a.*) × 49½ × 18¾ (*mean*) feet. Armament : 3—5 inch, 2—3 inch AA., 2—6 pdr. Carries 300 Mark II mines. 4 searchlights. H.P. (*trials*) 9761 = 19.5 kts. 8 Babcock boilers. Coal: 663 tons. Fitted as flagship.

Mine Layers—Second Line (OCM)—*continued.*

Photo, *U. S. Navy*

(*Pacific Fleet.*)

BALTIMORE (Cramps 1888). Displacement, 4413 tons. Complement, 351. Dimensions : 335 (*o.a.*) × 48⅔ × 19½ (*mean*) feet. Guns : 4—5 inch, 51 cal., 2—3 inch AA., 4—6 pdr., 2—1 pdr. Armour : 4″ deck. H.P. (*trials*) 8777 = 20 kts. Boilers : 8 Babcock. Coal : 1092 tons. Fitted as flagship.

Auxiliaries—Repair Ships (AR)—*continued.*

PROMETHEUS. 1926 *Photo, Ian Perman, Esq.*

PROMETHEUS (Mare Island N.Yd., 1908). **VESTAL** (New York N. Yd., 1908). 8100 tons, full load. Dimensions: 450 × 60 × 18 feet. Guns: **4**—5 inch, 50 cal., **1**—3 inch AA., **4**—30 cal. Boilers: *Prometheus*, 6 Babcock; *Vestal*, 2 White-Forster. Weight of machinery: *Prometheus*, 1100 tons; *Vestal*, 789 tons. H.P. 7500 = 16 kts. Oil: *Prometheus*, 872 tons; *Vestal*, 1412 tons. Complement, 466.

Auxiliaries—Store Ships (AF).

ARCTIC. 1926 *Official Photo.*

ARCTIC (1919), **BOREAS** (1919), **YUKON** (1920). 12,600 tons. Dimensions: $416\frac{1}{2} \times 53 \times 26\frac{1}{2}$ feet. Guns: **2**—5 inch, 51 cal., **4**—3 inch AA. (not always carried). Parsons geared turbines in *Arctic* and *Yukon*, Curtis in *Boreas*. Designed H.P. 2800 = 11 kts. Boilers: 4 Heine, except *Yukon*, 3 single-ended. Oil: 1794 tons. Complements: 166 (*Y*), 180 (*B*), 211 (*A*).

Auxiliary—Store Ships (AF)—*continued.*

1919 *Photo.*

BRIDGE (Boston N.Yd., May 18th, 1916). 8500 tons. Complement, 212. Dimensions: $423 \times 55\frac{1}{4} \times 20\frac{2}{3}$ feet (*mean* draught). Guns: **4**—5 inch, 50 cal., **1**—3 inch AA., **2**—3 pdr. Boilers: 2 White-Forster. H.P. 4000 = 14 kts. Reciprocating engines. 2 screws. Fuel: 1000 tons *oil.*

RAPPAHANNOCK. 1927 *Official Photo.*

RAPPAHANNOCK (Bremer-Vulkan, Vegesack, Germany, 1913, ex-North German Lloyd S.S. *Pommern*, seized 1917). 15,200 tons. Complement, 291. Dimensions: $471\frac{1}{6} \times 59\frac{1}{6} \times 24\frac{1}{4}$ feet. Guns: **4**—5 inch, 51 cal., **1**—3 inch AA. Boilers: 4 single-ended. I.H.P. 4850 = 11.5 kts. Coal: 3060 tons.

Auxiliaries—Colliers (AC).

NEREUS. *Photo added* 1921.

NEREUS (1913), **PROTEUS** (1912). 19,080 tons. Dimensions: $522 \times 62 \times 27\frac{2}{3}$ (*mean*). 2 screws. Boilers: 3 double-ended. H.P. 7000 = 14·5 kts. Fuel capacity (deadweight to designed draft): 10,500 tons cargo fuel, Bunker capacity, 1,925 tons. *Maximum* cargo capacity (close stowage): 11,800 tons coal + 1125 tons oil *or* 10,100 tons coal + 3050 tons oil. Guns: **4**—4 inch 50 cal. Complement, 181.

Auxiliaries—Colliers (AC)—*continued.*

ORION (1912). 19,250 tons. Dimensions: $536 \times 65 \times 27\frac{2}{3}$ feet (*mean*). 2 screws. Boilers: 3 double-ended. H.P. 6943 = 14 kts. Fuel capacity (deadweight to designed draft): 10,500 tons cargo fuel and 2000 tons own bunker fuel. *Maximum* cargo capacity (close stowage): 11,500 tons coal and 2575 tons oil. Guns: **4**—4 inch. Complement, 181. *Jason* is now an Aircraft Tender.

1919 *Photo, O. W. Waterman.*

NEPTUNE (1911). 19,480 tons. Dimensions: $542 \times 65 \times 27\frac{2}{3}$ (*mean*). 2 screws. Boilers: 3 double-ended. S.H.P. 5400 = 13 kts. Fuel capacity (deadweight to designed draft): 10,500 tons cargo fuel + 2000 tons own bunker fuel. *Maximum* cargo capacity (close stowage): 10,200 tons coal + 2925 tons oil *or* 11,700 tons coal + 1250 tons oil. Guns: **4**—4 inch. Has Westinghouse geared turbines. Complement, 181.

Auxiliaries—Ammunition Ships (AE).

Auxiliaries—Oilers (AO).

TRINITY.   1927 *Official Photo.*

BRAZOS.   1927 *Official Photo.*

PYRO.   1924 *Official Photo.*

NITRO, PYRO (both launched Dec. 16th, 1919, at Puget Sound N.Yd.). 10,600 tons. Dimensions : 460 × 61 × 21 feet. Guns : 4—5 inch, 2—3 inch AA. Boilers : 4 Babcock. S.H.P. 6700 = 13.3 kts. (*N.*), 13.2 kts. (*P.*). Parsons (geared) turbines. 2 screws. Fuel capacity : 1078 tons coal (*Nitro*), 1493 tons oil (*Pyro*). Fitted with plant for powder testing and cooling, also large cold storage capacity for meat, in addition to ammunition-carrying spaces. Complement, 195.

RAPIDAN (1919), **SALINAS** (1920), **TIPPECANOE** (1920), **RAMAPO** (1919), **SAPELO** (1919), **SEPULGA** (1920), **TRINITY** (1920). 16,800 tons. Dimensions : 463¼ (*p.p.*) × 60 × 26¼ feet (*mean* draught). Quad. Exp. reciprocating engines.† 3 S. E. boilers. I.H.P. 2900 = 10·5 kts. Guns : 2—5 inch, 51 cal., 2—3 inch AA. *Max.* cargo capacity : 11,145 tons oil fuel. Own fuel : 1109 tons oil. Complement, 107 (*Patoka* 156).

†Curtis turbine in *Trinity* and *Tippecanoe.*

BRAZOS (1919), **NECHES** (1920), **PECOS** (1921), all three by Boston N. Yd. 14,800 tons. Dimensions : 475⅔ (*o a.*) × 56 × 26⅔ feet *mean.* Recipro. engines. 4 B. & W. boilers in *Brazos*, 4 Ward in each of others. 2 screws. I.H.P. 6000 = 14 kts. Cargo capacity, 8050 tons. Own fuel, 828 tons. Guns : 4—5 inch, 51 cal., 2—3 inch. Complements : 136 (*B.*), 117 (*N.*), 156 (*P.*).

KANAWHA (& MAUMEE).   1919 *Photo, O. W. Waterman.*

CUYAMA (1916), **MAUMEE** (1915), **KANAWHA** (1914). 14,500 tons. Dimensions : 475½ × 56 × 26⅛ (*mean*). *Cuyama* and *Kanawha* reciprocating engines, 5590 H.P. *Maumee* 2-cycle Diesel motors 5000 H.P. Boilers : 2 Babcock in *Maumee*, 4 Babcock in each of others. Speed : 14 kts. 2 screws. Fuel capacity : 8050 tons cargo oil ; 824 tons own bunker oil. Guns : *Cuyama* 4—5 inch ; *Maumee*, *Kanawha* 4—4 inch. Complements : 136 (*C.* and *K.*) 146 (*M.*).

Auxiliaries—Repair Ships—(AR).

1925 *Photo, W. W. Stewart, Esq.*
(*Pacific Fleet.*)

MEDUSA (Puget Sound N.Yd., April 16th, 1923). 10,620 tons. Dimensions : 460 × 70 × 20 feet. Guns : 4—5 inch, 51 cal., 2—3 inch AA., 2—6 pdr., 4—30 cal. Parsons geared turbines. Designed S.H.P. 7000 = 16 kts. 2 Bureau Modified Thornycroft boilers. Oil : 1834 tons. Complement, 466 (including an exceptionally full technical staff).

Note.—The *Medusa* was specially designed with a view to the execution of permanent as well as temporary repairs. She carries two 8 ton derricks, besides one 20 ton, one 10 ton and two 8 ton shear legs. Machinery is installed aft. Equipment includes a medical and hospital section.

KAWEAH (1919), **LARAMIE** (1920), **MATTOLE** (1920), 14,450 tons. Dimensions : 446 (*o.a.*) × 58 × 25½ feet. Guns : 2—5 inch, 51 cal., 2—3 inch AA. Reciprocating engines and 3 S. E. boilers. H.P. 2800 = 11 kts. Cargo capacity, 8850 tons. Own fuel, 1288 tons. Complement, 107.

Auxiliaries—Oilers (AO)—continued.

SARA THOMPSON (ex-s.s. *Gut Heil*, Armstrong, 1888, purchased 1918). 5850 tons. Dimensions : $321 \times 40\frac{1}{4} \times 21\frac{5}{8}$ feet. I.H.P. 1300 = 9 kts. Cargo capacity : 3826 tons. Own fuel : 494 tons (drawn from cargo holds.) (Used as receiving ship at Cavité.) Complement, 70.

ROBERT L. BARNES (1917, acquired 1918). 3850 tons. Dimensions : $258\frac{1}{2}$ (*o.a.*) $\times 43\frac{1}{4} \times 15$ feet. I.H.P. 1100 = 8.5 kts. Capacity : 1806 tons. Own fuel, 103 tons. (Used for Oil Storage, Guam.) Complement, 67.

Auxiliaries—Cargo Ships (AK).

(For appearance, see *Antares* under Auxiliaries—Miscellaneous.)

CAPELLA (1920), **SIRIUS** (1919), **SPICA** (1919), **VEGA** (1919). 11,450 tons. Dimensions : $401 \times 54 \times 24\frac{1}{2}$ feet. Guns : 2—5 inch, 51 cal., 4—3 inch AA. Curtis geared turbines. 3 Babcock boilers. H.P. 2500 = 11.5 kts. Oil : 1222 tons. Complement. 106.

REGULUS (1920). 10,550 tons. Dimensions : $392 \times 52 \times 24$ feet. Guns : 2—5 inch, 51 cal., 4—3 inch AA. Recipro. engines, 3 single-ended boilers. H.P. 2500 = 11 kts. Oil : 1180 tons. Complement, 106.

1924 Official Photo.

KITTERY (ex-s.s. *Präsident*, 1905). 3330 tons. Dimensions : $293\frac{2}{3}$ (*o.a.*) $\times 40\frac{1}{2} \times 13\frac{1}{4}$ feet. Guns : 4—3 inch. 2 screws. Boilers : 2 single-ended. I.H.P. 1400 = 15.5 kts. Coal : 351 tons. Complement, 102.

Auxiliaries—Transports (AP).

1929 Official Photo.

CHAUMONT (Hog Island, 1920). 10,700 tons. Dimensions : $448 \times 58 \times 23$ feet. Guns : *Nil.* 1 screw. G.E. Curtis geared turbines. Boilers : 6 Babcock. S.H.P. 6000 = 15 kts. Oil : 1473 tons. Complement, 249.

Auxiliaries—Transports (AP)—continued.

1920 Photo.

HENDERSON (1916). 10,000 tons. Complement, 424. Dimensions : $483\frac{5}{6}$ (*o.a.*) $\times 61 \times 20$ feet (*mean* draught). Guns : 8—5 inch, 51 cal., 2—3 inch, 2—3 pdr., 2—1 pdr. H.P. 4000 = 14 kts. Reciprocating engines. Boilers : 3 Babcock. 2 screws. Fuel : 1400 tons *oil*. Has Sperry gyro. stabilisers. To take 2000 men and 32 horses.

Note.— A second transport, *Heywood*, of same dimensions as *Henderson*, was authorised for construction several years ago, but there appears to be no prospect of her being laid down for some time to come.

Auxiliaries—Hospital Ships (AH).

RELIEF. *1927 Official Photo.*

RELIEF (Dec., 1919, Philadelphia N.Y.). 9800 tons. Dimensions : 460 (*p.p.*) $\times 61 \times 19\frac{1}{2}$ feet. Designed H.P. 5250 = 16 kts. Parsons (geared) turbines. 2 screws. 3 Babcock and Wilcox boilers. Oil : 1951 tons. Complement, 397.

Auxiliaries—Hospital Ships (AH)—continued.

1920 Photo.

MERCY (ex-Ward Liner *Saratoga*, built by Cramp, 1907), 9,450 tons. Complement, 377. Dimensions : $429\frac{5}{6}$ (*o.a.*) $\times 50\frac{1}{6} \times 22\frac{3}{4}$ feet. Boilers : 8 S.E. I.H.P. 8500 = 18 kts. Coal : 1776 tons. Purchased 1917.

Auxiliaries—Oceangoing Tugs (AT).

BAY SPRING (1920). About 800 tons. Dimensions : 150 (*o.a.*) $\times 27\frac{2}{3} \times 14$ feet. Guns : *nil.* H.P. 850 = 11 kts.

ALGORMA, BAGADUCE, CONTOCOOK, IUKA, KALMIA, KEOSANQUA, KEWAYDIN, KOKA, MAHOPAC, MONTCALM (ex-*Kineo*), **NAPA, PINOLA, SCIOTA, SUNNADIN, TADOUSAC, TATNUCK, UMPQUA, WANDANK.** All launched 1919-20. **ALLEGHENY** (1917), **SAGAMORE** (1917). 1000 tons. Dimensions : $149\frac{1}{3}$ (*p.p.*) $\times 30 \times 14\frac{2}{3}$ feet. Guns : 2—3 inch AA. I.H.P. 1800 = 13 to 14 kts. Oil : 279 tons.

UNDAUNTED (1917). 450 tons. Guns : 1—3 inch AA. I.H.P. 1000 = 11.5 kts. Oil fuel 329 tons.

CHEMUNG (ex-*Pocahontas*, 1916), **WANDO** (1916). 575 tons. Dimensions : $123\frac{1}{2}$ (*o.a.*) $\times 26\frac{2}{3} \times 11\frac{1}{2}$ feet. Guns : 2—3 pdr. H.P. 800 = 11 kts. Oil fuel 147 tons.

ARAPAHO (1914), **TILLAMOOK** (1914). 575 tons. Guns : 2—3 pdr. H.P. 800 = 10 to 11 kts. Oil : 142 tons.

Auxiliaries—Oceangoing Tugs (AT)—continued.

LYKENS (1899). *About* 1000 tons. Dimensions : 157 (*p.p.*) × 29 × 15 feet. Guns : **1**—3 inch. H.P. 1000 = 14 kts.

SONOMA (1912) and **ONTARIO** (1912). 1120 tons. Dimensions : 175 (*p.p.*) × 34 × 12½ feet (*mean*). Guns : **1**—3 inch, **1**—3 inch AA. Speed : 13 kts. Coal : 440 tons (*average*).

PATAPSCO (1908), **PATUXENT** (1908). 755 tons. Dimensions : 148 (*p.p.*) × 29 × 12¼ feet. Guns : **1**—3 inch AA. H.P. 1160 = 13 kts. Coal : 324 tons.

GENESEE (ex-*Monocacy*, 1905, bought 1917). 1000 tons. Guns : 2—3 inch. I.H.P. 1000 = 15 kts. Coal : 286 tons.

NAVAJO (ex-*General Hubbard*, bought 1907). 800 tons. Dimensions : 141¼ (*o.a.*) × 27½ × 14 feet. Guns : **2**—3 pdr. H.P. 935 = 12 kts.

CHALLENGE (ex-*Defiance*, 1889, bought 1918). 515 tons. Guns : **2**—3 pdr. Speed : 14 kts.

Notes.—*Carrabasset* has been transferred to Coast Guard. Other and Smaller Tugs attached to Naval Districts, rated as " Harbor Tugs."

Mine Vessels—Mine Sweepers (AM).

1920 *Photo.*

(" BIRD " CLASS—43 BOATS.)

LAPWING, OWL, ROBIN, SWALLOW, SANDERLING, CHEWINK, CORMORANT, GANNET (all built by Todd S. B. Co., Tebo Yacht Basin, Brooklyn, N. Y.).

TANAGER, ORIOLE, GREBE, MALLARD, ORTOLAN, PEACOCK (all built by Staten Id. S.B. Co., N. Y.).

AVOCET, BOBOLINK, LARK, PIGEON (all built by Baltimore D. D. & S. B. Co.).

PELICAN, FALCON, SEAGULL, TERN (all built by Gas Engine & Power Co., Morris Heights, N. Y.).

Mine Vessels—Mine-Sweepers (AM)—continued.

TURKEY, WOODCOCK, QUAIL, PARTRIDGE (all built by Chester S. B. Co.).

SANDPIPER, WARBLER, VIREO, WILLET (all built by Philadelphia Navy Yard).

SWAN, WHIPPOORWILL, BITTERN (all built by Alabama S. B. & D. D. Co., Mobile).

WIDGEON, TEAL, BRANT (all built by Sun S. B. Co., Chester).

KINGFISHER, RAIL (both built by Puget Sound Navy Yard).

EIDER, THRUSH (both built by Pusey & Jones, Wilmington).

FINCH, HERON (both built by Standard S. B. Co., N. Y.).

PENGUIN (built by New Jersey D. D. & T. Co., Elizabethport).

All built 1918-19. Displacement : 950 tons *normal.* Dimensions : 187⅝ (*o.a.*) × 35½ × 9⅝ feet (*mean* draught). Guns : **2**—3 inch AA. Machinery : 1 set triple expansion and 2 B. & W. boilers. Designed I.H.P. 1400 = 14 kts. Oil fuel only : 275 tons. Complement, 59.

Notes.—*Gannet, Pelican, Sandpiper* and *Teal* sometimes serve as Aircraft Tenders, when each carries a seaplane aft ; *Chewink, Ortolan, Seagull, Quail*, are Submarine Tenders ; *Pigeon* and *Penguin* are engaged in patrolling Chinese rivers ; *Redwing* has been transferred to Coast Guard ; *Falcon, Mallard, Ortolan, Pigeon, Widgeon* equipped as Submarine Rescue Vessels ; *Whippoorwill* at Pearl Harbor.

Auxiliaries—Miscellaneous (AG).

ANTARES.   1924, *Official Photo.*

ANTARES, EMPIRE STATE (ex-*Procyon*, both 1919). All details as *Capella* class of Cargo Ship, described on an earlier page, except complement, 197. *Procyon* is loaned to State of New York for School Ship ; *Antares* flagship Training Squadron, Scouting Fleet, Atlantic, and is fitted as Target Repair Vessel, carrying special photographic apparatus for recording results of target practice.

GOLD STAR (ex-*Arcturus*, 1920). All details as Cargo Ship *Regulus*, described on an earlier page, except complement, 124.

Auxiliaries—Miscellaneous (AG)—continued.

Photo added 1920.

HANNIBAL (ex-S.S. *Joseph Holland*, 1898). Ex-Fuel Ship. 3550 tons. Dimensions : 274 × 39¼ × 15½ feet. Guns : 1—6 inch 40 cal., 2—3 inch AA. Complement, 163. H.P. 1100 = 9 kts. Coal : 855 tons. Has been used for Surveying Duties.

For Duty with Naval Reserves.

Ex-Battleship *Illinois* ; Monitor *Cheyenne* ; obsolete Gunboats *Wheeling, Dubuque, Paducah, Topeka, Wilmington, Essex, Wilmette* ; old Yacht, *Hawk* ; various Eagle Boats and Submarine Chasers previously described. *Annapolis* : loaned to Pennsylvania State as a School Ship.

Notes.

Officially Revised, 1931, from materials furnished by courtesy of the Commandant, U.S. Coast Guard, Treasury Department, Washington, D.C. Photos also official unless otherwise acknowledged.

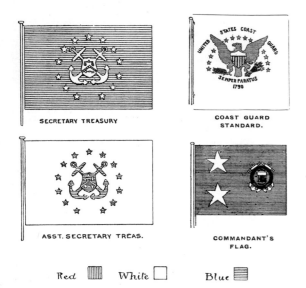

SECRETARY TREASURY

COAST GUARD STANDARD.

ASST. SECRETARY TREAS.

COMMANDANT'S FLAG.

Red ▦   White ☐   Blue ▤

I.—ADMINISTRATION.

The U.S. Coast Guard forms part of the Military Forces of the United States, operating under the Secretary of the Treasury in peace, and as part of the Navy, subject to the orders of the Secretary of the Navy, in time of war or when the President shall so direct. (Act of January 28th, 1915.)

Secretary of the Treasury .. The Hon. A. W. Mellon.

*Assistant Secretary of the Treasury** The Hon. Seymour Lowman

Commandant .. .. .. Rear-Admiral F. C. Billard.

8 Chief of Divisions (Inspection, Operations, Personnel, Supplies and Accounts, Intelligence, Construction and Repair, Engineering, Communications).

2 Boards (Life-Saving Apparatus, Inter-Departmental Board on International Service of Ice Observation, Ice Patrol and Ocean Derelict Destruction).

* The Assistant Secretary has immediate supervision of the Coast Guard.

II.—ORGANIZATION (SHIPS).

The vessels of the service are for the most part grouped in divisions, each of which is under the command of a Division Commander, who is one of the ranking officers of the service.

The Divisions are as follows :—

Headquarters.
1. North-Western Division, Pacific Coast Seattle, Wash.
2. California   „   „   „   .. San Francisco, Cal.
3. Eastern   „   Atlantic   „   .. Boston, Mass.
4. New York   „   „   „   .. New York, N.Y.
5. Norfolk   „   „   „   .. Norfolk, Va.
6. Gulf   „   Gulf   „   .. Mobile, Ala.
7. Lakes   „   Great Lakes .. Saulte Ste. Marie, Mich.
8. Bering Sea Fleet, composed of vessels detailed from Northern and Southern Divisions from May to October each year.

Other ships, unattached to the Divisions perform independent duty.

IIa. ORGANIZATION (DISTRICTS, &c.).

Headquarters of Coast Guard at Washington, D.C.

The Coast (and Great Lakes) of the United States are divided into 13 Districts, each being under a District Commander. (*Note.*—These Coast Guard Districts extend over areas different to those of the "Naval Districts" of the Regular Navy.) 1st—9th District extend along Atlantic and Gulf seaboard ; 10th, 11th, 12th Districts on Great Lakes ; 13th District Pacific Coast and includes Station at Nome, Alaska. Number of C.G. Stations in each District varies between 8 and 41.

III.—TRAINING, REPAIR, STORE ESTABLISHMENTS.

Coast Guard Academy (Fort Trumbull, New London, Conn.). Four years' course for Cadets. Entry by Competitive Examination.

Coast Guard Training Station (Fort Trumbull, New London, Conn.). Receives and trains recruits.

Coast Guard Depot (Arundel Cove, South Baltimore, Md.). For overhaul and repair of vessels stationed on Atlantic Coast, boat-building, &c.

Coast Guard Stores. At Brooklyn N.Y. and San Francisco, Cal. for purchase and issue of supplies to ships and stations.

Coast Guard Radio Repair and Supply Base. At Philadelphia N.Y. Issue and repair radio supplies to ships and stations.

IV. PERSONNEL.

(Total authorized complement, 12,277).

Uniforms similar to U.S. Navy, but C.G. Shield replaces Naval Star on sleeve and shoulder.

Ranks :—Rear-Admiral (1).
Engineer-in-Chief (1).

	Line.	Engineering.	Constructor.	District Commander.
Captain	21	8	..	
Commander ..	42	12	1	..
Lieut.-Commander	50	24	1	4
Lieut.	106	..	3	10
Lieut. (j.g.).. } Ensign .. }	130	..	..	..
Chief Warrant Officers	89	..	..	..

Warrant Officers total 848.* Pay of Commissioned and W.O. as equivalent grades U.S.N. Age limit, 64.

Petty Officers and Men, 11,137. Enlist for 1, 2 or 3 years; pay as U.S.N.

* Excluding temporary entries.

V.—AVIATION.

10 Aviation Stations authorized and 3 stations in operation, 1 being built. Additional stations to be put in operation each year. 4 Seaplanes in active operation.

5 Twin Motor (engine above wing), large type flying boats under contract, all radio equipped and fitted for life-saving and rescue work.

Notes on subsequent description of Vessels.

Re-classified 1924, as (*a*) Cruising Cutters, 1st Class ; (*b*) Cruising Cutters, 2nd Class ; (*c*) Coast Guard Destroyers ; (*d*) Harbour Cutters and Harbour Launches ; (*e*) Patrol Boats.

Ships arranged alphabetically. Classes comprising several ships inserted under earliest name in alphabetical order.

Length is *o.a.* Beam is *moulded.* Draught is *max.* Tonnages are *displacement.*

Stations in italics and Signal Letters in leaded type, usually after description of ships, e.g., *Acushnet* stationed at *Woods Hole, Mass.*, Signal Letters **GVHP.**

ABEL P. UPSHUR.   1931 *Photo.*

5 *Newport News* : transferred 1930. **Geo. E. Badger, Herndon, Hunt, Abel P. Upshur, Welborn C. Wood.** All built 1920. Displacement : 1215 tons (1308 *full load*). Dimensions : 314½ ×31 ×9¾ feet. S.H.P. 28,000 =35 kts. Westinghouse geared turbines. 4 White-Forster boilers, 27,500 square feet heating surface. 2 screws. Guns : 3—4 inch, 50 cal., 1—1 pdr.

2 Aylwin Class. 2 Cushing Class.

CASSIN.   1931 *Photo.*

1 *New York S. B. Co.* : **Ericsson*** (1914). 1090 tons (1211 *full load*). Parsons geared turbines with reciprocating engine (port shaft only) weighs 364 tons. Boilers : 4 Thornycroft—26,936 sq. ft. heating surface. Trials : 29·29 kts.
1 *Bath I.W.* : **McDougal** (1914). 1025 tons (1139 *full load*). Two sets Parsons turbines and two reciprocating. Machinery weighs 325 tons. Boilers : 4 Normand—21,509 sq. feet heating surface. Trials : 30·7 kts. Guns (both) : 3—4 inch, 50 cal., 1—1 pdr.
(All other particulars as given under *Cushing* Class, in U.S. Navy Section.)
*Has very low mainmast.
2 *Bath I.W.* : **Cassin, Cummings** (1913). 1020 tons (1139 *full load*) Parsons turbines and reciprocating engines (on port shaft only). Machinery weighs 329 tons. Boilers : 4 Normand—21,509 sq. feet heating surface. Oil fuel : 312 tons. Trials : *Cassin* 30·14, *Cummings* 30·57 kts.
Guns : 3—4 inch 50 cal., 1—1 pdr. (All other particulars as given under *Aylwin* Class, in U.S. Navy Section.)

4 Conyngham Class.

PORTER.   1931 *Photo.*

2 *Cramp* : **Conyngham** (1915), **Porter** (1915). 1090 tons (1205 *full load*.) Designed H.P. 18,000 =29½ kts. Parsons geared (cruising on starboard shaft only) turbines. Machinery weighs 375 tons. Boilers : 2 White-Forster—24,000 sq. ft. heating surface. Oil : 308 tons. Trials : *Conyngham*, 29·63 kts.; *Porter*, 29·58 kts.
1 *New York S.B. Co.* : **Wainwright** (1915). 1050 tons (1265 *full load*). Designed H.P. 17,000 =29½ kts. Parsons geared (cruising on port shaft only) turbines. Machinery averages 369 tons. Boilers : 4 Normand—21,500 sq. ft. heating surface. Trials : 29·67 kts. Oil : 308 tons. (*Jacob Jones* of this type lost during war.)
1 *Fore River* : **Tucker** (1915). Displacements as *Conyngham*. Designed H.P. 17,000 =29½ kts. Curtis geared (cruising on both shafts) turbines. Machinery weighs 369 tons. Boilers : 4 Yarrow—21,500 sq. ft. heating surface. Oil : 309 tons. Trials : 29·56 kts.
Guns (all four) : 3—4 inch, 50 cal., 1—1 pdr. (All other particulars as given under *Conyngham* Class in U.S. Navy Section.)

3 Allen Class.

SHAW.   1928 *Photo, Lieut.-Com. G. Finlay, U.S.C.G.*

1 *Bath I.W.* : **Davis** (1916). Details as *Allen*, in U.S. Navy Section.
1 *Mare Island Navy Yard* : **Shaw** (1916). Displacement, H.P. and speed as *Rowan*. Parsons geared (cruising on port shaft only) turbines. Boilers : 4 Thornycroft. Trials : 29·5 kts. During War, cut in two by R.M.S. *Aquitania*, steamed stern first to Portland (England) and rebuilt by H.M. Dockyard, Plymouth.
1 *Cramp* : **Wilkes** (1916). 1110 tons (1124 *full load*). Designed H.P. 17,000 =29·5 kts. Parsons geared (cruising on starboard shaft only) turbines. Machinery weighs 367 tons. Boilers : 4 White-Forster. Trials : 29·58 kts.
Guns (all three) 3—4 inch, 50 cal., 1—1 pdr. (All other particulars as given under *Allen* Class in U.S. Navy Section.)

CHELAN.   *1929 Photo.*

Name.			Station.	Signal Letters.
ITASCA	..	..	*Honolulu T.H.*	**GVDM.**
SEBAGO	..	..	*Stapleton N.Y.*	**GNDT.**
SARANAC	..	..	*Galveston Texas*	**GVDN.**
SHOSHONE		..	*Unalaska Alaska*	**GVFM.**
CAYUGA	..	..	*Building.*	

Built 1930 by Gen. Eng. & Dry Dock Co., Oakland.

CHELAN	..	..	*Seattle, Wash.*	**GVKN.**
CHAMPLAIN	..	..	*Stapleton, N.Y.*	**GNDR.**
MENDOTA	..	..	*Norfolk, Va.*	**GNDS.**
PONTCHARTRAIN	..	*Mobile. Ala.*	**GVKP.**
TAHOE	..	..	*San Francisco, Calif.*	**GNDQ.**

All built 1928-29 by Bethlehem Shipbuilding Corporation at Quincy, Mass. Steel, 1 Screw. 1975 tons. Dimensions : 250 (o.a.) × 42 × 16 feet. Turbine-Electric engines (1 main, 2 auxiliary). H.P. 3220 = 16 kts. Guns : 1—5 inch, 1—3 inch, AA., 2—6 pdr. Radius 8,000 miles.

GRESHAM (1897). Steel, 1 screw. 1090 tons. Dimensions : 205½ × 32 × 12½ feet. Speed : 14 kts. Guns : 2—3 inch, 50 cal., 2—6 pdr., 1—1 pdr. (*Mobile Ala.* **GVFD.**)

Cruising Cutters—*continued.*

TAMPA.

Name.				Station.	Signal Letters.
HAIDA	..	..	..	*Port Townsend, Wash.*	**GVKW.**
MODOC	..	..	..	*Wilmington, N.C*	**GVBR.**
MOJAVE	..	..	..	*Boston. Mass.*	**GVBT.**
TAMPA	..	..	..		**GVKT.**

All built 1921. Steel, 1 screw. 1780 tons. Dimensions : 240 × 39 × 16½ feet. Guns : 2—5 inch, 1—3 inch AA., 2—6 pdr. S.H.P. 2600 = 16 kts. Machinery : Turbo-electric (General Electric Curtis Turbine).

Cruising Cutters—*continued.*

NORTHLAND.   *Photo added 1927.*

NORTHLAND (Newport News Shipbuilding Co., 1927). Built of steel, hull being of exceptionally massive construction, to withstand ice pressure. Forefoot cut away to above w.l. Displacement : 2050 tons. Dimensions : 216 (o.a.) × 39 × 15 feet (*mean draught*). Two 6-cyl. 4-cycle Diesel engines with electric drive. Total B.H.P. 1200 = 11 kts. 1 screw. Guns : 2—4 inch, 50 cal., 2—6 pdr. For Bering Sea Patrol. (*San Francisco, Cal.,* **GNDP.**)

      1920 Photo.

OSSIPEE (1915). Steel, 1 screw. 908 tons. Dimensions : 165¾ × 32 × 11¾ feet. Speed : 12 kts. Guns : 2—3 inch, 2—6 pdr. (*Portland, Me.* **GVBW.**)

> (*For appearance, v. photo under* " *Auxiliaries—Mine Sweepers,*" *in U.S. Navy Section.*)

REDWING (1919.) Ex-Navy Minesweeper, taken over 1924. Steel, 1 screw. 1210 tons. Dimensions : 187⅝ × 35½ × 13 feet (*mean draught*). Speed : 14 kts. Guns : 2—3 inch, 23 cal., 2—1 pdr. (**GVKM.**) (*Astoria, Oregon*).

Cruising Cutters—*continued.*

SEMINOLE (1900). Steel, 1 screw. 860 tons. Dimensions : 188 × 29½ × 12 feet. Speed : 14 kts. Guns : 2—1 pdr. (*Sault St. Marie, Mich.* **GVFP.**)

Photo wanted.

SENECA (1908). Steel, 1 screw. 1445 tons. Dimensions : 204 × 34 × 17¼ feet. Speed : 13 kts. Guns : 2—4 inch, 50 cal., 2—1 pdr. (*Stapleton, N.Y.,* **GVHL.**)

1920 *Photo.*

TALLAPOOSA (1915) Steel, 1 screw. 912 tons. Dimensions : 165¾ × 32 × 11¾ feet. Speed : 12 kts. Oil fuel only. Guns : 2—3 inch, 50 cal., 2—6 pdr. (*Juneau Alaska*).

Cruising Cutters—*continued*

TUSCARORA (1902). Steel, 1 screw. 739 tons. Speed : 14 kts. Dimensions : 178 × 30 × 11 feet. Guns : 2—6 pdr. (*St. Petersburg, Fla,* **GVFS.**)

1919 *Photo, U.S. Navy Publicity Bureau.*
UNALGA (1912). Steel, 1 screw. 1181 tons. Dimensions : 190 × 32½ × 14 feet. Speed : 13 kts. Guns : 2—6 pdr. (**GVHS.**)

Note to Photo.—Additional searchlights are now carried and boats removed from poop.
YAMACRAW (1909). Steel, 1 screw. 1082 tons. Dimensions : 191⅔ × 32½ × 13 feet. Speed : 13 kts. Guns : 2—3 inch, 50 cal., 2—6 pdr. (*Savannah, Ga.,* **GVHR.**)

15 Cruising Cutters. Second Class.

ACUSHNET (1908). Steel, 1 screw. 800 tons. Dimensions : 152 × 29 × 13¾ feet. Speed : 12 kts. Guns : 2—1 pdr. (*Woods Hole, Mass.* **GVHP.**)

1929 *Photo.*
APACHE (1891). Iron, 1 screw. 740 tons. Dimensions : 185½ × 29 × 9¼ feet. Speed : 12 kts. Guns : 3—6 pdr. (*Baltimore, Md.* **GVBS.**)

Photo. See following columns.

Name.	Station.	Signal Letters
CAHOKIA	*Eureka, Calif.*	**GVDK**
KICKAPOO	*Rockland, Maine.*	**GVFQ**
MASCOUTIN	*Norfolk, Va.*	**GVFB.**
SAUKEE	*Key West*	**GVFR**
TAMAROA	*San Diego, Calif.*	**GVCF.**

Built 1919-1920 as seagoing tugs; transferred from U.S. Shipping Board 1921. Steel, 1 screw. 729-767 tons. Dimensions : 151¼ × 27½ × 15 feet. Speed : 11 kts. Guns : 2—1 pdr. *Kickapoo* fitted as Ice Breaker. *Cahokia* and *Tamaroa* are oil-fired; others coal.

Cruising Cutters—*continued.*

Cruising Cutters—*continued.*

CARRABASSET.   *Photo added 1927.*

CARRABASSET (1919). Ex-Fleet Tug taken over from Navy Dept., 1924. Steel, 1 screw. 1133 tons. Dimensions: 155¾ × 30 × 17½ feet. Speed: 13½ kts. Guns: 2—1 pdr. **(GVKL.)**

TAMAROA.   *1931 Photo.*

(*See previous column.*)

KANKAKEE.   *1929 Photo.*

KANKAKEE ... ... *Evansville, Ind.* ... ...
Built 1919. Steel hull, wood deckhouses. 383 tons. Dimensions: 182 × 34 × 3½ feet. Guns: none. Speed: 12 kts. River Steamer for flood relief.

                                  1931 Photo.

MANHATTAN (1918). Steel, 1 screw. Ice Breaker, Salvage Vessel, Tug and Fire Float. 406 tons. Dimensions: 120¼ × 24 × 11¾ feet. Speed: 12 kts. Guns: 2—1 pdr. (*New York, N.Y.* **GVCL.**)

PAMLICO (1907). Steel, twin screw. 451 tons. Dimensions: 158 × 30 × 5⅔ feet. Speed: 11 kts. Guns: 2—6 pdr. (*Newbern, N.C.* **GVHJ**).

PEQUOT.   *Photo added 1927.*

PEQUOT (ex-Minelayer *General Samuel M. Mills*, built 1909, transferred from War Department 1922). Steel, 1 screw. 950 tons. Dimensions: 166½ × 32½ × 11¼ feet. (*Curtis Bay, Md.* **GVCM.**)

(For *Saukee v. Cahokia.*)

SHAWNEE (1921). Steel. 900 tons. Dimensions: 158¼ × 30 × 14 feet. Guns: 2—1 pdr. Built by Union Con. Co., Oakland, Cal. (*S. Francisco, Calif.* **GVCB.**)

                                  1920 Photo.

SNOHOMISH (1908). Steel, 1 screw. 879 tons. Dimensions: 152 × 29 × 15½ feet. Speed: 12 kts. Guns: 1—3 inch, 50 cal. (*Port Angeles, Wash.,* **GVHN.**)

(For *Tamaroa v. Cahokia.*)

Harbour Cutters and Harbour Launches.

Detailed to larger Maritime Ports to enforce Customs and Navigation Laws and the regulation of the anchorage and movements of vessels.

Arcata (1903). Wood. 1 screw. 138 tons. Dimensions: 85 × $17\frac{1}{2}$ × $10\frac{1}{3}$ feet. Speed: 11 kts. Guns: **1**—1 pdr. (*Port Townsend, Wash.*, **GVHC.**)

Calumet (1894). Iron. 1 screw. 170 tons. Dimensions: $94\frac{1}{2}$ × $20\frac{1}{2}$ × 9 feet. Guns: None. Speed: 12 kts. (*New York, N.Y.*, **GVDR.**)

Name.	*Station.*	*Signal Letters.*
Chautauqua	*New York N.Y.*	**GVJM.**
Chicopee	*Portland, Maine*	**GVJL.**
Chippewa	*Sault Ste. Marie, Mich.*	**GVJK.**
Chulahoma	*S. Baltimore, Md.*	....

All built 1919. Wood. 215 tons. Dimensions: 88 × 20 × $8\frac{3}{4}$ feet. Speed: 10 kts. Are Ex-Navy Tugs taken over by Coastguard. *Chincoteague* and *Choptank* of this class, sold 1925.

Davey (1908). Steel, 1 screw. 182 tons. Dimensions: $92\frac{1}{2}$ × 19 × $10\frac{1}{6}$ feet. Guns: *Nil.* Speed: 10 kts. (*New Orleans, La.*, **GVHM.**)

Golden Gate (1896). Steel, 1 screw. 240 tons. Dimensions: 110 × $20\frac{1}{2}$ × $9\frac{5}{6}$ feet. Speed: 12 kts. (**GVFH.**)

Guard (1914). Wood. 52 tons. Dimensions: 67 ft. 7 in. × $12\frac{1}{2}$ × $6\frac{1}{4}$ feet. Speed: 9 kts. (*Friday Harb., Wash.*, **GVHW.**)

Guthrie (1895). Iron, 1 screw. 149 tons. Dimensions: 88 × $17\frac{1}{2}$ × 9 feet. Speed: 11 kts. (*Philadelphia, Pa.*, **GVBQ.**)

Hudson (1893). Iron, 1 screw. 179 tons. Dimensions: $96\frac{1}{2}$ × 20 × 9 feet. Speed: 12 kts. (*New York, N.Y.*, **GVDQ.**)

Leopard (1920). Wood. Dimensions: 94 × 24 × 12 feet. (*Curtis Bay, Md.*)

Mackinac (1903). Steel, 1 screw. 241 tons. Dimensions: 110 × $20\frac{1}{2}$ × $10\frac{1}{2}$ feet. Guns: None. Speed: 12 kts. (*Boston, Mass.*, **GVHB.**)

Raritan (1905). Steel. 1 screw. 220 tons *gross*. Dimensions: 103 × 22 ft. 8 in. (*New York, N.Y.*)

Winnisimmet (1903). Steel, 1 screw. 182 tons. Dimensions: $96\frac{1}{2}$ × $20\frac{1}{2}$ × 9 feet. Speed: 12 kts. (*Norfolk, Va.*, **GVFW.**)

Wissahickon (1904). Steel, 1 screw. 194 tons. Dimensions: $96\frac{1}{2}$ × $20\frac{1}{2}$ × $9\frac{1}{2}$ feet. Speed: 12 kts. (*New York, N.Y.*, **GVHD.**)

Harbour Cutters and Harbour Launches—*continued.*

(Ex-Submarine Chasers.)

Name	(late *SC*).	*Station.*	*Signal Letters.*
Cook	(438)	*New London Conn.*	**GVKC.**
Cygan	(335)	*Ketchikan, Alaska*	**GVKR.**
Smith	(155)	*Oakland, Cal.*	**GVKQ.**
Tingard	(183)	*San Pedro, Cal.*	**GVJT.**

Built 1917-18, taken over 1919-20. Wood. 75 tons. Dimensions: 110 × $14\frac{3}{4}$ × 6 feet. Speed: 11 kts. Guns: **1**—1 pdr. (Twin screw, petrol.)

17 Launches.

Numbered between AB.1. and AB.25.

Displ: 45 tons gross average.

Length from 63ft. to 41ft.

1931 *Photo*

33—125 ft. steel Patrol Boats: ***Active, Agassiz, Alert, Antietam, Bonham, Boutwell, Cahoone, Cartigan, Crawford, Cuyahoga, Diligence, Dix, Ewing, Faunce, Frederick Lee, General Greene, Harriet Lane, Jackson, Legare, Marion, McLane, Montgomery, Morris, Nemaha, Pulaski, Reliance, Rush, Tiger, Travis, Vigilant, Winona, Woodbury, Yeaton.*** 220 tons. Dimensions: 125 × $23\frac{1}{2}$ × $6\frac{3}{4}$ feet. Guns: **1**—3 inch. 23 cal.

Swift (1917). Wood Dimensions: 66 × $13\frac{1}{2}$ × $3\frac{1}{4}$ feet. Speed: 16 kts. (Twin screw, petrol.) (*San Francisco, Cal.*, **GVHT.**)

Patrol (1917). Wood, 23 tons. Dimensions: $68\frac{3}{4}$ × 14 × $3\frac{3}{4}$ feet. Speed: 9 kts.

PETREL. 1929 *Photo.*

13 steel Patrol Boats: ***Corwin, Dallas, Dexter, Eagle, Forward, Gallatin, Mahoning, Nansemond, Naugatuck, Patriot, Perry, Petrel, Wolcott.*** 210 tons displacement. 99′ 8″ × 23′ × 8′. Diesel engines. Guns: **1**—3 inch, 23 cal.

CG 182. *Photo added* 1927.

194 wooden Patrol Boats: ***CG—100*** to ***CG—302.*** (1924-25) 37 tons displacement. Dimensions: 74′ 11″ × 13′ $7\frac{1}{2}$″ × 4′. Gasoline engine. Guns: 1—1 pdr. 16 boats lost or disposed of.

URUGUAYAN FLEET.

RECOGNITION SILHOUETTES.

Scale: 1 inch = 160 feet.

Vanguardia *class.*

Corsario *class.*

B. de R. Branco.

18 DE JULIO.

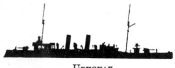

Uruguay.

Monte Video.

Minister of War and Marine : General Estanislao Mendoza y Duran.

Director of Navy : Captain F. Garcia Martinez.

Personnel : 1306.

Naval Attaché, London : Lieut. Carlos Travieso.

Mercantile Marine : (From "Lloyd's Register," 1928 figures.) Total *gross* tonnage, 50,601.

Ports, Yards, &c.

MONTEVIDEO.—There is a fort here, but only for returning salutes. The National Dock (Dique Nacional) is operated by the Naval Authorities. Length, 459 feet. Breadth, 55 feet. Maximum depth, 17 feet. Steam and electric pumps can empty dock in eight hours. Dique Maúa (south of city) is property of Monte Video Gas Co. Dimensions : 272 × 50 × 12 feet 4 inches to 15 feet 2 inches. Has 2 steam pumps and 25 ton crane, also fixed and moving cranes. The firm Varadero del Cerro have a yard, well equipped for repairs, with a small slipway. The National Port Administration bought the Varadero Lussich, a repairing yard with a small slipway during 1919.

Old Cruiser.

1918 *Photo, A. J. Carbone.*

MONTEVIDEO (ex-*24 de Agosto*, ex-*Dogali*, ex-*Salamina*, Elswick, 1890, purchased from Italy, 1908). 2050 tons. Complement, 250. Dimensions : 250 (*p.p.*) × 37 × 16¼ feet (*max.* draught). Guns : **4**—6 inch, **6**—3 pdr., **6** M.G. Torpedo tubes : **4** *above water.* Armour : 2″—1″ deck, 4½″ gun shields, 2″ conning tower. Machinery : 2 sets horizontal and 4 double-ended boilers. H.P. 7500 = 17 kts. Coal : 480 tons.

Torpedo Gunboat & Training Ship.

URUGUAY (Vulkan, Stettin, 1910). 1150 tons. Complement, 125. Dimensions: $278\frac{3}{4}$ ($p.p.$) $\times 30\frac{5}{6} \times 12$ feet (*max.* draught). Guns (Skoda): 2—4·7 inch, 45 cal., 4—12 pdr., 6—1 pdr. (Vickers). 4 M.G. Torpedo tubes: 2—18 inch *above water*. Armour: $\frac{2}{3}$" nickel steel over boilers and engines. 4 Normand boilers. H.P. 8,000 = 23 kts. Coal: 210 tons = 3,000 miles at 10 kts.

Note.—Is fitted for service as Training Ship for midshipmen. Old Gunboat, *Gen. Suarez*, is a Harbour Training Ship.

Training Ship.

Now rigged as Silhouette.

DIEZ Y OCHO DE JULIO. 678 tons. Complement, 85. 4 small guns and 2 machine guns. Speed, 12 kts. Re-fitted and re-boilered 1920.

Gunboat.

1918 *Photo, A. J. Carbone.*

BARON DE RIO BRANCO (ex-*Maldonado*). Old paddle-wheel gunboat. 300 tons. Carries 4 small Q.F. and 2 M.G. Speed, 14 kts.

Tenders.

VANGUARDIA class.

1918 *Photo, A. J. Carbone.*

CORSARIO class.

1918 *Photo, A. J. Carbone*

INGENERIO, LA VALLEJA, ORIENTAL, OYARVIDE. These are four armed tugs, built about 1908, displace about 60 tons each. Guns: 3 pdr. or M.G. Speed, 13 kts. Three other tugs, *Chapicuy, Corsario, Yaguary*, also exist, and are classified as tenders. No information has been supplied to assist in determining which of the seven ships named above belong to *Vanguardia* class or which to *Corsario* class. 1 Tug building at Cant. Riuniti, 1931.

VENEZUELA

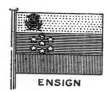 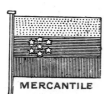

ENSIGN   MERCANTILE

Personnel :

Minister of War and Marine : General C. Jiménez Rebolledo.

Warship Port : Puerto Cabello. Steel floating dock here 282 × 90 × 22 feet. (2400 tons capacity) built in five sections on self-docking system, and worked by electricity. Also a wooden floating dock, 180 × 60 × 19 feet (1200 tons capacity). Both these docks are Government property.

Mercantile Marine : ("Lloyd's Register," 1930 figures). Total *gross* tonnage, 62,026.

RECOGNITION SILHOUETTES.

Scale 1 inch = 160 feet.

MIRANDA.

J. F. RIBAS.

GENERAL SALOM.

M. SUCRE.

VENEZUELAN FLEET.

Gunboats.

1918 Photo, by courtesy of T. I for Rees, Esq.

MARISCAL SUCRE (ex-Spanish *Isla de Cuba*, 1886, captured by U.S., 1898, and sold to Venezuela, 1912). 1125 tons. Dimensions : 192 × 30 × 12¼ feet (*Mean* draught) 13 feet (*Max.* draught). Guns : 2—4 inch, 2—6 pdr., 6—3 pdr., 2—1* pdr. H.P. 2000 = 13 kts., *max.* continuous speed, 10 kts. Coal : 200 tons. Endurance : 2200 miles at 9·5 kts. Complement, 100.

    * 1—1 pdr. transferable to boat mounting.

1920 Photo, by courtesy of T. I for Rees, Esq.

GENERAL SALOM (ex-*Restaurador*, purchased 1900 ; built as U.S. private yacht *Atlanta*, 1884). 750 tons. Dimensions : 240 × 26 × 13 feet (*max.* draught). Guns : 1—12 pdr., 4—6 pdr., **1** machine. H.P. 1900 = 10 kts., *max.* continuous speed 8 kts. Coal : 200 tons. Endurance : 2000 miles at 8 kts. Complement, 65.

Gunboats—*continued*

MIRANDA (Clydebank, 1895 ; purchased from Spain, 1898). 200 tons. Dimensions : 135 × 19 × 8 feet. Guns : 1—6 pdr. H.P. 315 = 10 kts. Coal : 36 tons. Endurance : 850 miles at 8 kts. Complement, 46. Carries 30 Mauser rifles.

Armed Tug.

Photo by favour of Ellis Greu & Co., N.Y.

JOSÉ FELIX RIBAS (ex-*Zumbador*, built 1894). 300 tons. Dimensions : 127 × 23 × 12 feet. Guns : 2—6 pdr. Speed, 10 kts. Coal : 60 tons. Endurance : 1440 miles at 10 kts. Complement, 44. (Being reconstructed.)

Transport.

Brigantine **Antonio Diaz**, used as Naval Coal transport. 300 tons. Dimensions : 109 × 24·5 × 11 feet. Complement, 16. Is armed to some extent.

ROYAL YUGO SLAV NAVY.

Revised 1931 by courtesy of the Ministry of Marine.

FLAGS.

ROYAL STANDARD

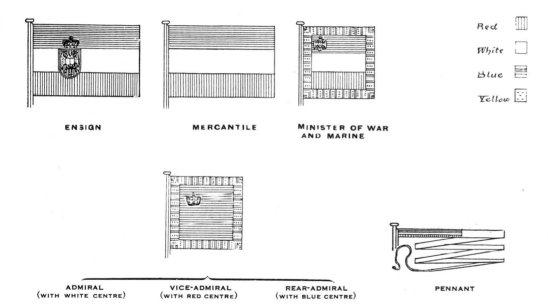

ENSIGN

MERCANTILE

MINISTER OF WAR AND MARINE

Red

White

Blue

Yellow

ADMIRAL
(WITH WHITE CENTRE)

VICE-ADMIRAL
(WITH RED CENTRE)

REAR-ADMIRAL
(WITH BLUE CENTRE)

PENNANT

ADMINISTRATION.

Minister of War and Marine : General Dragutin Stojanovitch.

Commander in Charge of Fleet : Admiral Victor Wilkerhauser.

Naval Attaché in London : Captain Vladimir Mariashevitch.

Personnel : 487 officers. 5,500 petty officers and men.

(Reserve) : 164 officers. 570 petty officers and men.

Colour of Ships : Light grey.

Mercantile Marine : From " Lloyd's Register," 1931. Total *gross* tonnage, 361,606.

Displacements are " standard."

UNIFORMS.

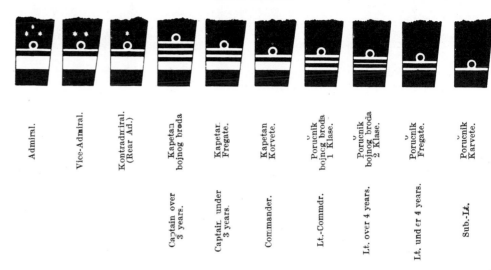

Admiral.

Vice-Admiral.

Kontradmiral.
(Rear Ad.)

Kapetan
bojnog broda

Captain over
3 years.

Kapetan
Fregate.

Captain under
3 years.

Kapetan
Korvete.

Commander.

Porucnik
bojnog broda
1 Klase.

Lt.-Commdr.

Porucnik
bojnog broda
2 Klase.

Lt. over 4 years.

Porucnik
Fregate.

Lt. under 4 years.

Porucnik
Karvete.

Sub.-Lt.

For relative ranks :

Engineers have silver grey between the stripes.

Paymasters have red between the stripes.

Constructors have purple between the stripes.

Warrant Officers have brown between the stripes.

Surgeons have an Aesculapias snake on the curl.

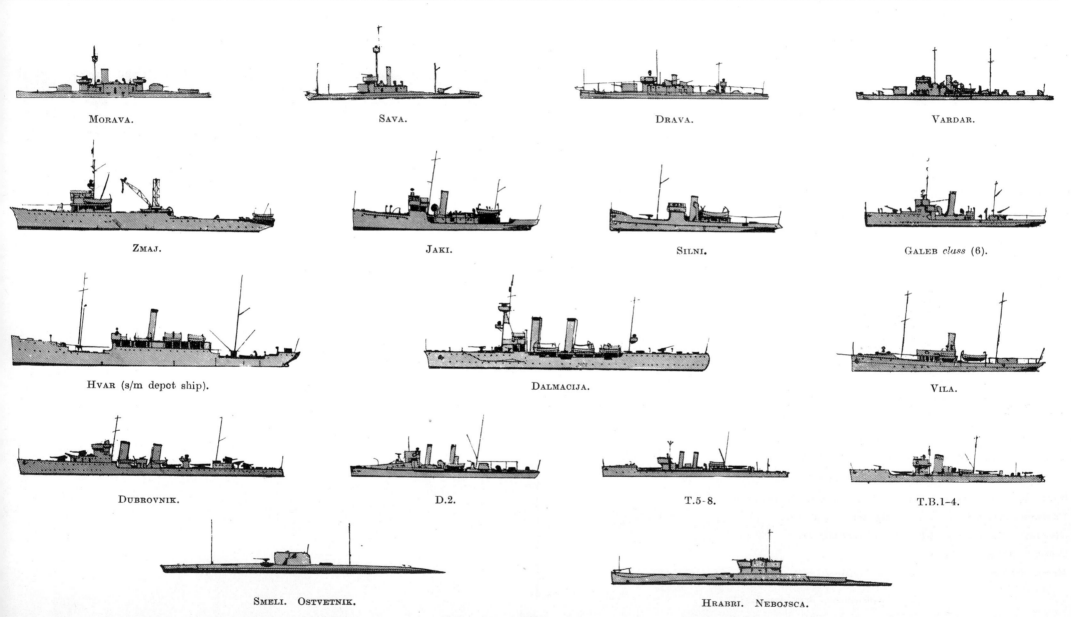

MORAVA.   SAVA.   DRAVA.   VARDAR.

ZMAJ.   JAKI.   SILNI.   GALEB *class* (6).

HVAR (s/m depot ship).   DALMACIJA.   VILA.

DUBROVNIK.   D.2.   T.5-8.   T.B.1-4.

SMELI. OSTVETNIK.   HRABRI. NEBOJSCA.

Cruiser (*Used for training purposes.*)

DALMACIJA.

1931 *Photo, Official.*

1931 *Photo, Official.*

DALMACIJA (ex-German *Niobe*, Weser Yard, 18th July, 1899). Displacement: 2370 tons. Dimensions : $342\frac{1}{4} \times 38\frac{1}{2} \times 17\frac{1}{4}$ feet (*max. draught*). Guns : **6**—3.3 inch, 55 cal. (83 *m/m*) AA. (These are guns of a new and powerful Skoda model, with a maximum range of 18,000 yds.) Torpedo tubes: originally carried **2**—19.7 inch, *above* water. Armour (Krupp) : 2″ deck (amidships), ¾″ deck (ends), $3\frac{1}{2}$″ glacis to engine room hatches, 3″ C.T. Machinery : 2 sets 4-cylinder triple expansion, 2 screws. Boilers : 5 Schulz-Thornycroft. Designed H.P. 8000=21 kts. Coal, *normal*, 380 tons ; *maximum*, 580 tons.

Note.—Purchased from German Government in 1926 and underwent extensive refit and alterations at Cattaro. Tripod mast fitted 1931.

Flotilla Leader.

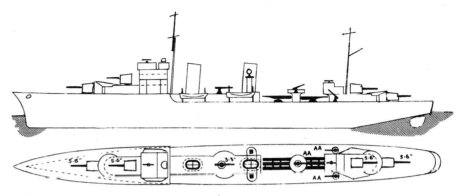

DUBROVNIK.

DUBROVNIK (October 11, 1931, Yarrow).

Displacement : 1,880 tons (*standard*), 2,400 (*normal*). Dimensions : $371 \cdot 5 \times 35 \times 11 \cdot 7$ feet.

Guns : **4**—5·6 inch (140 m/m),

(Skoda) **1**—3·3 inch A.A.,

2—small A.A.,

Tubes : **6**—21 inch.

Machinery : Parsons geared turbines. 3 Yarrow boilers.

D.H.P. 42,000=37 kts.

Fuel : Radius :

Note.—Designed to meet particular specifications and should be a fast and economical steamer. The re-appearance of the Skoda gun is noteworthy, the calibres being unusual. Note the position of the A.A. guns by after shelter deck, after control position and removal of searchlight from the bridge to athwart second funnel. S.L. platforms are stayed away from funnel to avoid all vibration. She is the first Yarrow destroyer to have a clipper bow.

8 Torpedo Boats (*Torpiljarke*) (ex-Austrian).

1931 Photo, Official.

4 Ex-Austrian boats: **T1—T4** (ex-*76T*—*79T*, Stab. Tecnico, Trieste 1913-15). Displacement: 262 tons. Fuel: 18 tons coal, 24 tons oil.

1931 Photo, Official.

4 Ex-Austrian boats: **T5—T8** (ex-*87F*, *93F*, *96F*, *97F*, Ganz-Danubius Co., Porte Ré, Fiume, 1913-15). Displacement 266 tons, Fuel: 20 tons coal, 34 tons oil.

Details of **T1—T8.** Dimensions: 188·3 × 18·7 × 4·9 feet. Guns: 2—66 m/m. and 1 M.G. Torpedo tubes: 2—18″. Designed H.P. (turbines) 5000=28 kts. (24 reported best speed now) Yarrow boilers.

4 Submarines.

HRABRI.

1928 Photo, Abrahams.

Hrabri, Nebojsca (Armstrong, 1927). Displacement: $\frac{975}{1164}$ tons. Speed: $\frac{15\cdot5}{10}$ kts. Armament: 2—4 inch AA. 6—21 inch torpedo tubes. Generally similar to British L50 type. Radius 5000 miles at 9 kts.

Names mean *Gallant* and *Dreadnought*.

HRABRI class.

(Carries a second gun on Conning Tower.)

OSTVETNIK.

1930 Photo, M. Bar.

Smeli (Dec. 1st, 1928), **Ostvetnik** (Feb. 14th, 1929). Laid down at Nantes, 1927, by At. & Ch. de la Loire. Displacement, $\frac{630}{800}$ tons. 227×18×14 feet. H.P. $\frac{1410}{1000}=\frac{14\cdot5}{9}$ kts. Armament: 1—4 inch Skoda, 1—1 pdr. AA., 1 M.G.; 4 bow and 2 stern, 19.7 inch tubes. Complement, 43.

Names mean *Ardent* and *Vindictive*.

2 Coastal Motor Boats.

Uskok, Cetnik. Delivered by Messrs. John I. Thornycroft & Co., Ltd., in May, 1927. Dimensions : 55 × 11 feet Machinery : 2 Thornycroft motors of 375 H.P. each=37 kts. *nominal* (40 kts. actually obtained). Auxiliary engine fitted for cruising, equal to 800 miles radius. 2 Lewis guns, 2—18 inch torpedoes. 4 D.C., and smoke floats.

Minelayers (*Minonosci*).

SOKOL.

1924 *Photo, by courtesy of the Navy Department.*

6 boats : **GALEB, LABUD, JASTREB, KOBATZ, ORAO, SOKOL** (1917-18). Displacement : 330 tons. Guns : 2—3·9 AA., 4—3 pdrs. Complement : 71. Names mean *Seagull, Swan, Hawk, Sparrowhawk, Eagle* and *Falcon*.

Minesweepers.

D2.

1931 *Official Photo.*

D2 (ex-Austrian t.b., *T.B.*36, 1886). Displacement : 78 tons. H.P. 900=17 kts. 128 feet long. Guns : 2—37 m/m. Triple expansion engines. Complement : 16.

5 boats : **MALINSKA, MARJAN, MELJINE, MIJET, MOSOR** (1931. Yarrows Adriatic Works, Kralvevica). Displacement : 130 tons. Similar to *Albona* type (Italy). H.P. 280= 9 kts. Guns : 1—11 pdr.

Aviation Depot Ship.

ZMAJ. Built in 1928 by Deutsche Werft, Hamburg : burnt out and re-built in 1929-30. Displacement : 1870 tons. Dimensions : 251 × 44·8 × 11·8 feet. Guns : 1—4 inch AA. Machinery : 2 compressorless M.A.N. diesels each 1630 H.P. (3260 H.P.) = 15 kts. 2 screws. (*Zmaj = Kite*).

1931 *Official Photo.*

Danube Flotilla.—River Monitors.

River Monitors—*continued.*

DRAVA.

1931 *Photo, by courtesy of the Navy Dept.*

DRAVA (ex-Austrian *Enns*, 1913). 530 tons. Dimensions: $203\frac{1}{4} \times 34\frac{1}{2} \times 4\frac{1}{4}$ feet. Guns: **2**—4·7 inch **+ 3**—4·7 inch howitzers, **2**—66 m/m., **7** M.G. Armour: $1\frac{1}{2}''$ Belt and Bulkheads, $1''$ Deck, $2''$ C.T. and Turrets. Designed H.P. 1500 = 13 kts. Boilers: Yarrow. Fuel: Oil only, 70 tons. Complement, 86. Built under Austro-Hungarian 1912 Naval Programme; ceded to Yugo-Slavia 1920. Sister ship *Basarabia* now in Roumanian Navy.

MORAVA.

1924 *Photo, by courtesy of the Navy Dept.*

Note overhanging rails at stern, for launching and hauling in boats.

MORAVA (ex-Austrian *Körös*, Budapest, 1892). 390 tons. Dimensions: $177\frac{1}{6} \times 29\frac{1}{2} \times 4$ feet. Designed H.P. 1200 = 10 kts. Boilers: Yarrow. Guns: **2**—4.7 inch (35 cal.), **2**—66 m/m. **2** M.G. Armour: $2''$ Belt, $\frac{3}{4}''$ Deck, $3''$ Turret, $2''$ C.T. Complement, 79-80. Coal: 80 tons.

SAVA (ex-Austrian *Bodrog*, Neupest, March, 1904). 380 tons. Dimensions: $183\frac{3}{4} \times 31\frac{1}{4} \times 4$ feet. Designed H.P. 1200 = 9 kts. Boilers: Yarrow. Armament: **2**—4·7 inch (45 cal.) **2**—66 m/m. **2**—M.G. 1 or 3 machine. Armour: $1\frac{1}{2}''$ Belt and Bulkheads, $1''$ Deck, $3''$—$1\frac{1}{2}''$ Turrets and Conning tower. Complement, 79. Coal: 62 tons.

1921 *Illustration, R. F. Scheltema, Esq.*

VARDAR (ex-Austrian *Bosna*, 1915). 530 tons. Dimensions: $190\frac{1}{4} \times 34\frac{1}{2} \times 4\frac{1}{4}$ feet. Guns: **4**—4·7 inch, **2**—66 m/m. **7** M.G. Armour: $1\frac{1}{2}''$ belt and bulkheads, $1''$ deck, $2''$ C.T., $2''$ turrets and cupolas. H.P. 1600 = 12 kts. Oil: 75 tons. Complement, 100. Sister to *Bucovina*, now in Roumanian Navy.

S/M Depot Ships.

HVAR.   *1928 Photo.*

HVAR (ex-*Vintali*, ex-*Solun*) Sir Jas. Laing & Sons, Ltd., Sunderland, 1896 (Rebuilt 1927). 3,600 tons. Speed : 12 kts.
SILNICA (ox-*Najade*, 1891). 370 tons. Speed : 9 kts. Guns : 2—3 pdr. Name means *Dew*.

Tugs.

1931 Official Photo.

SILNI (1914). Displacement : 200 tons. H.P. 670=10 kts. Name means *Powerful*.

Tugs (continued).

1931 Photo, Official.

JAKI (1915). Displacement : 370 tons. H.P. 1,200=15 kts. Name means *Forceful*.
MOCNI (1889). 260 tons. H.P. 400=11 kts.
MARLJIVI (1898). 130 tons. H.P. 300=12 kts.
SNAZNI (1917). 100 tons. H.P. 300=10 kts.
USTRAJNI (1917). 160 tons. H.P. 250—9 kts.

Yacht.

VILA (ex-*Dalmata*) (1896). 230 tons. H.P. 325=12 kts. Name means *Nymph*.

Training Ship.

JADRAN (1932). Displacement : 720 tons. Diesel engines. H.P. 375=8 kts.

BRITISH NAVY.

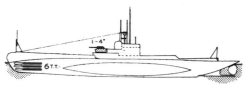

Plan of *Swordfish* class.

KEMPENFELT launched October 29, 1931.

FALCON.   1931 *photo, favour of Messrs. Yarrow.*

CHALLENGER built for research work by Fisheries Board : to be employed on Surveying duties.
  Constructed at Chatham D.Y. 1930–31.
  Dims.: 220 (*o.a.*) 200 (*p.p.*) × 36 × 12½ feet.
  Displ.: 1,400 tons.
  Triple expansion engines, oil fired. H.P. 1,200 = 12½ knots. 1 screw. Oil = 340 tons.

CHINA.

MING–SAN.   1931 *Photo.*

Built by Kiangnan D.Y., Shanghai, 1931.
  Displ.: 600 tons. Dims.: 210 × 27 × 6½ feet.
  Guns : 1—4·7″, 1—4″, 2—3″ A.A., 2—6 pdrs.
  Speed : 18 knots. Coal : ? tons. Complement : 115.

FRANCE.

SURCOUF (p. 200). Armament : 2—8″, 2—37 mm. A.A., 4 M.G. A.A., 8 tubes.

  Can submerge in less than two minutes.
  Is to carry a small seaplane.

ORPHÉE (p. 204), launched November 10, 1931.

Second class s/ms : Those building under 1929–30 programmes are to have 1—4″, 2 M.G. A.A. guns and 9 tubes. They
  will be able to submerge in less than 45 seconds.

HALBRONN (p. 203), ***PIERRE MARRAST*** (p. 203), ***GUSTAV ZÉDÉ*** (p. 204) and ***PIERRE CHAILLEY***
  (p. 201) are to be disposed of.

ALGERIE (p. 177). Side armour is 4 inches only. Inside bulges with hull thickness of 40 M.M.

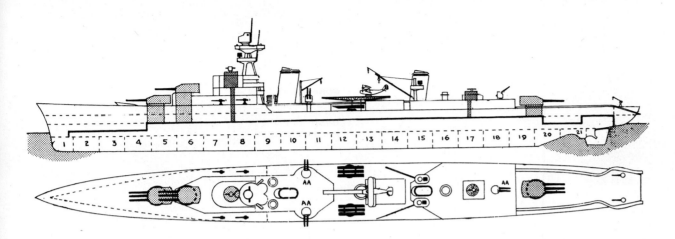

FRANCE.

"EMILE BERTIN" (p. 185).

Length (*approx.*) 574 feet (175 *m.*).

Armament : 9—6 inch.   Speed = 30 knots.
6—3·5 or 4" A.A.
4 or more—37 mm. A.A.
Fitted for mine laying.

It is not yet decided whether a main mast will be fitted.

The new cruisers of **"LA GALISSONINIÈRE"** *class* will be based on this design, with armour capable of resisting 6 inch gunfire.

Dimensions reported to be
590 × 57·4 × 16·4 ft, (180 × 17·5 × 5 m,)
and Displacement raised to 7,729 tons.

LE MALIN *class* (p. 189).

Torpedo Armament = **7** tubes, 21·7 inches, and not **8** inch quadruple mounts.
MILAN and **EPERVIER** will be similar.
CASSAID *class* will have 4 funnels.

Experimental type *leader* (p. 189).

Armament : 6—5·5 inch gun in twin mounts.
1—3 inch A.A.
6—37 mm. A.A.
4—D.C. Throwers.
9—21·7 Tubes (triples).

Experimental type *destroyer* (p. 189).

Armament : 4—5·1 inch gun in twin mounts.
2—37 mm. A.A.
9—21·7 Tubes (triples).

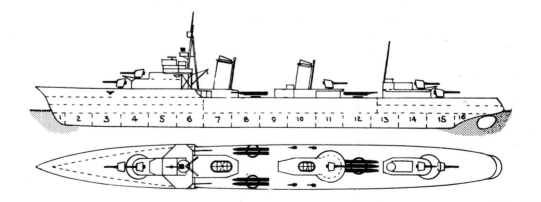

ITALY

PERSIA.

ZARA.

1931 *Photo, Official.*

(Note caps to funnels.)
Destroyer *"ALVISE DA MOSTO"* (p. 272) should read *"ALVISE CADAMOSTO."*

4 Motor Vedettes only are building at Cant. Navili Parseno i-Naples,

"CHABROKN" (24/7/31.)
"SIMORGH" (3/8/31).
"KARKASS" (24/8/31).
"CHAH HAAZ" (12/9/31).

2 Motor Gunboats at Cant. Navali Riuniti-Palermo.
BABR (2/3/31).
PALANG (?/11/31).

860126